A HISTORY OF
GEOGRAPHICAL DISCOVERY
AND EXPLORATION

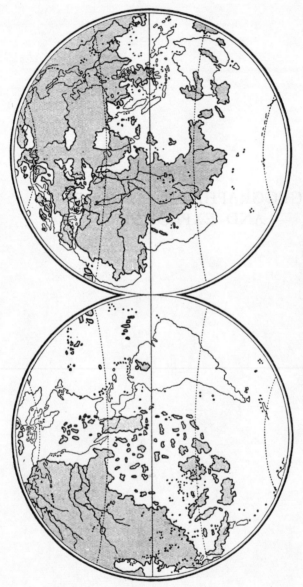

THE WORLD ACCORDING TO BEHAIM, 1492

Behaim's map is here shown superimposed on the map of the world as it is
known to-day, the land masses in outline representing discoveries made since
Behaim's time.

Reproduced by courtesy of Messrs George Philip and Son, Ltd.

A HISTORY OF
GEOGRAPHICAL DISCOVERY
AND EXPLORATION

BY

J. N. L. BAKER B.Litt. M.A.

READER IN HISTORICAL GEOGRAPHY IN THE
UNIVERSITY OF OXFORD

NEW EDITION REVISED

G
80
B3
1967

COOPER SQUARE PUBLISHERS, INC.
NEW YORK
1967

Published 1967 by Cooper Square Publishers, Inc.
59 Fourth Avenue, New York, N. Y. 10003
Library of Congress Catalog Card No. 66-30785

PRINTED IN THE UNITED STATES OF AMERICA
by SENTRY PRESS, NEW YORK, N. Y. 10019

PREFACE TO THE FIRST EDITION

WHILE many excellent works deal at length with special periods or topics of geographical discovery, no single book covers the whole ground in a manner quite suited to the needs of the increasing number of students now reading honours courses in geography in the universities of this country. This book attempts to meet those needs, but it is hoped that it may also be of interest to a wider circle who wish to have a connected account of exploration. It lays claim to be little more than a compilation. My indebtedness to those who have already contributed to this subject will be apparent from the list of works quoted in the bibliographical note and in the footnotes to the various chapters. For any accidental failure to acknowledge my sources I here offer my apology.

Although making full use of secondary authorities, I have tried to introduce as many original sources as space would allow. It has been impossible to deal with all periods or all explorers in the same detail, and parts of the later chapters are little more than a catalogue of work done. Even a catalogue, however, has its uses, and I hope this will enable students to follow up the work of explorers in greater detail than I have been able to do.

For the general arrangement and for the choice of material I am alone responsible. I hope that there is enough originality of treatment in parts of this book to commend it to those who wish to study the connexion between the progress of discovery and the facts of geography.

I hope that the maps will be of real help in the reading of this book, but they are in no sense to be regarded as a substitute for a good atlas, since they do not show all the places mentioned in the text, and all but essential details have been omitted from them. For their compilation I am greatly indebted to Miss M. M. Middleton, who has generously given much time and skill in transforming my own rough sketches.

My thanks are due to those who have helped me at various stages in the preparation of this book ; to Mr E. Heawood and the Library staff of the Royal Geographical Society ; to Mr J. H. Reynolds ; and to Mr P. A. Seymour. I am specially indebted to Mr E. W. Gilbert, Lecturer in Geography in the University of Reading, who read the greater part of the manuscript and made a

3

number of useful suggestions, particularly in the chapters relating to North America; and to Dr R. N. Rudmose Brown, who not only gave me the benefit of his expert advice on the chapters relating to Polar exploration, but has helped me in ways too numerous to mention at every stage in my work.

For permission to make long extracts from their published works I am indebted to the Council of the Royal Geographical Society; to the Council of the Hakluyt Society; to Mr John Murray, who has allowed me to quote extensively from Sir H. Yule's *The Book of Ser Marco Polo*, Sir A. Kitson's *Life of James Cook*, and the various works of Livingstone; to Messrs Sampson Low, Marston and Co., Ltd., for similar permission to use H. M. Stanley's *Through the Dark Continent*; and to Messrs George Routledge and Sons, Ltd., for permission to quote from several volumes in their excellent "Broadway Travellers" series. For permission to reproduce Figs. 1 and 2 my thanks are due to Dr M. Cary and Mr E. H. Warmington, and to Messrs Methuen and Co., the publishers of their *Ancient Explorers*. Grateful acknowledgment is due also to Messrs George Philip and Son, Ltd., for supplying the drawing of Behaim's globe reproduced as the frontispiece.

J. N. L. B.

September 1931

PREFACE TO THE SECOND EDITION

THE chief changes in the present edition are the correction of known mistakes, the alteration of statements as required by recent research, and the addition both of references to explorations made since 1930 and of new works.

My thanks are due to many kind critics, whether reviewers or correspondents, who have helped me in this task, and to those who, in using the first edition, have been good enough to refer to it in generous terms. Limitations of space have not allowed me to adopt all the suggestions I have received, and I regret particularly that I could not refer at greater length to the theoretical side of exploration, which is so important. I hope the addition to the bibliography of several works dealing with this subject will help students to remedy this defect.

I am again particularly grateful to Professor R. N. Rudmose Brown and to Mr E. W. Gilbert for their help.

J. N. L. B.

August 1937

CONTENTS

PART I

BEFORE THE NINETEENTH CENTURY

GEOGRAPHICAL DISCOVERY AND EXPLORATION

PART II

THE NINETEENTH CENTURY AND AFTER

CONTENTS

ABBREVIATIONS

J.R.G.S. : *Journal of the Royal Geographical Society.*
Proc. R.G.S. : *Proceedings of the Royal Geographical Society.*
G.J. : *Geographical Journal.*
P.M. : *Petermann's Mitteilungen.*

MAPS

9

BIBLIOGRAPHICAL NOTE

THE following list is not exhaustive : for more complete bibliographical notices the *Geographisches Jahrbuch* should be consulted. The most recent collected bibliography is that of K. Kretschmer, *Die Literatur zur Geschichte der Erdkunde vom Mittelalter an* (1907–25), in Band xli of that work, while the same article refers to similar compilations covering the period from 1883 onward. The York Gate Library catalogue (second edition, 1886), the *Catalogue of the Library of the Royal Geographical Society* (1895), and the *Katalog der Bibliothek der Gesellschaft für Erdkunde zu Berlin* (1903) may still be consulted with profit. The *Bibliographie géographique*, which has appeared annually either in the *Annales de géographie* or separately since 1891, and is now enlarged and known, since 1931, as *Bibliographie géographique internationale*, should be consulted for recent publications.

At the beginning of each chapter, or in the footnotes, will be found references to works bearing particularly on that region or period : these are, with one or two exceptions, not mentioned below.

WORKS COVERING THE WHOLE PERIOD UP TO THE DATE OF THEIR PUBLICATION

The History of Maritime and Inland Discovery ("Lardner's Cabinet Cyclopedia"), 3 vols. (1833).

V. SAINT-MARTIN, *Histoire de la géographie et des découvertes géographiques* (1873).

O. PESCHEL, *Geschichte der Erdkunde*, 2nd edition, edited by S. Ruge (1877).

F. P. LEMOSOF, *Le Livre d'or de la géographie* (1902). Brief biographical notices of explorers up to the end of the nineteenth century.

M. B. SYNGE, *A Book of Discovery* (1912). An account of the more important explorers.

J. JACOBS, *Geographical Discovery*, revised edition. A useful sketch ending about the year 1912.

J. S. KELTIE and O. J. R. HOWARTH, *History of Geography* (1913). A short, excellent sketch, including much geographical discovery.

R. E. DICKINSON and O. J. R. HOWARTH, *The Making of Geography* (1933).

SIR PERCY SYKES, *A History of Exploration* (1934).

L. OUTHWAITE, *Unrolling the Map* (1935).

The Romance of Exploration (1936) (Anonymous).

O. OLSEN, *La Conquête de la terre* (6 vols., 1933–37).

COVERING SHORTER PERIODS, OR DEALING WITH
SPECIAL TOPICS

F. EMBACHER, *Die wichtigeren Forschungsreisen des neunzehnten Jahrhunderts* (1880). A useful chronological summary.

C. R. LOWE, *Maritime Discovery* (2 vols., 1881). Deals with maritime exploration from the earliest times.

S. RUGE, *Geschicte des Zeitalters der Entdeckungen* (1881). The best work dealing fully with this period.

R. CRONAU, *Amerika : Die Geschicte seiner Entdeckung* . . . (2 vols., 1896).

J. KEANE, *The Evolution of Geography* (1899). A useful sketch up to and including Magellan's voyage.

S. GÜNTHER, *Entdeckungsgeschicte und Fortschritte der wissenschaftclichen Geographie im neunzehnten Jahrhundert* (1902). The best account of this period.

P. GAFFAREL, *Histoire de l'expansion coloniale de la France depuis 1870 jusqu'en 1905* (1905).

C. G. D. ROBERTS, *Discoveries and Explorations in the [Nineteenth] Century* (1906). The only work of its kind in English.

H. MEYER, *Das deutsche Kolonialreich* (2 vols., 1909–10).

E. HEAWOOD, *A History of Geographical Discovery in the Seventeenth and Eighteenth Centuries* (1912). Invaluable for this period.

S. GÜNTHER, *Das Zeitalter der Entdeckungen* (4th edition, 1919). A short but useful sketch with a select bibliography.

G. FRIEDERICI, *Der Charakter der Entdeckung und Eroberung Amerikas durch die Europäer* (3 vols., 1925–36).

V. T. HARLOW, *Voyages of the Great Pioneers* (1929).

H. R. MILL, *Record of the Royal Geographical Society* (1930).

E. G. R. TAYLOR, *Tudor Geography, 1485–1583* (1930).

A. P. NEWTON (ed.), *The Great Age of Discovery* (1932).

H. E. BURTON, *The Discovery of the Ancient World* (1932).

G. C. HENDERSON, *The Discoverers of the Fiji Islands* (1933).

J. E. GILLESPIE, *A History of Geographical Discovery, 1400–1800* (1933).

E. G. R. TAYLOR, *Late Tudor and Early Stuart Geography* (1934).

J. C. BEAGLEHOLE, *The Exploration of the Pacific* (1934).

J. HOLLAND ROSE, *Man and the Sea* (1935).

SIR CLEMENTS MARKHAM and J. S. KELTIE, "Review of British Geographical Work, 1789–1889," in *Royal Geographical Society Supplementary Papers*, vol. iii, pp. 149–199.

Papers dealing with the work of other nations during the nineteenth century up to 1889 will be found in the *Report of the Fourth International Geographical Congress*, 1889.

Similar papers covering the period from 1889 to 1912 (approximately) are reprinted in the *Report of the Tenth International Geographical Congress*, 1913. In particular mention should be made of those on the

BIBLIOGRAPHICAL NOTE

work of Britain (by O. J. R. Howarth and Miss M. I. Newbigin), of France (by G. Grandidier), and of Germany (by F. Hahn).

Useful summaries of exploration, and many maps, will be found in E. Reclus' *Géographie universelle* and in the *Allgemeine Länderkunde*.

The early collections of travel are dealt with in M. Böhme, *Die grossen Reisesammlungen des 16. Jahrhunderts und ihre Bedeutung* (1904). For an account of the more important English collections of travel, from Hakluyt to Pinkerton, reference may be made to the writer's paper, " Some Sources for the History of Exploration," in *The Geographical Teacher*, vol. xiii, p. 307.

A very large number of original authorities have been reprinted by the Hakluyt Society. Between 1847 and 1898 this society issued a hundred volumes in its first series ; since that year seventy-nine volumes have been issued in the second series. In addition, the society has published an edition of the collections of Hakluyt and Purchas and of the narratives of John de Plano Carpini and William de Rubruquis. Many of these volumes contain introductory material and explanatory notes of great value. These works are indispensable.

For the nineteenth century the publications of the Royal Geographical Society are invaluable, containing accounts of, or references to, the most important discoveries. These are (1) the *Journal of the Royal Geographical Society* (50 vols., 1830–80) ; (2) the *Proceedings of the Royal Geographical Society* (old series, 22 vols., 1855–78 ; new series, 14 vols., 1879–92) ; (3) the *Geographical Journal* (since 1893 : 2 volumes yearly) ; (4) *Supplementary Papers* (4 vols., 1881–93). The index volumes, particularly to the *Proceedings* and the *Geographical Journal*, and the index to supplements to the *Geographical Journal* (1918–32), are indispensable.

Among the foreign periodicals *Petermann's Mitteilungen* stands preeminent, and is particularly valuable for its maps. It has been indexed from its beginning in 1855 to 1934.

PART I

BEFORE THE NINETEENTH CENTURY

CHAPTER I

THE MEDITERRANEAN WORLD [1]

I. INTRODUCTION

THE history of geographical discovery tells of the evolution of the map of the world from its simplest and most elementary beginnings in antiquity to the highly specialized form which is known to-day. To preserve continuity in the story it is not necessary to go farther back than to the Greeks, who did more than any other early people to develop the science of geography, and acquired a considerable knowledge of the world. Other peoples, neighbours of the Greeks or directly associated with the Mediterranean region, come into the picture from time to time, but their contributions were relatively small, or were made so long ago that all record of them has been lost.

The first people who need be considered are the Minoans, whose civilization in Crete spread to the lands of the Eastern Mediterranean, and may even have reached the Atlantic. The island of Crete was naturally favoured for the dispersion of culture, and the Minoans came to know Egypt, and to exchange products with the Egyptians, as early as 2000 B.C. Later they extended their knowledge to Cyprus and the Levant in the east, and to Sicily and Italy in the west. Perhaps, too, they learned something of the whole of the Western Mediterranean, although of this there is no certainty. But by the year 1000 B.C. the unsettled conditions in the Mediterranean region led to a cessation of Minoan activity.

The Phœnicians succeeded to the Minoans as leaders in geographical exploration. They too were helped by certain geographical advantages in their homeland, for the coastline of the Eastern Mediterranean improves north of the Carmel peninsula, and the mountains, coming nearer to the sea, throw off peninsulas and

---

[1] The standard authorities for this period are:

E. H. BUNBURY. *A History of Ancient Geography* (2 vols., 1879).
H. F. TOZER, *A History of Ancient Geography* (2nd edition, with additional notes by M. Cary, 1935).
M. CARY and E. H. WARMINGTON, *The Ancient Explorers* (1929).
W. H. SCHOFF, *The Periplus of the Erythræan Sea* (1912).

islands, making harbours sufficiently good for ships of light draught ; south of the Carmel peninsula there are no natural harbours, and the silt brought by currents from the North African coast is an insuperable difficulty. The Phœnician cities grew up on this northern coastline, within sight of Cyprus, which itself was within easy reach of Asia Minor and the Ægean Sea. Local products, like the cedar-trees, the sand—useful for the glass industry—or the murex from which ' purple ' was obtained, formed the basis of trade, while through the mountains or along the coastal plain routes led to the richer countries of Mesopotamia and Egypt. It is probable that the Phœnicians were immigrants from the Persian Gulf, where they had learnt their seamanship, and that some of their progress was due to influences received from Cyprus, whither they had come from Crete.

Phœnician exploration did not extend as far as has sometimes been assumed. In the Mediterranean the Phœnicians dominated the Levant by about 1200 B.C., and soon after displaced the Minoans in the western basin.

The Greeks in turn succeeded to the Phœnicians, and with them progress is more continuous and knowledge more certain. Their earliest notions, as revealed in the Homeric poems, were very limited, for although certain facts stand out with almost striking clarity—the lotus of Tripoli, Charybdis (Straits of Messina), the winds and weather of the Mediterranean Sea—their geographical horizon was not far distant from Greece.

The remarkable expansion of ' Greece ' which began about the year 800 B.C. materially contributed to the growth of geographical knowledge. In this unsystematic movement of fishermen, merchants, pirates, and colonists the Greeks spread themselves over the Mediterranean waters, and by the year 500 B.C. had some general knowledge of the whole of their shores. Egypt and the coasts of Cyrene were known by about 650 B.C., Sicily had been reached by 800 B.C., Colæus discovered the Straits of Gibraltar about 650 B.C., and Massilia dates from about 600 B.C. In the Adriatic, and particularly on the eastern shore, Greek traders were active, and Hecatæus, who wrote about 500 B.C., was able to make use of the information they obtained. In the Black Sea the fish and the minerals of Northern Asia Minor attracted the Greek traders, and from 800 B.C. onward they gained increasing knowledge of the coastal fringe.

II. Exploration by Sea

The one connecting-link between the Greek colonies was the sea, and it was on the sea that geographical knowledge made its earliest progress. It will therefore be convenient to deal first with the

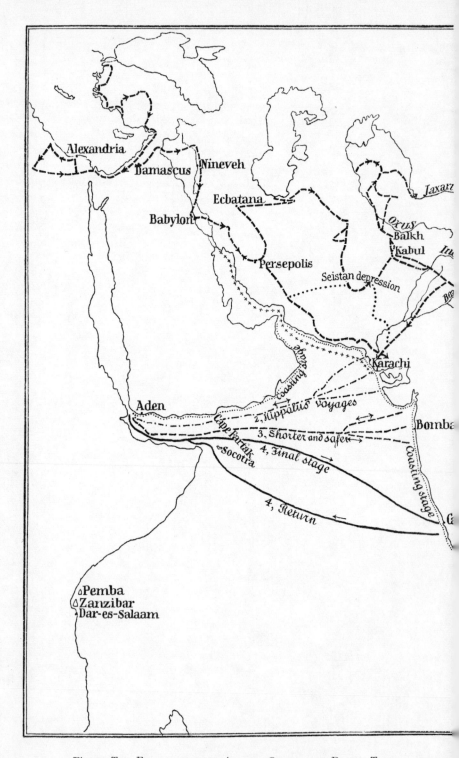

Fig. 1. THE EXPLORATION OF ASIA IN GREEK AND ROMAN TIMES

The voyage of the trader Alexander was made during the reign of the Emperor Hadrian, and should not be confused with the explorations of Alexander the Great.

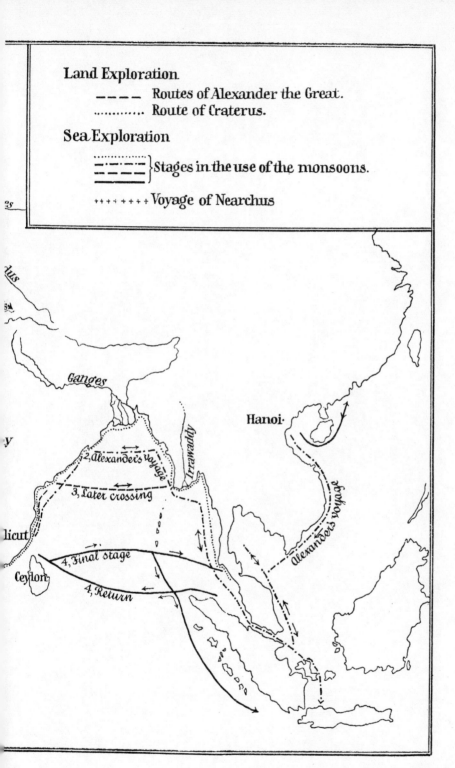

Land Exploration
      – – – – Routes of Alexander the Great.
      .... Route of Craterus.
Sea Exploration
      } Stages in the use of the monsoons.
      ++ ++ ++ ++ Voyage of Nearchus

Ganges

Hanoi.

Irrawaddy

2, Alexander's voyage

3, Later crossing

Alexander's voyage

licut

4, Final stage

Ceylon

4, Return

sea expansion of the Greeks, and for this purpose it is necessary to look first to the Erythræan Sea (*i.e.*, the Indian Ocean). Here the pioneers of exploration were the sailors of Egypt and the kingdoms of Mesopotamia, while the Phœnicians, who sailed their "ships of Tarshish "[1] on the waters of the Red Sea, were also active long before the arrival of the Greeks. But about the year 510 B.C. a Greek named Scylax was sent by King Darius of Persia to explore the river Indus. He is said to have followed the river eastward to the sea—but this may refer to his starting-point (*i.e.*, the Kabul river)—and then to have reached the Red Sea. There seems to have been some confusion about the results of this voyage, and some deny that it was ever made ; yet it is difficult to account for such knowledge of Southern Arabia as Herodotus possessed without admitting the genuineness of the exploit of Scylax.

More important, however, was the voyage of Nearchus, undertaken in order to transport a part of the army of Alexander from India to the Persian Gulf. Nearchus was instructed to examine the details of the route along which he sailed, and carried out his orders with such care that it is still possible to identify many of the places described by him, in spite of known changes in the coastline. The voyage from the Indus to the Tigris took five months, but this included two long delays, first in the " port of Alexandria," perhaps near, but not necessarily the same as, the modern Karachi, and again at the other end of the route, at the mouth of the Sitacus river. Nearchus was assisted by a native pilot, whose presence shows that the voyage was not one of real discovery.

Alexander projected the exploration of the coasts of Arabia, but all that was done before his death in 323 B.C. was to examine the western shore of the Persian Gulf, the eastern shore of the Red Sea, and the coast of Hadramaut.

Shortly after this the Ptolemy dynasty in Egypt (323 B.C.) began the exploration of the Red Sea, and during the next century considerable progress was made. Somaliland was frequently visited, as well as parts of Egypt which could be approached from the Red Sea. The exploration was partly of a military character, and received much stimulus from the elephant trade. When, however, the Western Mediterranean began to require more luxury articles the elephant trade gave way to commerce in less bulky commodities, and the Greeks began to make longer voyages, which ultimately took them to India.

The first Greek to reach India from Egypt was Eudoxus. On the first occasion (*c.* 120 B.C.) he was accompanied by an Indian who had been blown from India to the coast of Africa, while on his return from the second voyage (*c.* 115 B.C.) Eudoxus himself was driven out of his course on to the Ethiopian shore. There he

[1] Doubtless a general term. *Cf.* "East Indiaman." Tartessus was in Spain.

discovered traces of a ship which had come, men said, from Gades, and he determined to make a third voyage to India from Spain. He sailed along the coast of Morocco, and obtained evidence on which he concluded that the whole voyage was practicable ; but after re-turning to fit out a larger expedition he was lost, and the whole exploit became surrounded with fable.

The advent of the Roman power in Egypt after 30 B.C., and the increase in luxury trade, led to greater commerce on the Indian Ocean, and to the discovery of the sailing route to India. At first traders followed the coast round from the mouth of the Red Sea to some port on the west coast of India. This was a lengthy, slow, and expensive business, and it was not until early in the reign of Tiberius (A.D. 14–37) that a trader named Hippalus discovered the use of the monsoon winds by sailing direct from Cape Fartak to the delta of the Indus. This was a discovery of the greatest importance, and it has been said that " Hippalus deserves as much honour in Roman annals as does Columbus in modern history." [1] It was, however, improved upon by successive traders, who first began to sail from some point near the modern Aden to Bombay, and finally (c. A.D. 50) shaped a course from Aden to ports on the southern part of the Indian coast. The result of these discoveries was a considerable increase in the trade of the Indian Ocean, and a very material advance in geographical knowledge.

The changed situation is reflected in the important *Periplus of the Erythræan Sea*, written about the year A.D. 60, apparently for the use of merchants. It describes the coast of Africa for a considerable distance beyond Cape Guardafui, and in outline to the modern Zanzibar. The southern coast of Arabia and the greater part of the west coast of India also receive minute and accurate treatment. Beyond these points the author is less accurate, although he had heard of Ceylon, the Malay Peninsula, and China. He refers to the silk trade of the latter country, which is said to follow one of two routes, the first leading through Central Asia to Bactria, and the second crossing the mountains to India, and making use of the Ganges valley. This implies that at the time the *Periplus* was written Roman merchants did not know that it was possible to reach China by sea.

During the century which followed the writing of the *Periplus* the farthest limits of Greek and Roman penetration in the Indian Ocean were reached. On the African coast traders pushed to Zanzibar and beyond, perhaps as far as Dar-es-Salaam. Of India they gained greater knowledge by frequenting some of the more important cities. They discovered a sailing route across the Bay of Bengal during the reign of Hadrian (117–138), established direct contact with China in 166, and reached the port of Cattigara (? Hanoi) in Cochin-China.

[1] Schoff, *Periplus of the Erythræan Sea*, p. 6.

Yet the knowledge thus obtained was confused by the geographers. Ptolemy made many mistakes about the Far East, and assumed that beyond the coasts of China there lay another land which was connected to Africa, and so turned the Indian Ocean into a vast lake.

By contrast with their expansion over the Indian Ocean, the Greeks and Romans made comparatively little advance in the Atlantic. It is possible that a single Greek trader, Midacritus, reached Brittany or Cornwall in search of tin before the year

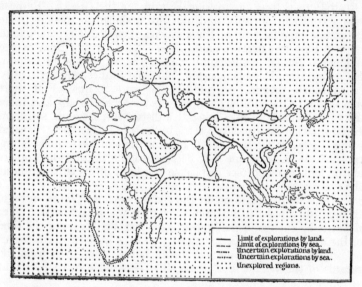

Fig. 2. THE WORLD AS DISCOVERED BY ANCIENT EXPLORERS

500 B.C., but this was an isolated venture, and its repetition was made impossible by the growing power of Carthage.

The Carthaginians made at least two important Atlantic voyages. About the year 500 B.C. Himilco visited the west coast of Europe, and reached Ireland. From the vague and unsatisfactory accounts of the voyage preserved by Avienus in his *Ora Maritima*, dating from the fourth century A.D., it appears that Himilco either explored the Atlantic Ocean or was blown across it to the Sargasso Sea, though Dr Cary finds no need to carry the Carthaginians so far, and declares that all the phenomena mentioned could be found near Gades. It is clear that, whatever the ultimate end, the voyage was of small importance.

More successful, however, was the expedition of Hanno, who was sent, about 470 B.C., to establish Carthaginian settlements on the west coast of Africa, and is said to have taken 30,000 people with him. Doubtless this is an exaggeration, but Hanno succeeded in planting a colony on the west coast, and made exploratory voyages about as far south as Sierra Leone. The descriptions of the geographical features along the coast, the grass fires in the interior, and the gorillas (*i.e.*, chimpanzees) leave no room to doubt the genuineness of the voyage, but it became surrounded by fable, and Pliny states that Hanno sailed round Africa to Arabia.

About the time that Nearchus was sailing the waters of the Indian Ocean Pytheas was discovering Britain for the Greeks. Pytheas was a trader of Massilia, and was also a skilled astronomer. He determined the latitude of Massilia with remarkable accuracy, and he was able to make valuable observations on the tides of the Atlantic. But of greatest importance was his voyage to Britain. He set out from Massilia, coasted Spain and France, and apparently sailed round Britain. In addition he made a number of short journeys into the interior, and collected information about a more distant land called Thule, lying at a distance of six days' sail from Britain. This may perhaps refer to Iceland.[1] He then travelled along the North German coast, but the limit of his journey is uncertain. Some maintain that he reached the Baltic, while others are perhaps more correct in placing the limit of his exploration at the river Elbe.

There is no reason to doubt the genuineness of Pytheas' voyage, though geographers like Strabo thought it was a fabrication. Yet the striking change in the knowledge of the West between the time of the *Periplus* of Scylax (*c.* 336 B.C.) and the work of Eratosthenes (*c.* 240 B.C.) must in some way be explained, and, apart from the records of the voyage of Pytheas, it is reasonable to connect that advance with his exploration.

No farther advance in the Atlantic Ocean was made until the beginning of the first century B.C., when traders other than Phœnicians or Carthaginians reached the " tin islands " of Scilly, but this voyage was of little importance. With the invasion of Britain by Cæsar, however, a new era began, and thereafter Britain was regularly visited, and remained no longer a land of mystery. After A.D. 43 the Roman generals began the systematic conquest of the island, and thereby extended geographical knowledge practically to the limits of the coastline.

Meanwhile Roman fleets had sailed along the northern coast of Germany, reaching the Ems river in 12 B.C. and the entrance to the Baltic in A.D. 5. This marked the limit of exploration eastward in the Atlantic.

Of the African islands, the Canaries, which had almost certainly been seen by the Carthaginians, were effectively explored by Juba

[1] Dr Cary rejects the suggestion of Iceland, and prefers Norway.

after 25 B.C., while Madeira, which may have been visited in the fifth century, was rediscovered in 80 B.C. A recent attempt has been made to prove that the Carthaginians also reached the Azores, but the evidence, in the shape of coins, is not entirely satisfactory, and it is doubtful whether the sailors of the Mediterranean world ever penetrated so far to the west.

There remain for consideration certain voyages which had for their object the circumnavigation of Africa. The limits of Phœnician navigation in the Indian Ocean are not known with certainty, but it may be assumed that at least they reached the entrance to the Red Sea; some critics extend their journeys much farther, and if the story of Herodotus is believed they were the first to circumnavigate Africa. According to this account, Pharaoh Necho sent an expedition to the east coast of Africa, and its leader returned through the Straits of Gibraltar (*c.* 600 B.C.). The voyage took two years; the geographical conditions do not make such a feat impossible; and the problem of supplies, always a difficulty until quite recent times, was solved by landing, sowing corn, and waiting for it to ripen.

Much controversy surrounds the story, but the truth is that it can be neither proved nor disproved. All that can usefully be said is that it exerted no strong influence on later geographical thought, and none at all on human action.

A voyage made by order of King Xerxes of Persia about 485 B.C. also had for its object the circumnavigation of Africa. This time it was undertaken by Sataspes, who tried the reverse route to the Phœnicians, sailed through the Straits of Gibraltar, and reached a country inhabited by a race of small people. The difficulties of navigation made progress impossible, and Sataspes returned. There is no doubt about the reality of those difficulties, and it may be that Sataspes told the truth about his voyage. At least the evidence is sufficient, although the failure to carry out the whole voyage cost Sataspes his life when he returned. A third voyage, that of Eudoxus, has already been mentioned in connexion with his Indian exploits, and with this the attempts to sail round Africa come to an end. The classical world reached the conclusion that what had not been done could never be done, and Ptolemy brought his west coast of Africa to an abrupt and unsatisfactory end on the edge of the map, and cut off all entrance to the Indian Ocean by a great unknown land.

III. EXPLORATION BY LAND

The continent in which greatest progress was made during the classical period was Asia, and with that continent the story of land exploration may fittingly begin. Here, as on the Indian Ocean,

23

the pioneers were not the Greeks. Assyrian armies penetrated into the recesses of Armenia and to Asia Minor, as well as to the borders of Egypt, while the Egyptians extended their own knowledge as far as the valleys of the Euphrates and the Tigris.

The spread of Greek colonies round the borders of Asia Minor and their trading activities naturally led to a gradual acquisition of knowledge of that region, but it was not until about the year 600 B.C. that the Greeks appear to have reached Mesopotamia. The rise of the Persian Empire, however, gave them greater opportunities, and the royal road through Asia Minor to Susa afforded an easy line of approach. The result of this new contact is, perhaps, reflected in the writings of Hecatæus (c. 500 B.C.), who knew something of Western India, the Persian Gulf, and the Caspian Sea, and is the first to make mention of the river Indus.

The Greeks continued to frequent Asia, and when Herodotus wrote his *History* (c. 443) he was able to add considerably to the geography of the continent. Much of his information was scrappy and inaccurate, but he did not profess to be writing a geographical account. A few parts, such as Mesopotamia, he knew from personal experience ; for other regions of the Persian Empire he seems to have drawn upon some official and statistical information. Of the lands to the north of the Black Sea he had also much new knowledge to record, for Greeks had penetrated the Steppe land east of the Don, then considered to be the boundary of Asia, and had learnt something of that vast open country, which degenerates into desert on the east and stretches northward to the Ural Mountains. The details of the Caucasus Mountains and the Caspian Sea are also, on the whole, accurately known.

In other ways the Greeks were increasing their knowledge of Asia. Ctesias (c. 398 B.C.) gave an account of the routes from Asia Minor to India, and during his residence at the Persian Court collected highly coloured stories about the latter country. In Asia Minor and in Armenia the marches of the Greeks, graphically described by Xenophon, led to greater and more detailed knowledge of the difficult mountain regions through which they passed.

But the most decisive event in the progress of geography was the great march of Alexander from Greece to India. It is not necessary to follow him through the country already known in outline—that is, Asia Minor, Syria, and Mesopotamia. In 331 B.C. he defeated Darius at the battle of Arbela, to the south of Nineveh, crossed the western mountains of Persia, and marched to Persepolis, where he spent the winter. In the following spring Alexander moved to Ecbatana, the modern Hamadan, where he established a depot preparatory to his conquest of the remainder of the Persian Empire. After some minor campaigns in the difficult mountain region that lies to the south of the Caspian Sea Alexander marched eastward to

Bactria, but on the way was obliged to make a diversion to the southward, which took him as far as the Seistan depression in Persia. Returning by the Helmand valley, he reached the foot of the Hindu Kush Mountains, where he remained for the rest of the winter. Early in 329 B.C. Alexander crossed the Hindu Kush to Balkh, whence he pushed on to the valleys of the Oxus and the Jaxartes. The latter river marked the limit of his progress in Central Asia, and was thought to be not only the boundary of Asia, but also the same as the Don river of Southern Russia. A number of minor expeditions were now made against the tribes of the mountain country of Turkestan, after which Alexander recrossed the Hindu Kush, and late in the year 327 invaded India, one portion of his army advancing by the Khyber Pass and crossing the Indus at Attock, and a second, under his personal command, approaching by the more devious route through Chitral, where Sir Aurel Stein has recently found interesting relics of the march. The Punjab was invaded, and the Greek army penetrated as far as the river Beas, when a mutiny made retreat necessary. Following the Indus to the south, to the neighbourhood of the modern Hyderabad, Alexander sent some of his troops home by sea under the command of Nearchus, but himself conducted a second detachment through the very difficult country of Makran and Southern Persia. The march was made in the heat of the summer, and many of the troops and animals died on the way. Alexander kept close to the shore of the Arabian Sea, and when he arrived at Gulashkird was joined by the third branch of the army, under Craterus, who had followed a more northerly route through Persia. Alexander had thus returned to that portion of Asia which was well known before his expedition, and his subsequent visits to Susa and Ecbatana added little fresh knowledge, while the projected expedition to Arabia never took place, owing to his death in 323 B.C.

The magnitude of the work of Alexander the Great makes it difficult to realize the revolution in geographical knowledge that resulted from his campaigns. The Greeks were brought into contact with a new world, and the old, vague rumours of the country to the east of Mesopotamia were converted into real knowledge of Persia, a small but very important part of Central Asia, and Western India. Not only were the geographical features of these new countries brought to light, but the campaigns gave the Greeks first-hand knowledge of a great number of isolated geographical facts of which they had hitherto been ignorant. The great mountain chains of Asia and the river system of Western India, to mention but two, were important not only for the geography of Asia, but also for the study of geography in general, for the Greeks could find nothing like them in their own country. Thus both in general and in regional geography these expeditions were of the greatest importance.

Further knowledge of India came from the embassy of Megasthenes (*c.* 29′ B.C.), who lived for some time in the valley of the Ganges—a region hitherto unvisited by the Greeks—and wrote an account of the country and its people. His knowledge was confined to the great Indo-Gangetic plain, and although he had heard of Ceylon as a large island lying a considerable distance from the coast, he was ignorant both of the peninsula of India and of the delta of the Ganges. The most important single feature of Indian agriculture, the summer monsoon, was noticed by Megasthenes, as well as the general social and economic condition of the people. His work remained the chief authority on India during the classical period.

About the same time a project of Alexander was revived, and Patrocles was sent to explore the Caspian Sea in order to discover a new route to India. He was only able to examine the southern part of the sea, but he collected information about neighbouring regions, and unfortunately concluded that there was a sea-route from the Caspian to India. Much confusion followed from his reports, but at least they seemed to confirm the wrong belief that the Caspian was connected with the Northern Ocean.

The coming of the Romans to Asia, and particularly the formation of the province of Asia (Western Asia Minor) in 126 B.C., led to further exploration of this region and of parts of Armenia. It was to the knowledge which directly resulted from the Mithridatic wars that Strabo (*c.* A.D. 19) was indebted for his improved account of these regions.

In Arabia also the Romans made an important advance. Apart from a few indications of trade-routes, the country was practically unknown until Gallus, in 25 B.C., led an expedition from Haura, on the Red Sea coast, in the north of Hejaz, to the borders of Hadramaut. The object of the expedition, according to Strabo, was " to conciliate or subdue the Arabians." That writer adds :

He [Augustus] was also influenced by the report which had prevailed from all time, that this people were very wealthy, and exchanged their aromatics and precious stones for silver and gold, but never expended with foreigners any part of what they received in exchange. He hoped to acquire either opulent friends, or to overcome opulent enemies.

The failure to discover this El Dorado was attributed to treachery on the part of allies who

neither guided them by a safe course by sea along the coast, nor by a safe road for the army, but exposed both the fleet and the army to danger, by directing them where there was no road, or the road was impracticable, where they were obliged to make long circuits, or to pass through tracts of country destitute of everything.[1]

From this account it may be inferred that the Romans saw Arabia

[1] The quotations are from H. C. Hamilton and W. Falconer's translation of Strabo ("Bohn's Library," 3 vols., 1854–57), vol. iii, p. 210.

as it really was, and found it necessary to excuse a failure. Yet if Gallus did all that he is reputed to have done his journey was remarkable, and his is the only exploration of Arabia undertaken in classical times.

In other directions also the Romans made advances. They penetrated to the east of the Euphrates after 20 B.C., and Greeks in their service reached Merv and Kandahar. One hundred and forty years later a merchant had followed up the silk route beyond Merv and Kashgar, and his agents gained some general knowledge of China. Still later these traders reached the Lob Nor. Thus by

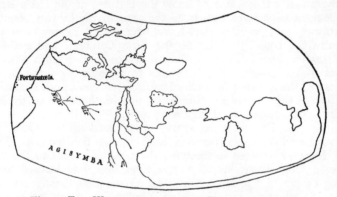

Fig. 3. THE WORLD ACCORDING TO PTOLEMY, c. A.D. 150

land, as well as by sea, the Romans had come into direct contact with the Chinese.

By the time of Ptolemy (c. 150) the bounds of Roman knowledge in Asia had been considerably extended. A glance at his map will show some of the serious errors into which he fell. He was quite wrong about the whole of the southern coastline of Asia, and assumed that beyond China there was land, while the island of Ceylon was magnified out of all recognition. Yet he reflected the new developments along the Chinese trade-route and corrected the former errors about the Caspian Sea. This latter improvement was due to Roman exploration in the Caucasus region and the lands round the Black Sea, although there is reason to believe that Ptolemy did not do full justice to the new information which had been obtained. Yet a comparison of the information of Ptolemy with that of any of his predecessors shows how extensive was knowledge in his day. If many of his ideas were wrong, at least he bears witness to the spread of geographical knowledge from the Ægean to the borders of China.

The geographical conditions which have delayed the progress of African exploration in modern times also prevented the peoples of

27

the Mediterranean world from making much advance. There is only one entrance to the country from the north—that is, by the Nile valley ; elsewhere the desert presents a barrier which has been almost insuperable until quite recent times. Even in the Nile valley the extent of the sudd region made exploration very difficult, and no one in classical times passed beyond this obstacle. It marked the limit of penetration by the Egyptians, the first of the African explorers ; it stopped the advance of Nero's expedition, the last that tried to advance up the Nile during classical times.

Early in the sixth century the Greeks were established in Egypt, and gradually they came to know the features of the Delta lands, while some penetrated farther, to the oases of the Libyan Desert or southward into Nubia. Herodotus, who visited Egypt, knew personally the country as far as the First Cataract, and gathered information about the more distant Meroë in the south and the oases of the desert. Yet he seems to be quite ignorant of the extent of the Sahara ; he guessed wrongly, like many other classical writers, at the cause of the Nile flood ; and he thought that the Nile in its upper course flowed from west to east.

Under the Ptolemies exploration progressed more rapidly, but they reached the upper course of the river from the Red Sea. They did, however, succeed in verifying the reported source of the Blue Nile in Lake Tana, known to the Egyptians, and learned something of the highlands of Abyssinia. From Egypt, too, there was a steady advance, and the vague information about the country beyond the great bend of the Nile was gradually replaced by more accurate knowledge. Hence by the time of Strabo the Nile to Meroë and the oases of the Libyan Desert were well known, while there was some, though less certain, knowledge of Abyssinia and Somaliland.

The Romans added more precise information about the borders of Abyssinia, finding another way thither as a result of their campaign against the Queen of Ethiopia in 25 B.C., while in the reign of Nero they undertook an expedition to explore the sources of the Nile. This latter party reached the sudd region, which is well described by Seneca.[1] The men arrived at impenetrable marshes, and saw two rocks from which fell a river with great force. The latter statement presents a difficulty, but it need not be assumed that Nero's party ever saw the Ripon Falls, which Speke reported were called " the Stones " by the natives. Although this expedition failed in its main purpose, it penetrated farther than any other Greek or Roman had done in the valley of the Nile, and its limit was not passed until the nineteenth century. One other valuable piece of information about the Nile region came from the activities of a trader, Diogenes, who seems to have pushed inland from the east

[1] *Naturales Quæstiones*, Book VI, § 8.

coast and to have seen the snow-covered mountains of Kenya and Kilimanjaro. He also heard of lakes in the interior, and may even have visited Lake Victoria, and have been told about the Ruwenzori group. As was almost inevitable, this information got muddled in the course of repetition, but Marinus and Ptolemy were both able to point to lake sources for the Nile, and if they fell into the mistake of supposing that the lakes were fed by the snows of Mounts Kenya and Kilimanjaro they at least made a happy guess at the real origin of the Nile.

For the knowledge of the rest of Africa, where exploration was entirely unconnected with that of the Nile basin, the classical world was chiefly indebted to the Romans, who displaced the Carthaginians after 146 B.C. The main outlines of the Atlas country from Tunis to Morocco were thus added to the map. Beyond this region few penetrated.

Herodotus had reported the story of some young men who crossed the desert from Libya and reached a river flowing from west to east. If this story is genuine there can be little doubt that they saw the Niger river, perhaps near to Timbuktu. But Herodotus drew a wrong conclusion from this discovery, for he made the Niger the upper course of the Nile. The region was never again visited during the classical period.

In 19 B.C. Balbus crossed from the coast of Tripoli to the region of Fezzan, and this journey may have been extended by Flaccus, in about A.D. 70, to the Sahara, and later by Maternus to the region of Lake Chad. Here perhaps is to be located the country of Agisymba, which Marinus placed south of the equator, but which seems to have been part of the Sudan.

Farther westward Paulinus crossed the Atlas Mountains in A.D. 42, and discovered the river Gir on the southern side. Some critics have tried to identify this river with the Niger, but such speculations are unnecessary. There is no reason to believe that Paulinus crossed the Sahara, and there are a number of streams on the southern borders of the Atlas region which might easily have been discovered. Further, some confusion has been introduced into the question of West African geography through attempts to attach too much precision to Ptolemy's statements. He was a skilled astronomer, but he had to rely for his data, in a great many cases, upon routes and estimated distances, with the result that his positions cannot possibly be accurate. Hence the attempt to locate Ptolemy's Nigir and Gir rivers is almost useless except as a pleasant recreation.

The exploration of the continent of Europe, so far as it was known in classical times, was very largely the work of Roman armies. The expansion of Greek colonies along many parts of the seaboard, and the activities of their traders from centres like

Massilia, contributed to the knowledge of small areas, but with a few exceptions they knew comparatively little of the interior.

Of the north-east—that is, Scythia—some vague knowledge had reached the Greeks in Homer's day, and Herodotus was able to add considerably to the accounts of the land north of the Black Sea. Yet here knowledge was limited to well-defined routes, and did not extend a great distance from the shores of the Euxine, and even as late as the time of Strabo the Dnieper was reported to be navigable only for a distance of about seventy miles. "Neither in ancient times nor in the Middle Ages did Mediterranean travellers pursue their explorations far northward into Russia." [1]

A second line of Greek advance was along the Lower Danube, which was comparatively well known by the time of Herodotus, though of its upper reaches he was quite ignorant. Here the Roman expedition under Tiberius, in 16 B.C., was the first to gain definite knowledge.

In France the Greek traders from Massilia advanced up the Rhône valley early in the fifth century, and seem to have heard of Lake Geneva, but here again knowledge was very scanty, and the real exploration of the country was due to Julius Cæsar. It is therefore to Roman campaigns that one must turn for an account of substantial geographical progress. In the Balkans a series of wars, beginning in 199 B.C. and continuing until 28 B.C., filled in many details wholly unknown to the Greeks. In the Alpine regions the invasions of the Carthaginians led to more direct knowledge, and Polybius was able to make a correct survey of several routes across the mountains. Similarly in Spain Roman conquerors brought the first accurate knowledge of the country behind the east coast plain. In France the campaigns of Cæsar and his lieutenants produced similar results, while those of Tiberius between 16 B.C. and A.D. 12 increased the knowledge of the South of Germany, and Drusus (9 B.C.) gathered information about North Germany as far as the river Elbe. Much of this new discovery is reflected in the pages of Strabo, whose *Geography* has been described by Bunbury as "not only the most important geographical work that has come down to us from antiquity, but . . . unquestionably one of the most important ever produced by any Greek or Roman writer." He collected all the available geographical material and reduced it to order, thus preserving a vast body of matter which would otherwise have been lost, and leaving a comprehensive system of geography. Although his work is not strictly a record of exploration it requires, and deserves, detailed treatment, especially since it contains much useful information about Europe.

Of all the authorities whom Stabo used, by far the most important is Eratosthenes ; he cites him continually, and from him he derived

---

[1] Cary and Warmington, *op. cit.*, p. 111.

both the plan of his work, and the greater part of his scientific views. After him come Hipparchus, Polybius, Ephorus, Artemidorus, and Posidonius, all of whom contributed extensive material for the treatment of various sides of his subject. In particular, it was from Polybius that he derived his interest in historical geography, and learnt to take a comprehensive view of the history of mankind, and of the earth's surface as the sphere of its operation and as modifying its development. Posidonius furnished him with a large store of observations about the phenomena of physical geography, together with miscellaneous information on numerous subjects which he had collected in the course of his extensive travels. Of this latter kind also were the valuable contributions of Artemidorus. Besides these, there were numerous other writers on geography, of whose compilations and narratives Strabo availed himself for special countries, and additional details were supplied from local sources.[1]

Strabo had poor ideas of the shape and form of the countries of Europe, but he had accumulated much geographical knowledge about them. Thus in Spain he speaks of the Pyrenees as " an unbroken chain of mountains stretching from north to south " and forming the boundary between Celtica and Iberia—a curious mixture of considerable and accurate knowledge with no sense of position. Of the peninsula as a whole, however, he gave a good description, and laid particular stress on that region known to the ancients as Tartessus, to Strabo as Bætica, and to modern geographers as Andalusia, of which he described the mineral and agricultural wealth. His account ends with descriptions of the Balearic Islands and of Gades.

In France, as in Spain, Strabo had a confused idea of the mountain systems, and the features of the west coast were imperfectly known. But of the country as a whole, and in particular of its southern and south-eastern parts, Strabo has left a good description. He derived much of his information from the writings of Cæsar, and relied on the same authority for Britain. Hence of the latter his account is meagre. The south coast he considered ran from opposite the Pyrenees to the mouth of the Rhine, a natural mistake in view of his errors in the topography of France and Spain, and as he thought this was the longest side of the island he placed its northern extremities too far south. To the north of Britain lay Ireland, but of these regions and of the Far North he had no knowledge, and rejected such facts as Pytheas had collected.[2]

Of the Alpine mountains and North Italy Strabo again had a good general idea, which two extracts will illustrate.

As for the Alps, their base is curved and gulf-like, with the cavities turned towards Italy ; the central parts of the gulf are near the Salassi, while the extremities take a turn the one as far as . . . the recesses of the Adriatic, the other to the Ligurian seaboard as far

[1] H. F. Tozer, *Selections from Strabo* (1893), p. 46.
[2] Maps of Spain and France will be found in vol. ii of the Loeb translation.

as Genua . . . where the Apennine Mountains join the Alps. But immediately at the base of the Alps there lies a considerable plain.[1]

Of the inner regions he says :

Throughout the whole of the mountainous country of the Alps there are, indeed, not only hilly districts which admit of good farming, but also glens which have been well built up by settlers ; the greater part, however, and in particular the neighbourhood of the mountain crests, where, as we know, the brigands used to congregate, is wretched and unfruitful, both on account of the frosts and of the ruggedness of the soil.[2]

Similar extracts would show his good general knowledge of Southern Italy. His account of the country round the Bay of Naples, " the most blest of all plains," with its wealth of grain and wine, and its enervating effect on the inhabitants, may be instanced as one of his many good descriptive pieces.

Northern Germany as far as the Elbe was described by Strabo less fully than the countries already considered, but again he showed a good general knowledge of its geography. Beyond the Elbe, however,

those parts of the country . . . near the ocean are wholly unknown to us. For of the men of earlier times I know of no one who has made this voyage along the coast to the eastern parts that extend as far as the mouth of the Caspian Sea.[3]

Southern Germany beyond the longitude of the Elbe was but vaguely known, being, as Strabo pointed out, the land about which fabulous stories were invented, including the mythical " Rhipæan Mountains " and " Hyperboreans." Of the regions to the north of the Black Sea Strabo knew very little. He says : " the whole country towards the north from Germany as far as the Caspian Sea is a plain, but whether any people dwell beyond the Roxolani we do not know." [4]

Strabo had little new information about the Balkan peninsula, but he recognized its main features, one of which, of great significance in the history of the region, is here described :

Now the whole Illyrian seaboard is exceedingly well supplied with harbours, not only on the continuous coast itself, but also in the neighbouring islands, although the reverse is the case with that part of the Italian seaboard which lies opposite, since it is harbourless. But both seaboards in like manner are sunny and good for fruits, for the olive and the vine flourish there, except, perhaps, in places here and there that are utterly rugged. . . . But the whole of the

---

[1] *The Geography of Strabo*, with an English translation by H. L. Jones (" Loeb Classical Library," 8 vols., 1917-32), vol. ii, p. 283.

[2] *Ibid.*, vol. ii, p. 283.

[3] *Ibid.*, vol. iii, p. 171.

[4] H. L. Jones, *op. cit.*, vol. iii, p. 223. The Roxolani " roam the plains between the Tanais [Don] and Borysthenes [Dnieper]."

country situated above this is mountainous, cold, and subject to snows, especially the northerly part, so that there is a scarcity of the vine not only on the heights, but also on the levels. These latter are the mountain plains.[1]

That part of the work which deals with Greece is the least satisfactory, and adds no new knowledge.

After the time of Strabo comparatively little progress was made. In Britain, as already described, the Roman armies marched throughout the country, with the result that its geography became better known. About the middle of the first century an unknown Roman knight crossed from Vienna to the shores of the Baltic, and this journey resulted in much greater knowledge about Northern Europe and Germany, while in Transylvania the successful campaigns of Trajan in the early years of the second century were " veritable journeys of exploration," [2] and led to the opening up of a new route through Moldavia to the Black Sea. This advance is recorded by Ptolemy, whose account of Britain and of the countries to the south of the Baltic Sea is much superior to that of any of his predecessors. With him the age of classical exploration ends for all practical purposes : Europe was now well known west of the Elbe and south of the Danube, and, with less accuracy, much farther to the eastward.[3]

[1] H. L. Jones, *op. cit.*, vol. iii, pp. 269–271.
[2] Cary and Warmington, *op. cit.*, p. 119.
[3] Ptolemy's work has recently been made available to students in an authoritative text for the first time by Professor J. Fischer in *Claudii Ptolemœi Geographiœ Codex Urbinas Grœcus* (4 vols., 1932). See the review by Mr E. Heawood in *G.J.*, vol. lxxxii, p. 65. See also *Geography of Claudius Ptolemy*, translated and edited by E. L. Stevenson, with an introduction by Professor J. Fischer (1932).

CHAPTER II

THE MIDDLE AGES [1]

I. To the Time of Marco Polo

THE geographical work of Ptolemy marks both the end of the great era of classical geography and the beginning of a period which can only be called one of decay. The great expeditions in Africa on which he relied for his geographical accounts were not repeated ; the trade with Asia passed into the hands of Oriental middlemen ; and in Europe the decline of the Roman Empire closed many areas to the people of the Mediterranean. From the third to the fifth century there was stagnation, relieved only by the journeys of Christian pilgrims to the East. Even in these cases, however, the contribution which was made to geographical discovery was very small. Thus one of the best known of the pilgrims, Etheria (St Sylvia) of Aquitaine, visited Lower Egypt, Sinaitic Arabia, Syria, and Mesopotamia, and reached Edessa, on the borders of Persia. She returned across Asia Minor to the Bosporus. She left an account of her travels which is of great interest to the scholar of pilgrim literature, but almost valueless to one in search of geographical information. Her successors, like the author of the *Short Description of Jerusalem*, or Theodosius (*c.* 530), or Antoninus of Placentia, mix up geographical facts with vivid, and perhaps genuine, accounts of holy relics. Thus the last includes accounts of the earthquake which ruined Tripolis in 551, the silk trade of Tyre, the parting of the river Jordan every year

[1] The authorities for this chapter are as follows:

C. R. BEAZLEY, *The Dawn of Modern Geography* (3 vols., 1897–1906). This standard work for the period 300–1420 has been extensively used.

A. P. NEWTON (ed.), *Travel and Travellers in the Middle Ages* (1926).

C. R. BEAZLEY (ed.), *The Texts and Versions of John de Plano Carpini and William de Rubruquis* (Hakluyt Society, 1903).

SIR HENRY YULE, *The Book of Ser Marco Polo*, 3rd ed., edited by H. Cordier (1903), with the supplementary volume, *Marco Polo: Notes and Addenda* (1920).

—— *Cathay and the Way Thither*, new edition by H. Cordier (Hakluyt Society, second series, vols. xxxiii, xxxvii, xxxviii, and xli).

G. LE STRANGE, *Clavijo: Embassy to Tamerlane* ("Broadway Travellers" series, 1928).

R. H. MAJOR, *India in the Fifteenth Century* (Hakluyt Society, first series, vol. xxii).

SIR HENRY YULE, *Friar Jordanus: Mirabilia Descriptă* (Hakluyt Society, first series, vol. xxxi).

at Epiphany, and the presence of the pillar of salt which was once Lot's wife. To these he adds picturesque details about the Ethiopians he met in Jerusalem, the " Saracen " beggars in the desert of Sinai, the ships of " India " which he saw in the Red Sea, the Nilometer at Aswan, and the " splendid but frivolous " city of Alexandria. It is all very interesting, but it can hardly be called progress in the geographical field.

A contemporary of Antoninus, by name Cosmas, has earned notoriety by reason of his book called *Christian Topography*, written about the year 547. Professor Beazley called it " systematic nonsense " ; and it is little more than a curiosity. The Bible was used to support a theory of a flat earth, centred on Jerusalem and boxed in by heavens which in turn were cut up by a firmament which lay between the old and the new earth. In fact, the world was like the Tabernacle of Moses.

Cosmas had visited the sources of the Nile, knew Abyssinia well, and may have made a trading voyage to India, yet his efforts to harmonize geographical facts and theological beliefs led him to deny the sphericity of the earth and the existence of the Antipodes. He had little influence on medieval thought.[1] But it is characteristic of the period that the most widely read works of geography were encyclopædic writings, of which the most famous was that of Isidore of Seville (*d.* 636). Isidore used the Bible, the *Collectanea rerum memorabilium* of Solinus (third century), and the *Historiarum adversum Paganos* of Orosius (fifth century) : Solinus himself reproduced much of the work of Pliny the Elder (*d.* 79). As Isidore was copied by many later writers a strange mixture of fact and fancy was inherited by geographers ; little information of value came from travellers themselves. Such may be said of Arculf, who visited the Levant about 670. He found that Alexandria was so large that it took him a whole day to walk through it ; it was a city of great commercial importance. Arculf knew something of the navigation of the Nile, and of the rainless yet fertile country through which it flowed. He was greatly impressed by the magnificence of Constantinople. He was an observant man, yet made unscientific deductions, for he passed " the isle of Vulcan," and saw a volcano which, he declared, gave out a cloud by day and fire by night, and was particularly active on Fridays and Saturdays.

In the eighth century the area which Christian pilgrims visited was disturbed by the invasions of Muslims, and journeys become both less numerous and more dangerous. One visitor, Willibard,

[1] On Cosmas see J. W. McCrindle, *The " Topographia Christiana" of Cosmas Indicopleustes* (Hakluyt Society, first series, vol. xcviii). On the writers of the period generally see J. K. Wright, *The Geographical Lore of the Time of the Crusades* (1925) ; H. C. Darby, " The Geographical Ideas of the Venerable Bede," in *Scottish Geographical Magazine*, vol. li, p. 84 ; E. G. R. Taylor, " Pactolus : River of Gold," in *Scottish Geographical Magazine*, vol. xliv, p. 130.

perhaps an Englishman by birth, spent ten years in travel, from the year 721. From Southampton he crossed to Rouen, traversed France and the Alps, visited Naples, Samos, and Cyprus, and spent four years in Palestine. His return journey was made by Constantinople and the sea-route. Willibard's narrative, dictated to a nun on his return, abounds in references to the miraculous, and has little geographical value.

The Christian pilgrims amuse by their quaint stories, but it is to be placed to their credit that in an age of great darkness they throw a little light. They maintained contact between the West and the East; and for men and women whose grandparents might have been wandering nomads they are deserving of much praise. The literature which their journeys inspired, and particularly the guide-books, is of value as throwing some light upon the routes most commonly used during the period.

In Central and Eastern Europe missionary activity was carried on successfully, and may have contributed to that movement of peoples from Scandinavia and the Baltic lands which did so much to affect the political developments of Europe in the eighth and following centuries. The " Northmen," whose home-lands held but limited resources, and to whom the temptation to use the sea must always have been very strong, were affected by the political and religious pressure of the Franks, and in turn threw themselves on the coastlands of Europe from Denmark to Sicily. With that political movement this book is not concerned. They also penetrated into remoter regions in Northern and Eastern Europe, and crossed the Atlantic to America.

To the east they followed two main routes, one skirting the northern end of the Scandinavian peninsula, the other passing up the Baltic Sea. By the first route they reached the White Sea; by the second they came to the mouth of the Duna river, up which they penetrated to the Dnieper, and so ultimately reached Constantinople and the Black Sea. At the beginning of the tenth century they had sailed into the Sea of Azov, up the river Don, to a portage over to the Volga, and so they arrived on the Caspian Sea (914).

Some of the knowledge thus acquired found its way to England through Othere the Norseman and Wulfstan the Dane, who were numbered among the small band of men whom Alfred the Great collected round him when he had leisure to establish a Court. Alfred was no mean scholar, and with the aid of the new information obtained from these men reconstructed the geographical chapters on Germany, the Baltic lands, and Northern Europe in the *General History* of Orosius, of which he made a translation.

Othere and Wulfstan represent respectively the northern and the southern movements eastward. The first had coasted to the North Cape of Europe, where the land ran due east, and on again to where

36

it turned due south, following it to Biarmaland—*i.e.*, the country about Archangel. Wulfstan had travelled along the coast of Prussia and Esthonia to the eastern end of the Baltic Sea.

The westward expansion of the Northmen across the Atlantic Ocean was made by means of stepping-stones—Iceland and Greenland. Iceland was first discovered by Irish monks about 795, but it was not reached by the Northmen until 867, when a colonist from the Faroe Islands was driven by storms to a large and mountainous country, which he called "Snowland." Shortly afterward the land was found to be an island, and in 870 a party of Northmen wintered there, and gave it the name it now holds. From 874 onward Norwegian emigrants began to settle on the island.

About the year 982 Eric the Red discovered Greenland, and here, as in Iceland, settlers followed, including missionaries. The inhabitants, who were all on the south-west coast, lived by fishing and cattle-breeding, and maintained themselves in some comfort for a long period. After the middle of the fourteenth century, however, intercourse with the home country gradually ceased, and the inhospitable geographical conditions led to the destruction of the colony.

Beyond Greenland the Northmen reached America.[1] It seems at least certain that Leif, son of Eric the Red, made a voyage to some part of the coast between Labrador and Cape Cod about the year 1000, and that some time later, perhaps in 1004, Karlsefni visited the lands already discovered and spent three winters there. Some scholars interpret the evidence differently, attributing the first discovery to Bjarni, about 986, and making Karlsefni's voyage of a much later date (1024).

Nor is there agreement as to the localities visited. The lands discovered by Leif were called Helluland (" the Land of Flat Stone "), Markland (" Woodland "), and Wineland. Mr Gathorne-Hardy places them respectively in Labrador or Newfoundland, considered as one 'land,' Nova Scotia, and New England. Others take the Northmen as far south as Florida, or to the Gulf of St Lawrence and even into the river itself. It is perhaps safest to conclude the localities reached cannot now be identified.

It is not certain that these voyages had any influence on subsequent discovery. Some knowledge of them was preserved by Adam of Bremen (*c.* 1070). Much later Henry the Navigator was in touch with Denmark, and may have been inspired by a reference in a work of Claudius Clavus (*c.* 1400) to suggest a northern voyage to the King of Denmark, or that ruler may have acted on his own initiative. There seems little doubt that a voyage was made, perhaps in 1462, and it may have resulted in the rediscovery of Greenland

[1] See G. M. Gathorne-Hardy, *The Norse Discoverers of America* (1921) ; M. Thordarson, *The Vinland Voyages* (1930) ; and H. Hermannsson, *The Problem of Wineland* (1936).

and of the mouth of the St Lawrence, but of this there is no certainty, and it was probably unconnected with the previous voyages of the Northmen. It is possible that Columbus while in Portugal, or Bristol merchants during their trading ventures to Iceland, or even to Portugal, heard of these events.[1] But all this is conjecture.

> It is unwise to argue *ex silentio* and positively to deny that the geographical discoveries of the Norsemen in the tenth and eleventh centuries had any influence upon the great explorers of the fifteenth century. On the other hand, we owe it to ourselves to admit frankly that we have no conclusive evidence that they did.[2]

There seems little reason to doubt the historical accuracy of the discovery of America by the Northmen. Attempts to connect the descriptions of places and features in the New World with the Fortunate Islands, such as Nansen made, appear to have little basis, while the Norse descriptions of America, vague though they are, receive confirmation from every other explorer in the same region. The success of their efforts to follow up an accidental discovery in a region in which navigation was not easy is a tribute to their courage and their enterprise, and for this, as for their work elsewhere, the Northmen must rank high among the pioneer explorers of the world. In their own age they were unequalled.

Soon after the Norse discovery of America Europe was involved in the Crusading movement, which went on throughout the Middle Ages. This movement is important, from the point of view of geographical discovery, for several reasons. It brought Europe into contact with the Arab world—and in particularly close contact with that world in Spain—and from the Arabs some geographical knowledge came to Europeans. It gave a considerable impetus to land travel, and was indirectly responsible for two very important journeys during the later Middle Ages. Trade increased with the Crusades, and with it grew the powerful Italian commercial cities, of which Venice, Genoa, and Pisa are conspicuous examples. It was this increased commercial activity on the waters of the Mediterranean Sea that contributed to the perfection of the medieval sailing maps, the *portolani*, which were the ancestors of the modern Admiralty Chart. And it was this same commercial development which led to increased efforts outside the Mediterranean, through which the Atlantic islands off the African coast were rediscovered. Further, the many journeys made to and from the Holy Land, and the establishment of Christian kingdoms in the Levant, added considerably to the knowledge of those parts of the world.

The voyages of Mediterranean sailors beyond the Mediterranean were spasmodic, and on the whole not productive of great results.

---

[1] See Beazley, *op. cit.*, vol. ii, pp. 514–548; S. Larsen, *The Discovery of America Twenty Years before Columbus* (1925); G. R. C[rone] in *G.J.*, vol. lxvi, p. 68; and E. Prestage, *The Portuguese Pioneers* (1933), pp. 186–187.

[2] Hermannsson, *op. cit.*, p. 84.

At the same time, the fact that they were being made in the neighbourhood of the west coast of Africa is of significance. The Venetians and the Genoese took the lead in these matters, and in 1270 Lancelot Malocellò rediscovered the Canary Islands. Shortly afterward (in 1281 or 1291) the Genoese sent galleys round the west coast of Africa, and these seem to have reached Cape Non. Their voyage

Fig. 4. OUTLINE SKETCH OF PART OF THE LAURENTIAN PORTOLANO

ended in disaster, and became surrounded with fable, so that they were said to have opened up trade with Ethiopia.

In the next century two expeditions from Portugal, one about the year 1336 and the second in 1341, were sent to the Canary Islands, for the purpose of exploration, and the results may perhaps be seen on the great Laurentian Portolano [1] of 1351. In 1346 Jayme Ferrer sailed from the island of Majorca for the " River of Gold," but was never heard of again. Interest was aroused in African ventures, and the *Book of the Spanish Friar*, published in 1350, gave an account of a journey first by sea to this same " River of Gold " and then inland to the Mountains of the Moon and to the dwelling of

[1] But see G. H. T. Kimble, " The Laurentian World Map, with Special Reference to its Portrayal of Africa," in *Imago Mundi*, vol. i, p. 29.

Prester John. From this work and from the Arabs Europeans got the idea of a branch of the Nile flowing from " the land of the Blacks" to the Atlantic.

Further voyages to the Canaries were made in 1382, about the year 1400, and in 1402, the last being a French expedition under Gadifer de la Salle and Jean de Bethencourt. A few years earlier, between 1380 and 1395, the Venetians Nicolò and Antonio Zeno claimed to have sailed into the North Sea and to have visited the Shetland and Faroe Islands and Iceland. It is now, however, generally admitted that the voyage was never made, but it gave rise to a misleading map, which puzzled cartographers for a century, and led Frobisher to believe that he had discovered a ' strait' when all he had found was an opening in Baffin Island.[1]

The importance of these voyages lies not in what was accomplished, but in the fact that they show quite clearly that European sailors were turning their attention to seas beyond the Mediterranean. It remained for the adventurers of Portugal to finish their work, and the Portuguese were to no small degree influenced by events which had been taking place on land. It was, in fact, the combination of land and sea ventures that finally led to the opening up of the sea-route to India.

The early land journeys, apart from Crusading ventures, are of small importance. Rabbi Benjamin, who visited the Jewish communities between Navarre and Bagdad in the years 1160–73, collected some information of a limited character, and was apparently a truthful witness, but his world was too narrow for his reports to be of real value. A little earlier Adelard (1110–14) travelled through Egypt and parts of Arabia, and translated into Latin the chief works of Saracen astronomy. In another region the Abbot Daniel journeyed from Little Russia through Byzantium to Cyprus, and thence to the Holy Land. The pressure of the Turks, however, was steadily closing the East to travellers of this kind when an event entirely changed the situation. In the early years of the thirteenth century Mongol invaders burst upon Eastern Europe. After a time it occurred to some Europeans that this non-Muslim people might be used with effect against the Turks, while at the same time they might also be won over to the Christian faith. The result was that two missions were sent to the Mongols, and from these missions has come the first really important record of exploration in the medieval period.

The first envoy, John de Plano Carpini, was a Franciscan, who received a commission from the Pope and began his journey on April 16, 1245. His immediate object was to convey a letter from

[1] For the relationship between the Zeno Map and the real map see Miller Christy, *The Silver Map of Drake's Voyage* (1900). For Frobisher see below, Chapter VIII.

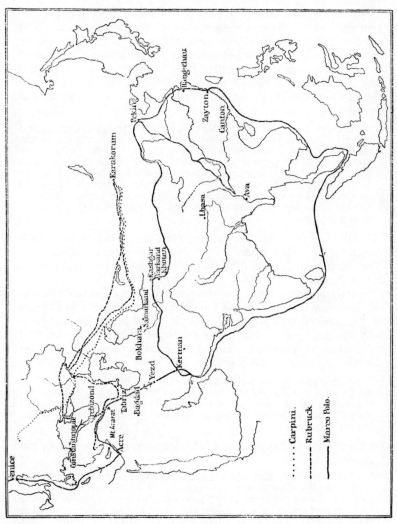

Venice
Constantinople
Trebizond
Acre
Mt Ararat
Tabriz
Bagdad
Yezd
Bokhara
Samarkand
Kashgar
Yarkand
Khotan
Kerman
Karakorum
Peking
Yung-chau
Zayton
Canton
Ava
Lhasa

.... Carpini.
-- -- -- Rubruck.
———— Marco Polo.

Fig. 5.   The Opening up of Asia in the Middle Ages

the Pope to the Grand Khan of the Mongols. He travelled to Bohemia, and thence followed the usual route eastward to Cracow and Kiev, which town he left on February 4, 1246. Thence he went down the Dnieper, across the head of the Sea of Azov, over the Don near its mouth, thence east-north-east to the Lower Volga, about one hundred miles above Astrakhan, and so across the Aral-Caspian depression to the basin of the Syr Darya. Thence his route skirted the western prolongation of the Tian Shan Mountains, took him past the lake Ala Kul, and thereafter led him almost due east to the camp of the Mongols near Karakorum. This country he has described as

> in some part . . . full of mountaines, and in other places plaine and smoothe ground but everywhere sandie and barren, neither is the hundredth part thereof fruitefull. For it cannot beare fruite unless it be moistened with river waters which be very rare in that countrey. Whereupon they have neither villages nor cities among them except one which is called Cracurim and is said to be a proper towne. We ourselves sawe not this towne, but almost within half a day's journey thereof when we remained at Syra Orda which is the great court of their Emperour.[1]

He reached this Court on July 22, 1246, and remained there until November 13. He returned by practically the same route, reaching Kiev on June 9, 1247, and by the summer of that year had arrived at the Papal Court.

Such is the bare outline of the journey: its importance lies in the fact that Carpini brought back some very accurate knowledge of the country and people he visited. It is impossible to quote fully his descriptions, but a few selections will show the kind of information he obtained. Thus he gives the Slavonic names for the great rivers of South Russia:

> All this journey we went through the land of Comania, which is all plain ground, and hath four mighty rivers running through it: the first is called Neper . . . the second Don, . . . the third is called Volga which is an exceeding great river, . . . the fourth is called Iaec [Ural].[2]

Of the climate and vegetation of the Steppe region he gives a good account:

> In certain places thereof are small store of trees growing but otherwise it is altogether destitute of woods. Therefore all warm themselves and dress their meat with fires made of dung. The air also in that country is very intemperate. For in the midst of summer there be great thunders and lightnings, and at the same time there falleth great abundance of snow. There be also such mighty tempests of cold winds that sometimes men are not able to sit on horseback. . . . There is never any rain in winter but only in summer

---

[1] *The Texts and Versions of John de Plano Carpini and William de Rubruquis,* edited by C. R. Beazley, p. 108.

[2] *Ibid.,* p. 130.

albeit in so little quantity that sometimes it scarcely sufficeth to allay the dust or to moisten the roots of the grass. There is oftentimes great store of haile also. Likewise in the summer season there is on the sudden extreme heat and suddenly again intolerable cold.[1]

There is a good picture of the nomadic life :

> Their habitations be round and cunningly made with wickers and staves in the manner of a tent. But in the midst of the tops thereof they have a window open to convey the light in and the smoke out. For their fire is always in the midst. Their walls be covered with felt. Their doors are made of felt also. Some of these tabernacles may quickly be taken asunder, and set together again, and are carried upon beasts' backs. Other some cannot be taken insunder, but are stowed upon carts. And whithersoever they go, be it either to war or to any other place, they transport their tabernacles with them. They are very rich in cattle as in camels, oxen, sheep, and goats. And think they have more horses and mares then all the world besides.[2]

There are many other interesting points that could be illustrated from the record of Carpini's travels if space allowed, but these are enough to show something of the very thorough nature of his report.

William of Rubruck, the second envoy, was sent out to the same region by King Louis IX of France, at that time engaged in the Sixth Crusade. He left Acre in the spring of 1252, and journeyed by sea to Constantinople, where he remained until May of the following year. He then sailed to Sudak, in the Crimea, where he engaged carts for the journey, and as a result doubled the time required for a journey on horseback. His route was very similar to that of Carpini. The Etil, the third of the four great rivers, to which William gives their classical names, was passed on August 8. Continuing more or less due east for thirty-four days after crossing the Ural river, he arrived in the basin of the Syr Darya, and changed his direction to south-east. He proceeded by a mountainous route, possibly over the north-west outliers of the Alexander range, for another seven days. At the end of this period, on November 8, he reached the Talas valley and the town of Kenchat. The following day another village, nearer the mountains, was reached. Rubruck says :

> I enquired what mountains they were, which I understood to be the mountains of Caucasus which are stretched forth and continued on both parts to the sea, from the west unto the east : and on the west part they are conjoined unto the foresaid Caspian Sea, whereinto the river of Volga dischargeth his streams.[3]

This shows that William's geographical knowledge had not advanced beyond the one single mountain range of Asia which was known to

[1] Beazley, *op. cit.*, pp. 108–109. [2] *Ibid.*, p. 109. [3] *Ibid.*, p. 226.

43

classical writers. Continuing, the party passed the mountains and entered into

> a most beautiful plaine having high mountaines on our right hand and on the left hand of us a certain sea or lake which containeth fifteen days journey in circuit.

This was the modern Lake Balkash. From this point he proceeded, as Carpini had done, past the Ala Kul, and across Mongolia to the Court of the Grand Khan, which he reached on December 26. Thence, after some delay, William moved with the Court to Karakorum, where he remained until July 6, 1254. He returned by much the same route to the Volga, apparently a little to the north of his outward journey, but instead of returning to the Black Sea received permission to go through Asia Minor ; he reached Corycus, on the coast of Cilicia, on May 5, 1255.

The narrative of William of Rubruck is more difficult to follow than that of Carpini, and it apparently aroused little interest until the sixteenth century. None the less, it supplements in many respects the earlier writings of Carpini. Thus there is an account of the great trade in salt from the region round the mouth of the Don.

> Towards the borders of the said province there be many great lakes upon the banks of which are salt pits or fountains the water of which so soon as it entereth into the lake becometh hard salt like unto ice. And out of those salt pits Batu and Sartach have great revenues : for they repair thither out of all Russia for salt ; and for each cart load they give two webbes of cotton. . . . They come by sea also many ships for salt which pay tribute every one of them according to their burden.[1]

Another interesting point relates to the Caspian Sea, about which he says :

> This sea is compassed in on three sides with the mountaines but on the north side with plain ground. A man may travel round about it for four months. And it is not true, which Isidore reporteth, namely that this sea is a bay or gulfe coming forth of the ocean: for it doth in no part thereof join with the ocean but is environed in on all sides with land.[2]

Isidore was an encyclopædic writer of the early seventh century, and borrowed his ideas from the classical authors. They had changed their opinion about this sea, for Herodotus correctly described it as an inland sea. By the time of Strabo this had become an arm of the ocean. Ptolemy corrected this error, but the early and medieval writers went back to the older theories. One of these was Solinus, who, about the third century, compiled a book called *Collectanea Rerum Memorabilium*, which in turn supplied the basis for Isidore's work. William of Rubruck was able, by

---

[1] Beazley, *op. cit.*, p. 187.   [2] *Ibid.*, p. 217.

actual exploration, to revive the idea put forward by Herodotus 1700 years earlier.

A last illustration gives a picture of irrigation in the fertile region watered by the Syr Darya and Amu Darya. Near to Kenchat

> there descended a great river down from the mountains which watered the whole region according as the inhabitants would give it passage, by making divers channels and sluices : neither did this river exonerate itself into any sea but was swallowed up by an hideous gulf into the bowels of the earth : and it caused many fens and lakes. Also I saw many vines and drank of the wine thereof.[1]

The narratives of these two men are of interest now because of the light they throw on Central Asian geography. Their importance in the thirteenth century was rather different. It is true that they gave to Western Europe the first really accurate account of Central Asia and the Mongol peoples, and thus opened up a great field for further exploration, as well as filling in a blank on the map. But their narratives contained in addition vague accounts of other peoples. Thus Rubruck, in describing the peoples who lived beyond the Court of the Grand Khan, speaks of " Great Cathaya the inhabitants whereof (as I suppose) were of old time called Seres. For from them are brought most excellent stuffs of silke." Rubruck is the first to make explicit the connexion between Cathaya and the land of Seres. Among classical writers Pomponius Mela (A. D. 43) was the first European who had any idea of land beyond the Bay of Bengal. By the time of Ptolemy there was definite knowledge of the country in which the town of Seres was located and from which silk came. With the decline in geographical knowledge which accompanied the fall of the Roman Empire this land was forgotten, and it was left to John de Plano Carpini and William of Rubruck to bring it once more within the known world. For this alone their work would have been of great value : in addition they were the pioneers in a movement which led to the opening up of Asia for a short period.

But this process of rediscovering Asia was greatly helped by the unification of a large part of the country by the Mongols, " as important a fact for the commerce of the Middle Ages as the discovery of America for the men of the Renaissance." [2] These people opened up two of the three great trade-routes between east and west.

> One, the Egyptian road, remained in the hands of the Muslims and closed to Europeans, though the Venetian galleys still brought back their cargoes of spices and silk from the great terminus port of Alexandria. But the other two, the Persian-Syrian and long sea-route and the Trans-Asiatic land-route, were now thrown open.[3]

[1] Beazley, *op. cit.*, p. 225.
[2] Quoted from R. Grousset, *Histoire de l'Asie*, in A. P. Newton, *Travel and Travellers in the Middle Ages*, p. 136.
[3] Newton, *op. cit.*, p. 137.

GEOGRAPHICAL DISCOVERY AND EXPLORATION

In 1255 two Venetian traders, Nicolò and Maffeo Polo, reached Serai by the Black Sea route already used by the envoys to the Grand Khan. Their return was prevented by the unsettled state of the country, and so they travelled to Bokhara, and thence to the Court of the Grand Khan, somewhere near Peking. After an absence of fourteen years they came back to Acre, bearing a message for the Pope. They had penetrated into Asia farther than any other European.

These men returned to the East in 1271, and took with them Marco, son of Nicolò, who has left an invaluable record of the journey. From Acre[1] they went northward through Armenia, skirted the north side of Lake Van, and passed through Tabriz and Yezd to Ormuz. Here they proposed to take ship for the East, but, disliking the unseaworthy appearance of the boats, turned inland, and crossed Persia to Balkh. Their route then lay over the Pamirs to Kashgar, where they began their journey through the towns that lay at the foot of the Kuen Lun range. From Yarkand and Khotan they continued eastward, passing to the south of Lob Nor, crossing Ordos, and so reaching Peking. Even now their journeys were not over, for the Venetians lived in China for seventeen years. This long residence gave Marco Polo an opportunity to see something of the great Chinese plain, to travel through Shansi, Shensi, and Szechwan, to the distant Yunnan, and even to Burma, and to visit Cochin-China. For three years he was Governor of a Chinese city, and there, as throughout his journeys, he was a very keen and accurate observer of all he saw. Thus his book gives an admirable picture of the route to China, of China itself, and of the Chinese.

The Venetians returned to Europe by the sea-route, sailed through the Straits of Malacca, skirted the south coast of India and passed along its western shores, and again reached Ormuz. Thus the homeward journey supplemented, in an important way, the land-route to Asia, for hitherto no European, with the possible exception of Cosmas, had sailed the Indian Ocean since classical times, and none had ever come from so far as a Chinese port. Marco Polo's travels were thus a first-hand commentary on the two great trade-routes which the Mongols had opened up.

It is impossible in a short space to do justice to the man who has appropriately been described as "incomparably the greatest traveller and the most magnificent observer of the whole Middle Ages."[2] A few illustrations will suffice to indicate the scope and content of his record.

First there is the great port of Ormuz, which Polo calls Hormos.

> Merchants come thither from India, with ships loaded with spicery and precious stones, pearls, cloths of silk and gold, elephants'

[1] See *The Most Noble and Famous Travels of Marco Polo*, edited by N. M. Penzer (1929).   [2] Dr Eileen Power, in Newton, *op. cit.*, p. 132.

teeth, and many other wares, which they sell to the merchants of Hormos, and which these in turn carry all over the world to dispose of again. In fact, 'tis a city of immense trade. . . . It is a very sickly place, and the heat of the sun is tremendous. . . . The people sow their wheat and barley and other corn in the month of November, and reap it in the month of March. The dates are not gathered till May, but otherwise there is no grass nor any other green thing, for the excessive heat dries up everything.[1]

Marco Polo gives a very good account of the caravan-route across Central Asia to China, and the following extract brings out the significant geographical facts of its difficulties and limitations:

Lop is a large town at the edge of the Desert, which is called the Desert of Lop, and is situated between east and north-east. . . . Now, such persons as propose to cross the Desert take a week's rest in this town to refresh themselves and their cattle; and then they make ready for the journey, taking with them a month's supply for man and beast. On quitting this city they enter the Desert.
The length of this Desert is so great that 'tis said it would take a year and more to ride from one end of it to the other. And here, where its breadth is least, it takes a month to cross it. 'Tis all composed of hills and valleys of sand, and not a thing to eat is to be found on it. But after riding for a day and a night you find fresh water, enough mayhap for some 50 or 100 persons with their beasts, but not for more. And all across the Desert you will find water in like manner, that is to say, in some 28 places altogether you will find good water, but in no great quantity; and in four places also you find brackish water. . . . In making this journey 'tis customary for travellers to keep close together [for fear of being lured away by spirits]. All the animals too have bells at their necks so that they cannot easily get astray. And at sleeping-time a signal is put up to show the direction of the next march. So thus it is that the Desert is crossed.[2]

The desert route led ultimately to the Court of the Grand Khan at Peking, of which Polo gives a most elaborate account. He then passes on to describe China, which he saw for himself during his long residence in the country. He tells of the excellent system of communication maintained by the Grand Khan. " Now you must know," he writes,

that from this city of Cambaluc proceed many roads and highways leading to a variety of provinces, one to one province, another to another; and each road receives the name of the province to which it leads. . . . And the messengers of the Emperor in travelling from Cambaluc, be the road whichsoever they will, find at every twenty-five miles of the journey a station which they call *Yamb*, or, as we should say, the " Horse-Post-House." And at each of those stations used by the messengers, there is a large and handsome building for them to put up at. . . . At some of these stations, moreover, there shall be posted some four hundred horses, standing ready for the use of the messengers; at others there shall be two hundred, according

[1] Yule, *Book of Ser Marco Polo*, vol. i, pp. 107–109.
[2] *Ibid.*, vol. i, pp. 196–197.

to the requirements, and to what the Emperor has established in each case. At every twenty-five miles, . . . or anyhow at every thirty miles, you find one of these stations, on all the principal highways leading to the different provincial governments ; and the same is the case throughout all the chief provinces subject to the Great Kaan. Even where the messengers have to pass through a roadless tract where neither house nor hostel exists, still there the station houses have been established just the same, excepting that the intervals are somewhat greater. . . . On all these posts taken together there are more than 300,000 horses kept up, specially for the use of the messengers. . . . The thing is on a scale so wonderful and costly that it is hard to bring oneself to describe it.[1]

One product of China, coal, was in great use, and Marco Polo thus describes it :

All over the country of Cathay there is a kind of black stones existing in beds in the mountains, which they dig out and burn like firewood. If you supply the fire with them at night, and see that they are well kindled, you will find them still alight in the morning ; and they make such capital fuel that no other is used throughout the country. It is true that they have plenty of wood also, but they do not burn it, because these stones burn better and cost less.[2]

Marco Polo was much impressed by the number and richness of the cities of China and the magnitude of its trade. Thus the town of Sinju (Ichang) was, he said,

of no great size, but possessing a very great amount of shipping and trade. . . . It stands on the greatest river in the world, the name of which is Kian. It is in some places ten miles wide, in others eight, in others six, and it is more than 100 days' journey in length from one end to the other. This it is that brings so much trade to the city [of Sinju] ; for on the waters of that river merchandize is perpetually coming and going, from and to the various parts of the world, enriching the city, and bringing a great revenue to the Great Kaan. And I assure you this river flows so far and traverses so many countries and cities that in good sooth there pass and repass on its waters a great number of vessels, and more wealth and merchandize than on all the rivers and all the seas of Christendom put together. It seems, indeed, more like a sea than a river ! . . . If this city, of no great size, has [15,000 vessels at it at one time], how many must there be altogether, considering that on the banks of this river there are more than sixteen provinces and more than 200 great cities besides towns and villages, all possessing vessels ?[3]

Near to this little port was " the most noble city of Kinsay [Hang-chow], beyond dispute the finest and the noblest in the world." It was " so great that it hath an hundred miles of compass." In it were twelve thousand bridges of stone ; twelve guilds of different crafts ; a lake " which has a compass of some 30 miles " ; streets paved with stone or brick ; three thousand baths, some of them

[1] Yule, *op. cit.*, vol. i, pp. 433–434.   [2] *Ibid.*, vol. i, p. 442.
[3] *Ibid.*, vol. ii, p. 170.

" large enough for 100 persons to bathe together " ; and the ocean
sea within twenty-five miles. " I repeat," says Polo,

> that everything appertaining to this city is on so vast a scale, and
> that the Great Kaan's yearly revenues therefrom are so immense,
> that it is not easy even to put it in writing, and it seems past belief
> to one who merely hears it told.[1]

Polo's account of China, and, indeed, of all the lands he saw, is
so remarkably good that it is difficult to select the more interesting
portions. He left China by the port of Zayton (Chuan-chau, in
Fukien), which was

> frequented by all the ships of India, which bring thither spicery and
> all other kinds of costly wares. It is the port also that is frequented
> by all the merchants of Manzi [i.e., the Lower Yangtse valley], for
> hither is imported the most astonishing quantity of goods and of
> precious stones and pearls, and from this city they are distributed
> all over Manzi. And I assure you that for one shipload of pepper
> that goes to Alexandria or elsewhere, destined for Christendom,
> there come a hundred such, aye and more too, to this haven of
> Zayton; for it is one of the two greatest havens in the world for
> commerce.[2]

On his return, by sea, Marco gathered a little information about
the Arab sphere of influence in the Indian Ocean. " Madagascar,"
he wrote,

> is an Island towards the south, about a thousand miles from Socotra.
> . . . You must know that this Island lies so far south that ships
> cannot go further south or visit other Islands in that direction
> except this one, and that other of which we have to tell you, called
> Zanghibar. This is because the sea-current runs so strong towards
> the south that the ships which should attempt it never would get
> back again.[3]

Here, obviously, is the limit of knowledge ; and beyond it, very
significantly, " is found the bird *Gryphon*," not, Polo says, " half
lion and half bird as our stories do relate ; but enormous as they
be they are fashioned just like an eagle," yet are strong enough to
seize an elephant in their talons, and carry him high into the air.

Marco Polo's book deals with countries outside his own route.
He refers to Japan, the islands of the East Indies, and Northern
Europe, but his accounts are all based upon what he was told or
guessed, and have little value.

Though Marco Polo obtained no immediate recognition, his work
was later to have great influence on geographical thought and
exploration. His ideas were reproduced in the maps of the later
Middle Ages, and notably in the Catalan map of 1375,[4] while among

---

[1] Yule, *op. cit.*, vol. ii, p. 190.   [2] *Ibid.*, vol. ii, p. 235.   [3] *Ibid.*, vol. ii, p. 412.
[4] See *The Catalan World Map of the R. Biblioteca Estense at Modena*, with
memoir by G. H. Kimble (R.G.S., 1934), and, for another example, Behaim's
globe, Fig. 7.

49

the students of his book were Henry the Navigator and Christopher Columbus. His travels had been undertaken partly for commercial reasons, partly to take some answer from the Pope to the Grand Khan; and they succeeded in opening a door through which missionaries and traders were quick to pass. For a little while the door remained open, and messages came back from Asia to Europe. Then it was closed, and remained so until another people, the Portuguese, found another route, round Africa, and once more opened the East to the trader and to the missionary. Yet if Marco Polo's work was to that extent a failure, in another direction it was a success, for it produced perhaps the most fascinating work of travel ever written, one which will be of value for all time.

II. THE SUCCESSORS OF MARCO POLO

Shortly after Marco Polo left Europe on his remarkable travels the first Christian mission was sent to the Tartars. Of this venture of 1278 little is known, and it is probable that it did not penetrate to inner Asia. The " true founder of the Latin Church in China " is John of Monte Corvino, who was born about the year 1247 and died about the year 1328. He carried on his missionary work first at Tabriz, then for thirteen months in Southern India, and finally, from about the year 1293 to his death, in China. It is only natural that his work should figure largely in his letters, but they are by no means devoid of geographical interest. He describes, and explains, the climatic conditions of Southern India, and gives a long account of the people. His reference to the cinnamon trade of Ceylon, his account of the foreigners, mainly Arabs and Jews, who lived " in the regions by the sea," and his explanation of the use of the monsoon winds for navigation are some of the more important matters dealt with in the letters. Of the navigation he writes :

> They cannot make the voyage but once a year, for from the beginning of April till the end of October the winds are westerly, so that no one can sail towards the west ; and again 'tis just the contrary from the month of October till March. From the middle of May till the end of October the wind blows so hard that ships which by that time have not reached the ports whither they are bound run a desperate risk, and if they escape it is great luck.[1]

On his journey from Tabriz to Peking John was accompanied by " Master Peter of Lucolongo, a faithful Christian man and a great merchant."

Another missionary, Andrew of Perugia, was at work in Peking from about 1308 to 1318, and afterward at Zayton, " the greatest port in the world." Though he wrote home from this latter place,

[1] Yule, *Cathay and the Way Thither*, edited by H. Cordier, vol. iii, p. 66 (Hakluyt Society, second series, vol. xxxviii).

he gives no information about China, "because it would be a long matter to write and would seem incredible to those who heard it."

Further information about India is furnished by Friar Jordanus, who went there for the first time perhaps as early as 1302, and wrote two letters from India in 1321 and 1323, in addition to composing his *Mirabilia*, which may be dated about 1328–30.[1] This book professes to be a description of marvels, but is in effect a short geographical treatise on a large part of the world. It deals most fully with India, of which its writer had personal knowledge, but once outside this rather narrow limit inaccuracies and fables creep into the narrative. For some parts of India Jordanus is very reliable, and many of his summary statements are models of brief and accurate description.

After a short and generally accurate account of Persia Jordanus passes to "India the less"—*i.e.*, the south coast of Baluchistan and the west coast of India as far as Malabar. A great number of the salient features are noticed : the deserts, the dark skins of the people, the equality of day and night, the peculiarity of fruits like the jack and mango, and trees such as the tadi and banyan. He is the first European to describe the Parsees, whose burial customs differed so widely from those of the Hindus.

In "Greater India" he was attracted by the elephant and the spices and fruits. Beyond India, and so beyond the limits of his personal observation, Jordanus tells of "more than 10,000 inhabited islands." In this "India" "everything is indeed a marvel. Verily it is another world." Yet all was not fanciful, for the elephants in Cambodia are faithfully described.

Of "India Tertia"—*i.e.*, East Africa—Jordanus says : "I have not indeed seen its many marvels, not having been there, but have heard them from trustworthy persons." He does know of "the emperor of the Ethiopians whom you call Prestre John," and that in Arabia, which "hath very great deserts, pathless and very dry," there grew "choice incense and myrrh." Jordanus had been there, but of the country he says : "I can tell but little."

Much more important is the work of Friar Odoric, who was born about 1274 and died in January 1331.[2] He began his travels about the year 1316 and ended them in 1330. He was in Western India in 1321 and in Northern China between 1322 and 1328.

His outward journey was made by the normal trans-Persian route, starting from Constantinople, passing through Trebizond, Tabriz, and Bagdad to Ormuz, whence he sailed for Tana, in Salsette. He visited Malabar, Ceylon, and Madras, and then, sailing eastward,

---

[1] Yule, *Cathay and the Way Thither*, vol. iii, p. 29. See also *Mirabilia Descripta*, edited by Sir Henry Yule (Hakluyt Society, first series, vol. xxxi).

[2] For an account of Odoric see Yule, *Cathay and the Way Thither*, vol. ii (Hakluyt Society, second series, vol. xxxiii).

touched at Sumatra, Java, perhaps Borneo, and Cochin-China, eventually reaching Canton. This city, three times as big as Venice, and situated one day's voyage from the sea, " hath shipping so great and vast in amount that to some it would seem well nigh incredible." Odoric then journeyed to Northern China, going by way of Hang-chow, called by him Causay and by Marco Polo Kinsay. Of this great city he has left an important account. Passing through Nanking, Odoric went " by fresh water channels "—*i.e.*, the Grand Canal—to the Hwang-ho, and then to Peking. The Hwang-ho " passeth through the very midst of Cathay, and doth great damage to that country when it breaks its banks, just as the Po does by Ferrara." Odoric spent " full three years " in Peking. He adds some interesting details about the Chinese which are un-recorded by Marco Polo. " 'Tis a mark of gentility . . . to have the nails long . . . and with the women the great beauty is to have little feet ; and for this reason mothers are accustomed, as soon as girls are born to them, to swathe their feet tightly so that they can never grow in the least."

Odoric returned through the modern Ordos and Shensi to Tibet. He seems to have visited Lhasa, and, if not the first European to do so, he is at least the first who has left an account of it. His subsequent route cannot be determined with certainty, but probably lay through Kabul to Khorasan, along the south of the Caspian Sea, and through Tabriz. His account of his travels is of great interest and importance. It has suffered somewhat from comparison with that of Marco Polo, but it deserves to be read for its own merits. Odoric is " the first European who distinctly and undoubtedly mentions Sumatra and the Rejang of that island " ; he notices, too, the use of the blowpipe by the aborigines of the East Indies ; and, as already shown, he supplements the narrative of Marco Polo in some interesting details. He was unlearned, he cared little for the rigours of religious life, he loved to travel and see new countries, but with it all he preserved his sense of proportion, and if he re-ported travellers' tales he has also recorded important facts, so that his work must remain one of the most valuable documents of this period of European intercourse with the East.

The last of the missionaries of whom mention need be made is Marignolli, who left Avignon in 1338 and, after some delay in Italy, reached Constantinople on May 1, 1339. The winter of that year was passed, probably, at Serai, and the journey continued to the East in the following spring. It was not, however, until about June 1342 that Marignolli reached China. He spent three or four years in Peking, and then went to Zayton, whence he sailed for India. The date of his departure is uncertain, but was in the year 1346 or 1347. From India he went to Ormuz, and thence over-land to a number of places, including Bagdad and Jerusalem. By which route he left Palestine is not known, but he touched at Cyprus, visited Italy, and arrived back in Avignon in 1353.

In addition to describing some of the features of Southern China, Ceylon, and Southern India, Marignolli includes passages which give some idea of his conceptions of geography. He discusses the four great rivers of Paradise. Phison, a river which was lost in the sands, had part of its course in China ; it was crossed by Marignolli, and was the " biggest river of fresh water in the world." It seems to be a confused combination of many great rivers, including the Hwang-ho, Ganges, and Oxus. Another instance of his confusion is in the " white sea beyond Hungary where now are the Wallachians," which formed part of the western boundary of the dominions of Shem. It appears to be a greatly exaggerated Russian lake, Bielo Osero, which lies due east from Leningrad, and forms part of the river Volga. This great lake appears on the map of Fra Mauro.[1]

Marignolli claims to have taken great pains in investigating the marvels of the world. He had travelled " in all the chief countries of the earth and in particular to places where merchants from all parts of the world do come together, such as the Island of Ormes," and he had never seen the monsters reported by other travellers. Yet giants, monstrous serpents, and certain animals with countenances almost like that of a man do exist. Marignolli rejected the idea of the Antipodes, and thought that " God willed not that men should be able to sail round the world."

Missionary activity was only one form of European penetration of the East : Marco Polo was a trader, and others of his profession followed. It was partly for their benefit that Marino Sanudo wrote his *Opus Terræ Sanctæ* in 1321. It was not primarily a geographical work, but was written to urge the prosecution of a new Crusade which should capture Egypt and so abolish the Muslim trade monopoly. Sanudo illustrated his work by maps which show that, although he knew much about the trade-route to the East, he was ignorant of the location of the more important towns. Aden he placed in Africa ; he was unaware that Ormuz was on an island ; he had no accurate knowledge of the Indian ports ; and he did not think that the Red Sea was navigable. To set against this ignorance he had a good knowledge of the great trade-route from Syria to Bagdad, and argued that since traders had already gone overland to India there was no reason why the Venetian merchants should not establish their trade on this route.

Another piece of evidence illustrating this trading activity is to be found in Pegolotti's book, which was written about the year 1340, and forms part of a larger work by a certain Pagnini.[2] The

[1] Yule, *Cathay and the Way Thither*, vol. iii, p. 247.
[2] On Pegolotti see Yule, *Cathay and the Way Thither*, vol. iii, pp. 137-172.

author called it *The Book of the Descriptions of Countries*, though Pagnini gave it a more accurate description, *Practica della Mercatura*. It was apparently compiled for the information of Florentine merchants, and does not represent any actual journey of the writer, who was never in Eastern Asia. The book opens with " information regarding the journey to Cathay for such as will go by Tana and come back with goods." The second chapter deals with the needs of merchants. " In the first place you must let your beard grow long and not shave." Information about servants, the mode of travelling, and food is followed by notices of charges on merchandise and transport expenses. The road itself " from Tana to Cathay is perfectly safe, whether by day or by night, according to what merchants say who have used it." That remark alone is a significant comment on the commercial relations of Europe and China at this time, and the whole work, written by a merchant for the use of merchants, is invaluable for an account of medieval commerce.

One merchant, the Venetian Nicolò de Conti, has left a record of his own journeys to the East. He is only one of a number of Venetians who opened up commercial relations with Persia and more distant countries in the fifteenth century.[1] He began his travels in Damascus, and journeyed by way of Bagdad and Basra to Ormuz, whence he sailed to Cambay. After a short expedition inland he made his way round the coast of India to Bengal. He went up the Ganges to Cernove and beyond, after which he made a land journey to Burma, first

> through mountains void of all habitations for the space of seventeen days and then through open plains for fifteen days more, at the end of which time he arrived at a river larger than the Ganges, which is called by the inhabitants Dava. Having sailed up this river for the space of a month he arrived at Ava.

Nicolò de Conti then visited Java, and perhaps Cochin-China and China, before returning to Calicut and Cambay. The return journey was made by Socotra, Aden, Ethiopia, Jedda, and Egypt, thence to Tripoli, and finally to Italy. This intrepid merchant arrived back in Venice in the year 1444, after an absence of twenty-five years. Poggio Bracciolini, who gives the account of Conti's adventures, says that " he went further than any former traveller penetrated, and he appeared to be a truthful person." Bracciolini includes in this narrative some account of the Nile sources and Abyssinia.

The writers so far considered had travelled extensively, and in some cases without any very definite object. But Clavijo, who next merits attention, only went to the Court of Timur, and was not there very long : his visit was strictly limited to business. Yet he was

[1] See R. H. Major, *India in the Fifteenth Century* (Hakluyt Society, first series, vol. xxii).

an observant man, and his record of the embassy to Samarkand in 1403–4 gives a valuable picture of the last days of the Emperor Timur.

Clavijo went by sea from Spain to Constantinople, of which he has left a most valuable description. From Trebizond he journeyed overland to Tabriz, and so across the Kara Kum Desert to the Syr Darya, and on to Samarkand. His book gives many interesting geographical details of the route.

> It is to be noted that from Tabriz all the distance to Samarkand Timur has established relays of horses kept ready at command so that his messengers may ride on his missions night and day without let or hindrance. The post-houses have been built at intervals of a day's journey apart, or sometimes of half a day's journey. In some post-houses a hundred horses will be found, in others only fifty, while in a few there may be as many as two hundred: and thus the high road all the way to Samarkand is served.[1]

The Oxus river, rising in the mountainous region north of Afghanistan, flows down

> through the plains of Samarkand, finally passing out into the lands of Tartary, from whence the discharge of its waters is into the Caspian Sea.[2]

This account, derived from hearsay, agrees with a Persian writer of the same time, who states definitely that the Oxus did enter the Caspian. While it is known that there have been considerable changes both in the rivers and in the Caspian and Aral Seas, the question of the actual course of the Oxus is still a matter of dispute, and will perhaps never be settled.

Clavijo gives a picturesque description of the city of Samarkand, lying in a plain, and surrounded by a rampart of earth, with a very deep ditch.

> The city itself is rather larger than Seville, but lying outside Samarkand are great numbers of houses which form extensive suburbs. These lie spread on all hands for indeed the township is surrounded by orchards and vineyards. . . . In between these orchards pass streets with open squares; these are all densely populated, and here all kinds of goods are on sale with bread stuffs and meat. Thus it is that the population without the city is more numerous than the population within its walls.[3]

So numerous are the orchards that the houses of the great men are hidden from sight. Through the streets of the city and through the gardens

> pass many water conduits, and in these gardens are the melon beds and cotton-growing lands.[4]

[1] *Clavijo : Embassy to Tamerlane*, translated and edited by Guy le Strange ("Broadway Travellers" series, 1928), p. 155.
[2] *Ibid.*, p. 199.
[3] Guy le Strange, *op. cit.*, pp. 285–286.   [4] *Ibid.*, p. 286.

Camels daily bring in loads of melons from the country.

> The soil of the whole province of Samarkand is most fertile, producing great crops of wheat. There are abundant fruit-trees also with rich vineyards : the live stock is magnificent, beasts and poultry all of a fine breed. . . . Baked bread is everywhere plentiful and rice can be had cheap in any quantity.[1]

The approach to the city was through a lofty mountain range,

> and the pass that traverses it is a narrow cleft where the passage seems to have been cut through by the hand of man, with the mountain wall on either side rising vertical to an immense height. The roadway itself is quite level, passing deep down in the cleft. Here, in the midst of the surrounding heights stands a village, and the place is known as the Iron Gates. In the whole length of this mountain range there is no other pass to cross it, save this one, which is thus the Guard House of the Imperial city of Samarkand. It is only by this one pass that all who travel up to Samarkand from [Afghanistan] can come : nor can those who go down from the Imperial city voyaging to India travel by any other route. The Lord Timur is sole master of these Iron Gates, and the revenue is considerable to the state from the customs imposed on all merchants who come from India going to the city of Samarkand and to the regions beyond.[2]

Clavijo points out that Timur also controlled the other "Iron Gates," at the eastern end of the Caucasus range, near to Derbend, so that "those who would come from Tartary to Persia must pass through these." Between the two was a great territory all under the control of Timur.

Very different from the missionaries, the traders, and the Ambassador was the last of the travellers, Hans Schiltberger. Taken prisoner by the Turks at Nicopolis, in 1396, when he was only fourteen years of age, he remained in bondage or semi-freedom until 1427. He was captured by Timur after his victory at Angora in 1402, and so saw something of the Court of Samarkand, and must have been there at the time of Clavijo's visit. After Timur's death, in 1405, he visited the modern provinces of Tobolsk and Tomsk, in Siberia, and gave an account of them. His subsequent enforced journeys took him to other parts of the Near East, including the Crimea and, perhaps, Egypt.

Schiltberger set down his experiences in his *Reisebuch*, which also contains much descriptive matter relating to these new lands. Of some of the countries which he describes, as India, he had probably no personal knowledge ; he claims to have visited Egypt, but his account of it hardly carries conviction. Yet he knew of the trade of Alexandria, he appears to have had access to some reliable source of information about the Red Sea, and he gives an account of the life of Mohammed and of the practices of his followers which is very creditable.

[1] Guy le Strange, *op. cit.*, pp. 286–287.   [2] *Ibid.*, pp. 204–205.

It is to be remembered that Schiltberger passed a great portion of his life wandering through strange lands. The circumstances of his life, his youth, and the company with which he would be obliged to associate all doubtless contributed to the inaccuracies which have been recorded in his book. Yet his is " the first important contribution of a German to the literature of European expansion." [1] Like that of Marco Polo, his book is based on a long period of residence in the lands described, and while it does not approach the standard of value of the work of the Venetian, it is important for its few new details, among the most valuable of which are those relating to Siberia.

The penetration of Asia by Europeans in the century after the journey of Marco Polo must be regarded merely as an episode : it had no permanent results. It came to an end partly because the conquests of the Turks imposed an intolerant Mohammedanism on a great part of Asia, and partly because the Tartar dynasty was driven out of China in 1370, and thus one factor making for security was removed. Yet it was a remarkable century of expansion, and its records form some of the most interesting and valuable documents in the history of discovery.

[1] Beazley, *Dawn of Modern Geography*, vol. iii, p. 257.

CHAPTER III

THE ARABS [1]

ALTHOUGH the Arab geographers have no direct contact with those of Europe, yet because of the indirect influence which they exercised they must find a place in the history of discovery. Their chief importance is that they preserved some of the traditions of the classical period in an age when Western Europe was incapable of appreciating their value ; they also record the travels of some remarkable men, who saw parts of the world closed to Europeans, although it must be admitted that Arab travel had little influence on the geographical thought of Europe.

Arab geography falls broadly into two categories, descriptive and mathematical. The latter, which is highly specialized, and which owed much to the *Geography* of Ptolemy, translated into Arabic in the early years of the ninth century, will not be considered : it belongs rather to the history of geography. It formed part of the general astronomical work of the Arabs, which was of a high order, and certainly superior to that of the Greeks. Their religion made accurate determinations of latitude and longitude necessary for the construction of horizontal sundials to indicate the noonday prayer-time, to secure the geographical co-ordinates of Mecca, toward which the face was turned in prayer, and to ensure success in casting horoscopes. " One result of outstanding importance that emerged from Arabic determinations of longitudes was the correction, by shortening some 17°, of Ptolemy's exaggerated figure for the length of the Mediterranean Sea." [2]

The descriptive geography of the Arabs was helped considerably by the spread of their political influence, thus giving them a large area in which to travel, and bringing them into contact with higher forms of civilization. The yearly pilgrimage to Mecca, and the comparative ease and cheapness of travel among their coreligionists, also assisted the spread of knowledge, while trade, both by land and

---

[1] Most of the material in this chapter has been taken from B. Carra de Vaux, *Les Penseurs d'Islam*, vol. ii (1921).

On the Arabs generally see also :

    C. SCHOY, " The Geography of the Moslems of the Middle Ages," in the *Geographical Review*, vol. xiv, pp. 257 *et seq.*

    C. R. BEAZLEY, *The Dawn of Modern Geography*.

    J. K. WRIGHT, *The Geographical Lore of the Time of the Crusades* (1925).

[2] Schoy, *op. cit.*, p. 267.

by sea, contributed to the same end. The Arab world extended from the Atlantic Ocean to the borders of the Pacific, and for a considerable distance down the east coast of Africa. Their traders crossed the Sahara ; they came in contact with Europeans in Spain and in Sicily ; and they met Orientals in India and in China.

One of the earliest of the Arab geographers is Ibn Khordadbeh, whose work dates from about the year 850. Being an official, he had access to much valuable statistical information. His book *On Routes and Kingdoms* is, however, disappointing. It includes a brief account of his scientific views, derived from the Ptolemaic 'school,' and a valuable summary of the great trade-routes of the Arab world, but it is spoiled by the introduction of fabulous stories, such as that of whales twelve hundred feet long. These defects reduce Ibn Khordadbeh to the rank of an undiscriminating compiler.

Another Arab geographer of the early period is Jakoubi, whose work dates from the year 900, and who has been called the father of Arab geography, because of the use that was subsequently made of his works by other writers. From his youth he desired to know all he could about distant countries. He was an experienced traveller, and had obtained a great deal of information from the cross-examination of others from the East and from the West. As a result he produced a compendium of information, *The Book of Countries*, giving details of the names of places, their distances from one another, their physical geography, and a number of facts relating to their human geography. The mere list of contents shows that Jakoubi had a good idea of the wide nature and scope of the subject. He was a serious writer, and, unlike so many later Arab geographers, he did not mix up fact with fable.

The next geographer who may be taken as typical of the early period also illustrates the ease of movement within the Muslim world. Ibn Haukal made a journey to the East in 953, and met, in the valley of the Indus, another geographer, Istakhri, who himself subsequently wrote a book on *Climates* illustrated by maps. This work forms the foundation of the *Book of Ways and Kingdoms*, which Ibn Haukal finished in 988, and which gives a geographical, political, and statistical description of the various provinces of the empire of the Khalifs. His information was, as he explains, that " which makes geography a science which interests princes and peoples of all classes," and was of a very comprehensive character. It derives additional importance from the fact that it furnishes a description of the Muslim Empire at the height of its power.

Even more valuable, however, is the great work of Mas'oudi, who had travelled over the Muslim world from Spain to China, and appears to have visited Madagascar. He wrote the *Meadows of Gold*, which is not strictly a geographical work, but which does

59

contain much geographical information : its aim was to be a kind of cyclopædia of knowledge. He had very limited ideas of Europe, and borrowed much from earlier writers, but on some points he was well informed. The Caspian he knew to be an inland sea, and he is the first Arab geographer to indicate the existence of the Sea of Aral.

Edrisi, though not the greatest of the Arab geographers, has perhaps most interest for Europeans. Educated at Córdoba, Edrisi spent a considerable time in travel, both in Europe, where he reached the shores of France and England, and in Asia Minor. He went to live at the Court of Roger II, King of Sicily, and wrote his book about the year 1170. Living in Sicily, he was able to obtain much information from passing sailors and from merchants, and he gives a wealth of information about Christian Europe not found in earlier Arab works. His maps, however, are defective. At the same time, he exercised an important influence on Christian geography, an influence indirect rather than direct, due to the geographical location of Sicily and his own Arab connexions. This is perhaps best seen in the navigation charts, which early reached a high level in Sicily.

The last of the typical Arab geographers is Jakout, who was born about 1196, and who spent much of his time in the famous libraries in Merv. He compiled two " dictionaries," geographical and biographical, which were rich in detail, paid little attention to mythical stories, and included valuable notices of natural phenomena. Although not the originator of this kind of work, Jakout produced books which, because of their accuracy, were regarded as models, and he has been called the greatest Arab geographer.

During the Arab period journeys devoted strictly to exploration are not numerous. It is recorded that one such expedition was made to the sources of the Nile ; it reached the Mountains of the Moon and the lake whence the river sprang. Yet Arab maps of Africa scarcely differ from those of Ptolemy, and it may be that this expedition, if ever made, was merely a repetition of the earlier trading venture of Diogenes.

Another exploit was the expedition of Sallam to the Great Wall of China, during which he was commissioned to search for the mysterious people of Gog and Magog. His journey was made through Armenia to the Volga river, round the Caspian Sea to the Ural and Altai Mountains, and back through Bokhara to 'Iraq.

Among the expeditions by sea, Edrisi records one in the Atlantic Ocean. Much mystery surrounds this voyage, made first to the northern waters, known as the Sea of Darkness, and afterward toward the equator, but it is possible that the story does represent some early Atlantic exploration. The mention of the discovery of an island far removed from Europe, inhabited by " red " men with smooth hair and tall figures, may perhaps have its origin in some early attempt to explore Madeira. If this story is genuine it is the first record of Atlantic exploration since classical times.

In the Indian Ocean the fable associated with the name of Sindbad the Sailor undoubtedly points to early maritime enterprises in those waters, and probably represents the early record of a voyage from Madagascar to Ceylon. In addition there is an important *Relation* of Arab and Chinese voyages in the Indian Ocean, dating from the ninth century. It is said to have every appearance of truthfulness, and it gives the details of a voyage made in the year 879. It also throws valuable light on the people and commerce of the Far East —that is, China, Java, Ceylon, and India. It mentions the two great Arab ports of Siraf and Basra. Of great interest also are the nautical instructions, which date from the end of the fifteenth century, but which give information going back for at least five hundred years in Arab history. One of the authors appears to have been the pilot who guided the Portuguese fleet from Malindi to Calicut on Vasco da Gama's first voyage. The works, which are in manuscript, resemble the modern pilot books, but, in addition to the information there given, include accounts of trade-routes.

Two of the best-known figures in Arab geography remain for notice, and both owe their reputation to the extent of their travels. They form a third class of geographer, supplementing the work of the compiler and the real explorer. The first, Albiruni, died in the year 1084, after a life spent in travel and in study. He was born in Khiva, spent part of his life in the country south of the Caspian Sea, and accompanied Mahmud of Ghazni on his Indian invasion about 1027. Many details of his life and work have been preserved in Jakout's biographical dictionary, to which reference has been made. Among the works of Albiruni were a description of India, the *Chronology*, dealing with the methods of reckoning time employed by various people, and the *Canon*, a geographical book. The valuable contributions to geographical knowledge which he made included a description of the routes leading from the Ferghana to Eastern Turkestan, and of the cities of that province, and some account of Nepal and Tibet. His description of India and its institutions at the beginning of the eleventh century is also a work of considerable importance.[1]

The other great figure in Arab travel is Ibn Battuta, whose extensive journeys alone would demand notice. He was born at Tangier, and when twenty-two years of age set out for Alexandria. Having travelled over the greater part of Egypt, he visited Palestine, and then went to Mecca. Returning from Arabia, he went to 'Iraq and Persia, and then visited Mecca a second time. Making his way back again to Palestine, he next crossed Asia Minor and visited Russia, and perhaps reached Siberia.

[1] See E. C. Sachau, *Alberuni's India* (2 vols., 1910).

From his Russian travels he returned to Constantinople, and began another long journey overland through Turkestan and Afghanistan to India, where he was employed by the ruler of Delhi, who sent him on a mission to China in 1342. In the course of his journey he called at the Maldive Islands. Ibn Battuta then returned to Morocco, but was not satisfied so long as there remained any Muslim countries unvisited. Accordingly he went first to Spain, and then crossed the Sahara to Timbuktu. He returned to Fez, where he dictated an account of his travels which forms one of the most interesting and remarkable works ever compiled. He died in 1377.

Ibn Battuta was

> the only mediæval traveller who is known to have visited the lands of every Muhammadan ruler of his time, quite apart from such infidel countries as Constantinople, Ceylon, and China. . . . [His work was] primarily intended to present a descriptive account of Muhammadan society in the second quarter of the fourteenth century. Ibn Battuta's interest in places was subordinate to his interest in persons. He is the supreme example of *le géographe malgré lui*, whose geographical knowledge was gained entirely from personal experience and the information of chance acquaintances. For his details he relied exclusively on his memory.[1]

Yet with all its deficiencies Ibn Battuta's book is full of interesting matter, and much of it has a high value. His record is a fitting end to an important interlude in the history of discovery.

[1] H. A. R. Gibb, *Ibn Battuta: Travels in Asia and Africa* (" Broadway Travellers" series, 1929), pp. 9, 12. This is a selection of his travels: the author is preparing a complete version for the Hakluyt Society.

CHAPTER IV

THE SEA-ROUTE TO THE FAR EAST [1]

AT the beginning of the fifteenth century Central, Southern, and South-eastern Europe was fully occupied with domestic problems. Internal weakness in Germany followed from the disruption of the great duchies and the quarrels with the Papacy. In France the long struggle with the English was still in progress. In Italy, apart from the political troubles associated with the Papacy, there was intense rivalry between the great cities of the north. In the south-east the Turks had overthrown the Serbian empire, and were only checked in their progress in Europe by attacks delivered in Asia Minor by the army of Timur.

By contrast the political conditions in the Iberian peninsula were relatively stable. The Moors were driven into the mountains of Granada, but the crusading spirit of the Christians was still alive. The Portuguese had attained their present territorial limits in 1262, and, as soon as they were able, were anxious to continue the Holy War. Isolated from Spain, and with a wholly maritime outlook, Portugal was ready by the year 1415 to move southward.

The expansion of Portugal over the ocean, and the discovery of the sea-route to India by her sailors, owe much to the work of Henry, generally known as " the Navigator," though he took no active part in maritime enterprises. Henry was inspired by a number of motives. To quote the chronicler Azurara, " he had a wish to know the land that lay beyond the Isles of Canary and that cape called Bojador, for that up to his time neither by writings nor by the memory of man was known with any certainty the nature of the land beyond that cape." To this scientific aim he added a wish to extend the empire and the trade of Portugal, to carry out

---

[1] The authorities for this chapter are :

C. R. BEAZLEY, *Henry the Navigator* (1895).
E. PRESTAGE and C. R. BEAZLEY, *The Discovery and Conquest of Guinea* (Hakluyt Society, first series, vols. xcv and c).
E. G. RAVENSTEIN, " Diogo Cão and Bartholomew Dias," in *G.J.*, vol. xvi, p. 625.
—— *Vasco da Gama's First Voyage* (Hakluyt Society, first series, vol. xcix).
LORD STANLEY OF ALDERLEY, *The Three Voyages of Vasco da Gama* (Hakluyt Society, first series, vol. xlii).
K. G. JAYNE, *Vasco da Gama and his Successors* (1910).
F. HUMMERICH, *Vasco da Gama* (1896).
E. PRESTAGE, *The Portuguese Pioneers* (1933).

a crusade against the Moors, to learn the extent of Muslim dominion in Africa, and to find an ally in some African king who was a Christian—*i.e.*, Prester John. Although he may not have aimed at the discovery of a sea-route to India in 1415, it is possible that this object was before him in his later exploits.

Henry was much helped by the political situation at home and by the expedition to Ceuta in 1415, from which he gained some personal knowledge of the trade of the Niger country. He owed much to the improvements in the ships of Portugal which had gradually been carried out. The caravel, purely Portuguese in its origin, began life as a fishing-vessel or coastal trader in Portugal, and retained its characteristics down to the end of the fifteenth century. During the later period of Henry's life it was a light ship, not more than 200 tons, provided with three or more masts rigged with lateen sails. Its merit was that it could sail close to the wind.

The steady improvement in the compass also made navigation more secure. The compass was certainly in use in Europe in the latter half of the twelfth century, but in or about the year 1302 the improvement was made of fixing to the pivoted needle a light card on which was painted a wind-rose.

Further, new knowledge was being steadily accumulated, and this was put at Henry's disposal by his brother Pedro, who toured Europe in order to obtain books and maps.

The geographical conditions, real or imaginary, on the west coast of Africa were such as to hamper explorers. In spite of the many earlier voyages, the limit of knowledge was placed at Cape Bojador, and that cape was, in theory, guarded by fierce currents. The trade-winds, blowing constantly from the north-east, seemed to offer small prospect of a safe return, while the inhospitable coast could furnish little in the way of food and water. The problem of crossing the fiery zone of the tropics had also to be solved.

It was not Henry's task to find a solution to these many difficulties. Living in seclusion on his promontory of Cape St Vincent, he collected information, trained pilots, encouraged explorers to further efforts, and saw to it that the interest in ocean exploration did not diminish. At times the political intrigues in Portugal were too strong for him, but on the whole the country never relaxed its efforts during his lifetime. It was no small achievement to secure the discovery of a large part of the west coast of Africa and to set many ships on the route to India. For it is as one stage in the progress of the Portuguese from Lisbon to Calicut that the work of Henry must be judged : it was the first and in many respects the most difficult period in which he worked.

For convenience the discovery of the sea-route to India may be divided into five stages, the first of which extends from the expedition to Ceuta in 1415 to the rounding of Cape Bojador in 1434.

This may be called the preparatory stage, and is marked by a large number of voyages to the Atlantic islands and the west coast of Africa. Twelve years were spent in the effort to get round Cape Bojador, a task which was ultimately accomplished by Gil Eannes. Thus one serious difficulty had been overcome.

The second stage, from 1434 to 1462, was marked by steady progress along the coast of Africa. From 1436 to 1441 there was a slight break in the course of events due to an expedition to Tangier and troubles at home, but improving conditions on the west coast of Africa, graphically and appropriately marked by the name Cape Verde, made the chances of progress considerably greater. The earlier discoveries were made in a land described by Azurara as " no less sandy than the deserts of Libya, where there is no water, no tree, no green herb," but now the " green land " appeared to the sailors like " some gracious fruit garden ordained for the sole end of their delight. . . . When the men in the caravels first saw the palms and lofty trees . . . they understood well that they were close to the river of Nile at the point where it floweth into the western sea, the which river is called Senegal." Cape Verde was discovered in 1445, and in 1462, two years after Henry's death, the Portuguese sailed into the Gulf of Guinea, and reached the point later chosen for their fort of El Mina.

After a break the exploring voyages were renewed in 1470, but the third period covers only the short space of five years. During this time regular expeditions were sent out under contract to make definite discoveries, and in this way the Portuguese became acquainted with the remainder of the Guinea coast, and by 1475 had reached Cape Catherine, 2° beyond the equator.

The fourth period begins in 1482, and is occupied by the voyages of two men, Diego Cam and Bartholomew Dias. Cam made his first voyage in 1482, when he continued the coastal expeditions of his predecessors, and carried the Portuguese flag as far as the modern Cape St Mary, in latitude 13° 26' S. Here, and at the mouth of the Congo, which he discovered, he set up pillars to mark his progress. In 1485 he made a second voyage, cruising along the coast already explored, and landing occasionally to seize natives. He set up his third pillar at a cape called Monte Negro, in latitude 15° 41' S., and a fourth was erected on Cape Cross, about 6° farther to the south. Cam probably went a little beyond this cape before he died. To his credit must be placed the discovery of 1450 miles of coastline, a feat of considerable magnitude, and not rendered less difficult by the Benguela Current and the south-east trade-winds.

As a result of reports which reached Portugal from West Africa of a king named Ogané whose territory was within measurable distance of the coast, two expeditions were sent out to find the priest-king and to reach India. Covilham went to Egypt in 1487 and reached India by sea. He reported that it was possible to sail to India round Africa.

The second expedition under Dias left Lisbon in 1487 for the Congo, where his real exploration began. He made a survey of the coast as far as Walfish Bay. He was by this time finding difficulty with the currents which sweep round South Africa, but, sailing first southward well beyond the Cape of Good Hope, and into the region of the 'brave west winds,' then eastward, and finally northward, he reached Mossel Bay. With difficulty he followed the coast eastward to the mouth of the Great Fish river. On his return voyage he rounded the Cape with ease, leaving it behind with a following wind. He had found the region stormy, but the pretty story of Cabo Tormentoso and its renaming by an optimistic king rests on the not too trustworthy authority of Barros, while a contemporary writer says that Dias gave the Cape its present name. Dias reached Lisbon in December 1488, after a voyage which had added 1260 miles to the known coast of Africa.

After some delay this task of completing the discovery of the sea-route to India was entrusted to Vasco da Gama, whose main work was to cover the eight hundred miles of unknown coast between the limit already reached by Dias and the region well known to Arab sailors. Had he done no more Da Gama would have won his place in the ranks of great explorers, yet this was but a small part of his achievement, and took only a month to complete. What is really remarkable is that he made a voyage which, if the time spent in India is deducted, occupied twenty-one months, of which on his outward journey three were spent on the open sea.

Of Vasco da Gama little is known apart from his three voyages to India. He was probably born in 1460, and appears to have had considerable experience afloat before he was called on to command the expedition of 1497. Of that expedition there is only one contemporary account, written by an unknown member of it, and this throws little light either on the character of the leader or on the conduct of the voyage. The fleet consisted of four vessels, of which two had been specially built for the voyage, and was manned by 118 men all told. Its commander was supplied with the latest information available in the books and maps of the time, and took with him the best scientific instruments that the country could produce. Thus equipped, the vessels left the Tagus river on July 8, 1497, and, favoured by good weather, reached the island of São Thiago, in the Cape Verde group, on July 27. They left again on August 3, and from this date until November 4 no land was seen, nor is it possible to say with certainty what course was followed. In the *Journal* it is stated that the whole fleet sailed as far as El Mina, but this seems to be wrong, because the same authority asserts that after sailing for fifteen days they had made 200 leagues from

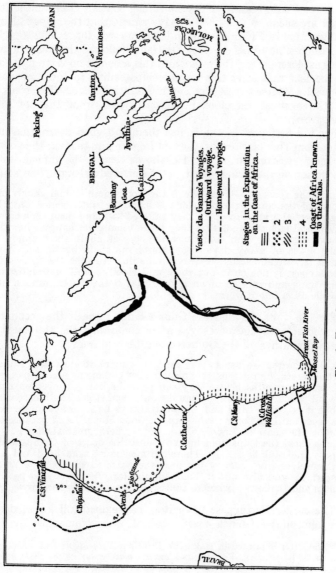

Fig. 6. The Sea-route to India

the Cape Verde islands, and were sailing south. Other authorities either are silent on this point or say vaguely that the ships sailed in the direction of El Mina. As no land was seen for so long a period it is impossible to believe that Da Gama followed the route of previous explorers along the coast, and this assumption is strengthened by the fact that after this voyage ships sailing to India regularly followed a course across the South Atlantic Ocean. The track of Da Gama must therefore be reconstructed from that of later navigators.

For the first part of the course there is a good description in a letter from Thomas Stevens, the first Englishman to make the voyage to India, written in 1579. He shows clearly the difficulties of navigation off the Guinea coast. " We arrived at length," he writes,

> unto the coast of Guinea which the Portuguese so call chiefly that part of the burning zone which is from the sixth degree unto the equinoctial ; in which part they suffered so many inconveniences of heat and lack of winds that they think themselves happy when they have passed it. For sometimes the ship standeth there almost by the space of many days ; sometimes she goeth but in such order that it were almost as good to stand still. And the greatest part of this coast is not clear but thick and cloudy ; full of thunder and lightning and rain so unwholesome that if the water stand a little while all is full of worms.[1]

For the course beyond the Guinea lands there is the account of Linschoten's voyage of 1583. After confirming the statement of the bad weather off the Guinea coast, he continues :

> The nearer we are to the land, the more it stormeth, raineth, thundereth, and calmeth ; so that most commonly the ships are at least two months before they can pass the line. They then find a wind which they call a " general wind " and it is a south-east wind : but it is a side wind and we must always be sideways in the wind almost until we come to the Cape of Good Hope. And because that upon the coast of Brazil, about 18° S., lieth great shallows . . . to pass them the ships hold up most unto the coast of Guinea and so pass the said flats. . . . Therefore men must take heed and keep themselves from coming too near the coast to shun the calms and storms ; and also not to hold out too far off, thereby to pass the flats and shallows ; wherein consisteth the whole Indian voyage.[2]

The earlier Portuguese navigators had gained full knowledge of the inhospitable Guinea coast. Cabral, who commanded the fleet

---

[1] The letter is printed in Hakluyt's *Principal Navigations* (vol. vi, p. 377), and in C. R. Beazley, *Voyages and Travels mainly during the Sixteenth and Seventeenth Centuries* (2 vols., 1903), vol. i, p. 152. All quotations from Hakluyt's *Principal Navigations* are taken from the Maclehose edition of this work. For a description of the route, written soon after Da Gama's voyage, see "Esmeraldo de situ orbis," by Duante Pacheo Pereira, translated and edited by G. H. T. Kimble (Hakluyt Society, second series, vol. lxxix), p. 170.

[2] Beazley, *Voyages and Travels*, vol. ii, p. 170.

in 1500, went to the other extreme and actually reached Brazil. It seems probable that Da Gama, perhaps by accident, but with ultimate success, took the middle course, and was thus the first to navigate the real sailing-route to the East. Following the circuitous track for over five thousand miles, he saw land on November 4, and, continuing along the coast to the southward, " cast anchor in a bay to which the name of St Helena was given." Here the Portuguese first came in contact with the Hottentot peoples of South Africa, described in the *Journal* as of brown or blackish colour, whose food was the flesh of seals, whales, and gazelles and the roots of herbs, and who were completely ignorant of the spices which the Portuguese sought, but were much interested in round bells and tin rings and in the copper coins which the sailors distributed.

After a stay of eight days the ships continued the voyage to the southward, and after several attempts, in the words of the *Journal*, " at last on Wednesday [November 22] at noon, having the wind astern, we succeeded in doubling the Cape [of Good Hope] and then ran along the coast." In three days Mossel Bay was reached and natives again encountered. These supplied an ox in exchange for three ivory bracelets, entertained the crews with music—" a pretty harmony," the *Journal* says, " for negroes who are not expected to be musicians "— and with dancing " in the style of negroes." The store ship was broken up and burnt before departure. Eight days after leaving Mossel Bay the ships passed the last of the pillars set up by Dias, and thus entered the unknown region of Africa. Here they had to contend with the Agulhas Current, which was so strong that on December 20 they were actually carried back on their course. Fortunately, " being favoured during three or four days by a strong stern wind we were able to overcome the currents which we had feared might frustrate our plans." The writer of the *Journal*, perhaps recalling the mutiny which had compelled Dias to turn back at this point, adds, " henceforth it pleased God in His mercy to allow us to make headway. We were not again driven back."

For the next four days the ships kept close inshore, passing Natal on Christmas Day, and then put out to sea, until shortage of water and food made it " necessary to seek a port." On January 11 a small river was discovered affording suitable anchorage. Natives were again seen, but clearly belonged to a different race. They were tall, lived in straw huts, and appeared to be both prosperous and generous. The country gave every sign of being well populated, and was named " the Land of Good People," while the river was called the Copper river from the abundance of that metal in the possession of the natives. Continuing northward, the fleet reached the mouth of the Quilimane river on January 22, and remained here

69

for thirty-two days, taking in supplies and effecting repairs. The low-lying and marshy country seems to have done little to improve the health of the men, for soon after leaving sickness broke out in an alarming manner. At length, still going northward, the fleet reached the sphere of Arab influence, and at Mozambique came across four Arab dhows "laden with gold, silver, cloves, pepper, ginger, pearls, and rubies," all of which articles were apparently traded to the natives. Here, too, information was obtained as to their future course along the east coast of Africa, the difficulties of which were increased at the outset by the Mozambique Current, which flows rapidly between Madagascar and the mainland. After a false start they finally got away on March 27.

There is no need to follow them in their progress along the coast, hampered as it was by the hostility of the Arab traders. At Malindi a pilot was obtained, and a new stage in their voyage began. Favoured by the monsoon wind, they made a good passage across the Indian Ocean, and at the end of twenty-three days sighted the lofty wall of the Western Ghats. Coasting a little way to the southward, they came to anchor on May 23 near to Calicut.

The reception of the Portuguese was hardly warm, for the *Journal* records that " the first greeting was in these words : ' May the devil take thee. What brought you hither ? ' They asked what [the messenger] sought so far away from home and he told them that we came in search of Christians and spices." This search was soon rewarded. As to Christians, the Portuguese were quite misled, and believed that the Hindu gods were the same as their own. This is curious when it is remembered that no similar mistake was made about the Muslims. The latter were, they thought, responsible for all the misfortunes that they suffered. Of the spices, and the trade of Calicut generally, the *Journal* gives a good account. Not only was that place the centre of a fertile district producing ginger, pepper, and cinnamon of an inferior quality, but it was also the collecting port for the merchandise of the East. To it came cinnamon from Ceylon, cloves from Malacca, and tin from Malaya. Of great interest also is an appendix to the *Journal* which gives the information which the Portuguese were able to collect about the countries which lay beyond Southern India. Here is to be found an account of the Coromandel coast of India ; of the spices, sapphires, and rubies of Ceylon ; of Sumatra ; of Siam, whose king owned four hundred war-elephants ; of Pegu, through which country came the musk of inner Asia ; of Tenasserim, the land of Brazil wood ; and of Bengal, where there was " much corn and much cloth of great value."

At length

on Wednesday the 29 of August the captain-major and the other captains agreed that inasmuch that we had discovered the country we had come in search of, as also spices and precious stones . . . it would be well to take our departure. . . . We therefore left for Portugal greatly rejoicing at our good fortune in having made so great a discovery.

There is no need to go into the details of the return voyage. Three months were taken to cross to Africa, and the crews were so reduced in numbers and strength that one of the ships had to be abandoned near Mombasa. Thereafter, with winds and currents in their favour, the two remaining ships made a good passage, and the first reached Lisbon on July 10, 1499. Da Gama, who had gone with his brother to the Azores, did not reach Portugal for some weeks, but the exact date of his arrival is not known. It should be noticed that the route on the homeward voyage across the Atlantic Ocean differed considerably from that taken on the outward voyage. On this occasion winds and currents alike favoured direct sailing from the Cape of Good Hope to the Cape Verde Islands. On a subsequent occasion (1502) the island of St Helena was discovered on this route.

A few general facts about this remarkable voyage are worth mention. It covered nearly 24,000 nautical miles, and occupied 630 days, of which half were spent on the open sea. The influence of the currents and winds is seen in the average daily run, which was as high as 93 miles from Malindi to India and from the Cape to the Rio Grande on the return passage, but was only 54 miles from the Cape Verde group to St Helena Bay on the outward journey, and dropped to 26 when running against the Agulhas Current, and to 25 on the homeward voyage from India to Africa. Of the crew, whose number is not known with certainty, about half died in the course of the voyage.

It is unnecessary to say much of the results of Da Gama's work, but it is well to bear in mind that if his discovery revolutionized the history of Europe its effects were no less strikingly felt in the East. An entirely new element, the sea, was introduced into Indian history. The Far East very soon felt the influence of the West, for European sailors immediately followed out the trade-routes which the Portuguese had tapped in India. And it is a little humiliating to realize that as a result of this new contact the Asiatic peoples lost their confidence in the white man, who was no longer able to travel freely in and enjoy the hospitality of Eastern countries.

It is rather astonishing to find that European nations were apparently slow to realize the change that had taken place. This is well reflected in the maps of the period. The great map of La Cosa, and the manuscript drawings of 1502, of which there are three specimens—an anonymous work and the maps of Cantino and Canerio—show with reasonable accuracy the new facts. The

71

anonymous map was, almost certainly, a compilation from charts executed by a member of Da Gama's expedition, of which unfortunately no specimens remain. But whatever may be said of the manuscripts, printed maps were very slow to make any changes, and the familiar outline of Ptolemy was not easily displaced. In 1506 it was annotated by Reisch to indicate some of the more important changes, but it was not until the edition of 1508 that an entirely new map found its way into the *Geography* of Ptolemy, nor until 1513 that his work was revised in the light of the new discoveries.

Da Gama made a second voyage to India in 1502, with a fleet of fifteen ships, but was not thereafter employed until 1524, when he returned to the East as Viceroy of Portuguese India. Many abuses had already crept into the administration of the new possessions, and Da Gama spent the last months of his life in a fruitless effort to check corruption and re-establish the prestige of the Government. The task proved too much for a man now probably in his sixty-fifth year and no longer able to endure hardship in a tropical country, and before it was completed Da Gama died at Cochin, on December 24, 1524.

Probably enough has been said of Da Gama as an explorer for some appreciation of his great work : of the man himself little is known except in his later years, when his temper was soured by ill-health. All Portuguese writers of the sixteenth century agree that he was a brave leader and a fearless administrator. Judged by present standards, he was cruel and obstinate. He could 'question' hostages by pouring boiling oil on them ; he could leave 300 dead and dying men, with their wives and families, to the mercy of the open sea ; he could order disobedient Portuguese women to be flogged through the streets of an Indian town. Yet he could also share with good spirit the hardships of his men, and by timely encouragement stay a panic during an earthquake. If his conduct as Viceroy was sometimes harsh he at least astonished both Portuguese and Indians by his refusal to accept presents, and he saw to it that his authority was respected. That in an Eastern land was the beginning of wisdom. His character is not inadequately represented in the pages of Astley's *Collection of Travels*, where he is said to be " fit for all that was intrusted to his conduct as Captain, as Discoverer, and as Viceroy."

Important as was the arrival of the Portuguese at Calicut, it was only one stage in their advance to the Pacific. In India itself their progress was not very rapid. Goa was finally acquired in 1510 ; trade was opened up with Bengal in 1518, though this was an isolated venture, and it did not become regular until the Governorship of Nuno da Cunha (1529–38) ; and in 1543 Salsette Island was ceded to the Europeans.

To the eastward the Portuguese first reached Ceylon in 1507. Two years later the great Viceroy Albuquerque took charge of affairs, and progress was rapid. His policy was to extend the territorial basis of the Portuguese empire so that the commercial sphere should be wider and more secure ; to make commerce a Crown monopoly ; and to remain on friendly terms with any who would help to undermine the Muslim power in the East. The Portuguese naval victory off Diu in 1509 was followed by the seizure of Goa, and, later, by an expedition to Malacca, which was finally taken in 1511. This in turn led to penetration still farther eastward, for Malacca was the key to the trade-routes of the Archipelago and the China Seas. Its capture not only drew the Portuguese onward, but also gave them some security for further exploration and trade.

After the fall of Malacca a fleet under the command of Antonio d'Abreu was sent to the Archipelago, and although no details of the voyage have been preserved, it seems that the Portuguese reached Amboina, south of Ceram, a very important centre of the clove trade, and it is reasonable to suppose that they touched at the intermediate islands of Borneo, Celebes, and the Moluccas. The pacific nature of this expedition probably helped the Portuguese to extend their influence in the Archipelago, and although no portion of the Moluccas was annexed until after 1526, trade was regularly carried on after 1511.

Canton was reached in 1516, and within twenty-four years there were said to be over one thousand Portuguese houses in the Chinese port of Liampoo. By 1520 the traders had penetrated inland to Peking.

In 1518 the Lu-chu Islands were reached, and in 1542 Japan came within the realm of Portuguese commerce.

Meanwhile, something had been done to open up the lands between India and China. During the siege of Malacca an embassy had been sent to the Court of Siam, and reached the capital, Ayuthia, on the Menam river above Bangkok. Subsequently the Portuguese settled in some numbers in the country, and frequently used it as a stopping-place when the north-east monsoon winds made navigation in the China Seas difficult and dangerous. A second expedition under Antonio de Miranda sailed round the Malay peninsula as far as Trengganu, from which place a long and arduous journey on foot was made to Ayuthia. If the account of this exploit is reliable Antonio de Miranda deserves credit as the first European explorer of Lower Siam.

An expedition to Burma was dispatched after the fall of Malacca, and was followed by regular trading voyages and, about the middle of the century, by Dominican missionaries.

The opening up of Indo-China is due to the misfortunes of Mendez

Pinto, a man of whom many hard things have been said. He was robbed off the small state of Ligor, and with the owner of the cargo, Antonio de Faria, set out in 1540 to catch the thieves. From Patani he went to Pulo Condore, an island off the mouths of the Mekong, and thence went to the mainland, where he heard of Tonlé Sap and of great mineral wealth. Thence he coasted as far as Hainan, and finally went back to the mainland at Turan, the centre of overland trade with China by way of the Mekong and Songkoi rivers. After further adventures the Portuguese reached China.

The Portuguese were not the first Europeans in the Far East, and they were not to hold the trade monopoly for very long: they had been anticipated by those travellers whose activities have been recorded in an earlier chapter, and they were soon to be ousted by the Dutch. Yet in the short space of fifty years they had accomplished a very considerable work. The vagueness which surrounded the Island Archipelago had now gone; the certainty of rich trade had been established; and the power of the white man had been consolidated in a region not suited to Europeans. And if the Portuguese had been helped by some geographical conditions to establish themselves in the East they paid the penalty of attempting to settle in the tropics, and to this unhealthy geographical environment part of their decline was due. This is, however, not the whole explanation. The union with Spain in 1580, the smallness of their numbers in the East, the vigour and persistence of the attacks of other European nations, and the counter-attractions of South America must all be considered as factors in the decay of the Portuguese Empire.

It is possible that the Portuguese while searching for a route round Africa accidentally discovered Brazil. As long ago as 1894 Mr Yule Oldham argued that such a discovery took place before 1448, in which year Andrea Bianco drew a map on which was a land mass with a legend the interpretation of which is uncertain. According to Mr Yule Oldham, it reads, " Authentic island is distant 1500 miles to the west "; and if one adopts the length of a degree used by Bianco on an earlier map, Brazil was, in fact, 1520 miles west of Cape Verde. Mr Yule Oldham's views were not generally accepted, in spite of strong support from Dr J. Batalha-Reis. It is now clear that the voyage of Cabral in 1500, which resulted in greater knowledge of Brazil, was not an accident, but was planned deliberately,[1] and may be regarded as the successor of a project of 1498 which had come to nothing.

[1] See Prestage, *op. cit.*, p. 277.

CHAPTER V

CHRISTOPHER COLUMBUS AND HIS SUCCESSORS [1]

WHILE the Portuguese were steadily pushing their way down the west coast of Africa an event happened which very materially affected the history of Europe. It is sometimes referred to as the discovery of America, but to men of the fifteenth century it meant merely the discovery either of some islands previously known only through fabulous stories or of some islands known to exist off the south-east coast of Asia. The subsequent discovery of a great continent lying between Europe and Asia was, at the most, only a rediscovery of America.

To Christopher Colombus belongs the credit for initiating these new discoveries. He was born at Genoa in the year 1451, and belonged to a poor family of weavers. He first went to sea in 1474 or 1475, when he made a voyage to the Levant. In 1477 he visited England, but the story of his further journey to Iceland is probably an invention. Late in 1479 he settled in Lisbon, got to know the leading men in Portuguese exploration, and probably took part in a Portuguese voyage to the Guinea Coast in 1482. This last experience, and the general information he had collected, gave him his passion for further discovery. But he unsuccessfully pressed his schemes in Portugal and left that country for Spain in 1484. Here, with the help of his brother, a map-maker, and the Pinzon family, well known in the trading world, he developed his ideas, secured the help of influential churchmen, and, perhaps

---

[1] The following are the main sources for this chapter :

Select Documents illustrating the Four Voyages of Columbus, edited by Cecil Jane (Hakluyt Society, second series, vols. lxv, lxx).

CECIL JANE, The Voyages of Christopher Columbus (1930).

SIR CLEMENTS MARKHAM, Christopher Columbus (1892).

H. HARRISSE, Christophe Colomb (1884).

—— Christophe Colomb devant l'histoire (1892).

—— John Cabot and Sebastian his Son (1896).

H. VIGNAUD, Etudes critiques sur la vie de Colomb avant ses découvertes (1905).

—— The Columbian Tradition on the Discovery of America (1920).

FILSON YOUNG : Christopher Columbus and the New World of his Discovery (2 vols., 1906). Popular account.

C. R. BEAZLEY : John and Sebastian Cabot (1898).

J. A. WILLIAMSON : The Voyages of the Cabots and the English Discovery of North America under Henry VII and Henry VIII (1929). This elaborate and scholarly book appeared after 'this chapter was written. It will certainly take its place as the standard work on the subject.

because of his religious enthusiasm rather than through any sound and intelligible plans, ultimately won the approval of the Queen of Spain.

The position occupied by Columbus in the history of geographical discovery is so important and so conspicuous that all efforts to find out the whole truth about him are welcome. Many critics have taken away the frills of romance, and one, H. Vignaud, has endeavoured to show that most of the traditional stories associated with his name are erroneous. Much controversy has raged round the aims and beliefs of Columbus. It has been asserted that he never intended to discover the Spice Islands by sailing westward across the Atlantic, but that he was merely looking for an island in that ocean. There were many mythical islands on the maps of the period.[1] Brandan was supposed to have been visited by a saint of that name in A.D. 578, and men continued to look for it as late as the year 1721. Antilla was thought to have been reached by the Archbishop of Oporto in 734 and by others in 1414. Brazil attracted the attention of Bristol merchants late in the fifteenth century. All these islands appear on the great globe of Behaim, which dates from the year 1492, and which represents the most advanced geographical knowledge of that time. This globe also shows no land mass between Europe and the Asiatic islands.

The traditional story of Columbus and Toscanelli has been a commonplace of history for so long that it is unnecessary to do more than refer briefly to it. According to the story, Toscanelli, a learned Italian, sent a letter to a Portuguese named Martins, expressing the view that it was possible to reach Asia by sailing westward, and illustrating his letter by a map. Columbus wrote to Toscanelli explaining his own project, whereon Toscanelli replied by sending him a copy of his letter to Martins and the map. He thus encouraged Columbus to proceed with his scheme of sailing to the west, and stressed the political and commercial advantages which would follow its successful accomplishment.

Vignaud has tried to prove that the whole of the story of Toscanelli and Columbus is a fraud, and that any western voyage of Columbus based on the arguments drawn from Toscanelli's map is unsound. He suggests that the story was invented by the brother of Columbus, who palmed it off on Las Casas, who in turn was responsible for deceiving Ferdinand Columbus, the son and biographer of Christopher. It is not necessary to enter into the details of the controversy, but, assuming that Vignaud's point is established, it might be urged that others besides Behaim had access to the knowledge on which the latter constructed his globe, and that from it, or a similar production, it was possible to argue in favour of a westward route to the Indies. There is no proof that Columbus

[1] See W. H. Babcock, *Legendary Islands of the Atlantic* (1922).

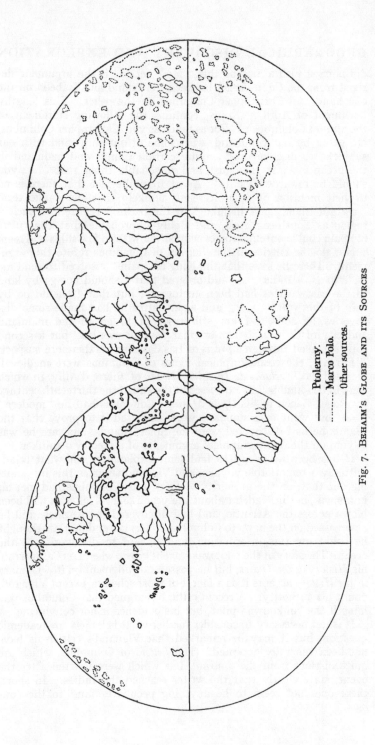

Fig. 7. BEHAIM'S GLOBE AND ITS SOURCES

——— Ptolemy.
·········· Marco Polo.
——— Other sources.

did not see such a map as this. More serious is the argument derived from the *Capitulation* between Ferdinand and Isabella on the one hand and Christopher Columbus on the other. This lengthy document of April 30, 1492, contains the following statement of the aims of Columbus : " For as much as you, Christopher Columbus, are going by our command, with some of our ships and with our subjects, to discover and acquire certain islands and mainland in the ocean . . . it is a just and reasonable thing that . . . you should be rewarded for it." Apart from the fact that there is no explicit mention of Asia, it seems unlikely that the vague term " certain islands and mainland in the ocean " referred to such a region as South-east Asia, and highly improbable that the rulers of Spain could contemplate its acquisition with so few ships and men.

Nor do the entries in the *Journal* of Columbus refute this argument. There he says that the King of Spain " resolved to send me . . . to . . . India . . . and ordered that I should not go by land to the eastward as had been customary, but that I should go by way of the west " . . .; and again, after he had made some discoveries, he adds, " I am still resolved to go to the mainland and city of Guisay." The original *Journal* was lost, but a second copy survived through a *précis* of Las Casas and is therefore suspect.

Further, the cosmographical views of Columbus were medieval. He used the *Tractatus de Imagine Mundi* of Pierre d'Ailly, in which were to be found beliefs expressed at the end of the thirteenth century by Roger Bacon in his *Opus Majus*. Columbus had no ' modern ' ideas, but went to a standard work and used it to prove that the islands he had discovered were the Spice Islands, unaware he was relying on the cosmographical arguments of a medieval thinker.

It has been necessary to find some explanation for what is admittedly a remarkable voyage, and Vignaud supplies this by pointing out that, on the authority of Las Casas, Columbus had met an unknown pilot in Madeira about the year 1484. This man had been blown across the Atlantic, and had discovered the Antilles, and he now passed on the news to Columbus. The latter doubtless thought he could use this information, and so add to discoveries in the ocean. The story of the pilot was current gossip when Las Casas wrote his *History of the Indies*, but he passed no judgment on it. Gomara in his *History* accepts it as a fact, but most scholars, except Vignaud, doubt his authority. A recent critic has argued that Columbus was himself the ' unknown ' pilot, but his evidence is not convincing.

It is not necessary to consider further what is largely an academic question, but it may be remarked that Vignaud's criticisms have not been generally accepted. The *Letters* of Columbus, which are quite distinct from the *Journal*, but which were written after the event, state clearly that the writer reached the Indies. In short, there does not seem to be anything peculiarly fatal to the conventional ideas except Columbus and his biographers. If he only occasionally spoke the truth it may counteract their alleged habitual lying. It yet remains to be proved that he definitely set out for some Atlantic island.

M. Charles de la Roncière recently found a map which, he claimed, showed the aims of Columbus, perhaps an Atlantic island and the coast of Asia. His arguments have not, however, carried conviction. Another map, drawn in Turkey in 1513, but based in part on material captured from Spaniards, which is thought to show that Columbus annotated a map similar to Behaim's globe and marked Atlantic islands, Japan (Haiti), and the mainland of Asia (Cuba), may also reveal his ideas. But Jane in his recent works is wisely vague, as, indeed, was Columbus. The latter, he suggests, " contemplated the possibility of reaching Cipangu and Catayo, . . . [and] Antilla or other islands in the Ocean," but had a further object—to discover land whose position cannot be fixed and of which he himself had no clear conception.[1]

It is more profitable to know what Columbus accomplished. Leaving Spain on August 3, 1492, and the Canary Islands on September 9, he followed a westerly course until, in about longitude 68° W., on October 7, he changed his course to south-west. As this change had been suggested by Pinzon the day before, its adoption has been used by critics to dispute the claim of Columbus to find the Indies by sailing westward. Four days later land was sighted. The Indians called it Guanahani, and it is probably Watling Island, in the Bahama group.[2] After discovering other islands in the group Columbus reached Cuba, which he described to his crew as Cipangu, on October 28. After some exploration of the interior and the discovery of the tobacco plant he sailed to Haiti. When Cuba was seen to be something other than Cipangu, Haiti was so described, though Columbus called it Española. He left the island on January 16, 1493, and, steering first north-east and then due east, made the Azores after thirty-four days, and was back in Spain early in March.

Apart from the discovery of new land, the identity of which was not established, Columbus had boldly sailed into the Atlantic and had found islands in regions in which mythical islands were shown on maps. He had made a pioneer voyage of immense importance, and had shown that it was possible to return from the lands he had found. Hence the claim that he discovered the sailing-route across the Atlantic. This, however, may have been accidental, and,

---

[1] On M. Roncière's discovery see *G.J.*, vol. lxv, p. 247, and *Annales de géographie*, vol. xxxiv, p. 193. On the Turkish map see *G.J.*, vol. lxxxii, p. 267 ; P. Kahle, " The Lost Columbus map of 1498," in the *Aligarh Muslim University Journal*, vol. ii, No. 2 ; and *Piri Reis Haritasi* (a reproduction of the map with text by Yusuf Akcura, 1935).

[2] See the admirable summary by R. T. Gould in *G.J.*, vol. lxix, p. 403.

in view of the later courses taken by Columbus, was obviously not understood. It may, too, have been due to one of the pilots who sailed with him.[1] Contemporary opinion gave him credit for greater things. Some thought he had found the Indies ; others very soon suspected that a hitherto unknown continent had been discovered.

The main object of the second voyage of Columbus, in 1493, was to complete his work of the previous year, to the eastward of Haiti, where the colony of Navidad had been established. On this occasion he shaped a more southerly course, and sighted land on Sunday, November 3, calling it Dominica, a name which it still retains. The discovery of a number of the smaller islands followed. From

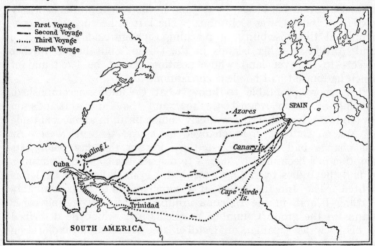

Fig. 8. THE FOUR VOYAGES OF CHRISTOPHER COLUMBUS

Dominica, by Marie Galante and the Leeward Islands, including Montserrat, Nevis, St Christopher's, and Santa Cruz, Columbus reached Puerto Rico, and finally arrived off the settlement on Haiti. He found it abandoned, and learned that the colonists had been killed by natives. To replace it he established the new town of Isabella, whence parties went inland for gold to the Cibao Mountains.

Columbus next sailed along the south coast of Cuba, and then put across to Jamaica. The northern coast of that island was discovered, and then the explorer returned to complete his examination of the southern shore of Cuba. He came to the conclusion that this was no island, but part of the mainland of Asia. At last Columbus got back to Isabella, and sailed thence for Spain on March 10, 1495, taking with him gold, specimens of birds, fruits, and plants, including

[1] For a contrary view see G. E. Nunn, *Geographical Conceptions of Columbus* (1924).

maize and yams. He steered first to Guadeloupe, and then north-eastward in the face of the trade-winds. So long and difficult was the passage that Cadiz was not reached until June 11. The outward voyage had taken forty-one days : the homeward voyage occupied sixty-two. These figures show the difficulties which sailors had to face, and are a strange commentary on the alleged knowledge of seamanship possessed by Columbus.

The third voyage of Columbus began on May 30, 1498. He sailed to the Cape Verde Islands, intending to follow the parallel of 8° 30' due westward, but the calms off the African coast upset his plans, and ultimately he reached the island of Trinidad on August 1, after a voyage of sixty-two days from Spain. Here pearls were discovered, and the fresh water of the Orinoco river was observed far out in the ocean. After leaving Trinidad Columbus sighted the mainland of South America near Paria, but he did not delay to investigate the discovery. When he reached Haiti he was made a prisoner, and sent home to Spain.

The next great figure in the history of the discovery of the New World now appears on the stage. Much controversy has raged round the achievements of Amerigo Vespucci. By some he is regarded as a very important explorer : by others as a man of no importance at all, except in so far as he was a respectable beef-contractor in Spain. Vespucci claimed to have made four voyages, in the years 1497, 1499, 1501, and 1503. The most recent, and in general the most reasonable, discussion of the controversy rejects the first and the fourth voyages.[1] The ' first ' voyage, which is accepted as genuine by a number of scholars, was supposed to have resulted in the discovery of the coast of Mexico from the Bay of Campeachy and of part of the east coast of the United States of America.

The second voyage was made in the company of Ojeda, though the two men did not work together. Ojeda reached the coast of South America near to Surinam, and followed it to beyond the Gulf of Maracaibo. Vespucci appears to have struck the coast in about latitude 5° S., and to have carried out some exploration supple-mentary to that of Ojeda. If this voyage is genuine he discovered Brazil.

The third voyage, in the service of the King of Portugal, was made along the east coast of South America, which Vespucci seems to have examined from about latitude 5° S. to latitude 50° S. This was a most important discovery, and, if genuine, entitles Vespucci to rank very high among the explorers of the Age of Discovery.[2]

---

[1] See A. Magnaghi, *Amerigo Vespucci* (2 vols., 1924), and E. Heawood in *G.J.*, vol. lxvi, p. 339.
[2] The fourth voyage of Vespucci was to have been made to Malacca, but came to an end at Bahía, in South America.

About the same time the Spaniards were very active on the coasts of South America. Alonso Nino in 1500 landed some Spaniards on the island of Marĝarita, the centre of the pearl-fishery, and investigated the mainland westward of Cumana. In the same year Vincente Pinzon reached latitude 8° 20′ S., on the coast of Brazil, and Rodrigo de Bastidas completed the discovery of the northern coast, from the Gulf of Maracaibo, which had been reached by Ojeda, to the Gulf of Darien.

It is probable that by this time many Spaniards realized that a new world had been discovered. But to Columbus the islands of the West Indies were merely a barrier between himself and Asia, and he tried on his fourth voyage to penetrate through the unknown obstacle to Asia. His real work of discovery began on the coast of Honduras at the end of July 1503. The coast was followed southward to the Gulf of Darien, and no passage leading westward was discovered, though when near to the modern Greytown Columbus heard of a country called Veragua which contained gold, and which he thought was somewhere near to the river Ganges.

The work of Columbus was now over. He died in 1506, and even then had probably not realized all that the new discoveries implied. His name is preserved in a number of places in the New World, and his achievements are commonplaces in history. Even allowing for the serious criticisms that have been brought against him or his biographers, he must always remain the central figure in the great era of European expansion across the oceans of the world.

While Spaniards and Portuguese had been directing their attention southward across the Atlantic the English had been content with smaller and less ambitious projects. For a long period the sailors of the West, and of Bristol in particular, had carried on trade in fish and salt with Ireland and Iceland. They complained to Henry VII in 1486 that this traffic was declining. But they did more than complain. In 1480 a certain John Jay financed an expedition to find the island of Brazil, thought to lie to the west of Ireland. It met with no success, in spite of a voyage lasting for six weeks.

From the year 1490 onward the Bristol merchants sent out every year two, three, or four ships in search of this island of Brazil. They were therefore prepared for John Cabot. How far Cabot was indebted to Columbus can never be known, but, on his own evidence, he was well versed in seamanship, and he appears to have worked out the problem of a westward voyage to the Indies from his own experience. His reasoning was as sound as it was ingenious.

He says that on previous occasions he had been to Mecca, whither spices are borne by caravans from distant countries. When he asked those who brought them what was the place of origin of these spices, they answered that they did not know, but that other caravans came with this merchandise to their homes from distant countries, and these again said that the goods had been brought to them from other remote regions. He therefore reasons that if the easterners declare to the southerners that these things come from places far away from them, and so on from one to the other, always assuming that the earth is round, it follows as a matter of course that the last of all must take them in the north towards the west.[1]

In any comparison between the work of Cabot and that of Columbus one other fact must be considered. If Cabot had the advantage of a later start, he made his voyages in a much higher latitude, where the geographical conditions were far less favourable, and although he made use of the summer months, it was no light task to sail across the stormy waters of the North Atlantic.

In 1496 John Cabot was granted a patent to

sail to all parts, regions, and coasts of the eastern, western and northern sea . . . to find, discover, and investigate whatsoever islands, countries, regions, or provinces of heathens and infidels, in whatsoever part of the world placed, which before this time were unknown to all Christians.[2]

He made his first voyage in 1497, but little is known of the course taken or of the country reached. It is reasonably certain that he saw Newfoundland or Nova Scotia, though the report that he had followed the coast for three hundred leagues is probably an exaggeration, since he was away from Bristol only for three months.

The success of the first voyage justified a second, and Cabot probably sailed again in May 1498. Nothing certain is known of this voyage. If the map of La Cosa can be taken as evidence Cabot must have followed the coast for a long distance, " as far as the Delaware or the Chesapeake and perhaps a little farther." [3] It is significant that when the Spanish sovereigns granted a patent to Ojeda in 1501 they instructed him to

go and follow that coast which you have discovered, which runs east and west, as it appears [i.e., the north coast of South America], because it goes towards the region where it has been learned that the English were making discoveries.[4]

The second voyage was a failure, for it had not revealed the wealth of Eastern Asia. The discovery of the fishing grounds off Newfoundland was the only material benefit derived from John Cabot's projects. This trade in fish attracted sailors of all nations. It is almost certain that the French made some discoveries near

[1] J. A. Williamson, *The Voyages of the Cabots* (1929), p. 31. Professor E. G. R. Taylor, *Tudor Geography* (1930), should also be consulted for this period.

[2] *Ibid.*, p. 26.

[3] *Ibid.*, p. 196. The usually accepted date of the La Cosa map is 1500. Mr G. E. Nunn disputes this and suggests 1508 (*The Mappemonde of Juan de la Cosa*, 1934). His arguments are not conclusive.

[4] *Ibid.*, p. 43.

Newfoundland, although the results of their work cannot be described with precision.

Meanwhile the Portuguese from the Azores had joined in the exploration of northern waters. In 1500 Gaspar Corte Real rediscovered Greenland, and on a second voyage in the following year he sailed from Greenland to the North American coast, which he followed to the land discovered by Cabot. He never returned from this voyage, and his brother Miguel, who went out to Newfoundland in 1502, also disappeared. Yet another expedition was dispatched in 1503, but found no trace of the missing explorers.

One Portuguese, by name Fernandez, who may have accompanied Gaspar Corte Real to Greenland, came to England, and with some Bristol merchants received a patent to make discoveries in lands " which before this time were and at present are unknown to all Christians." This may mean that they proposed to explore the region of Davis Strait between Cabot's discoveries and those of Corte Real, but although voyages were made, in 1501 and in 1502, very little is known about them. That they revealed something of promise may be inferred from the fact that the Bristol merchants continued to send ships to these northern waters for a number of years. Finally Sebastian Cabot made a voyage from Bristol in 1509. There is much confusion about this expedition, but there is every reason to guess that it was successful in finding something which resembled a ' passage ' through or round the lands already discovered. Dr Williamson suggests that he passed through Hudson Strait into Hudson Bay, was prevented by ice and a discontented crew from getting farther, and came back to follow the North American coast as far south as latitude 38°. On his return he found a new King, Henry VIII, who was unwilling to give him more help, and after three years he transferred his services to Spain. When he came back to England in 1548 Sebastian Cabot was accepted as an authority on northern discovery, and was soon giving advice on the proposal to explore the North-east Passage.

CHAPTER VI

THE SPANIARDS IN THE NEW WORLD [1]

I. THE GULF OF MEXICO AND FLORIDA

THE fourth voyage of Columbus had failed to settle the problem of a water-route to the East through the new lands that had been discovered, although it had limited the area in which such a passage might be found. It was therefore mainly with the object of discovering such an opening that the Spaniards prosecuted their explorations in the Gulf of Mexico, and within a very short period had solved the problem of its coastline. The insularity of Cuba, guessed at by Juan de la Cosa in 1500, was proved beyond doubt eight years later, while in 1513 Ponce de Leon discovered Florida, although he was not aware that it was part of the mainland. A number of small expeditions were sent to various points on the Gulf coast, and finally in 1519 Pineda followed the shore from Florida to the borders of Mexico. This, together with earlier voyages, finally established the fact that there was no through route to Asia opening off this part of the Atlantic. The Spaniards next turned their attention to the eastern coast of Florida, and in their efforts to find a passage examined the country as far north as Chesapeake Bay, which was reached in 1526. The further history of the exploration of this coast is told elsewhere.[2]

Meanwhile, adventurers from Cuba had discovered a part of the coast of Yucatan in 1517, and had reported that they found " thickly peopled countries, with masonry houses, and people who covered their persons and went about clothed in cotton garments, and who possessed gold and who cultivated maize fields." [3] A second expedition the next year confirmed the report, and led to the dispatch of a well-organized party in 1519 under Hernando Cortes, with definite orders to explore the new country. The early impressions of the adventurers confirmed their wildest hopes, for they

---

[1] The main works dealing with this period are quoted in footnotes. In addition the elaborate *Narrative and Critical History of America* (8 vols., 1886–89), by Justin Winsor, has been consulted. The excellent cartographical illustrations and the wealth of bibliographical references render it indispensable. Sir Clements Markham, *The Conquest of New Granada* (1912), has also been used. F. A. Kirkpatrick, *The Spanish Conquistadores* (1934), should now be referred to.

[2] See p. 92 and pp. 115–116.

[3] *Bernal Diaz del Castillo*, edited by Alfred Maudslay (" Broadway Travellers " series, 1928), p. 59. This works deals in a short form with the conquest of Mexico, being an abbreviated edition of the author's longer work on the conquest of New Spain (Hakluyt Society), quoted below.

believed they had reached a land which contained " as many riches as that from which Solomon is said to have obtained gold for the temple." [1] After a short stay in the unhealthy coastal regions near the modern Vera Cruz Cortes began his march inland toward the city of Mexico. On the journey he took advantage of the enterprise of one of his captains to send a party up the snow-clad volcano Popocatepetl, from the top of which could be seen the great lake in which the capital was built. Cortes chose a route which enabled him to approach the city from the south, and arrived at his goal at the beginning of November 1519.

The attention of the Spaniards was soon distracted by troubles along their line of communication with the coast, and ultimately they were obliged to fight their way out of Mexico City and retreat by a route round the northern end of the lake toward the country of friendly Indians near the seaboard. Here they recruited their strength, received small but welcome reinforcements, and made elaborate preparations for a second advance. This time they were completely successful, and Mexico City fell in August 1521.

The conquest of the lands on all sides of Mexico City naturally followed from the overthrow of the city itself, and although the motive was not a desire to acquire knowledge, but to gain wealth, the geographical horizon of the Spaniards was very considerably widened. The historian Bernal Diaz records that " Cortes always had lofty thoughts and in his ambition to command and rule wished to copy Alexander of Macedon." [2] He sent expeditions in all directions, " established the great cities " of Oaxaca, Zacatula (in the state of Guerrero), Colima, Vera Cruz, Panuco, and Coatzacoalcos, the modern Puerto Mexico, and then sent his armies beyond the boundaries of the modern state of Mexico.

Alvarado was dispatched to Guatemala, which he partially conquered, and Cristobal de Olid was sent to Cuba, with instructions to

> shape his course for Higueras [Honduras] . . . to endeavour to found a town at some good harbour, and to bring the natives of the province to peace, and to seek for gold and silver, and to make enquiries and endeavour to find out if there was a Strait, and what harbours there were on the south coast, if he should reach it. [3]

He reached the southern shore of the Gulf of Honduras, and sent parties to explore the inland country, but his disloyalty to Cortes led to the dispatch of a punitive expedition, some members of which, after failing to murder the rebel leader, invoked the aid of

[1] Hernando Cortes, *Five Letters*, translated and edited by J. B. Morris (1928), p. 21. This work, with that of Diaz quoted above, provides authoritative accounts of the conquest of Mexico. Both books form part of the excellent series known as " The Broadway Travellers."

[2] *Bernal Diaz del Castillo* . . ., translated by Alfred Maudslay, vol. iv, p. 272 (Hakluyt Society, second series, vol. xxx).

[3] *Ibid.*, p. 285.

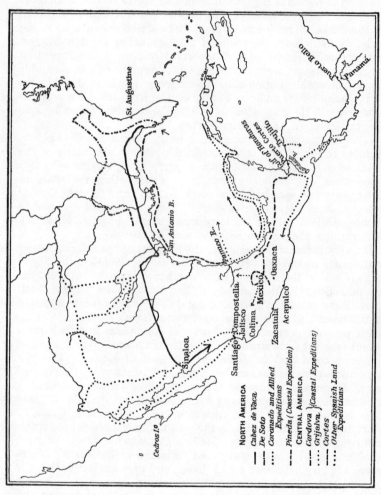

NORTH AMERICA
Cabez de Vaca . . . . —
De Soto . . . . —··—
Coronado and Allied
   Expeditions . . . . . . ·······
Pineda (Coastal Expedition) —··—
CENTRAL AMERICA
Cordova . . . . . } (Coastal Expeditions)
Grijalva . . . . . }
Cortes . . . . ·······
Other Spanish Land
   Expeditions . . . . . . —···—

Fig. 9. Spanish Exploration in Central and North America

the law to secure his death. Cortes was by this time anxious about the fate of the second expedition, and decided to investigate the situation in person. He set out from the city of Mexico in October 1524, and marched through the province of Tabasco to the Gulf of Honduras. The journey, graphically described in one of the leader's own letters, was marked throughout by great hardships, and was unproductive of any important results. Once arrived on the Gulf, however, his exploring parties accomplished a considerable amount of work. Cortes himself founded a new town, now known by the name of its founder, Puerto Cortes, from which he sent out expeditions. He then sailed on to Trujillo, and this in turn became the starting-point of exploring parties.

While Cortes was pacifying the country behind Trujillo his subordinate Sandoval was trying to do the same in the valley of the Chamelecon. Here he met with a party of Spaniards who had made their way through Nicaragua. Thus within the space of three years the Spaniards had carried their arms through Central America from Mexico to Panamá. Cortes returned by sea to Mexico, while a part of his force made a long and difficult march back through the modern Salvador and Guatemala.

It is now necessary to return to the progress of Spanish discoveries in the north of Mexico. Here, as in the south, the fall of the city of Mexico led to the dispatch of a number of expeditions from the capital. By 1522 the conquerors had reached the Pacific coast, establishing there the port of Zacatula. In the opposite direction their armies had scoured the country as far as the Panuco river. Their progress northward, if slow, was continuous and took them far into the present territories of the United States, to California on the west coast and to Texas on the Gulf of Mexico. The first important step was taken by Nuno de Guzman, who advanced from Mexico and conquered the provinces of Jalisco and Sinaloa. This advance was at once large and important, yet it might not have been followed up but for a curious event. A Spaniard, Cabez de Vaca, had landed in Florida in 1528, and after a series of adventures had reached Mexico in 1536. He brought with him stories of great wealth in the hitherto unexplored countries of the north. There seemed to be good reason for his belief, and so it was put to the only possible test. Three years later a Franciscan, Marcos de Niza, who made a journey northward into the modern states of Arizona and New Mexico, saw from a distance one of the " Seven Cities of Cibola," and by his glowing reports confirmed the earlier story of de Vaca. The result was the dispatch of the expedition of Francisco Vasquez de Coronado in 1540.[1]

[1] On the expeditions of Coronado and Cabez de Vaca see F. W. Hodge and T. H. Lewis, *Spanish Explorers in the Southern United States* (1925), from which the quotations and some of the detail for Fig. 9 are taken.

THE SPANIARDS IN THE NEW WORLD

The Coronado expedition was of far-reaching importance from a geographical point of view for it combined with the journey of de Soto in giving to the world an insight into the hitherto unknown vast interior of the northern continent and formed the basis of the cartography of that region. It was the means also of making known the sedentary Pueblo tribes of the south-west [of the United States of America] and the hunting tribes of the great plains, the Grand Cañon of the Colorado and the lower reaches of that stream, and the teeming herds of bison and the absolute dependence on them by the hunting Indians for every want.[1]

Before Cibola was reached a party of the most efficient men were sent toward the north and west in search of the sea-coast. They reached a river at a point fifteen leagues from its mouth, and found an inscription on a tree saying : " Alarcon reached this place ; there are letters at the foot of the tree." This referred to a complementary expedition which had sailed from San Blas to the head of the Gulf of California, and which had returned because it could make no further progress. Alarcon reported that Lower California was a peninsula. The land party passed round the head of the Gulf, and followed the coast southward for a short distance into Lower California.

Another expedition detached from the main body was sent from Cibola to visit a river reported to exist beyond the desert country.

> After they had gone twenty days they came to the banks of a river which seemed to be more than three or four leagues [*i.e.*, nearly ten miles] in an air line across to the other bank of the stream which flowed between them. This country was elevated, and full of low twisted pines, very cold, and lying open toward the north, so that, this being the warm season, no one could live there on account of the cold. They spent three days on this bank looking for a passage down to the river, which looked from above as if the water was six feet across, although the Indians said it was half a league wide.[2]

Thus was described the first sight of the Grand Cañon of the Colorado.

The search for wealth now took the Spaniards south-eastward across the Rio Grande and the Pecos river, where they found the all-important bison. Ten days after crossing the Pecos " they came to some settlements of people who lived like Arabs." They had seen " the cows " for two days past, and they found that the people lived in tents made of the tanned skins of the cows, always followed the animals, and when necessary killed them for food.

Having reached the Colorado river of Eastern Mexico, the main army returned to its starting-point by a more direct route, while Coronado proceeded with a small party to Quivira, the district reported to be wealthy, which seems to have been in the region where the Arkansas and Kansas rivers approach near to each other.

---

[1] Hodge and Lewis, *op. cit.*, p. 280.   [2] *Ibid.*, p. 309.

Again the Spaniards were disappointed, for " neither gold nor silver nor any trace of either was found among these people. Their lord wore a copper plate on his neck and prized it highly."

Coronado reached Mexico again in the summer of 1542, but his report completely destroyed his reputation, and his expedition seems to have received less attention than it deserves, for, although " the grand pageant resulted in disappointment for all," the geographical results were of considerable importance.[1]

It is now necessary to go back to the events which had been happening in the country lying to the north of the Gulf of Mexico. In 1528 Pánfilo de Narvaez led an expedition to Florida in virtue of the right given to him to conquer and colonize the country between Eastern Mexico and Florida. The party landed on the west coast of Florida, near Tampa Bay, and marched parallel with the coast until they reached Appalachee Bay. By this time they had lost touch with the ships, and found themselves stranded in an unknown country. They built five boats, and started off again, only to lose touch with one another, until finally about eighty Spaniards collected on the " Island of Misfortune," off the coast of Texas, in November 1528. During the winter their numbers were reduced to fifteen. One of the survivors, Cabez de Vaca, went to the mainland, and spent five years living with the natives. At length, with a companion, he made his way southward, crossed the Brazos and Colorado rivers, and reached San Antonio Bay. He finally escaped to Mexico, reaching San Miguel, 100 leagues from Compostella, in April 1536 and Mexico City in the following July. He went back to Europe, and landed at Lisbon on August 10, 1537.

" In the time," he says,

> we traversed from sea to sea ; and from information gathered with great diligence there may be a distance from one to another at the widest part, of two thousand leagues ; and we learned that on the coast of the south sea there are pearls and great riches, and the best and most opulent countries are near there.[2]

As already explained, this remarkable journey had an important bearing on the expedition of Coronado.

When Cabez de Vaca reached Spain, hoping to receive large rewards for his news, he found that the governorship of Cuba and Florida had been granted to Hernando de Soto, a soldier who had already served with distinction in Central America and in Perú. Cabez refused to divulge all he knew about the land he had seen, but he said enough to convince his friends " that it was the richest

---

[1] The Spaniards continued to send expeditions into the north of Mexico throughout the century, and at its close began the settlement of what is now New Mexico. The importance of this journey was fully recognized by contemporary writers.   [2] Hodge and Lewis, *op. cit.*, p. 120.

country in the world," [1] and de Soto tried in vain to enlist his services. De Soto accordingly set sail for Cuba, and eventually reached Florida in May 1539.

The expedition of de Soto, like that of Coronado, is of first-rate importance, and the two form " the most elaborate efforts of the Spaniards to explore the interior of North America. . . . Between them they nearly spanned the continent from Georgia to the Gulf of California." [2] That of de Soto was the first extensive exploration of the Southern United States ; it furnished the earliest descriptions of the life and manners of the Southern Indians ; and it resulted in the discovery of the Mississippi river, down which the survivors of the expedition sailed on their return journey.

It is impossible to follow in detail the route taken by de Soto, but its main features can be reconstructed from the various accounts of the journey which have been preserved. One of his earliest inquiries after landing in the neighbourhood of Tampa Bay was for " any country where gold and silver might be found in plenty." [3] The Indians directed him " towards the sunset," where the people were so rich that they went to war in golden hats. The search thus begun took the Spaniards to the head of Appalachee Bay, whence they marched through the modern state of Georgia, until further reports of a wealthy land " in the direction of the sun's rising " led to a change, which brought them within two days' journey of the Atlantic. Then further reports of gold " towards the north " took the Spanish army inland to the Appalachian Mountains and to the Alabama river, which they followed to the country of ' Manilla near its mouth. Obliged " to go in quest of a country where subsistence might be had for the winter," the Spaniards turned toward the north-west, crossing the Mississippi probably near to the modern Memphis, and following its western bank for some distance in the hope of discovering " a path to the northward whereby to come out on the South Sea." Unsuccessful, the party returned " towards the south," and then made their way westward to the Ozark plateau, " a very rough country of hills," but were finally obliged to return to the Mississippi. A further search to the westward in a more southerly latitude was no more successful, and de Soto at last determined to go southward to the sea. A captain sent to find the way reported " that he found no road nor any way by which to pass the great bogs which extend out from the Rio Grande " (*i.e.*, Mississippi), whereupon de Soto " sickened and died." The command devolved upon Luis de Moscoso, who marched westward in the hope of reaching Mexico. Passing from one Indian tribe to another, " and at each remove through lands which became more

---

[1] *Narratives of the Career of Hernando de Soto*, edited by E. G. Bourne (2 vols., 1905), vol. i, p. 6.
 [2] *Ibid.*, vol. i, p. v. [3] *Ibid.*, vol. i, p. 35.

sterile," until faced with starvation, Moscoso " determined to return to the town where the Governor Soto died, as it appeared there was convenience for building vessels with which we might leave the country." So the Spaniards made their escape, " came out by the mouth of the river, . . . and kept close along the coast " until the Panuco river was reached, and they were " well received by the Christians."

Thus ended the splendid failure of de Soto. If the identification of his route is in the main correct he nearly reached the land of Quivira, where the party under Coronado turned back. Like Coronado, he failed in his main purpose, but his expedition added greatly to the geographical knowledge of the world. One account of it was published in an English translation by Richard Hakluyt, in 1607.

Later in the sixteenth century the Spaniards made repeated efforts to colonize and to explore Florida, in spite of the disasters that had attended their earlier efforts. In 1558 an expedition was fitted out to examine the coastline with a special view to settlement, but although a colony was set up, it rapidly fell into decay. The country, however, attracted the French, who established themselves there in 1560, and were a source of continual annoyance to the Spaniards, since they occupied an important strategical position, favourably situated for attacks on the colonies and on the treasure-ships. The result was that the Spaniards reasserted themselves, and an important expedition was sent out in 1565. Its commander, Mendez, disposed of the French, and did a certain amount of exploratory work on the coast both of Florida and of the country farther north. He also founded the city of St Augustine, where, in spite of hardships and mismanagement, the Spaniards were able to exist throughout the remaining years of the century.

While the Spaniards under de Soto and Coronado were opening up new if unpromising lands in the north their compatriots in the south had discovered the great wealth of the Inca kingdom. Their early ventures in Central America were unsuccessful, but in the year 1513 Vasco Nuñez de Balboa succeeded in crossing the Isthmus of Panamá, and from the Gulf of San Miguel saw the Pacific Ocean. Lured on by reports of wealth, a large number of expeditions were sent out to explore the narrow strip of land which connects Mexico and South America. They had to contend with great difficulties, which were clearly indicated by Balboa himself in a letter to the King of Spain.

> The nature of the land is such that if he who has charge of the government sleeps, he cannot awake when he wishes, for this is a land that obliges the man who governs to be very watchful. The country is difficult to travel through, on account of the numerous rivers and morasses and mountains, where many men die owing to

the great labour they have to endure, for every day we are exposed to death in a thousand forms.[1]

When Pedrarias reached Central America in 1514 he found the Spaniards established at Darien, whence the explorers of the neighbouring regions brought " all the gold they could lay their hands on," and in the process ruined the country. From Darien the Spaniards explored the land immediately to the westward ; one of their number, Gaspar de Morales, reached the Islands of Pearls ; another followed the northern coast almost to the modern Puerto Bello ; Balboa carried ships from Acla across the isthmus, and sailed on the Gulf of San Miguel, but was detected in a conspiracy against Pedrarias and executed, and the Governor himself completed the voyage to Panamá, where he founded a city in 1519.

The country to the south-west of Panamá had been examined by Spaniards under Gonzalo de Badajos and Epinosa a few years before the founding of the new port, which now became the starting-point of a number of new expeditions. Already in 1518 one of these expeditions had explored the coast for 100 leagues from Panamá to Cape Blanco, whence a return was made by land. One ship, however, went on to " the gulf which they call San Lucar . . . at the commencement of the land of Nicaragua." Three years later the coast was followed beyond " the place where Leon and Granada now stand " to the Gulf of Fonseca, while an independent party was sent " to subdue and settle Nicaragua." From Nicaragua the Spaniards made contact with their countrymen who had come south from Mexico. A number of other expeditions were sent out, both from Panamá and from Honduras, and gradually in the process of conquest the main features of Central America became known.

In the meanwhile the Spaniards in Mexico continued the work of coastal exploration from the point reached by those from Panamá. The first expedition was sent out in 1527, and by 1530 Tehuantepec, Acapulco, and Zacatula had been occupied. Explorers went farther north in 1532, although their exact discoveries are unknown, and in the next year Lower California was reached. It was thought to be an island, but this was disproved by Francisco de Ulloa, who penetrated to the head of the Gulf in 1539. He subsequently followed the coast of the peninsula, rounded Cape San Lucas, and discovered the western shore for some distance beyond Cedros Island. In the following year Alarcon also reached the Colorado river, and ascended it for a few miles. Finally in 1543 an expedition under Juan Rodriguez Cabrillo carried the exploration of the west coast perhaps as far as Cape Mendocino, or even beyond the cape to about latitude 44° N.

[1] *Narrative of the Proceedings of Pedrarias Davila . . .*, by Pascual de Andagoya, edited by Sir Clements Markham (Hakluyt Society, first series, vol. xxxiv), p. v. This work contains the accounts of a large number of voyages made in Southern Central America.

GEOGRAPHICAL DISCOVERY AND EXPLORATION

II. SOUTH AMERICA

The foundation of the city of Panamá in 1519 marks the beginning of the search for the wealthy kingdom of the Incas. Some vague stories of its existence had reached the Spaniards through the voyages of Morales and Andagoya [1] to the land of Biru, lying to the south-west of Darien, but the real credit for the discovery of Perú belongs first to Bartolomé Ruiz, and then to his superior officer, Francisco Pizarro. The latter sailed from Panamá in November 1524, but after numerous attempts, spread over nearly three years, only succeeded in reaching the river San Juan. During all that period " they discovered no good land. All was swamp and inundated country, without inhabitants." [2] From the San Juan river Ruiz went on with a small ship, crossed the equator, and saw "places very rich in gold and silver, and inhabited by more intelligent people than they had previously met with," and brought back samples of both the minerals and the people. Pizarro was so heartened that he continued his voyage as far as Tumaco, whence he returned to Panamá. He then went to Spain, where he received the right to discover and conquer this newly found country, and at the beginning of 1531 set out on his enterprise. His first halt was on the island of Puna, whence he passed on to Tumbez, where the work of exploration and conquest began. After founding a settlement in the Piura valley Pizarro marched to the province of Cajamarca, which was "noted throughout the kingdom for its riches." His road lay on the borders of the desert, and he found all the villages were located in the river valleys, where water for irrigation was plentiful.[3] Arrived at Cajamarca, he discovered wealth far greater than he could have expected, and learned of equally rich provinces to the south. Expeditions were accordingly sent out to Cuzco and the neighbouring country, where they found a " grand and stately " city, and, judging by what they saw, concluded that it must be very rich. The large amount of booty which they took back to Pizarro at Cajamarca was sufficient evidence of their success, and by the end of 1533 Pizarro himself had marched to Cuzco and made himself master of the city.

Perú now became the starting-point of a number of new ventures which took the Spaniards far into the interior of South America.

[1] Pascual de Andagoya, *op cit.*, p. 9 (Morales) and p. 40 (Andagoya). Pizarro served in the expedition of Morales.
[2] *A True Account of the Province of Cuzco*, by Francisco Xeres, edited by Sir Clements Markham (Hakluyt Society, first series, vol. xlvii), p. 5. This work gives an account of the discovery of Perú by an eyewitness. *Cf.* also Pascual de Andagoya, *op. cit.*, and Pedro de Cieza de Leon, *Chronicle of Peru* (Hakluyt Society, first series, vol. xxxiii).
[3] For a good account of the geography of this region see Cieza de Leon, *op. cit.*, p. 215.

From the original settlement in the Piura valley Benalcazar marched northward to Quito in 1533, and began the systematic conquest of Ecuador. His subsequent movements are so closely connected with those of others operating from the north coast in search of El Dorado that their further consideration may be postponed. Meanwhile, the city of Lima had been founded in 1535, and very soon Cieza de Leon was able to describe it as " the largest city in the whole kingdom of Perú, and the most important " after Cuzco.

In the same year Almagro set out on an expedition through the modern Bolivia to Chile. His march lay across extremely difficult country, over mountains which were not only excessively steep and rugged, but covered with snow. The passage was said to have cost the lives of 10,000 Indians and 150 Spaniards, and when at length the survivors arrived on the plains of Chile they found no country at all comparable in mineral wealth with that which they had left. Almagro penetrated far into the country, reaching about latitude 37° S., but news of the renewal of war in Perú hastened his return, and he effected no permanent conquest.

While Pizarro was in Cuzco in 1539 he " received tidings that beyond the city of Quito, and beyond the limits of the empire formerly ruled by the Incas, there was a wide region where cinnamon grew ; and he determined to send his brother, Gonzalo, that he might conquer such another land "[1] as he himself had found. Gonzalo marched from Cuzco to Quito by way of Piura and Guayaquil, and began his exploration on Christmas Day, 1539. After about six weeks " they commenced the passage of the snowy Cordillera, where the snow fell in such quantities, and it was so cold, that many Indians were frozen to death." On the other side they reached an uninhabited country, where " during two months it did not cease to rain for a single day." Here, in the valley of the Napo, Pizarro left most of his party, and went with a few of the more active " in search of a road if any could be found, to pass onwards ; because all the country they had as yet traversed, which was nearly 100 leagues, was dense forest where in many parts they had to open a road by main force, and with the blows of hatchets." Progress was slow and difficult, and all advance parties brought the same report, that " the land was covered with dense forest, full of lagoons and swamps, which could not be forded." Pizarro therefore halted to build a ship, and when it was finished the explorers continued their journey, some on board and others on shore, until after two months they heard of " an inhabited land well supplied

[1] See *Expeditions into the Valley of the Amazons*, edited by Sir Clements Markham (Hakluyt Society, first series, vol. xxii), from which the quotations which follow are taken. For a defence of Orellana see *The Discovery of the Amazon according to the Account of Friar Gaspar de Carvijal and other Documents* (with an introduction by J. T. Medina, translated from the Spanish by B. T. Lee, edited by H. C. Heaton, 1934).

with provisions and rich in gold, and in all other things which they wanted." Francisco de Orellana was sent on ahead in the ship "to load [it] with provisions, and return up the river to relieve the people." Orellana reached the place indicated in three days, found no provisions, and continued his voyage down the Amazon to the sea. He appears to have found himself in a position where return was impossible, nor had he assurance that if he returned he would meet Pizarro.

Pizarro followed, and sent out two parties to look for Orellana, without success, and the expedition reached the junction of the Napo and the main stream, to find only one man, who had been put ashore by Orellana. They struggled on for another 100 leagues, and then, finding "it was impossible to navigate up the river, . . . they plunged into the forest opening a road with axes and bills." Excluding those who sailed away with Orellana, 4000 Indians and 210 Spaniards died; the remainder, "clothed in skins, on foot, without shoes, worn out and thin so that they scarcely knew each other," re-entered Quito in the beginning of June 1542.

This journey, together with a number of later explorations in the forested country to the east of the Andes, not only brought new ideas about the great rivers of the world, but forced the Spaniards to conclude that the mineral regions were strictly limited.[1]

By the year 1540 Perú had been conquered, and the Spaniards were able to renew the exploration of Chile. This time, under the leadership first of Valdivia,[2] and later of Mendoza, the country was more fully explored, and in some measure settled.

When Valdivia advanced into the Coquimbo valley he began what was, of necessity, a different kind of settlement from that of Perú, for with a few exceptions the Spaniards in Chile were farmers, since there were no large mineral deposits which could be easily developed. But the progress of settlement was delayed, and at times brought to a standstill, by the hostility of the natives, which increased in intensity as the Spaniards moved southward into the forested mountains. The country was opened up first as far as the town of Valdivia, which was founded in 1552, and shortly afterward beyond it, to about the latitude of 40° S. At the same time expeditions by sea reached the Strait of Magellan, and Valdivia planned an exploration of the whole of the southern coastline, because his "lieutenant-general on sea," Juan Bautista de Pastene, reported that the existing charts were inaccurate. This sea expedition was to be linked up with one on land, about which Valdivia wrote: " in April [1552] I founded Villa Rica, which is the place whence the North Sea [i.e., the Atlantic Ocean] is to be explored ; . . . and I shall go along conquering and exploring until I reach the mouth of

---

[1] Cieza de Leon, *op. cit.*, pp. 112, 406.
[2] Details of Valdivia's conquest are taken from R. B. Cunninghame Graham, *Pedro de Valdivia, Conqueror of Chile* (1926).

the Strait [of Magellan]." He thought that strait lay only 2° south of the town of Valdivia, and that he would have reached it in the summer of 1552 but for " a very full river over a mile wide."

To the east Valdivia sent a party to explore the country on the other side of the Andes, and there found a great river, probably the Negro or the Colorado. In addition he conquered the province of Cuyo, now in the republic of Argentina. But Valdivia did not live long enough to complete his plans, for he was killed fighting against the Indians shortly after he had announced his grand expedition to the south. He had done very good service in Chile, whose prosperity he tried to make equal to that of other parts of America, and if his work was less spectacular it was at least as difficult and as successful as that of Pizarro or any other great leader in the Spanish conquest of America.

Under Mendoza the Spaniards pushed still farther south, and in 1577 discovered the archipelago of Chiloé. But the new country suffered in its early years from the small forces available and the unfavourable comparisons drawn between it and what is now Bolivia, where the great silver-mines of Potosí were discovered in 1545. In Chile the Spaniards were occupied with intermittent warfare throughout the century : in Potosí the country was soon peopled, Spaniards and Indians rushed to make their fortunes, and in a very short time Potosí had displaced Cuzco as the richest city in South America.[1]

Perú itself was not free from the troubles of civil war, and it was partly to rid himself of a number of lawless soldiers that the Viceroy, the Marquis of Canete, dispatched Pedro de Ursua on his expedition to the Amazon valley.[2] He doubtless had other motives, for " certain rumours prevailed in those times, both in the city of Lima and throughout the provinces of Perú (which had been spread by Indians from Brazil), respecting rich provinces, which they had seen, as they said, when on their road from the coast of Brazil. . . . In these provinces dwelt the gilded man." In this way the adventurers of Perú were drawn into that search for El Dorado which had been engaging the attention of Spaniards in the north-west of South America for thirty years.

The expedition left Lima in 1560, and by July had reached the Huallaga, one of the headstreams of the Amazon ; at the end of September " they lost sight of the mountains and came into a very flat country, and henceforth the country continued to be flat until they reached the coast of the north sea." Their early attempts to locate the "rich country" were a failure, for " the name was not

[1] On Potosí see Cieza de Leon, *op. cit.*, pp. 386–392.
[2] This expedition is fully dealt with in *The Expedition of Pedro de Ursua and Lope de Aguirre*, edited by W. Bollaert (Hakluyt Society, first series, vol. xxviii). The quotations which follow are from this work.

even known to the natives." By the end of the year some members of the party were dissatisfied, " for they had journeyed more than seventy leagues, and had neither met with the rich provinces for which they were in search, nor even found any sign by which they might ascertain in what direction to search." Discontent grew to mutiny, and on January 1, 1561, Ursua was murdered while a part of the expedition was absent " discovering two empty villages." Fernando de Guzman now took charge, and the expedition, still divided in its allegiance, moved down the river, but their story is one long record of plots and quarrels, out of which " the cruel beast Aguirre " emerged as leader. It is not certain which course they took, but probably they went from the Amazon up the Rio Negro to the Orinoco, by which they reached the Atlantic. If one may judge by the confusion which followed from this expedition its value to geography was very small. Of Aguirre it was said that " he mixed himself up in so many seditions in various parts that he could not be tolerated in the country," and he was hunted down and shot in Venezuela.

The earliest efforts of the Spaniards to establish themselves on the north coast of South America, as represented by the expeditions of Ojeda and Nicuesa to the Gulf of Darien in 1510, had merely resulted in skirmishes with the natives and the exploration of scattered pieces of territory along the seaboard. Gradually, however, the initial difficulties were overcome, and the Spaniards spread themselves in small settlements along the whole coast. Cumana was founded in 1520, Santa Marta in 1525, Coro two years later, and Cartagena in 1532.

The expeditions which explored the country from the north coast fall broadly into three groups. In the north-west Cartagena became the starting-point for a number of journeys into what was later known as New Granada, and by making use of the great valleys of the Magdalena and Cauca rivers the Spaniards reached the plateau of Bogotá. The first step in this direction was taken in 1532, when a part of the lower valley of the Magdalena river was explored. The following year Heredia reached Cartagena, and led a party up the Sinu river, while in 1534 Spaniards from the same starting-point reached the Cauca valley. The real conquest of New Granada was, however, due to Quesada, who organized a large force and set out from Santa Marta in 1536. Part of the army went by land, part by the Magdalena river, and the latter section, after some early disasters, at length managed to join the main body on the Magdalena, near to its junction with the Cauca. Quesada now followed the Magdalena river through uninhabited country, where the natural conditions were very difficult, until at length he was obliged to abandon the main valley and make use of that of the Opon. Here he discovered signs of a civilized community, which he soon found to be living on the plateau of Bogotá, called by him " the valley of palaces." The subjugation of the Chibchas followed, and

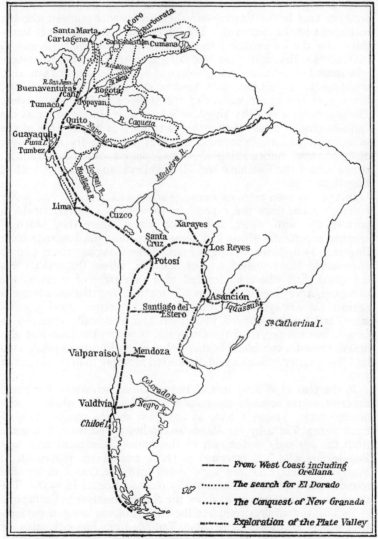

Fig. 10. SPANISH EXPLORATION IN SOUTH AMERICA UP TO 1600

on this plateau Quesada founded the town of Santa Fé de Bogotá in August 1538.

The second centre from which expeditions set out was Coro, where

99

the merchants of the company of Velsers of Augsburg had established themselves. In 1530 one of their servants, Alfinger, started to find a fabulous golden city thought to lie to the southward. The expedition went to the Magdalena valley, and thence plunged into the mountains to the eastward. The whole party suffered great hardships, and the leader died : those who were left made their way to the Cucuta valley, and so reached Coro, after an absence of two years.

A second expedition, under George of Spires, set out in 1536, and, avoiding the mountains, soon became involved in the forests and swamps of the upper valleys of the Orinoco and Amazon rivers. The search for a wealthy kingdom led the adventurers as far as the Caqueta river, whence they returned to Coro in 1538. One of the subordinate officers, Fedreman, who was following the main body, deserted, and, undertaking a journey on his own responsibility, struck across the Casanare and Meta valleys, and actually reached Bogotá in 1538.

In 1541 an even more extensive journey was made by Philip von Huten. From Coro the expedition went by sea to Burburata, a port on the north coast, and thence inland, where they heard of another expedition which had come down into the lowlands from Bogotá. Von Huten at length reached the Guaviare river, and so approached the so-called city of Macatoa, where the wealth was not great, but where he learned of a rich tribe of Indians, the Omaguas, who lived farther to the south. Von Huten advanced against the Omaguas, but they proved too strong for his small force, and he was obliged to retreat, and eventually returned to Coro. But his report of the Omaguas, of whom Orellana had also heard, caused a considerable stir, although no European penetrated into the country which he had discovered for more than two hundred years.

In the year 1538 there met at Bogotá three men whose combined experiences are some of the most remarkable in the whole history of discovery. Quesada had, as has been shown, reached Bogotá from Santa Marta by the Magdalena valley ; Fedreman had come from the lowlands to the east of the Andes ; the third man was Benalcazar, who had marched to Quito from Perú, passed on to Popayan, whence he sent expeditions into the Cauca valley and founded the post of Calí, and finally reached Bogotá in 1538. The three adventurers now went down the Magdalena river to Cartagena.

Two other journeys complete the outline of the story of exploration in the north-west. In 1538 Vadillo, from San Sebastian de Uraba, crossed the Abibe Mountains to the Cauca valley, and, with a much-reduced force, reached Calí. From this town he continued his journey by way of Popayan and Quito to the coast of Perú at Payta, at the exit of the Piura valley. Thus by two men, Benalcazar and Vadillo, the earliest Spanish settlement in Perú had been connected with the first discoveries in the Gulf of Darien and the later town of Cartagena. Cali was also reached in 1539 from the west coast, where Andagoya discovered the port of Buenaventura, and then pushed on through the forest-clad mountains, where he lost all his horses, to the Cauca valley.

The third scene of exploring activity was in the north-east, where repeated rumours of El Dorado led to an extensive examination of the country, and, at the end of the search, brought misfortune to the English adventurer Raleigh. In 1531 Diego de Ordaz ascended the Orinoco to the cataract of Alures, but was unable to proceed farther, partly because of the cataract itself, and partly because of the opposition of Indians. He was followed in 1533 by Alonso de Herrera, who ascended the Orinoco and entered the Meta river, where he was killed by the Indians. Shortly after this Von Huten made his remarkable journey, and all reports about the wealthy kingdom of the interior seemed to have received confirmation. A number of expeditions were fitted out, the most notable of which was that of Pedro de Ursua, to which reference has been made, and in spite of general failure enthusiasm was not quenched, though the area in which the mysterious kingdom might be found was restricted.

In 1569 Pedro Malaver de Silva, from Burburata, reached the inland plains of Venezuela, but failed to accomplish the main object of his journey. Other expeditions met with no more success at this time. Five years later Pedro made another attempt, and landed on the coast between the Orinoco and Amazon deltas, where all his party perished except Juan Martin de Albujar, who lived to spend ten years with the Indians, and eventually made his way to Margarita with wonderful stories of the wealthy kingdom of El Dorado.

Two years earlier, in 1582, Antonio de Berreo had made a remarkable journey from New Granada by way of the Cassanare, Meta, and Orinoco rivers to Trinidad, of which he became governor, and his own experiences, added to the reports of Juan Martin, led to the dispatch of another expedition in 1595, the year in which Raleigh made his attempt. Both of these efforts resulted in failure, and, with the exception of a few unimportant ventures, mark the end of the search for El Dorado in this century. Though unsuccessful, its prosecution had opened up a vast area of South America, much of which has never since been visited by Europeans.

In the earliest years of the sixteenth century the greater part of the east coast of South America had been examined very superficially, but apart from the north-east corner little was known in detail. The first expedition to make any substantial addition to knowledge was that of Juan Diaz de Solis, who, in 1515, made the important discovery of the estuary of the Plate river. The possibilities of this wide opening were obvious, and it is at least probable that a number of expeditions, whose details are unknown, examined the coast in this region, and further to the southward, in the hope of discovering a passage such as was found by Magellan a few years later. The estuary itself was explored in some detail by Sebastian Cabot in 1527. He ascended the Paraguay river to the mouth of the Bermejo, and the Paraná to the limit of navigation at the Apipe Rapids, and he found evidence of some wealth among the natives, but on the whole his expedition must be classed a failure.

By the Treaty of Tordesillas of 1494 the parts of South America that lay to the east of longitude 47° W. (approximately) belonged to Portugal, and the report of Cabot stirred the Portuguese into activity, the result of which was the foundation of a post of San Vincente near where the modern Santos stands (1531). Spain was thus obliged to meet a direct threat, and sent out the expedition under Pedro de Mendoza which arrived in the estuary of the Plate in 1535. The leader at once set about the establishment of a city which he called Buenos Aires, but the Indians were hostile, the Spaniards were few in numbers and were weakened by the dispatch of a large party up the river, and the settlement soon perished. The main result of the expedition, of which a somewhat inaccurate account has been preserved,[1] was far different from the intention of its commander. The river party, under Juan de Ayolas, sailed up the Paraná, and established themselves near to the modern Santa Fé. From this place Mendoza, " who was full of infirmities," returned to Spain. It is unnecessary to follow in detail the subsequent movements of the numerous small parties into which the main expedition became divided. In 1536 Juan de Ayolas reached the site of Asunción, where, in the following year, a Spanish settlement was established. From this point he ascended the Paraguay, and seems to have reached the confines of Perú, but was obliged to return to the Paraguay, and was murdered by the Indians.

On the return of Mendoza to Spain, Cabez de Vaca, the hero of an earlier adventure in North America, was dispatched to take command. When he arrived at the island of Santa Catherina he learned of the fate of Ayolas, whose death was attributed to the desertion of his second-in-command, Domingo de Irala. The new Governor

thought that, in order to succour as speedily as possible the Spaniards residing in the town of Asunción, as well as those in the port of Buenos Ayres, he would discover a road by *terra firma* from the island, and so make his way to those parts already mentioned where the Christians were, and that he would send the vessels round by sea to Buenos Ayres.

[1] " The Narrative of Ulrich Schmidt," printed in *The Conquest of the River Plate*, edited by L. L. Dominguez (Hakluyt Society, first series, vol. lxxxi), which also contains the account of the expedition of Cabez de Vaca.

The march inland was begun on November 2, 1541, and followed a route of which Pedro Dorantes had already made a reconnaissance.

> In nineteen days they crossed great mountains, cutting roads through the forests, to enable the men and the horses to pass, for all the land was uninhabited. And at the end of these nineteen days, having exhausted the provisions which they had carried . . . they discovered the first inhabitants.

By the beginning of December they had reached the Iquassu, a large tributary of the Paraná, which they followed in the main to the Paraná itself. Disappointed at not finding there the ships which had been ordered from Asunción, the Governor took possession of this river in the name of his Majesty, crossed over, and after a successful march arrived at the Spanish settlement on March 11, 1542. A month later the sick, who had been sent down the Paraná on rafts, also reached Asunción.

Cabez de Vaca at once set to work to re-establish the prestige and the power of Spain. A party was sent to rebuild the port of Buenos Aires " in the most convenient place, as the colony was necessary for the safety and welfare of all the Spaniards in the province, as well for those who might come there in future " ; friendly relations were established with the Indians, but when persuasion failed punitive expeditions were undertaken ; and some sort of discipline was introduced into the Spanish settlement. The Governor then went up the Paraguay, which, according to the report of Domingo de Irala, afforded the best route into the interior, and in due course reached the marshy country of Xarayes, of whose inhabitants the Spaniards had reported : " These people are agriculturalists, but they sow little, for they have not much land fit for cultivation, because most of it is inundated and covered with arid sand. They are poor and subsist chiefly by fishing in the lagoons near their villages." Exploration now became difficult, since provisions were running short and the Indians were " not precise in their indications." The leaders of the party advised a retirement, and Cabez de Vaca accordingly withdrew to the port of Los Reyes, " much dissatisfied at having gone no further." A small party, sent to carry the exploration beyond the point where the Governor had turned back, reported that the road lay " through a country so thickly covered with trees and brushwood that it was impossible to advance without cutting a path," and that " before attempting to enter that country it would be necessary to wait till the waters had subsided." Sickness and the mosquitoes at length compelled the Governor to return to Asunción, where the officers mutinied, made Cabez de Vaca a prisoner, and ultimately sent him back to Spain (1545).

For two years the Spaniards fought among themselves, until they saw that their very existence in the country was in danger. At length, in 1548, "Domingo Martinez de Irala assembled all the people and asked them if it pleased them that he should go with some people into the country to inquire if gold and silver were to be found." This proposition met with approval, and Irala went up the Paraguay and over to the headstreams of the Madeira until he came to a people who could talk Spanish and professed to be the subjects of Peranzures, who had already explored this country from Perú.[1] Irala soon received messages from Lima, and in turn sent four men to Perú, who journeyed by way of Potosí and Cuzco to Lima. In this way communication was first established from the east to Perú, and although it was not used immediately as a permanent line of contact, the discovery of the route was of considerable importance.

The connexion bétween the east and west coasts was further strengthened by two expeditions, the first of which, from Perú, resulted in the foundation of Santiago del Estero in 1553, while the second, from Chile, led to the establishment of Mendoza in 1559. In the following year the Spaniards began the settlement of Santa Cruz de la Sierra, and this marks the establishment of a real connexion between the Plate estuary and Perú, for by this route the trade of the Paraná-Paraguay valley passed to Europe.

[1] For the expedition of Peranzures and other Spanish exploration east of the Andes see *The War of Las Salinas*, edited by Sir Clements Markham (Hakluyt Society, second series, vol. liv), Appendices A, B, and C.

CHAPTER VII

MAGELLAN AND THE PACIFIC OCEAN TO 1600 [1]

THE great Age of Discovery is particularly notable for the achievements of three men, Christopher Columbus, Vasco da Gama, and Ferdinand Magellan. The results of the voyages of the first two have now been considered: it was the task of Magellan and his companions to link up the two areas of discovery, the New World and the Far East, by the first circumnavigation of the globe. This work was made possible by the discovery of the sea-passage connecting the Atlantic and Pacific Oceans which has ever since borne the name of Magellan.

From the first year of the sixteenth century explorers had given considerable attention to the east coast of South America, and it is reasonably certain that by the year 1519 the whole of it had been examined, at least superficially, as far as the entrance to Magellan's Strait. Whether or not the strait itself was known before Magellan's voyage is a matter of less certainty, but there is documentary evidence in favour of such a knowledge in the shape of the globes of Schöner, dated 1515 and 1520, and there is some other evidence. The general secrecy maintained by traders and early explorers must also be remembered. After a careful review of all the facts Dr Guillemard concludes that " the balance of evidence is in favour of more or less inexact knowledge of the existence of some antarctic break in the vast barrier which America opposed to a western passage." [2]

Ferdinand Magellan was born about the year 1480, served under the Portuguese in the East Indies, and probably took part in the exploration of the Spice Islands which followed on the fall of Malacca in 1511. He had also spent some time in Morocco. Leaving the service of the King of Portugal, he offered to make discoveries for Charles V, though stipulating that he would not trespass on the Portuguese ' sphere.' His instructions were somewhat vague, but were clear on this point.

[1] The standard works on Magellan and those for the more important Pacific voyages are given in footnotes below. Captain James Burney's *History of the Voyages and Discoveries in the South Sea, or Pacific Ocean* (5 vols., 1803–17), though old, is still valuable. It covers the period down to 1764.

[2] F. H. H. Guillemard, *The Life of Ferdinand Magellan* (1890), p. 197. This work is still the best life of Magellan. For accounts of his voyage see *The First Voyage round the World by Magellan*, edited by Lord Stanley of Alderley (Hakluyt Society, first series, vol. lii).

> Firstly, you are to go with good luck to discover the part of the ocean within our limits and demarcation. . . . Also you may discover in any of those parts what has not yet been discovered, so that you do not discover nor do anything in the demarcation and limits of the most serene King of Portugal . . . nor to his prejudice but only within the limits of our demarcation.[1]

The King of Spain amplified these instructions in a letter wherein he wrote :

> Inasmuch as I know for certain . . . that there are spices in the islands of Maluco, and chiefly you are going to seek them . . . my will is that you should straightway follow to the said islands.[2]

Magellan sailed from St Lucar on September 20, 1519, with a fleet of five ships which were " very old and patched up," according to the Portuguese Da Costa. His general route is indicated by the same writer. " The course which it is said they are to take is straight to Cape Frio, Brazil remaining on their right hand, until they reach the line of demarcation ; from thence they are to navigate to the west, and west-north-west, straight to Maluco." [3] It is unnecessary to follow the early part of the voyage across the Atlantic, except to remark that the experience of Magellan in the tropics was very similar to that of Da Gama, the ships going about the sea " hither and thither until fair weather came." They reached Cape St Augustin on November 29, and followed the coast southward until they arrived at Port St Julian (latitude 49° 20' S.) at the end of March 1520, and " remained there two whole months without ever seeing anybody." At the end of that period they were rewarded by the sight of some Patagonians, whose giant stature made a great impression on Pigafetta, the writer of the longest and best account of the voyage. In all they spent five months at Port St Julian, and it was during this period that " the masters of the other four ships plotted treason against the Governor," and " one of [the] ships, named *St James*, was lost in going to discover the coast " to the southward. The crew was saved, and made a difficult journey back to the winter quarters.

Sailing again toward the end of August, the ships reached Cape Virgins, where their great discovery was made. " We found, by a miracle, a strait . . . [which] is a hundred and ten leagues long, which are four hundred and forty miles . . . and it issues in another sea, which is called the peaceful sea." The passage of the strait was not easy, and though its real length is only about 320 miles, the voyage through took thirty-eight days. In the course of its exploration one ship deserted, so that when he reached the Pacific Ocean Magellan found his fleet reduced to three vessels.

Following the coast of South America northward for some distance, Magellan at length steered north-westward, and made the

---

[1] Stanley, *op. cit.*, p. xxviii.   [2] *Ibid.*, p. xxxiv.   [3] *Ibid.*, p. xliv.

passage across the ocean with the trade-winds behind him. This had some obvious advantages, but took the commander far from the many islands of the Pacific, and so imposed great hardships on the men. Their plight has been graphically described by Pigafetta.

Wednesday the twenty-eighth of November, 1520, we came forth out of the said strait, and entered into the Pacific Sea, where we remained three months and twenty days without taking in provisions or other refreshments, and we only ate old biscuit reduced to powder, and full of grubs, and stinking . . . and we drank water that was yellow and stinking. We also ate the ox hides which were under the main-yard . . . ; they were very hard on account of the sun, rain, and wind, and we left them for four or five days in the sea, and then we put them a little on the embers and so ate them ; also the sawdust of wood, and rats which cost half a crown each, moreover enough of them were not to be got. Besides the above-named evils this misfortune which I will mention was the worst, it was that the upper and lower gums of our men grew so much that they could not eat, and in this so many suffered that nineteen died. . . . Besides those who died twenty-five or thirty fell ill of divers sicknesses . . . in such manner that very few remained healthy. . . . During these three months and twenty days we went in an open sea while we ran fully four thousand leagues in the Pacific Sea. This was well named Pacific, for during this same time we met with no storm, and saw no land except two small uninhabited islands.[1]

The first land was sighted on January 24, 1521, and has been identified with Puka Puka, in the Paumotu Archipelago (latitude 14° 45′ S., longitude 138° 48′ W.). At the beginning of March they reached the Ladrones, but it was not until the middle of that month that the first really important discovery was made, when they arrived at the island of Samar, one of the Philippine group. After a short stay to refresh the crews Magellan pushed on, and reached Sebu, the most important port of the group, on April 7. Unfortunately, Magellan became involved in a native quarrel, and was killed fighting on the neighbouring island of Mactan on April 27, 1521.

His character has been well drawn by Pigafetta.

One of his principal virtues was constance in the most adverse fortune. In the midst of the sea he was able to endure hunger better than we. Most versed in nautical charts, he knew better than anyone the true art of navigation, of which it is certain proof that he knew by his genius, and his intrepidity, without anyone having given him the example, how to attempt the circuit of the globe, which he had almost completed.[2]

Like Da Gama, Magellan had shown a way to reach the Spice Islands ; he had succeeded where Columbus failed. He had proved that the world was round ; he had also demonstrated the possibility of its circumnavigation. As a sailor, a geographer, an explorer, Magellan was a great man, greater perhaps than either Columbus or Da Gama, possibly " the greatest of ancient and modern navigators."

[1] Stanley, *op. cit.*, pp. 64–65.　　　　　[2] *Ibid.*, p. 102.

The death of Magellan [1] and the treachery of the ruler of Sebu compelled the Spaniards to leave the Philippines. They sailed on to Borneo, to the city now known as Brunei, of which Pigafetta has left a good account.

> The city is entirely built on foundations in the salt water, except the houses of the king and some of the princes : it contains twenty-five thousand fires or families. The houses are all of wood, placed on great piles to raise them high up. When the tide rises the women go in boats through the city selling provisions and necessaries. [2]

From Borneo the course lay to the north-east, bringing the Spaniards to Mindanao, where they received instructions how to reach the Moluccas. Sailing on a south-easterly course past a number of islands, they sighted the Moluccas, " for which," says Pigafetta,

> we gave thanks to God, and to comfort ourselves discharged all our artillery. It need not cause wonder that we were so much rejoiced, since we had passed twenty-seven months less two days always in search of Maluco, wandering for that object among the immense number of islands. But I must say that near all these islands the least depth that we found was one hundred fathoms, for which reason attention is not to be given to all that the Portuguese have spread, according to whom the islands of Maluco are situated in seas which cannot be navigated on account of the shoals, and the dark and foggy atmosphere. [3]

It is of interest to find that the Portuguese, like the Phœnicians before them, attempted to shroud important discoveries in mystery.

The Spaniards, having accomplished their aim, spent some time enjoying the profusion of these islands. Here were to be found

> cloves, ginger, sagu, . . . rice, coconuts, plantains, almonds larger than ours, sweet and bitter pomegranates, sugar-canes, oil of cocoa and of sesame, melons, cucumbers, pumpkins, comilicai [ananas], which is a refreshing fruit the size of a water melon, another fruit like a peach called guave, and other eatable vegetables. They have also goats and fowls, honey produced by bees not larger than ants, which make their hives in trunks of trees. There are also parrots of many kinds, and amongst them are white ones . . . and red ones, which are the most sought after, not so much for the beauty of their plumage, as because they talk more clearly. [4]

[1] Mr G. E. Nunn has recently suggested that Magellan after leaving his strait sailed " parallel to the coast of South America as far north as the twentieth parallel of south latitude." He identifies the first land seen as Clipperton (10° 17′ N.) and Clarion (18° N.) Islands. In his view Magellan was aiming at Cipangu, which was thought to lie somewhere near the modern Central America (see frontispiece), while he argues that, had the conventional route been followed, birds would have given indications of land. In view of the blank in the west coast of South America on the Ribero map (1529), this last argument is of doubtful validity. See G. E. Nunn, " Magellan's Route in the Pacific," in *Geographical Review*, vol. xxiv, p. 615; and *The Columbus and Magellan Concepts of South American Geography* (1932). See E. Heawood, " The World before and after Magellan's Voyage," in *G.J.*, vol. lvii, p. 431.

[2] Stanley, *op. cit.*, p. 114.   [3] *Ibid.*, p. 124.   [4] *Ibid.*, p. 146.

The Spanish ships were badly in need of repair, and when, on December 21, the *Victoria* sailed for Spain the *Trinity* was left behind with her own crew and a number of men who did not wish to risk the voyage in the *Victoria*. The latter, laden fully with cloves, made for Timor, and then, "taking a west-south-west course . . . from fear of the Portuguese," sailed across the Indian Ocean with no prospect of replenishing provisions or of effecting repairs should the necessity arise. They deliberately avoided putting in to Mozambique, and only touched at the Cape Verde Islands, " constrained by extreme necessity." Here the thirteen men who went ashore were arrested; the rest of the sixty who left the Moluccas, now reduced in number to eighteen, entered the Bay of St Lucar on September 6, 1522. To the captain of the *Victoria*, Sebastian del Cano, went much of the honour and reward for the first

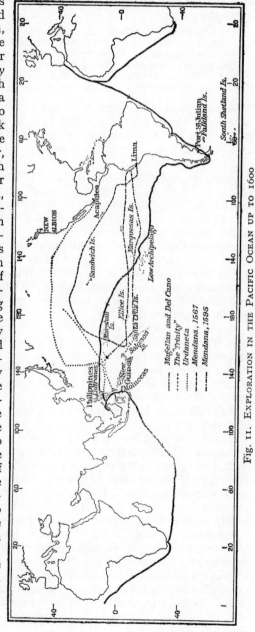

Fig. 11. Exploration in the Pacific Ocean up to 1600

109

circumnavigation of the world, but Ramusio more widely distributes the praise.

> Worthier, indeed, are our sailors of eternal fame than the Argonauts. ... And much more worthy was their ship of being placed among the stars than the old *Argo* ; for that only sailed from Greece through Pontus, but ours from Hispalis [Seville] to the south ; and after that, through the whole west and the southern hemisphere, penetrating into the east, and again returned to the west.[1]

Magellan had done more than sail round the world : he had shown that the Pacific Ocean might be used as an alternative route to the East. It is not surprising, therefore, to find that considerable progress was made in the discovery of that ocean during the century which followed his voyage. One of his own ships, the *Trinity*, made the first contribution to knowledge when in her efforts to return to America she reached a point in the Pacific in latitude 42° N., longitude 143° E. (approximately), but was unable to make headway, and was obliged to return to the Moluccas. A few islands were discovered, but the chief importance of the voyage was that it proved the existence of a wide ocean in a latitude considerably higher than that reached by Magellan.

The large island of New Guinea was discovered in 1526 by the Portuguese, and three years later its northern coast was again examined. Another claim to its discovery was made in 1543, while it was further explored in 1545.

Mystery surrounds the discovery of the Sandwich Islands. A local tradition exists to the effect that some Spaniards were wrecked on the islands in or about the year 1527. Another claim is made for their discovery in 1555, the evidence being a manuscript map in Madrid ; there is no other record of the voyage. Whatever may be the real facts, the visits of the Spaniards had little practical result, and the islands were in reality unknown until visited by James Cook in 1778.

In the year 1565 the Spaniards planted their first colony in the Philippine Islands, and in the same year Andres de Urdaneta succeeded, where many of his predecessors had failed, in crossing the Pacific from the west to the east. This feat he accomplished by boldly sailing into a high latitude, as far as 42° N., and so avoiding the region of the trade-winds, and this route was followed regularly after his pioneer voyage, and was popularly designated " Urdaneta's passage." Though little known in later years, Urdaneta must be ranked high among those who have made discoveries of great practical importance, for it became possible after his voyage to establish regular communication between the Spanish empire in the New World and their possessions off the east coast of Asia. He had a reputation as an experienced and good geographer,

---

[1] Stanley, *op. cit.*, p. 210.

and it seems that he volunteered to make this discovery. The actual route is described in De Morga's account of the Philippine Islands,[1] which also contains a useful sketch of the great trade-route from America to Eastern Asia. " They sail," he says,

> from the bay and port of Cabit with the first setting in of the south-westers . . . from the twentieth of June and later. . . . Having got out to the open sea they take advantage of the south-westerly gale, shaping their course eastward as much as possible to the latitude of fourteen or fifteen degrees. Then the north-east wind sets in . . . and as this is a headwind the course is changed and the ship's head put between north and east as much as the wind allows of ; by which they increase their latitude and so the ship is kept on until the south-west wind returns. [The ships pass the Ladrones and other islands, and having left these] there is a wide open sea where the ships can run free in any weather ; this is traversed with the winds that are met with for many leagues as far as forty-two degrees latitude, making for the coast of New Spain and looking for the usual winds which prevail in that latitude, and which in general are north-westerly, and at the end of a long navigation the coast of New Spain is reached.

Very shortly after this expedition a second, under Alvaro de Mendaña, added considerably to the knowledge of the Pacific Ocean.[2] The object of the expedition is of great interest in view of the stress that is often laid on documentary evidence in favour of early discoveries, for Mendaña was sent to find " certain islands and a continent " in the Southern Ocean, " because many men well versed in mathematics had deduced that they existed for certain in those positions." The expedition sailed from Lima in November 1567, and made its first discovery, in the Ellice Islands, on January 15, 1568. By the beginning of February they were off what they took to be a large land-mass, but which subsequently revealed itself as a cluster of islands, known as the Solomon Islands. Here the Spaniards remained until the middle of August: some, indeed, were for staying there permanently, induced to do so by the signs of gold which they thought they had observed. At the end of their stay there was much dispute as to their return route, and they subsequently sailed away to the northward, through the Marshall Islands, until they had arrived about the latitude of 30° N., when they put across to California and finally reached Lima by following the coast of America. The voyage is one of interest and importance, but it cannot be said to have been successful. The official record that " although they heard of better lands . . . they found no specimens of gold and silver, nor of merchandize, nor of any other

[1] *The Philippine Islands . . . at the Close of the Sixteenth Century*, by Antonio de Morga, edited by Lord Stanley of Alderley (Hakluyt Society, first series, vol. xxxix, pp. 355–356).

[2] See *The Discovery of the Solomon Islands*, edited by Lord Amherst of Hackney and Sir Basil Thomson (Hakluyt Society, second series, vols. vii and viii).

source of profit and all the people were naked savages " told against the explorers, and no further voyages were undertaken for some time.

Failure was not the only cause which retarded the progress of discovery, for the monopoly of the Spaniards was ended by the arrival in the Pacific, in September 1578, of an Englishman, Francis Drake.[1] It is possible that Drake made two important additions to knowledge. The account of the voyage as given in Hakluyt's *Principal Navigations* records that

> the seventh day [of September] wee were driven by a great storm from the entering into the South Sea . . . one degree Southward of the streight [of Magellan]. . . . From the Bay (which we called the Bay of Severing of Friends) wee were driven back to the Southward of the streights in 57 degrees and a terce : in which height we came to an anker among the Islands.[2]

If the ships really attained this latitude they must have gone beyond Cape Horn, and there is evidence that Drake gained an accurate knowledge of the small group of islands lying to the south of the continent. A manuscript map in the British Museum shows that the supposed Southern continent only consisted of a few islands, and bears the legend " Terra Australis Bene Cognita " ; a Dutch plaque executed in honour of Drake in 1586 also records the discovery ; the map in the second edition of Hakluyt's *Principal Navigations* (1598) was corrected to agree with the new knowledge ; and Drake himself claimed to have been to " the southernmost knowne land in the world."

The second discovery of Drake was of less general importance : he claimed to have reached the west coast of America in latitude 43° N., where no Spaniard had been before, and where he found a " faire and good Bay." [3] In later years this discovery played some small part in the search for a north-west passage.

Further confirmation of the existence of a north-west passage was given by the voyage of Francisco de Gali, who sailed across the Pacific from Mexico to the Philippines in 1582, and reported that to the east of Japan the current flowed toward the north, thus pointing

[1] Since this chapter was written Professor E. G. R. Taylor has discovered some very valuable documents illustrating this voyage. It appears that the original plan was not to go to the Moluccas, but to explore Terra Australis, as shown on the map of Ortelius (1570). Winter, who has apparently been unjustly accused of deserting Drake, proved that the constant westerly winds of the South Pacific Ocean made the voyage along the coast of Terra Australis impracticable. (See *G.J.*, vol. lxxv, p. 46.)

[2] Hakluyt, *Principal Navigations*, vol. xi, p. 112.

[3] Some identify this with San Francisco Bay : see Miller Christy, *The Silver Map of Drake's Voyage* (1900), p. 20. For a contrary view see G. Davidson, " Francis Drake on the North-west Coast of America in the Year 1579," in *Transactions and Proceedings of the Geographical Society of the Pacific* (second series, vol. v, 1908), and J. D. Hague, " The Drake Medal," in *Bulletin of the American Geographical Society* (vol. xl, pp. 449–469).

to an exit somewhere to the north of California. His voyage also seems to have led to the belief that Lower California was an island, although its earliest discoverers had proved otherwise. This error was not corrected until the eighteenth century.

Another voyage, about which there seems to be considerable doubt, had an important influence on the search for that passage. It was said to have been made by Juan de Fuca in 1592, and to have resulted in the discovery of a strait about latitude 47° N. His account ultimately found its way into the collection of Purchas, where it is stated that the Spaniards proposed to fortify this passage

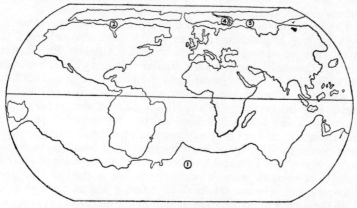

Fig. 12. OUTLINE SKETCH OF THE WORLD MAP OF A. ORTELIUS, 1570

Note the great southern continent, called Terra Australis Nondum Cognita (1); the North-west Passage (2); the North-east Passage (3); and Novaya Zemlya (4). A number of islands in the West Indies and elsewhere have been omitted.

in order to keep out the English. In later years the voyage of de Fuca was much used by the controversialists who argued in favour of the existence of the passage.

In the year 1595 another expedition from Perú explored the Pacific Ocean.[1] Organized, like the land expedition of Pedro de Ursua, " to disembarrass the land from many idle gentry," and placed under the command of Mendaña, its main object was " to go and subject and people the western islands of the South Sea," with the more immediate aim of revisiting the Solomon Islands. It sailed from Lima in April, with Pedro de Quiros as chief pilot, and on July 26 discovered a small island, which was named Magdalena. Shortly after a group of islands, the Marquesas, was reached. Then began a long voyage during which a few more islands were

[1] The narratives of this expedition will be found in *The Voyages of Pedro Fernandez de Quiros, 1595 to 1606*, edited by Sir Clements Markham (Hakluyt Society, second series, vols. xiv and xv).

sighted, but there were murmurs that those in command " did not know where they were going." At last they reached a volcanic island, Santa Cruz, on which a settlement was established. Trouble soon arose in the new colony, for some wished to abandon it, and, as Quiros remarks, there was " much dissoluteness and shamelessness and more than enough improper conduct." Mendaña and a number of other leaders died on the island, and finally Quiros conducted the expedition to the Ladrones, and ultimately to Manila. The attempted settlement " remained a spectacle for sentiment and reflection on the disastrous and brief course of events which took place in it," but although part of the plan had failed, the expedition did make some contribution to geographical knowledge.

The Spanish power in the Pacific Ocean had been threatened in 1578 by the Englishman Francis Drake, who also achieved the distinction of sailing round the world. Another Englishman, Thomas Cavendish, performed a similar feat in 1586–88, but apart from his raids on Spanish towns and shipping the voyage is of little importance. Much more serious, however, was the arrival of a Dutch fleet in the Pacific in the closing years of the century. For many years the Dutch had been fighting for their independence, and though it was not officially recognized in 1598 it had actually been secured. This in no way lessened their hostility to Spain, and as Spain and Portugal had been united under a single ruler in 1580 their energies were directed to the whole field of European discovery and colonization, both in America and in the Far East. With the decline of Spain, and her inability to defend her possessions, there went a corresponding growth in the power of the Dutch and a great extension of her colonial empire.

The first Dutch expedition to the Pacific was made in 1598, when James Mahu set sail from Rotterdam with five ships. The fleet arrived at the Strait of Magellan, and was then dispersed by storms. One vessel reached the Falkland Islands, which had already been discovered by John Davis in 1592 ; another was carried into a high southern latitude, and probably sighted the South Shetland Islands ; yet another successfully crossed the Pacific and reached Japan. Here its pilot, William Adams, was detained, and became so popular and so useful to the Japanese that he was obliged to remain in the islands for the remainder of his life, and died there about the year 1621.

Three months after Mahu had sailed Van Noort left Holland with four ships, and in the course of nearly four years sailed round the world. He returned to Amsterdam in August 1601, having made little addition to knowledge, though his voyage caused considerable stir in Holland and marks the beginning both of the Dutch supremacy and of the Spanish decline in the Pacific Ocean.

CHAPTER VIII
ALTERNATIVE ROUTES TO ASIA

I. Atlantic Voyages [1]

ALTHOUGH the results of the expeditions commanded by the Cabots and the brothers Corte Real had been disappointing, the nations of Western Europe continued to send vessels to the east coast of America to engage in the fishing industry or to make explorations in the hope of discovering a passage to Asia. Of these voyages one of the most interesting was that of Giovanni da Verrazano, made in the service of the King of France.[2] In 1523 he arrived at the island of Madeira, whence in the following year, by sailing westward, he reached " a new country which had never before been seen by anyone either in ancient or modern times." It is a little difficult to estimate the exact extent of Verrazano's discoveries, but at least he seems to have explored the coast from New Jersey to Cape Cod, and may have sailed from Florida to Cape Breton. " My intention in this voyage," he says, " was to reach Cathay, on the extreme coast of Asia, expecting, however, to find in the newly discovered land some such an obstacle as they have proved to be, yet I did not doubt that I should penetrate by some passage to the eastern ocean." He returned with a report of a narrow neck of land separating the Atlantic from the Pacific, and this feature found its way into a number of maps produced in the years immediately following that in which he made his discovery.

The Spaniards now entered into the search in the hope of discovering a shorter and better passage than that found by Magellan. Charles V sent Stephen Gomez " to go and discover Eastern Cathay . . . where you hope to discover as far as our Molucca islands, which all falls and lies within our limits and sphere of influence." The expedition was made in 1524–25, but its exact course is not known, and it certainly made no important discovery.[3]

---

[1] On these voyages in general see the following works:

    S. E. DAWSON, *The Saint Lawrence Basin* (1905).
    H. P. BIGGAR, *The Precursors of Jaques Cartier* (1911).
    N. M. CROUSE, *In Quest of the Western Ocean* (1928).

Authorities for the separate voyages are indicated in the footnotes below.

[2] For Verrazano see also *Henry Hudson the Navigator*, edited by G. M. Asher (Hakluyt Society, first series, vol. xxvii), Appendix.

[3] For a reconstruction of the voyage of Gomez see Biggar, *op. cit.*, p. xxvi.

In May 1527 two vessels under John Rut left the Thames "to seek strange regions." Their discoveries are recorded in a letter printed by Purchas,[1] from which it appears that the ships " came into 53 degrees, and there . . . found many great islands of ice," were unable to go farther northward, and so " entered into a good haven, called Saint John," where they found ships of the French and Portuguese fishermen. The results of this enterprise were of no importance.

The seas round the mouth of the St Lawrence river continued to be visited by a number of fishermen, but no important discovery was made until the arrival of Jaques Cartier in 1534 ; or perhaps it would be nearer the truth to say that no important discovery was made public. In particular it is surprising that the great opening known as Cabot Strait appears to have been overlooked, and that its discovery should be made by Cartier himself from the *western* side.[2]

Cartier sailed from Saint-Malo on April 20, 1534, and reached Cape Bonavista, Newfoundland, on May 10. Delayed here for ten days owing to the presence of ice, Cartier at length worked his way along the coast to the entrance to Belle Isle Strait, where once again ice stopped progress. Sailing again on June 9, Cartier examined the coasts round the entrance to the strait, both on the Newfoundland side and on the opposite coast of Labrador. Then, pushing through the straits, he made a careful study of the coast of Labrador and of the whole of the west coast of Newfoundland, noting with considerable precision details which would be of use to navigators and fishermen, and discovering many useful harbours. Of Labrador itself he had no high opinion. " If the soil were as good as the harbours," one account reads, " it would be a blessing ; but the land should not be called the New Land, being composed of stones and horrible rugged rocks ; for along the whole of the north shore I did not see one cartload of earth and yet I landed in many places." [3] Passing by way of a number of small islands and the Magdalen group to Prince Edward Island, he found there a land where " nothing is wanting but harbours," so that he was unable to go ashore and enjoy its obvious advantages. He sailed across what he called a bay (Northumberland Strait), and reached the mainland of the continent again, this time at Point Escuminac. At this time Cartier began to hope seriously that he might make some important discovery, for on reaching Chaleur Bay he found a large opening, where, " because of its depth and width and of the alteration in the coastline, we had hopes of discovering a strait." A thorough

[1] Purchas, *Pilgrimes* (Maclehose edition), vol. xiv, pp. 304–305.
[2] On Cartier see H. P. Biggar's edition of *The Voyages of Jaqıes Cartier* (1924), from which the quotations are taken.
[3] Biggar, *Cartier*, p. 22.

examination of the bay, however, showed that it offered no through passage, and the survey of the coast was therefore resumed. Eventually Anticosti Island was reached. The passage between the south of the island and Gaspé Peninsula was mistaken for a bay; the south coast was followed, the east cape rounded, and the passage on the north side was examined to see if it might prove to be a bay or a strait. Cartier went to the narrowest part, and found that the opening widened again, but the current was so strong that his boat could make no progress. At this point a meeting of captains, pilots, masters, and sailors " decided by a large majority to return home." Saint-Malo was reached on September 5.

In 1535 Cartier made his second voyage, " by the command and wish of the most Christian King of France, Francis the first . . ., for the completion of the discovery of the western lands, lying under the same climate and parallels as the territories and kingdom of that prince, and by his orders already begun to be explored." He sailed from Saint-Malo on May 19, passed through Belle Isle Strait in the early days of July, and by August 17 was at the mouth of the St Lawrence, where he had turned back on his first voyage. Indians assured him " that the river grew narrower as one approached Canada ; and also that, farther up, the water became fresh, and that one could make one's way so far up the river that they had never heard of anyone reaching the head of it." [1] Some time was, however, spent in an examination of the northern shore, and it was not until August 24 that the voyage up the river was begun. By September 7 the island of Orleans was reached, and a week later the ships were laid up in the St Charles river, near to which was the Indian village of Stadacona. The French were impressed with the nature of the country, writing that " the region is as fine a land as it is possible to see, being very fertile and covered with magnificent trees of the same varieties as in France."

Cartier now pushed on with the bark and two longboats in order to reach Hochelaga, of which he had heard. " During this time," the account records, " we saw and discovered as fine a country and as level a region as one could wish." On October 2 the French reached the village of Hochelaga, " near and adjacent to a mountain the slopes of which are fertile and cultivated, and from the top of which one can see a long distance. We named this mountain 'Mount Royal.' " A little later they visited the mountain, and from the top, they record,

we had a view of the land for more than thirty leagues round about. Towards the north there is a range of mountains running east and west, and another range to the south. Between these ranges lies the finest land it is possible to see, being arable, level, and flat. And in the midst of this flat region one saw the river extending beyond

[1] Biggar, *Cartier*, p. 107.

the spot where we left our longboats. At that point there is the most violent rapid it is possible to see, which we were unable to pass.[1]

After gathering as much information as they could about the river above the Lachine Rapids, and about other routes like that of the Ottawa river, the French returned downstream to the St Charles river, and there spent the winter. In December scurvy broke out, and by February there were not ten men who were in good health. Cartier fortunately heard from an Indian of a remedy, a juice from the leaves of a tree, which the Indians called *annedda*, and which seems to have been hemlock. The men after some hesitation tried this new medicine, and then so successful was it " that they almost killed each other to have it first."

On May 6, 1536, the ships sailed from their winter quarters, and they made their way south of Anticosti Island to Cape Breton Island, then across the entrance of Cabot Strait to Newfoundland, and so along its southern coast to Cape Race. On July 16 the explorers were back again in Saint-Malo.

Cartier made a third voyage in 1541, the object of which was " to discover more then was done before in the former voyages and attaine (if it were possible) unto the knowledge of the countrey of Saguenay," where there were " great riches." The fleet sailed on May 23, 1541, and in three months' time reached the St Charles river. Their subsequent attempt to get up the St Lawrence ended in failure, and the voyage made no addition to geographical knowledge.

Cartier's work was now finished. He had performed a task of the greatest value, and the results of his voyages, embodied in contemporary maps, show well the importance of his discoveries. If his efforts to reach Cathay were unsuccessful, and if his reports of wealthy countries beyond the rapids proved to be deceptive, he had at least discovered those fertile lowlands of the St Lawrence on which, half a century later, the French were to establish a new overseas dominion.

II. THE NORTH-EAST PASSAGE

The desire to reach the Spice Islands of South-eastern Asia had hitherto inspired nearly all the explorers, and two nations, Portugal and Spain, had already discovered ocean-routes to these islands. But in an age of intense nationalism, when the nations of Western Europe were thinking in terms of expansion and of monopoly, it was natural that those who had not succeeded in acquiring their own route to the East should continue the search, and continue it in regions hitherto unexplored. And while with the Spaniards and

[1] Biggar, *Cartier*, p. 168.

Portuguese religious motives played their part, with the English they were, at this date, not considered. As Michael Drayton crudely put it:

> A thousand kingdoms we will seek from far,
> And many nations waste with civil war, . . .
> And those unchristened countries call our own,
> Where scarce the name of England hath been known.

One may vary slightly the apt phrase of Professor Pollard, and say with truth that " the Tudor sea-dog who cared for Biblical precedents found his choicest exemplars in the Old rather than in the New Testament." [1]

It was this motive which led the English and the Dutch to attempt to reach the Indies by sailing round the north of Asia or of America; in general they were alone in trying to discover a passage by this route. The possibilities of it were clearly expressed in a letter of Robert Thorne to King Henry VIII, written in the year 1527.[2]

> I know it is my bounden duety to manifest this secret unto your Grace, which hitherto, as I suppose, hath beene hid : which is, that with a small number of ships there may bee discovered divers new lands and kingdomes. . . . To which places there is left one way to discover, which is into the North : for that of the foure partes of the worlde, it seemeth three parts are discovered by other Princes. . . . So that now rest to be discovered the sayd North parts, the which it seemeth to me, is onely your charge and duty. . . . Because the situation of this your realm is thereunto neerest and aptest of all other.

Thorne went on to explain the ease of navigation by this route and the riches that would follow from its discovery.

Of the expeditions toward the north those in search of a north-east passage began, and ended, first. They seem to have been stimulated by the return to England of Sebastian Cabot, who was regarded as an authority on navigation in high latitudes, and who, in 1553, was able to secure the formation of the " mystery and company of Merchant venturers for the discoverie of Regions, Dominions, Islands, and places unknown," or, as it is usually known, the Muscovy Company. Cabot drew up very valuable instructions for the first voyage, the destination of which was " Cathay, and divers other regions, dominions, Islands, and places unknowen." Sir Hugh Willoughby and Richard Chancelor were in command of the expedition, and carried with them a letter from Edward VI addressed to " the Kings, Princes, and other Potentates, inhabiting the North-east partes of the worlde, toward the mighty Empire of

---

[1] W. Hunt and R. L. Poole (editors), *The Political History of England* (1910), vol. vi, p. 306. On English enterprises in general see Sir William Foster, *England's Quest of Eastern Trade* (1933).
[2] Hakluyt, *Principal Navigations*, vol. ii, p. 161. See also Roger Barlow, *A Brief Summe of Geographie*, edited by E. G. R. Taylor (Hakluyt Society, second series, vol. lxix).

Cathay." They sailed from Deptford with three ships on May 10, 1553, and touched at Harwich, whence they crossed the North Sea to Norway, and followed the coast to the northward. The ships were separated in a storm, and that of Willoughby was not seen again. He and his men appear to have survived the storm, reached a high latitude, where they found land,[1] and to have subsequently "perished for cold" in Lapland. The second ship also disappeared in the storm, while Chancelor, left alone, returned to the coast of Norway and

> held on his course towards the unknowen part of the world, and sailed so farre, that hee came at last to the place where hee found no night at all, but a continuall light and brightnesse of the Sunne shining clearely upon the huge and mightie Sea. And having the benefite of this perpetuall light for certaine dayes, at length it pleased God to bring them into a certaine great Bay, which was of one hundred miles or thereabout over.[2]

Natives were met with, and the Englishmen learned that the country was called Russia, or Moscovie. In due course Chancelor made his way overland from the White Sea to Moscow, and returned with most valuable information about the country and its inhabitants, though it must be admitted that his contribution to the discovery of the North-east Passage was very small.

More extensive discoveries were made by Stephen Burrough, who had been master of Chancelor's ship in 1553, and who now sailed from the Thames on April 23, 1556. By the end of May he was off the North Cape, and he then followed the coast to the Kola river, where he met some Russian fishermen, and in their company continued his journey eastward. On July 15 he "went in over the dangerous barre of Pechora," whence after a stay of five days the voyage was resumed, and at the end of the month the Englishmen "were at an anker among the Islands of Vaigats."[3] Here they made the acquaintance of the Samoyedes, of whom Burrough reports,

> they have no houses, . . . but onely tents made of deers skins, which they under proppe with stakes and poles : their boates are made of deers skins, and when they come on shoare they carry their boates with them upon their backes: for their cariages they have no other beastes to serve them, but deere only. As for bread and corne they have none, except the Russes bring it to them.[4]

Mist, storms, and ice were now making navigation very difficult, until on August 22 they sounded, and decided that they "drew towards Nova Zembla. And thus," concluded Burrough,

[1] Probably a part of Novaya Zemlya.
[2] Hakluyt, vol. ii, p. 248.
[3] Now Vaigach. The old spelling has been retained in this section.
[4] Hakluyt, vol. ii, p. 339.

we being out of al hope to discover any more to the Eastward this yeere, we thought it best to returne, and that for three causes. The first the continuall North-east and Northerly winds. . . . Second because of great and terrible abundance of ice . . . third because the nights waxed darke, and the winter began to draw on with his stormes.[1]

On September 11 Burrough reached the Kola Peninsula, and wintered there, "expecting the approach of the next Sommer to proceede farther in our intended discoverie for the Ob." This project was not carried out, but the voyage is of peculiar interest not only because it set up a new limit of penetration into the Arctic seas, but also because it revealed very clearly the geographical difficulties attendant on all such voyages in high northern latitudes.

In 1568 a commission was given to James Bassendine and others for a voyage of discovery " for searching of the sea, and border of the coast, from the river Pechora to the Eastwards." Their instructions were to proceed eastward from the river Ob, if that should prove possible, but if the Kara Sea proved to be only a bay they were to return along its shores to Novaya Zemlya, and find out what connexion existed between Novaya Zemlya and the land discovered by Willoughby in 1553.[2] No records of this voyage have been preserved, nor is it even possible to say with certainty that it was undertaken.

In 1580 Arthur Pet and Charles Jackman were given a commission " for search and discoveries of a passage by sea from hence by Borough's streights and the Island Vaigats, Eastwards, to the countries or dominions of the mightie Prince, the Emperor of Cathay, and in the same unto the cities of Cambalu and Quinsay, or to either of them." [3] They were to carry out investigations similar to those proposed for Bassendine and his companions, and it is interesting to observe that all speculations as to whether the Kara Sea was a bay or not seem to have been absent from the minds of those who drew up the instructions.

The ships left Harwich on June 1, 1580, and reached Norway in ten days. They doubled the North Cape on June 22, and shortly after the two men parted company. Pet reached Novaya Zemlya, coasted southward along its western shore, and so reached the Bay of Pechora, whence he discovered the strait between Vaigats Island and the mainland. While off the island he met Jackman's ship, and together they " set saile to the Northwardes, to seeke if we could finde any way cleare to passe to the Eastward, but the further we went that way, the more and thicker was the ice so that wee could go no further." The two men conferred, and decided to return home, and by August 16 were back again at Vaigats Island. Six days later Pet saw Jackman's ship for the last time. Pet

---

[1] Hakluyt, vol. ii, p. 342.   [2] *Ibid.*, vol. iii, p. 119.   [3] *Ibid.*, p. 252.

rounded the North Cape on the last day of August, and reached the Thames on September 26. A note added to Smith's account of the voyage [1] reads : " The *William* with Charles Jackman arrived at a port in Norway . . . in October 1580, and there did winter : And from thence departed again in Februarie following, and went in company of a ship of the King of Denmark toward Island : and since that time he was never heard of."

Pet and Jackman failed to carry out their project to the full, partly because, like Burrough, they found the physical conditions were against them. But their voyage was evidently not considered a failure, for soon afterward other expeditions were sent to the same region, and it appears that about the year 1584 the English servants of the Muscovy Company had reached the mouth of the Ob river, and had also discovered the strait which bisects Novaya Zemlya.

At the same time it must be admitted that real progress in the north-east had scarcely been made. The theoretical arguments put forward by eminent scholars like Hakluyt or Mercator, and the evidence from the maps of Ortelius (1570) and Mercator (1587), show very considerable ignorance of the north coast of Asia. According to the map of Ortelius (Fig. 12), which was carried by Pet on his voyage of 1580, it was possible to sail from the southern end of Novaya Zemlya to Bering Strait on the same parallel of latitude, and although on Mercator's map there is one promontory stretching out beyond the parallel of 70° N., it is clear that his coastline represents little more than guesswork, arising from the fact that no one in Europe possessed accurate or even vague knowledge of these regions.

The voyage of Pet has a further interest in that it attracted considerable attention in Europe, and a report of it was taken by Barents on his last voyage. The Dutch and, to a less extent, the Russians soon realized the possibilities of opening up the northern route, and the former were anxious to exploit the commercial wealth of the newly found land of North Russia. As early as 1577 they had established a regular trade with the White Sea, and even before that date a Dutchman, Brunel, had gone overland from Russia, through the Samoyed territory, to Siberia, and had made a coasting voyage as far as the mouth of the river Ob. In 1584 Brunel accompanied an expedition to the north, and made unsuccessful efforts to get through the strait to the south of Vaigats Island, discovered four years previously by Pet.

The most important of the Dutch voyages [2] are connected with the name of William Barents, who first took part in Linschoten's expedition of 1594, the object of which was " to saile into the

---

[1] Hakluyt, vol. iii, p. 282.
[2] On these voyages see *The Three Voyages of William Barents to the Arctic Regions*, edited by Lieutenant Koolemans Beynen (Hakluyt Society, first series, vol. liv), from which the quotations are taken.

North seas, to discover the kingdoms of Cathaia and China, northward from Norway, Muscovia, and about Tartaria." The expedition left the Texel on June 6, and a month later "saw the land of Nova Zembla." Barents sailed up the west coast, and at the end of July reached the most northerly point, and on July 31 discovered the islands of Orange. Then, "finding that he could hardly get through to accomplish his intended voyage," and learning that his men would go no farther, Barents determined to make for Vaigats Island to pick up the other members of the expedition and find out what discoveries they had made. Arrived at the island, he met the other ships on August 15, and heard that they had penetrated into the Kara Sea, "and were of opinion that they had been about the river Obi," and that they had all but reached the extreme north of Asia. Linschoten, on the other hand, thought that Barents had sailed round Novaya Zemlya. Both were mistaken, and it is probable that Linschoten penetrated only a relatively short distance into the Kara Sea. Barents reached Amsterdam again on September 16.

The report of Linschoten encouraged the States-General to fit out a second expedition in 1595, "not only to discover the passage, but to send certain wares and merchandises thither." They had the advantage of the advice of Peter Plancius, "a learned cosmographer," who "set down the situation of the coasts of Tartaria, Cathaia, and China" for them. Seven ships were fitted out, and Barents sailed as chief pilot, leaving Amsterdam on June 18. In due course they reached Vaigats Island, and were able to sail for a short distance into the Kara Sea, but ice and contrary winds made progress impossible, and about the middle of September they returned to Holland, which they reached on November 18. The voyage had failed completely both to add to geographical knowledge and to increase the trade of the Dutch.

The States-General could not bring itself to sponsor another voyage, but the town of Amsterdam shouldered the responsibility, and sent out two ships, with William Barents as chief pilot. They sailed from Amsterdam on May 10, 1596, and, taking a more westerly course than was usual, in a month's time discovered Bear Island. On June 19 they saw land again, a large mass; and, says the chronicler of the voyage, "we sayled westward along by it till we were under 79 degrees and a half." The land now discovered was part of Spitsbergen, though the Dutch thought it was Greenland. After cruising about off this new land the ships returned to Bear Island, where Barents separated from the other ship, he sailing southward and his companion returning to the north. Barents reached Novaya Zemlya on July 17, and then proceeded to follow the west coast as on his first voyage. Within a month he had reached the islands of Orange, and began an examination of the east coast, intending to sail round Novaya Zemlya to Vaigats Island. This proved impossible, so he decided to return by the north, but was only able to reach Ice Haven, "where we were forced," says De Veer, the narrator of the voyage, "in great cold, poverty, misery, and griefe, to stay all that winter; the winde then being east-north-east." On September 11 they made a lucky find of driftwood, "an un-expected comfort in our need . . . which had been driven upon the shoare, either from Tartaria, Muscovia, or elsewhere, for there was none upon that land." This wood "served us not onely to build our house but also to burne and serve us all the winter long; otherwise without doubt we had died there miserably with extreme cold." Bears and, later, foxes were killed for food. The graphic account of this first winter in the Arctic regions leaves little room for doubt that the men suffered severely. Now frozen with the cold, now suffocated with the fumes and smoke from the fire, they had but little relaxation beyond attending to the fox-traps and, on Twelfth Night, making merry and proclaiming the gunner King of Novaya Zemlya. On January 24 some of them thought they had seen the sun: Barents did not believe them, and "divers wagers were laid." The incredulous lost their money. At the beginning of April they were able to indulge in a game of golf, "thereby to stretch our jointes," and with the arrival of May the men began to agitate for a return home. Toward the end of the month active preparations were made for return, the house was partly broken up, and necessary repairs to the boats were carried out. At length, on June 13, "committing ourselves to the will and mercie of God, with a west-north-west wind and an indifferent open water, we set saile and put to sea." It was no small task for two open boats, manned by men whose physique had been lowered by the hardships of an Arctic winter, to make the journey from Novaya Zemlya to Holland, and De Veer's record contains many references to the dangers and difficulties of the voyage. The boats were "much bruised and crushed with the cracking of the ice"; they were "in a thousand dangers to be cast away"; at times they "saw nothing but death" before their eyes. After a week's voyage William Barents, who had long been sick, died, which event, as De Veer explains, "put us in no small discomfort, as being the chiefe guide and onely pilot on whom we reposed our-selves next under God." At the end of July they met Russians at the southern end of Novaya Zemlya, and found "great store of lepel leaves [scurvy grass] which served us exceeding well . . . for as then we had many sicke men, and most of us were so troubled with a scouring in our bodies, and were thereby become so weake, that we could hardly row, but by means of those leaves we were healed thereof." On August 4 they saw the mainland of Russia, and followed the coast westward, and at the end of the month, at Kola, they met the commander of the other ship which had parted from them at Bear Island the year before. He brought a welcome supply of provisions, including a barrel of strong Swedish beer, salmon, and sugar, and after a day's rest the Dutch were able to continue their journey " comforted and relieved." They reached Amsterdam on November 1, 1597.

In May 1607 Henry Hudson sailed from the Thames on a voyage " to discover a passage by the North Pole to Japan and China." He reached the coast of Greenland, at some point which has not been identified, on June 13. He followed the coast to the northward for nine days, and then " steered away north-north-east hoping for an open sea . . . to fall with the bodie of Newland "—*i.e.*, Spitsbergen. He had deliberately chosen a westerly course at first, partly because of his " desire to see that part of Groenland which was to any Christian unknowne," and partly because he thought " it might as well have beene open sea as land, and by that meanes our passage should have been the larger to the Pole." Spitsbergen was reached on June 27, in latitude 78° N., and on July 13 the very high latitude of 80° 23′ N. was attained. Hudson saw a large piece of Spitsbergen two days later, and declared that it " stretched into 81 degrees," but he found himself " compassed in with ice in abundance," and was obliged to return. He tried in vain to find a passage between Greenland and Spitsbergen, for he says : " I meant to have made my return by the north of Groenland to Davis his Streights, and so for England." He reached Tilbury on September 15, after having made important contributions to knowledge. Not the least valuable part of his work was his report on the abundance of whales in the northern waters, whereby considerable stimulus was given to the English whale-fishery.

Hudson made a second voyage, " for finding a passage to the East Indies by the North-east," in 1608. Leaving the Thames at the end of April, he rounded the North Cape in the first days of June, and at the end of the month was off Novaya Zemlya. He tried to find a passage between Novaya Zemlya and Spitsbergen, but " by the meanes of the great plenty of ice, the hope of passage " was taken away. He therefore changed his plan, proposing " by the Vaygats to passe by the mouth of the river Ob, and to double that way to the north Cape of Tartaria, or to give reason wherefore it will not be." The attempt failed, and Hudson returned to London, convinced that a passage by the Pole did not exist, and that the only possible route lay by Vaigats Island.

Voyages in these northern waters continued in spite of all failure. The Danes [1] and the English made a few discoveries on the coasts of Greenland in the early years of the seventeenth century ; Hudson

---

[1] On the Danish voyages see *Danish Arctic Expeditions*, vol. i, edited by C. C. A. Gosch (Hakluyt Society, first series, vol. xcvi).

tried again in 1609 to discover a route to Cathay [1]; and the Dutch in 1611 and in 1612 made systematic efforts to penetrate the northern barrier of ice. Their efforts were not successful, but as a result of these two attempts the various pieces of imaginary land which dotted the seas to the east of Spitsbergen disappeared from the map, while Spitsbergen itself became better known. To this latter end the whaling fleets also contributed. The Muscovy Company's vessels made regular visits, and interlopers were not wanting. Although this was not strictly geographical discovery, it led to a much truer appreciation of these northern latitudes. Yet in spite of repeated failure and much better knowledge, attempts to penetrate to the Pole were subsequently revived, and had the support of the ablest geographers in England.[2] The Dutch continued their own efforts until 1624, when they abandoned their search for the North-east Passage.

III. THE NORTH-WEST PASSAGE

The search for the North-west Passage follows naturally on the two earlier phases of discovery that have been described, the search for a strait on the east coast of America and the attempts to find a north-east passage. The general theories underlying the belief in the practicability of such a passage were clearly expressed in *A Discourse written by Sir Humphrey Gilbert, Knight, to prove a Passage by the North-west to Cathaia, and the East Indies.*[3] The thesis well repays study not only for the arguments which it advances in proof of its author's contention, but also because of the light it throws upon contemporary geography. It was illustrated by a map drawn specially for the work, and this in itself is an item of considerable interest. Gilbert identifies the Americas with the classical island of Atlantis, and claims that it must be possible to sail round it. He is thus led to believe that a strait exists in the north similar to that found by Magellan in the south. " I am of the opinion," he wrote,

> that America by the north-west will be found favourable to this our enterprise, and am the rather imboldened to beleeve the same, for that I finde it not onely confirmed by Plato, Aristotle, and other ancient phylosophers: but also by all the best modern Geographers.

Among the latter were Gemma Frisius, Münster, Apianus, and Ortelius, whose important world map is particularly cited as evidence. From the existence of the passage Gilbert proceeded to argue that it led to China, for it was clear that if a land connexion existed between Asia and America either the Chinese would have made

[1] See below, p. 136.   [2] See Chapter XVII.
[3] For Gilbert's *Discourse* and map see Hakluyt, vol. vii, p. 158 *et seq.*

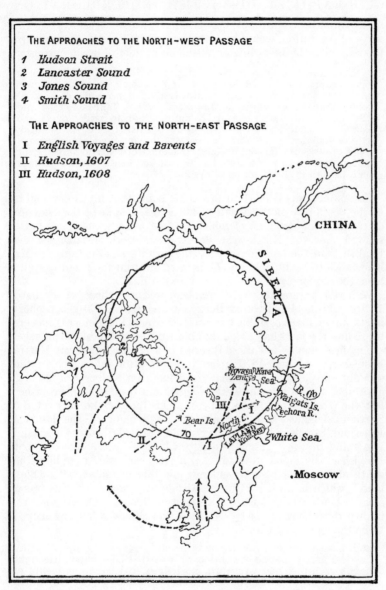

THE APPROACHES TO THE NORTH-WEST PASSAGE

1 *Hudson Strait*
2 *Lancaster Sound*
3 *Jones Sound*
4 *Smith Sound*

THE APPROACHES TO THE NORTH-EAST PASSAGE

I   *English Voyages and Barents*
II *Hudson, 1607*
III *Hudson, 1608*

CHINA

SIBERIA

Novaya Kara
Zemlya Sea
R. Ob
Vaigats Is.
Pechora R.
Bear Is.
North C.
70
LAPLAND
Kola
White Sea

.Moscow

Fig. 13. THE APPROACHES TO THE NORTH-EAST AND NORTH-WEST
PASSAGES

roads into the country or the Tartars, who lived always on the verge of starvation, would have migrated thither. He strengthened this argument by inventing an ingenious system of ocean currents.[1]

> Wherefore this current being proved to come from C. de buona Sperança to the fret of Magellan, and wanting sufficient entrance there, by narrownes of the straite, is by the necessity of nature's force, brought to Terra de Labrador, where Jaques Cartier met the same, and thence certainly knowen, not to strike over upon Island . . . and found . . . in Mar del Sur [the Pacific] on the back-side of America : therefore this current (having none other passage) must of necessity fall out through this our fret into the Mar del Sur, and so trending by the Moluccæ, China, and C. de buona Sperança, maintaineth itselfe by circular motion.

So anxious was Gilbert to prove his point that he threw doubts on the possibility of the North-east Passage, in spite of the evidence of the map of Ortelius, of which he had already made use. He showed that the North-west Passage was more suitable for the English than the long journey by the north-east, which experience had shown to be difficult, and he pointed out that the English would have the monopoly of this new way to the East.

Gilbert's arguments were supplemented by those of Richard Willes, who boldly declared that whatever theoretical geographers might put on maps or publish in books mattered little, since travellers who knew the facts had no doubt about the existence of the passage.

The first man to put these theories to a practical test was Martin Frobisher,[2] who sailed " to the North-west for the search of the straight or passage to China " shortly after Gilbert's *Discourse* appeared. With two ships, the *Gabriel* and the *Michael*, Frobisher left the Thames on June 7, 1576. On June 26 he was off the Shetland Islands, and by July 11 " had sight of the land of Friesland," on which no landing could be made because the land was " full of yce." Shortly afterward the *Michael* deserted, but Frobisher continued toward the north-west, and, rounding the south of Friesland (*i.e.*, Greenland), on July 20, sighted " an high land," which he called " Queene Elizabeths Forland " ; this was a small island to the north of Resolution Island. On August 11, finding the latitude to be 63° N., Frobisher entered what he believed to be the long-sought-for strait,

> and passed above fiftie leagues therein . . . having upon eyther hande a great mayne or continent ; and that land uppon hys right hande as hee sayled westward, he judged to be the continente of Asia, and there to bee devided from the firme of America, which lyeth uppon the lefte hande over against the same. This place he

---

[1] See the interesting speculations of Peter Martyr, quoted in A. P. Newton, *The Great Age of Discovery* (1932), pp. 150–152.
[2] On Frobisher see *The Three Voyages of Sir Martin Frobisher*, edited by Admiral Sir Richard Collinson (Hakluyt Society, first series, vol. xxxviii).

named after his name, . . . lyke as Magellanus at the south-weast ende of the worlde, having discovered the passage to the South Sea.[1]

Such is the account of George Best, who derived his information from Frobisher. Best illustrated his narrative with a map which clearly shows what he believed to have been done by Frobisher. Frobisher's ' Strait ' runs right across the north of America from Meta Incognita in the east to the Strait of Anian in the west, and the latter leads by a short passage to Japan and the Moluccas.[2] The passage is now known as Frobisher Bay.

The ship proceeded up the bay, and soon found human beings.

> They bee like to Tartars, with long blacke haire, broad faces, and flatte noses, and tawnie in colour, wearing Seale skinnes, and so doe the women, not differing in the fashion, but the women are marked in the face with blewe streakes downe the cheekes, and round about the eyes. Their boates are made all of Seales skinnes, with a keele of wood within the skin.[3]

Five men later went ashore, and never returned. Frobisher took an Eskimo away with him when he sailed on August 26. He arrived back in Harwich on October 2.

Frobisher had succeeded in rediscovering Greenland and in finding a new land which was later called Meta Incognita, and he thought he had found a new way to China. But much more important from the point of view of his future career was the discovery of " a peece of blacke stone, much lyke to a seacole in coloure, whiche by the waight seemed to be some kinde of metall or minerall." [4] On examination it was found to contain a small amount of gold. The result was that, in the words of Best,

> the hope of the same golde ore to be founde, kindled a greater opinion in the heartes of many to advaunce the voyage againe. Whereupon preparation was made for a newe voyage against the yeare following, and the captaine more specially directed by commission for the searching more of this golde ore than for the searching any further of the passage.[5]

The second voyage of 1577 was not, therefore, likely to produce much new geographical information. The ships left the Thames on May 26, and, sailing by the North Sea, they touched at the Orkney Islands, and saw Greenland in the beginning of July. " This Freeselande," says Best,

> sheweth a ragged and high lande, having the mountaynes almost covered over with snow alongst the coast full of drift ise, and seemeth almost inaccessible, and is thought to be an iland in bigness not inferior to England. . . .[6]

There is a note of disappointment in the record of Settle, who

[1] Collinson, *op. cit.*, p. 72. [2] Hakluyt, vol. vii, p. 256.
[3] *Ibid.*, vol. vii, p. 209. [4] Collinson, *op. cit.*, p. 75.
[5] *Ibid.*, p. 76. [6] *Ibid.*, p. 125.

has left one account of the voyage. " Here [in Friesland]," he writes,

> in place of odoriferous and fragrant smels of sweete gums and pleasant notes of musicall birdes, which other Countreys in more temperate Zones do yeeld, wee tasted the most boisterous Boreal blasts mixt with snow and haile, in the moneths of June and July, nothing inferior to our untemperate winter.[1]

Settle also gives a very good account of the Eskimo people who lived in the neighbourhood of Frobisher's ' Strait.' He thought as little of them as he did of their country, for he wrote :

> As the Countrey is barren and unfertile so are they rude and of no capacitie to culture the same to any perfection : but are contented by their hunting, fishing, and fouling, with raw flesh and warme blood to satisfie their greedy paunches which is their only glory.[2]

A small amount of exploration was carried out in the neighbourhood of the strait, but most of the time was spent in collecting ore, of which " about two hundred tunne " was placed on board. The ships left on August 23, and one reached Bristol, where the precious cargo was placed in the castle : the other ship arrived safely, after a separation during a storm.

The third voyage of Frobisher, in 1578, is of interest because of the elaborate plans to make a settlement in Meta Incognita.

> Bycause it was assuredly made accompt of, that the commoditie of mines, there already discovered, would at ye least countervaile in all respects, the adventurers charge, and give further hope and likelihood of greter matters to follow : it was thought needful, both for the better guard of those parts already found, and for further discovery of the inland and secreats of those countries, and also for further search for ye passage to Cataya (whereof the hope continually more and more encreaseth) that certain numbers of chosen soldiers and discreete men for those purposes should be assigned to inhabite there.[3]

The colony was to consist of forty mariners, thirty miners, and thirty soldiers. Fifteen ships sailed on this venture, from Harwich, at the end of May. They passed through the Channel, and when off North-west Ireland met a current " which seemed to us," says Best,

> to continue itselfe towards Norway and other the north-east partes of the world, whereby we may be induced to believe, that this is the same whiche the Portugalles meete at Capo d' buona Speranza, where, striking over from thence to the Straytes of Magellanes, and finding no passage there for the narrownesse of the sayde Straytes, runneth along into the greate Bay of Mexico, where, also having a let of lande, it is forced to strike backe agayne towardes the north-east, as we not only heere, but in another place also, further to the northwardes, by good experience this yeare have founde.[4]

---

[1] Hakluyt, vol. vii, p. 214.   [2] *Ibid.*, vol. vii, p. 228.
[3] Collinson, *op. cit.*, p. 226,   [4] *Ibid.*, p. 232.

This description of the currents of the Atlantic should be compared with the earlier speculations of Gilbert.

The ships saw Greenland on June 20, and on leaving it behind

> gave name to a hyghe cliffe in Weast England,[1] the laste that was in oure sight, and for a certaine similitude we called it Charinge Crosse.[2]

Early in July Frobisher's 'Strait' was reached, but was found to be frozen over. A bark containing the house to be erected on land was sunk, and the whole fleet narrowly escaped destruction in a storm, so that it was obliged to put out to sea again. They made a second attempt to enter, but in the fog reached a point which they had not seen before, and came across

> a swifter course of floud than before time they had observed. And truely it was wonderfull to heare and see the rushling and noyse that the tydes do make in thys place, with so violent a force that our shippes lying a hull, were turned sometimes rounde about . . . after the manner of a whirlpool.[3]

This seems to record the accidental discovery of what was later known as Hudson Strait : Frobisher subsequently declared that if it had not been for his instructions and his command of the fleet " he both would and could have gone through to the south sea." Best explained the strong current by saying that, having passed to the north-east, " it doth once againe rebound backe, by the coastes of Greenland, and from thence upon Frobisher's straights." There was much confusion about this new passage, and some thought it was connected with the real Frobisher's ' Strait.' At length the ships regained their objective, some ore was collected, and they returned home without leaving the colony behind. The fleet was scattered in a storm, and one ship claimed to have made a new discovery on her return voyage, " an unknowen channell full of rocks," which apparently they thought led to Frobisher's ' Strait.' In spite of Best's assertion that the hope of a passage was " furthered and encreased," the voyage failed. The cargo was not valuable enough to pay expenses ; no progress had been made in Frobisher's ' Strait ' ; and the only important discoveries were accidental, and were not thoroughly investigated. The voyage has one other interest, for a certain clergyman named Wolfall, although having " a good and large living " at home, accompanied the ships " for the only care he had to save soules, and to reform those infidels if it were possible to Christianitie." In spite of his willingness " to stay there the whole yeare if occasion had served " he only seems to have had the opportunity of ministering to the Englishmen, but he achieved the distinction of preaching two " godly sermons " in the barren lands round Frobisher's ' Strait.'

[1] This was a new name given to West Friesland.
[2] Collinson, *op. cit.*, p. 233.   [3] *Ibid.*, p. 240.

Frobisher suffered because he was a pioneer. His work was in general continued by John Davis,[1] who prosecuted the search for a passage in the sea which separates Greenland and the North American archipelago. He was financed by London merchants, of whom William Sanderson was the chief, and he set out to discover the North-west Passage unhampered by any body of colonists or any instructions to search for gold. The ships sailed from Dartmouth on June 7, 1585, and by July 20 discovered a land " which was the most deformed, rockie and mountainous that ever we saw," and which the captain named the " Land of Desolation." This was the southern portion of Greenland, along which they sailed, keeping more or less to the coast, until they again put in to land, in latitude 64° 15' N., into what was called Gilbert Sound, where is now situated Godthaab. From this point they sailed away to the north-west, and, crossing Davis Strait, " discovered land in 66° 40' of latitude, altogether void from the pester of ice." Some of the names which they gave to prominent features still survive, as Cape Dyer and Cape Walsingham, the north and south points of Exeter Sound. From this opening they sailed southward to the Cape of God's Mercy, at the northern side of Cumberland Sound, which appeared to be " a very faire entrance or passage . . . altogether void of any pester of ice, and the water of the very colour, nature, and quality of the maine ocean, which gave us the greater hope of our passage." As John Janes, who wrote the account of the voyage,[2] explains, " Our Captaine and Master searched still for the probabilities of the passage," and from various pieces of evidence came to the conclusion that it existed, but were unable to make a full exploration owing to bad weather conditions. Accordingly, Davis returned home, reaching Dartmouth at the end of September. At first sight the results of the voyage do not appear to be important. Davis wrongly thought that the " Land of Desolation " was a new discovery ; he did not appear to realize that it was unconnected with his subsequent discoveries round Cumberland Sound ; and he incorrectly believed the latter might prove to be the North-west Passage. He was quite definite about the existence of the passage, for he wrote to Walsingham that " the North-west passage is a matter nothing doubtful, but at any time almost to be passed, the sea navigable, voyd of yce, the ayre tolerable, and the waters very deep." Actually he had added a little more to Frobisher's discoveries in Greenland and put a new portion of the Canadian archipelago on the map.

[1] See *The Voyages and Works of John Davis the Navigator*, edited by Admiral Sir Albert Markham (Hakluyt Society, first series, vol. lix) ; *The Map of the World*, A.D. 1600 (Hakluyt Society, 1878) ; and Sir Clements Markham, *Life of John Davis* (1889).
[2] Printed in the work of Admiral Sir Albert Markham, quoted above, and in Hakluyt, vol. vii, pp. 381–393.

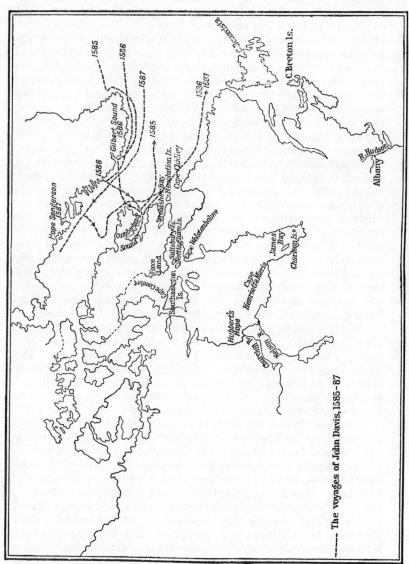

C. Breton Is.

R. Hudson.
Albany

Hope Sanderson 1587

1586

Gilbert Sound 1586

1587

1586

1585

1585

Resolution Is.
Frobisher Bay
Cape Walsingham

Cumberland Sound

Cape Chidley

Salisbury Is.
Southampton
Nottingham Is.
Is.

Foxe Land

Cape Comfort

Cape Henrietta Maria

James Bay

Charlton Is.

Hubbert's Hope

R. Churchill

R. Nelson

1536

1587

------ The voyages of John Davis, 1585-87

Fig. 14. The North-West Passage, First Stage

Davis made a second voyage " for the discovery of the North-west passage " in 1586, leaving Dartmouth on May 7. Greenland was sighted in the middle of June, " mightily pestered with yce and snow, so that there was no hope of landing." The positions given by Davis are not very accurate, so that it is impossible to say where he again saw land, but it seems to have been in the neighbourhood of Gilbert Sound. He remained here until July 11, spending the time in an examination of the fiords of the coast and the country of the interior. Here the crew found " tenne miles within the snowy mountaines, a plaine champion countrey, with earth and grasse, such as our moory and waste grounds of England are." On another day they " sailed into a mighty great river, directly into the body of the land, and in briefe found it to be no firme land, but huge, waste, and desert Isles, with mighty sounds and inlets passing betweene sea and sea." Taking a native guide with them, they continued their voyage to the northward, and by the beginning of August, in spite of difficulties from fog and ice, had reached the latitude of 66° 33' N., where a good harbour was found. " In this place," says the chronicler of the voyage, " we found it very hot, and we were very much troubled by a flie which is called muskyto, for they did sting grievously." [1] Sailing southward from this point, they eventually reached the entrance to Cumberland Sound, where once more they thought they " had great hope of a through passage," a hope which was increased because the land was " nothing but Isles." Continuing southward, they appear to have passed the entrance to Hudson Bay and to have discovered another inlet, perhaps Hamilton Inlet, in Labrador, where they " had a perfect hope of the passage, finding a mighty great sea passing betweene two lands west. The South land, to our judgement, being nothing but Isles, we greatly desired to go into this sea but the winde was directly against us." Without making any further discoveries the ships returned to England, arriving at the beginning of October.

Davis had divided his fleet, two vessels being sent " to seeke a passage Northward betweene Groenland and Island to the latitude of 80°, if land did not let us." The ships parted company on June 7, and two days later this eastern party met ice. By the twelfth of the month they were safe in an Iceland harbour, where they remained for four days. They left again on June 26, and, sailing to the north-west, saw Greenland, which they coasted until they reached Davis's "Land of Desolation," whence they departed for Gilbert Sound. Here they came across natives, and became on such friendly terms that Morgan, who wrote an account of this voyage,[2] records that the crew went ashore several times to play football with them. The Englishmen seem to have been a little rough, for, Morgan adds, " our men did cast them downe as soone as they did come to strike the ball."

[1] Hakluyt, vol. vii, p. 403.   [2] *Ibid.*, vol. vii, pp. 408–413.

These vessels arrived back in the Thames early in October 1586. Morgan has some interesting remarks to make about Iceland, where he found a merchant from Ipswich apparently visiting the island on business. He declares that " if we would go thither to fishing more than we do, we should make it a very good voyage."

Davis himself had drawn attention to the abundance of fish along the north-east coast of America, and had returned with a valuable cargo of sealskins. On purely economic grounds, therefore, this voyage was important and successful. To Davis, however, it left no room for doubt as to the existence of the passage. " I have now," he wrote to Mr Sanderson,

> experience of much of the North-west part of the world, and have brought the passage to that likelihood, as that I am assured it must bee in one of foure places, or els not at all. And further I can assure you upon the perill of my life, that this voyage may be performed without further charge, nay, with certaine profite to the adventurers, if I may have but your favour in the action.[1]

Davis began his third voyage on May 19, 1587, and by June 30 had sailed so far along the coast of Greenland that he reached latitude 72° 12′ N. John Janes, who wrote the account of the voyage, states:

> Now having coasted the land, which we called London coast . . . the sea open all to the Westwards and Northwards, the land on starboord side East from us, the winde shifted to the North, whereupon we left that shore, naming the same Hope Sanderson, and shaped our course West.[2]

All attempts to make progress to the north were frustrated by the ice, and the ships accordingly turned southward. By the end of July they were off what they called Lumley's Inlet, but which seems to have been Frobisher's 'Strait.' On the last day of the month " we fell into one of those overfals with a fresh gale of wind," and, Janes adds, " this day [July 31, 1587] and night we passed by a very great gulfe, the water whirling and roring as it were the meetings of tydes." [3] This appears to have been the entrance to Hudson Strait, for on the next day they named Cape Chidley, " the southermost cape of the gulfe." Having discovered the Darcie Islands, off North-east Labrador, and followed the coast to " almost 52° of latitude," Davis returned to England, reaching Dartmouth on September 15.

Davis had been farther north than any other explorer in the north-west, and had actually pointed to the true North-west Passage, though he had not found it. He had also added materially to the geographical knowledge of Greenland. On his return he wrote to his patron : " I have bene in 73 degrees, finding the sea all open, and fifty leagues betweene land and land. The passage is

[1] Hakluyt, vol. vii, p. 408.   [2] *Ibid.*, p. 418.   [3] *Ibid.*, p. 421.

most probable, the execution easie, as at my comming you shall fully know." [1] Davis was an able seaman and a careful explorer, and for his work in the north-west he deserves much credit. He assisted in the revision of the map of the world, and his hand can be traced in the new Molyneux globes and the " new map " which appeared at the end of the sixteenth century. He also wrote a book dealing with the problem of the North-west Passage, *The Worldes Hydrographical Discription*, and a useful manual of navigation called *The Seaman's Secrets*.

The next voyage of importance in search of the North-west Passage is that of Henry Hudson,[2] then in the service of the Dutch, in the year 1609. Leaving Amsterdam, he sailed toward Norway, and reached a point north-east of North Cape, in latitude 71° 46′ N. Prevented from getting eastward by calms and contrary winds, Hudson shaped his course by the Lofoten Islands, the Faroe Islands, and across the Atlantic, in face of the current which flowed from the south-west. At length, on July 3, he came across a large French fishing-fleet operating off Nova Scotia, and he also engaged in the fishing, catching a large number of cod. Soon after this land was seen, and a large river, in latitude 44° 1′ N., was discovered. He spent some days in the neighbourhood of this land, gradually working his way southward, past Cape Cod, and along the coast as far as latitude 35° 41′ N., which took him to the modern state of South Carolina. On the return to the north Chesapeake Bay was examined, and other exploration of an uncertain character carried out between it and the mouth of the Hudson river, which was reached at the beginning of August. Hudson ascended the river, and probably got as far as the site of the modern Albany, though the ship's boats passed a little distance beyond this point. Thence the ship returned down the river, and sailed for England, reaching Dartmouth early in November. Like many other explorers on the east coast of America, Hudson had added a few important details to the map, but had failed to find the strait which would lead through the continent to the South Sea.

Still with the object of discovering the North-west Passage, Hudson set out on his fourth and last voyage on April 17, 1610. Sailing through the North Sea, and as far north as Iceland, he reached Greenland at the beginning of June, and a few days later stated that he was off Frobisher's ' Strait.' This was a mistake due to the confused state of cartography at the time : on some maps it is shown as a strait separating Greenland from the " Land of Desolation," and in reality Hudson was merely off an indentation in

---

[1] Hakluyt, vol. vii, p. 423.
[2] On Hudson see *Henry Hudson the Navigator*, edited by G. M. Asher (Hakluyt Society, first series, vol. xxvii), and L. Powys, *Henry Hudson* ("Golden Hind" series, 1927).

the coast of South-east Greenland, for six days later he declared that he had sight of the land named Desolation by John Davis. From this land he sailed north-westward and westward, thus entering the strait which now bears his name.

Hudson was not the first to enter the strait, nor even the first to discover his bay. There is evidence that the Portuguese had some knowledge of Hudson Bay in the second half of the sixteenth century ; Frobisher and Davis had both discovered the strait ; and George Waymouth in 1602 had actually penetrated some distance into the strait. Waymouth's log-books were in the hands of Peter Plancius, the Dutch geographer, already mentioned, who took a keen interest in northern voyages. Perhaps he showed those documents to Hudson, and, if so, it may well be that Hudson merely followed up the hint of Waymouth that the new inlet was " a passage of more probability than Davis his Straights." [1]

On August 3 Hudson records in his *Journal* : " We put through the narrow passage, after our men had beene on land, which had well observed there, that the floud did come from the north, flowing by the shoare five fathomes. The head of this entrance on the South side I named Cape Wolstenholme."

Thus Hudson records the entry into his bay, and with that entry his *Journal* comes to an end. Nor is it possible, from the *Discourse* of Abacuk Prickett, to gain much further information about the subsequent discoveries of Hudson. He coasted the east side of the bay to its southern end, and spent the winter there. The crew suffered great hardship, and at length mutinied, putting Hudson and a few more adrift in a small boat, and these unfortunate men were not heard of again. The criminals had an adventurous voyage home, and eventually owed their safety to the skill of Robert Bylot. Bylot also brought back a map of his discoveries, which was later used by Foxe, but was eventually lost.

Hudson's voyage had been undertaken to find a north-west passage, and there was general belief that he had been successful. So far did this belief go that certain prominent men who had financed the venture now formed " the Company of the Merchants of London Discoverers of the North-West Passage," receiving in 1612 a charter of a remarkable character. It is there stated that a passage had been found by which the merchants " hope and propose to advance a trade to the great kingdoms of Tartaria, China, Japan, Solomons Islands, Chili, the Philippins, and other countrys " in the South Sea. It was partly to carry out this project and partly to discover the fate of Hudson that Thomas Button was sent on

[1] See *The Voyages of Captain Luke Foxe, of Hull, and Captain Thomas James, of Bristol*, edited by Miller Christy (Hakluyt Society, first series, vols. lxxxviii and lxxxix). The introduction to these volumes has been extensively used.

his voyage of 1612.[1] He received his instructions from Prince Henry, and was told that as the way to the bay was already known, he was not to waste time in its exploration. Once arrived in the bay, he was to remember that he was sailing to the west, and, the Prince observed,

> we would have you stand over to the opposite maine, in the latitude of some 58 degrees, where, riding at some headland, observe well the flood ; if it come in south-west, then you maie be sure the passage is that waie ; yf from the North or North-west, your course must be to stand upp into it.

Button sailed with two ships in April 1612, proceeded through Hudson Strait, discovered a cape on Coats Island, and eventually reached the western shore of the bay at a point significantly named "Hopes-check." From this point he sailed southward to a river that he named Port Nelson, which name still survives. Here the winter was spent, with much loss of life, and Button was obliged to abandon his own ship. He took advice as to his future course, and, as soon as he was able, sailed northward again, to look for a passage. He reached the latitude of 65° N. in Roe's Welcome, and, finding no passage, returned to the entrance to Hudson Strait in order to examine the tides which had been noticed by Hudson's men on their return voyage. He came to the conclusion "that those that were this way first, and himselfe the last yeere, were all of them deceived," and that the real passage lay to the north of Southampton Island. Button thus failed in his object, but he made careful observations, and to his credit must be placed the discovery of a very large part of the western shore of Hudson Bay.

His report led to the immediate dispatch of Captain Gibbons in 1614, but he was "driven into a Bay, called by his Company Gibbons his hole," on the coast of Labrador (latitude 58° 30' N.), and his voyage was a complete failure. Next year Robert Bylot, who had been with Hudson, Button, and Gibbons, went in search of the passage. This was the fourth voyage organized by "the Company of the Merchants of London Discoverers of the North-West Passage," and is of further interest because of the fact that William Baffin sailed as pilot, and wrote the account of the voyage. Like Bylot, Baffin was no stranger to the northern waters, for he had already made three Arctic voyages, to Greenland in 1612 and to Spitsbergen in the two following years.

Bylot left the Thames on April 16, 1615, and sighted Resolution Island on May 27. Hudson Strait was entered three days later, and its western exit was reached at the end of June, when Salisbury Island was sighted. Bylot then proceeded to examine the passage

---

[1] On these voyages see the work of Miller Christy cited above, and, for Baffin and Bylot, *The Voyages of William Baffin*, 1612–1622, edited by Sir Clements Markham (Hakluyt Society, first series, vol. lxiii).

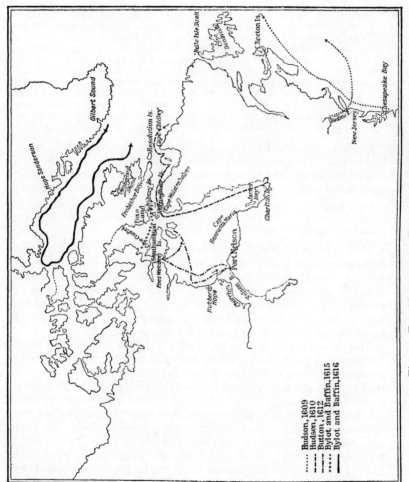

Fig. 15. The North-west Passage, Second Stage

to the north of Southampton Island, and on July 13 named Cape Comfort, because of the hope he had of finding a passage. But, as Baffin says,

> our sudden hopes weare as soon quayld, for the next morninge havinge dubbled the cape, when we supposed (by the account of the Tyde) we should be sett to the northward, it being little or no winde, we weare sett to the contrary, and that day having a good gale of winde we had not proceeded on our course past 10 or 12 leagues, but we saw the land trending from the Cape, round aboute by the west tyll it bore north-east and by east, and very thick pestered with ice, and the further we proceeded the more ice and shoaler water, with small show of any tyde. We seeing this our master soon resolved theare could be no passadge in this place and presently we bore upp the healme and turned the ships head to the southward.[1]

Bylot thus reached the entrance to Frozen Strait before turning homeward. He spent the remainder of the month at the western end of the strait, and then returned to England, which he reached early in September. Baffin's conclusions are interesting. He writes:

> Doubtless theare is a passadge. But within this strayte, whome is called Hudson's Straytes, I am doubtfull, supposinge the contrary. But whether there be or no, I will not affirme.

This opinion of Baffin carried great weight with the Merchant Adventurers, and they ceased to prosecute the search through Hudson Strait, turning instead to the earlier suggestion of Davis that the way led through the strait he had discovered. It was to examine this possibility that Bylot sailed in 1616, Baffin being again pilot, and also recorder of the voyage. Though Bylot was in command, Baffin seems to have gained all the credit.

The voyage began on May 26, 1616, and by the end of June Hope Sanderson was reached. From this point Bylot sailed steadily northward, giving names to prominent features on the coast of Greenland, and by July 3 had reached the modern Hayes Peninsula, where he named a cape after Digges and a sound after Wolstenholme, two great patrons of these northern voyages. Having reached the entrance to Smith Sound, Bylot could get no farther: his next discoveries are recorded on the west side of the bay. Jones Sound was discovered on July 11, and Lancaster Sound on the next day, but " here our hope of passage began to be lesse every day then other, for from this Sound to the southward wee had a ledge of ice betweene the shoare and us," says Baffin. They continued along the west side until reaching Cumberland Peninsula, then crossed back to Greenland, and finally sailed home, reaching Dover at the end of August. Baffin's judgment on the North-west Passage was now very definite, for he wrote to Sir John Wolstenholme that " the

---

[1] Markham, *Voyages of William Baffin*, pp. 131–132. Baffin's map is given at p. 103 of Markham's edition.

only hope was in searching Fretum Davis," but that as the result of his voyage " there is no passage nor hope of passage in the north of Davis straights." Thus ended this important and successful voyage. Bylot and Baffin discovered, and almost completely explored, Baffin Bay, and by discovering Smith Sound and Lancaster Sound pointed to two routes along which the discoverers of the nineteenth century pushed their way into the Polar seas. Baffin drew a map to illustrate this voyage, but it has unfortunately been lost, and much confusion arose subsequently as to the exact nature of his bay, until by the beginning of the nineteenth century its very existence was doubted. It would be of the greatest interest to know what Baffin's map was like, for in his conclusion that the passage was not to be found in that region he has been proved wrong.

In 1617 (?) Hawkridge conducted an expedition to Hudson Bay, but the voyage was a complete failure, and in 1619 Jens Munk, a Dane, reached Port Churchill, and spent the winter there. His voyage also was a failure, and, in addition to producing no geographical results, cost the lives of the whole party except Munk and two others. From this time down to 1631 no further efforts were made in search of the passage.

In 1630 the project was revived, and in the following year two expeditions were sent out, under Foxe and James. Both received instructions from the King, which have not been preserved, but from Foxe's account it is evident that he was directed to try first in that region where Baffin and Bylot had failed in 1615, then in the region where Button had wintered in 1612–13, and finally in the unexplored part of the bay between Port Nelson and James Bay, where Hudson had been cast adrift. So certain was Foxe of success that arrangements were made with the East India Company to bring back a cargo of pepper.

Foxe left England at the beginning of May 1631, and on June 22 reached the entrance to Hudson Strait. His passage through the strait occupied nineteen days, and he then found that the ice conditions made progress to the north-west impossible. Accordingly he sailed to the south-west, round the southern shore of Southampton Island and into Roe's Welcome, where he named a small, unidentified island. From here he turned to the south, to carry out his instructions " to search the passage diligently, all the Bay about untill I came to Hudson's [i.e., James] Bay." He examined the west coast with some care, though he failed to notice a large opening like Chesterfield Inlet, and arrived at Port Nelson on August 8. Ten days later he found a board which had been erected by Button in 1613. Foxe now proceeded to the discovery of the remaining part of the coast of Hudson Bay—that is, between Port Nelson and James Bay. He thought his chances of finding a passage very slight, and on August 26 records: "This low land thus trenting makes me doubt it will bring us with this shallow water to joyne with Hudson, and then leave us and fall away S., and there also must I leave it." At the end of the month Foxe met James and exchanged information, and he then continued his own exploration until September 2, when, he writes,

> I made motion at dinner for the N.W., declaring that now all this undiscovered land betwixt Mr Hudson's and Sir Thomas Button's [discoveries] was now perfectly finished by us . . . and now the further search of a passage this way was hopelesse, and there needed no more search in all the side of this bay, from 64° 30′ circularly to 55° 10′; and, seeing that we could not attempt the N.W. from Notinghams Ile (as I was instructed), for the heavie quantitys of Ice which had choaked all the three channels at our entering in the middle of July, now I did hope were disolved, or els never, and it was best to make tryall thereof whilest this good wind lasted.[1]

Leaving Cape Henrietta Maria, Foxe sailed to the north-east, and in due course reached the entrance to the passage north-west of Southampton Island. He followed the shore of Foxe Land, passing through Foxe Channel and reaching his highest latitude on September 22. Sickness and the lateness of the season compelled Foxe to return. He made his way back without further difficulty, except that he had many sick men among the crew, reaching the Downs on the last day of October. Foxe had performed three important pieces of work; he had completed the examination of Hudson Bay, he had penetrated far into Foxe Channel, and he had drawn a map of the whole region covered by the explorers of the North-west Passage. He believed that if such a passage existed at all it was through Roe's Welcome.

By contrast with that of Foxe, the voyage of Thomas James was singularly barren of results. He sailed from Bristol on May 2, 1631, and reached Hudson Bay about the middle of July. Finding it impossible to get to the north-west, he sailed to the south-west, and on August 11 he reports: "The land to the north of us did trend north by East and so made a point to the southward, and trended away west by south, which we followed, making it for that place which was formerly called Hubbert's Hope. And so it proved indeed; but it is now hopeless." Hubbert's Hope is probably the entrance to Churchill river, and from this point James followed the coast southward, being thus the first to discover part of the land lying between Port Nelson and James Bay, though Foxe subsequently overtook him and completed the discovery. It was James, however, who on September 2 named Cape Henrietta Maria at the north-west corner of his bay. James spent some time in an examination of his bay, and eventually wintered on

---

[1] Miller Christy, *op. cit.*, vol. ii, pp. 363-364.

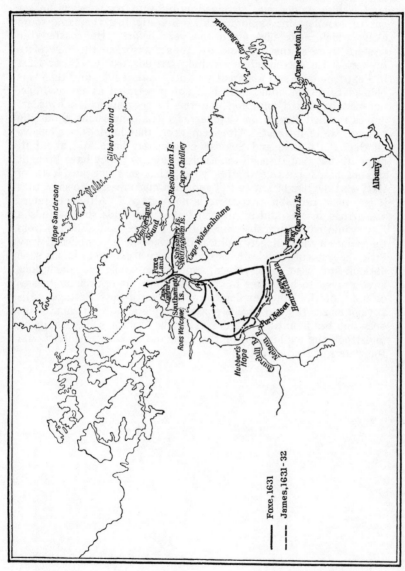

Fig. 16. The North-west Passage, Third Stage

Charlton Island, sinking his ship and building houses on the mainland. Here James was detained until July 1632, when he set out to complete his explorations by investigating the same route along which Foxe had failed the year before. He coasted the western shore of the bay, and by August 23 began this new piece of work. He succeeded in reaching latitude 65° 30′ N. at least in Foxe Channel, and apparently on its western side, and then was obliged to return home. He had not penetrated as far as Foxe, nor had he added anything material to geographical knowledge. James reached Bristol on October 22. His conclusions about the passage are of interest. After remarking that he does not believe all that Portuguese and Spanish geographers have said about it, he points out that through the English voyages "they have brought this supposed passage to this passe, that it must be North of sixty-six degrees of Latitude," and then gives reasons to show that it is "most probable that there is no passage." Although James was wrong in this and in his belief that the lands round Hudson Bay would never furnish commodities of trade, and although from the point of view of geographical discovery he accomplished very little, he yet surpassed all his contemporary explorers in his sane outlook and wise conservatism, and on the whole his conclusions have proved to be nearer to the truth than the optimistic guesses of most of the other explorers of the North-west Passage. His voyage marks the end of this phase of exploration : the next stage does not begin until the servants of the Hudson's Bay Company undertook the exploration of the mainland of North America and the waters of Hudson Bay.

CHAPTER IX

TERRA AUSTRALIS AND THE PACIFIC OCEAN, 1600–1800 [1]

I. THE PRECURSORS OF JAMES COOK

THE first voyage of importance made in the Pacific Ocean in the seventeenth century had for its object the discovery of some unknown land in the south of that ocean to which the name Terra Australis was sometimes given. The origin of the belief in the reality of this land dates back to classical times, when geographers held that some land existed beyond the uninhabitable tropics, or argued, on purely theoretical grounds, that some such land must exist. At the end of that period Ptolemy had actually put such a land-mass on the map, in the strip of country which joined Asia and Africa, and which stretched across the whole length of the Southern Ocean. Although during the early Middle Ages classical theories were disputed, or forgotten, in the later Middle Ages Ptolemy's theory exerted a considerable influence, and his maps survived by many years the discovery of a sea-route to India.

But if the belief in Terra Australis was a relic of classical geography, it also received the sanction of many reputable geographers in the second half of the sixteenth century. The famous map of Ortelius showed it quite clearly; and Mercator not only put it on his map, but argued that it must be there, because some such land-mass was necessary to balance the land in the Northern Hemisphere. This belief in the symmetrical arrangement of the earth did not receive universal acceptance, but it was in part responsible for the continuance or the revival of an old theory.

The existence of some such land seemed to be justified by recent discoveries. Magellan had passed through a strait : perhaps to the south lay this unknown continent. Drake was probably sent to follow its coasts, though his actual discoveries disproved its existence.[2] Later explorers like Schouten might add to discovery in one part, but also raise hopes for the future. Similarly, the discoveries of Quiros and Janszoon seemed to confirm the belief in this land-mass. There was therefore a problem of great importance awaiting solution : Did the continent really exist, and, if so, what was its character and extent ?

[1] The main authorities for this chapter are given in the footnotes below. In addition see the work of Captain James Burney, quoted on page 105 above.
[2] See above, p. 112, note 1.

It was to find this land in the south that Quiros and Torres set out from Callao on December 21, 1605.[1] Quiros issued long and detailed instructions to Torres as to the course to be followed. It was to be

> a W.S.W. course until the latitude of 30° [S.] is reached ; and when that is reached, and no land has been seen, the course will be altered to N.W. until the latitude of 10° 15' ; and if no land has yet been found, a course will be followed on that parallel to the west, in search of the island of Santa Cruz.

If Torres arrived alone he was to proceed to New Guinea, and " after coasting all along that land " to go to Manila. Quiros sailed on the above course until January 22, when he made a fatal decision. " On the 22nd we were in latitude 26°," h writes,

> with a squall and showers from the S.E. and with a great swell from the south. This brought out the timidity of some, saying : " Whither are they taking us, in this great gulf, in the winter season ? " . . . We were obliged, by the force of the winds and sea to stand on a W.N.W. course until we reached 25°.

They sighted an island, one of the Low Archipelago, four days later, and thereafter continued to pass islands, but it was not until February 10 that they came to one which had inhabitants ; it was Anaa, 200 miles east of Tahiti. Further islands were discovered, and on April 7 Quiros reached Taumaco, one of the Duff group, where the chief man told him of the existence of " as many as sixty islands, and a very large land which he called Manicolo." Thereupon Quiros turned southward, and reached the New Hebrides, off which he anchored on May 1, 1606. Here, he thought, was the southern continent, and he celebrated his discovery with a feast at which he read documents proclaiming that in the name of the King he took possession

> of this bay, named the bay of St Philip and St James, and of its port named Santa Cruz, and of the site on which is to be founded the city of New Jerusalem, in latitude 15° 10', and of all the lands which I sighted and am going to sight, and of all this region of the south as far as the Pole, which from this time shall be called Australia del Espiritu Santo, with all its dependencies and belongings.

Near by was a river which he named Jordan, and altogether Quiros thought he had found an earthly Paradise.

> I am able to say, with good reason, that a land more delightful, healthy, and fertile ; a site better supplied with quarries, timber, clay for tiles, bricks for founding a great city on the sea, with a port and a good river on a plain, with level lands near the hills, ridges, and ravines ; nor better adapted to raise plants and all that Europe and the Indies produce, could not be found.

[1] See *The Voyages of Pedro Fernandez de Quiros*, edited by Sir Clements Markham (Hakluyt Society, second series, vols. xiv and xv), from which the quotations are taken.

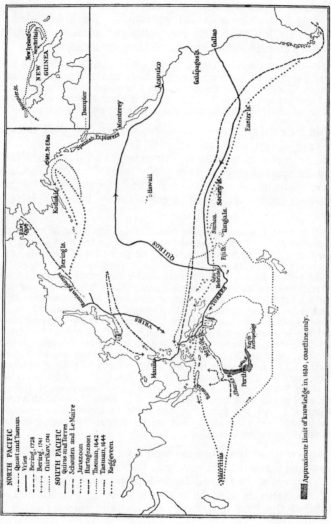

Fig. 17. The Precursors of James Cook

Quiros and Torres separated, by accident, and the former returned to America without making any more important discoveries, and fully confident that he would go back to finish his work. He presented no less than fifty memorials to the King of Spain for permission to explore his new-found land, declaring:

> By all that I have mentioned it appears clearly that there are two large portions of the earth severed from this of Europe, Africa, and Asia. The first is America which Christopher Colon discovered; and the second and last of the world is that which I have seen and solicit to people and completely discover for your Majesty.

After long delays Quiros gained his request, but died at Panamá in 1614 on his outward journey.

The independent voyage of Torres begins at the New Hebrides, where he parted from Quiros. He sailed "by the south-west course," but found no land, and then changed "to the north-north-west as far as eleven degrees and a half." "Here," he wrote,

> I fell in with the beginning of New Guinea the coast of which trends from east to west. . . . I could not go up it by the east side so I went coasting to the west, and on the south side it is all the land of New Guinea. . . . Having run three hundred leagues of the coast . . . we could not go forward on account of the numerous shoals and strong currents which there are throughout, so we had to go out by the south-west course. There were some very large islands and more were seen to the south. . . . [At the end of two months] we found ourselves in twenty-five fathoms of water and in five degrees latitude, and ten leagues from the coast, and we had gone four hundred and eighty leagues. Here the coast trends to the north-east. I did not reach it, because the bank is very shoal, so I went on running to the north . . . as far as four degrees when we fell in with a coast which also stretched from east to west. . . . We understood that it joined on with the coast we had left behind. . . . Lastly we ran along to the west-north-west beside the coast. . . . Here it was in this country where I found the first iron and bells of China . . . by which we understood more certainly that we were near the Moluccas, and so we went following this coast.[1]

Torres reached the Moluccas, and then sailed for Manila, where he wrote an account of his voyage in July 1607.

The voyage of Quiros and Torres is of great importance. Besides the New Hebrides and the southern shore of New Guinea, they discovered the Duff and Banks groups, and thirteen other coral

[1] See Appendix VI in De Morga's *Philippine Islands* . . ., edited by Lord Stanley of Alderley (Hakluyt Society, first series, vol. xxxix). A new translation of this letter, by Mr G. F. Barwick, is given in Appendix I of *New Light on the Discovery of Australia*, edited by H. N. Stevens (Hakluyt Society, second series, vol. lxiv). In this work Mr Stevens shows that Torres was acting as second in command to Captain Don Diego de Prado y Tovar, and claims that the *Relación* of the latter contains the first definite account of the discovery of Australia. On these points see E. A. Parkyn in *G.J.*, lxxvi, p. 252.

islands. They failed to achieve the main object of their expedition, but to them at least belongs the credit of having begun the search for Terra Australis.

With the arrival of the Dutch in the Pacific considerable progress was made in the discovery of pieces of the southern continent. A Dutchman named Linschoten, who had spent some time in the East, published on his return to Holland a *Discourse of Voyages*, in which he made it apparent that the way to the East was easy. He himself, as already explained, tried the North-east Passage without success. But his fellow-countryman Houtman went by the Cape route, and reached Java in 1596, and thereafter Dutch ships frequented the East Indies in such numbers as to be a very serious menace to the Spaniards. In 1602 the Dutch East India Company was founded, seven years later the Dutch secured the right to trade in the East, and in 1619 they founded Batavia, thus marking the beginning of their colonial empire.

Other Dutch sailors tried, with small success, the 'Spanish' route by way of Magellan's Strait. Some of these ventures have already been mentioned. Another, in 1614, was in the main successful, though it added nothing to geographical knowledge. Of much greater importance, however, was the voyage of Schouten and Le Maire.[1] Their objects were first to discover a new route to the South Sea, since all but members of the Dutch East India Company were forbidden to sail by either the Cape route or Magellan's Strait, and second to "discover great and rich countries in which ships would obtain rich cargoes, since . . . Le Maire said he had some knowledge thereof"[2] or, alternatively, to sail across the South Sea to East India for the purpose of trading there. They left the Texel on June 14, 1615, and on January 13, 1616, reached Port Desire. Eleven days later they made their great discovery, which can best be described in the words of the journal of the voyage:

> Early on the morning of the 24th we sighted land to starboard, lying not more than a good mile away. . . . The land ran east by south with very high mountains, which were all white with snow. We continued to sail along the land, and about noon we came to the end of it and saw more land east of the last, also very high and dangerous looking. These countries lay in our opinion about 8 miles from each other and there appeared to be a good channel between them both. . . . On the morning of the 25th we were close to the more easterly land. . . . We gave this the name of Staten-Landt, but the land to the west of us we called Mauritius de Nassauw. . . . We had a northerly wind to carry us into the channel sailing sou'-sou'-west with good progress. . . . In the evening the wind

[1] For the voyage of Speilbergen in 1614–17, and that of Schouten and Le Maire, see *The East and West Indian Mirror*, edited by J. A. J. de Villiers (Hakluyt Society, second series, vol. xviii).
[2] Derived probably from an account of the voyage of Quiros.

veered to the south-west and we then ran southward that night with a heavy roll from the south-west and very blue water, from which we opined and were certain . . . that it was the great South Sea, whereat we were very glad, holding that a way had been discovered by us which had until then been unknown to man, as we afterwards found to be the truth.[1] . . . Towards the evening [of the 29th] we again saw land to the north west. . . . It consisted entirely of high mountains covered with snow, and ends in a sharp corner, which we called the Cape of Hoorn, and which lies in latitude 57° 48′ S. [really 55° 59′ S.]

In the course of their voyage across the Pacific Schouten and Le Maire discovered a few islands in the Low Archipelago, and two islands to which they gave the names of Cocos and Verraders (now called Boscawen and Keppel respectively), and then made for the north shore of New Guinea, which was thought to be part of Terra Australis and joined to Staten Land. They made a fairly careful examination of the north coast, and two names, Vulcan and Schouten Islands, remain as a reminder of their visit. They finally reached Java, where their ship was confiscated ; they were sent home with Speilbergen on the ground that they could not have reached the Pacific without making use of one of the prohibited routes. Le Maire died on the way home : his father, after two years of litigation, vindicated his position and obtained compensation.

The Dutch at this time not only began their systematic conquest of the East Indies, but added a large piece of Australia to the map. Attempts have been made to prove that Australia was earlier known to the Spanish and Portuguese, and the claim is based on a number of early maps, dating from about 1530, on which various pieces of land are shown which, it is maintained, represent parts of the coast of Australia. As Mr Heawood has pointed out, the argument " rests almost entirely on the fact that early in the sixteenth century a certain unknown map-maker drew a large land, with indications of definite knowledge of its coasts, in a quarter of the globe in which Australia exists." The earliest map shows Sumatra, Java, and, separated by a narrow strait, Java la Grande, which certainly bears some resemblance to Australia. Very little was known at this time about land to the south of Java, and if emphasis is to be placed on the shape of Java la Grande it would be necessary to presuppose extensive coasting voyages, of which there is no evidence. If, on the other hand, it is maintained that the shape does not matter, then the map might quite well have been drawn from suggestions thrown out by Marco Polo or from a guess that the land was part of the southern continent. Two later maps, of 1578 and 1597, do in fact show Australia as part of the southern continent. On several grounds Mr Heawood rejects the claim to an

[1] In 1643 a Dutchman, H. Brouwer, discovered that Staten Land was merely a small island.

early discovery of Australia, and the same conclusion is reached by Wood, who has more recently examined the question.[1] At the same time it should be remembered that many early maps were based in part on information derived from local inhabitants, that it is, at the least, highly probable that Malay seamen knew something of the north coast of Australia and possibly of the west coast, and that some vague information about Australia may have reached Europeans through this source. As for the actual maps, Wood declares that "we should regard them not as prosaic records of historical facts, but as brilliant geographical romances, though the brilliant geographic imagination may possibly have had a fact or two to work upon."

The actual discovery of Australia must, therefore, in all probability, be placed to the credit of the Dutch, and, in particular, to Willem Janszoon in the year 1606. He had touched at New Guinea, and followed the coast to the south, but instead of continuing through Torres Strait (of which he was ignorant), he sailed into the Gulf of Carpentaria, and followed its eastern shore as far as Cape Keerweer ('Turn Again'), where the hostility of the natives obliged him to return. He thought that the new land which he had discovered was connected with New Guinea.

Between this voyage and the expedition of Tasman in 1642 a number of small but important discoveries were made. In 1616 Hartogszoon, sailing on a new course to Java, accidentally reached the west coast of Australia, at a small island which still bears his name (latitude 26° S.). He then followed the coast to the northward, thinking it was part of the southern continent. The west coast was reached again the next year, in latitude 21° 20′ S., and again in 1618, in latitude 22° S. In 1619 Houtman followed it through five degrees of latitude, from 32° 20′ S., and concluded that it belonged to the land already seen by Hartogszoon. Cape Leeuwin was sighted in 1622 ; the Gulf of Carpentaria was named in 1623 ; and in the extreme south the coast was followed to longitude 133° E. and Nuyts Land was named. Many of these discoveries were accidental, and there was still considerable confusion as to the relationship of one piece with another.[2] By 1630 the west and south coasts from Nuyts Archipelago to the North-west Cape were reasonably well known.

These voyages were followed by a much longer and more important expedition under Abel Tasman in 1642. His objects were

[1] See E. Heawood's article in *G.J.*, vol. xiv, p. 421, and G. A. Wood, *The Discovery of Australia* (1922), Chapter VI. For a recent exposition of the Spanish claim see the reference in note 1 above, p. 148.
[2] See the Dutch map of Terra del Zur. This and other useful maps will be found in the *Australasian School Atlas*, edited by J. G. Bartholomew and K. R. Cramp (1915). Many Dutch charts are reproduced in F. C. Weider, *Monumenta Cartographica*, vols. iv (1932), v (1933).

to explore the Indian Ocean beyond the track of ordinary trading-vessels, to find out whether Australia was part of the great southern continent or not, and to examine the northern coasts of New Guinea and determine whether or not it was an island. He sailed from Batavia to Mauritius, and thence first southward and then south-eastward. He appears to have reached latitude 49° S. in longitude 97° E., and, continuing to sail to the east, he saw land, to which he gave the name of Van Diemen, in honour of the Governor of the Dutch East Indies. Some attempt was made to examine the land, but the crew were frightened by the belief that it was inhabited by giants, and Tasman had to be content with an exploration of the coast, which was roughly charted as far as the Freycinet Penin-sula, lying in about the middle of the east coast. Tasman then sailed eastward, and on December 13 again saw land, which he called Staten Land, and which he thought was connected with the land discovered by Schouten and Le Maire in 1616. Actually it was part of the west coast of the South Island of New Zealand, in about latitude 42° S. Passing northward round the cape significantly named Foulwind, and beyond Cape Farewell, Tasman got between the South and North Islands without being aware of the fact. He then followed the west coast of the North Island to its northern end, and steered north-eastward across the Pacific.

The Tonga group was reached on January 21, and here Tasman turned to the west. Sailing past the Fiji Islands, he reached New Ireland (*i.e.*, Neu Mecklenburg), which he thought was part of New Guinea, followed the north coast of New Guinea to its western end, where he made a number of important discoveries, and so returned to Batavia.

Tasman's voyage was a splendid failure. He was unfortunate in that he sailed round Australia without seeing it, yet he definitely limited the area of the southern continent. He had false ideas about Australia, but he showed that at least it was not part of the southern continent. By discovering New Zealand he added another large land-mass to the map, but here again he was in error in supposing that it was part of the southern continent. In addition to making these discoveries he sailed over a vast stretch of the Southern Ocean, from Mauritius to the Tonga Islands, discovered the latter and many other small islands, and, with the help of his pilot, Visscher, recorded his discoveries on accurate charts. For this work he de-serves to rank as one of the most able and enterprising discoverers.

Tasman had been instructed to find a route to Chile, if possible, round the south of Australia, and this he claimed to have done. He was, however, unable to convince the Dutch East India Company that he had discovered the best way, and so was sent out again in 1644 to discover some passage to the south of New Guinea, to complete the work already done on the north coast, and to find out the general relationship between New Guinea and the various pieces of Australia and Tasmania which had been discovered.

The only evidence for this voyage is to be found in a letter from the Governor-General to the directors of the Dutch East India Company, and in maps, from which it appears that Tasman failed to fulfil the objects of the directors, but still held to the belief that New Guinea and Australia were one land. He did, however, prove beyond doubt that the earlier discoveries in the Gulf of Carpentaria belonged to the same land as those which had been made on the west and north-west. By 1644, therefore, the coast of Australia was generally known from Cape York to Nuyts Archipelago, and parts of the coasts of Tasmania and New Zealand had been visited.

This ended Tasman's work as an explorer. He had failed to find any new lands which would bring profit to the Dutch traders, and they were not prepared to undertake geographical exploration for its own sake. But he had performed great services to geography, and his record as an explorer in the South Pacific remained unsurpassed until James Cook arrived to complete his work.

Although the Dutch derived no profit from Australia, they did not entirely lose touch with the new continent. In 1648 a long coasting voyage, from Perth to Melville Island, was made, and ten years later a Dutch ship went as far south as Cape Leeuwin. The north-west coast was charted in 1678 from North-west Cape to the neighbourhood of Cape Levêque, while at the close of the century (1696) Vlamingh made an important survey of the west coast, on which he included the islands round Sharks Bay (which he discovered) and the Swan river. It is curious to find that the great discoveries of Tasman were not followed up by further explorations. One reason for this has already been suggested, a geographical cause arising from the poverty of the lands which had been found. To this must be added an historical explanation, for during the greater part of the period the Dutch were involved in serious political complications in Europe.

The next discoveries in the South Pacific were of a minor order, and consist of a large number of small, though often important, pieces of work. Of these the voyages of Narborough on the west coast of South America in 1669 produced a much improved chart of Magellan's Strait, while John Cook in 1683 performed a similar task for the Galapagos Islands. Cook was one of the renowned buccaneers, of whom William Dampier [1] must take first place so far as geographical discovery is concerned. In the course of one of his roving voyages Dampier reached Australia, in 1686, apparently near to Melville Island. He spent just over two months on the coast, but found no water, saw no animals, and learned to have a

[1] On Dampier, see *Dampier's Voyages*, edited by John Masefield, 2 vols. (1906), and C. Wilkinson, *William Dampier* (" Golden Hind " series, 1929).

great contempt for the people and their customs. "The inhabitants of this Country," he wrote, "are the miserablest people in the world." Of the land itself, he says : "It is not yet determined whether it is an Island or a Main Continent ; but I am certain that it joyns neither to Asia, Africa, nor America." Dampier had evidently at this point not heard of the work of Tasman, though on his second visit he carried one of Tasman's charts with him. Dampier's career after leaving Australia was full of adventure, including a canoe voyage from the Nicobar Islands to Sumatra and a small walking-tour in China, where he nearly lost his life through misunderstanding a Chinese funeral ceremony. Dampier left a full account of his journey, which makes good reading, though it added little to geographical knowledge.

In his second voyage of 1699 Dampier was in command of H.M.S. *Roebuck*. His object was to make a study of Terra Australis and to examine its physical geography, its people, and its mineral wealth. He originally intended to sail across the Pacific to the east coast of Australia, but was prevented by the late season from doing so, with the result that he went by the Cape of Good Hope, and reached the west coast near to Sharks Bay. He made a rough examination of the coast as far as Dampier Archipelago. Proceeding thence to New Guinea, and passing through the strait which now bears his name, he reached the north coast. He sailed eastward at some distance from the coast, and reached New Ireland, followed its east coast to what he called St George Bay, which is the strait at its southern end, and so reached New England. He continued right round this land, passed between it and New Guinea, and so got back to the north coast of the latter and began his homeward voyage. To the new land he thought he had discovered he gave the name of Nova Britannia. Dampier's voyages had not added much to geographical knowledge. Like the Dutch explorers, he had found only the barren parts of Australia. What Dampier had to say in its favour was theoretical : all that he had to report as an eyewitness was discouraging ; and it is not surprising, therefore, to find that his voyages were not followed by others. He himself reverted to the life of a buccaneer, and made another lengthy expedition in 1703, which is, however, of no importance in the history of geographical discovery.

Similar roving voyages were undertaken by the French, in the course of which Gouin de Beauchêne, in 1701, proved that Cape Horn, as shown on the charts in general use, was placed in too high a latitude. Early in the eighteenth century the French visited the Pacific in considerable numbers, and some of them did work of great scientific importance. Louis Feuillée described the coastal features of Chile and Perú ; Marcand discovered a new exit from the Strait of Magellan ; and Frézier improved the existing charts of the extreme southern parts of South America. More famous, if less successful, was the voyage of Bouvet in 1738-39. He set out to find ' Gonneville's Land,' discovered in the early years of the sixteenth century, and supposed to lie to the south of Africa. Bouvet sighted a high, snow-clad land on January 1, 1739, to which he give the name Cape Circumcision (latitude 54° S., longitude 27° or 28° E. of Tenerife). The land is now known as Bouvet Island.[1] Bouvet's expedition was of little importance in itself, though he returned with some information about the Antarctic ice, but it had an important influence on the work of James Cook.

Meanwhile the Dutch had been active in the South Seas. In 1707 Van Delft reached Australia at Melville Island. He hoped to find a passage to the south through Dundas Strait, but was disappointed, and spent some months in an examination of the coast. He produced a chart which showed an improvement over that drawn by Tasman. Fourteen years later Roggeveen began the last of the great Dutch voyages. His object was to search for the southern continent in a part of the ocean west of South America where land had been reported by an Englishman, Davis, about forty years earlier. Roggeveen was so far successful that he discovered Easter Island in April 1722, and then proceeded to the Low Archipelago and some of the islands in the Palliser, Society, and Samoa groups. Roggeveen subsequently touched at New Britain, sailed round the north of New Guinea, and so reached Batavia.

In 1740–44 Lord Anson was engaged in his famous, though from a geographical point of view rather disappointing, voyage round the world. The voyage resulted in the collection of much plunder, and gave valuable experience to a later explorer, John Byron, but is not otherwise of sufficient importance to require detailed examination.

Before turning to the new period inaugurated by Byron it is necessary to take a rapid glance at the growth of knowledge in the North Pacific. From the middle of the sixteenth century the European traders had kept up regular intercourse with Japan, and in the early years of the seventeenth century it was visited by both Dutch and English, as well as by Jesuit missionaries, who arrived in 1620. In spite of this, however, there was very little real knowledge of Japan, and almost complete ignorance of the Pacific Ocean to the north and north-east. There was a belief that wealthy islands existed there, and a rather vague story of their discovery by the Spaniards in 1584, and it was the desire to prove the truth of this rumour that led to the expedition of Quast and Tasman in 1639. The two captains began by improving the map of the Philippines and the neighbouring seas, saw Japan in about latitude 37°, and sailed for a long distance to the east, without finding the islands of

[1] Fo: the subsequent history of Bouvet Island see *G.J.*, vol. lxxii, p. 537.

gold. On their return they again saw Nippon in a slightly higher latitude, sailed round Kiushiu, and reached Formosa.

From the point of view of the Dutch company their voyage was a failure, but it was followed up by another of considerable importance, this time under Vries and Schaep. After reaching Japan the two men separated. Vries failed to establish the existence of a strait south of Yezo, though his charts place one there, and he apparently thought Yezo was part of Asia. Farther north he found a large island (Iturup ?) which he called Staten Island, and gave another name, Compagnies Landt, to a large mass which he thought to lie to the eastward. Sakhalin was reached, and was thought also to

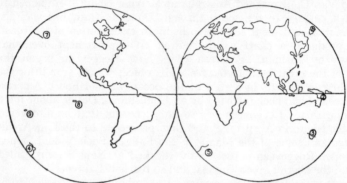

Fig 18. OUTLINE SKETCH OF THE WORLD MAP OF G. DE L'ISLE, 1700

Note Frobisher's 'strait' (1), the connexion of Australia and New Guinea (2), the appearance of Tasmania (3), and New Zealand (4), and a survival of the great southern continent, which is called Cap des Terres Australes (5). In the North Pacific Companies Land (6) and Gama Land (7) are shown. In the South Pacific are the Solomon Islands (8) and Santa Cruz (9). A number of islands have been omitted.

be part of Yezo. On the return journey Vries looked in vain for the islands of gold. Meanwhile Schaep had reached the Kurile Islands, in latitude 47° 8′ N.

The Dutch thus considerably extended the knowledge of part of the North Pacific, though Companies Land [1] was to bother cartographers for a hundred years. In about the same place appeared also from time to time a Gama Land, thought to have been discovered by the Spaniards in the early years of the seventeenth century. It was the task of Russian explorers to remove these errors from the map and add greatly to the accurate knowledge of the North Pacific. During the seventeenth century they had crossed Asia, and had reached the Pacific. It is even claimed by some that Deshnev in 1648 sailed from the north coast of Asia through what is now known as Bering Strait, but this has been doubted, and was certainly not generally accepted at the beginning

[1] Several variants of this ' land ' appear on the maps of the period.

of the next century. About the year 1697 the Russians arrived in Kamchatka and began the conquest of that peninsula, and ten years later they reached its southern end and sighted the nearest islands of the Kurile chain. In 1710 they obtained some further information of the region between Kamchatka and Japan, and this led to two expeditions to the Kuriles, in 1712 and 1713, when the islands were charted and Yezo was reached. This last was thought to be an archipelago. Six years later another expedition reached the Kuriles, but even then their geography was imperfectly understood. The work in this region was continued by Spangberg and his associates in 1738 and 1739. The Kuriles were again visited, and parts of the coast of Japan were reached, but the problem of Yezo remained unsolved. One ship, in a voyage eastward, failed to find any of the land reported to exist there. Spangberg had done much to establish the general relationship between Kamchatka and Japan, though, like other explorers in this region hitherto, he had not completely solved all the geographical problems.

Meanwhile vast strides had been made to the north and east. Vitus Bering[1] was entrusted with an expedition in 1728, with instructions to sail from Kamchatka " along the shore which bears northerly and which (since its limits are unknown) seems to be part of America " and to " determine where it joins with America." Bering reported that he carried out his instructions, and " came to latitude 67° 18' and turned back because the coast did not extend farther north and no land was near the Chukchee or East Cape and therefore it seemed to me that the instructions of his Imperial Majesty had been carried out." In the following year Bering searched the ocean for a land to the eastward which the inhabitants of Kamchatka said they had seen, but he failed to find it, and then " circumnavigated and charted the southern part of Kamchatka which up to this time had not been surveyed."

It is probable that the Russians saw part of the American continent in 1732, though they were unaware of this fact, and it was not until 1741 that they had definite knowledge of the New World. This was the result of the second expedition of Bering, whose voyage was one of a series undertaken to establish connexion with Japan, to prove definitely that Asia and America were not joined, and to discover America. Sailing from Kamchatka, the first search was for the elusive Gama Land in latitude 47° N., which naturally was not found. Bering then changed his course somewhat, and at the end of July 1741 sighted Mount St Elias and an island which he named St Elias (Kayak). From this point he began his return voyage, passing to the south of Kodiak Island, along the southern shore of the Alaska Peninsula, to the Shumagin Islands. A number of other islands were touched at or seen, and eventually, at the end of

[1] See *Bering's Voyages*, edited by F. A. Golder (2 vols., 1922, 1925).

October, Bering Island was reached. Here Bering died, but the crew, who were suffering very severely from scurvy, managed to recuperate, and in the following summer, under the command of Waxel, set sail in a small boat which they had built, and reached Kamchatka again in August.

Chirikov, who had accompanied Bering at the beginning of the voyage, had lost touch with his leader, and actually reached the American coast in a more southerly latitude. He followed the coast closely from Dixon Entrance, at the northern end of the Queen Charlotte Islands, to about the latitude of 58° N., and saw something of the coast for a considerable distance from that point. On the return voyage a number of the Aleutian Islands were discovered before Kamchatka was reached in the early days of October.

Nearly all the great problems of the North Pacific were solved by these voyages, so far as they lay within the scope of the instructions given to Bering. He had shown that the mysterious lands did not exist ; Spangberg had done much to clear up the question of Japan ; and it was reasonably certain that America was not joined to Asia, though this point had not been definitely proved. The value of the last voyage of Bering was much increased because of the record, left by the naturalist Steller, of the lands which were visited and their animal life. Russian fur-traders also took advantage of the prospects now opened up, and reached the Aleutian Islands about the year 1743. Other expeditions were made to America from time to time, and at some date between 1783 and 1787 a fur-station was established on Kodiak Island.

To complete the picture of the North Pacific before the voyages of Cook it is necessary to refer briefly to the Spanish explorers. Early in the seventeenth century Martin de Aguilar had reported the existence of what seemed to be the entrance to a strait, or the mouth of a river, in latitude 43° N., but practically nothing had been done to follow up the discovery. The activities of other nations in the Pacific in the eighteenth century, and in particular the explorations of the Russians and the voyage of Anson, revealed to the Spaniards the weakness of their position, and led to considerable activity both on land and on sea. In 1770 the post of Monterey was established, and four years later Juan Perez was sent northward along the coast with instructions to proceed as far as latitude 60° N., primarily to see what, if any, were the activities of other nations. Perez was supplied with maps based on recent Russian discoveries. He only succeeded in reaching latitude 55° N. and in charting a portion of the Queen Charlotte Islands, but he found no evidence of foreign settlements. A second expedition under Heceta and Quadra was dispatched in the next year, with instructions to reach a higher latitude than that attained by Perez, and, if possible, that of 65° N., and to examine the coast in more detail on the return journey. Heceta reached latitude 49°, and saw the mouth of the Columbia river ; Quadra sailed about as far as latitude 58° ; while a third vessel explored San Francisco Bay. The reports of the earlier explorers were not confirmed, and much yet remained to be done on the west coast before it could be said that it was well known.

II. The Age of Cook

The voyage of Commodore John Byron, begun in 1764, is the first of a series of expeditions which made great additions to the knowledge of the Pacific. He was specially ordered to examine " His Majesty's islands called Pepys Island and Falklands Islands " and to look for

> lands and islands of great extent, hitherto unvisited by any European power . . . in the Atlantic Ocean between the Cape of Good Hope and the Magellanic Streight, within the latitudes convenient for navigation, and in climates adapted to the produce of commodities useful in commerce.

The search for Pepys Island, reported to have been discovered in latitude 47° S. in 1684, proved fruitless, but Byron duly visited the Falklands, where Bougainville's French colony was established, and took possession of them for George III, believing that they were Pepys Island. The subsequent voyage of Byron across the Pacific resulted in the discovery of a number of islands and some indication, Byron thought, of a land to the southward, though no such land exists where Byron believed it lay.

The results of Byron's voyage were disappointing, but almost immediately after his return two more ships, under Captains Wallis and Carteret, were sent to explore the Pacific. The two ships separated at the western end of Magellan's Strait, and never met again during the voyage. Wallis sailed across the Pacific in a low latitude, and his most important discovery was the large island of Tahiti. Carteret sailed in a slightly higher latitude, and, failing to find Davis Land and other lands in the Pacific which appeared on contemporary maps, rediscovered the Santa Cruz group, though he was unable to locate the Solomon Islands in their position on the maps ; he subsequently found that they lay to the west of Santa Cruz. Carteret then discovered the strait separating New Ireland from New Britain, passed the Admiralty Islands, and so reached the East Indies. He also had failed to solve the riddle of the South Pacific, though he had filled in or corrected many details on the map.

Louis-Antoine de Bougainville, who had served the French in Canada, and in 1763 and again in 1765 had conducted colonizing expeditions to the Falkland Islands, went out a third time in 1766, to hand over the islands to Spain. He then proceeded to Rio de

Janeiro, where a store-ship joined him, and from that port he began his voyage round the world in July 1767. In the Pacific he first searched for Davis Land, and then continued westward in the hope of finding some solution to the problem of the southern continent. After touching at Tahiti Bougainville next discovered some islands to which he gave the name of Navigators' Islands (Samoa group). He visited the New Hebrides, which he rightly concluded were the same as the Australia of Quiros, passed through the Louisades, and, unaware of Carteret's recent discovery, sailed round New Ireland, and so reached the north coast of New Guinea. Bougainville returned to France in 1769, after a long and successful voyage, leaving the problem of the South Seas unsolved.

James Cook,[1] whose remarkable contributions to the geography of the Pacific Ocean were made shortly after the voyage of Bougainville, had, like that officer, served in Canada, where he had done excellent survey work both in the St Lawrence river and off the coasts of Newfoundland. In 1768 he was chosen to command an expedition organized by the Royal Society to observe a transit of Venus which was to take place in the following year. This was ostensibly the main object of the voyage, but Cook received further instructions to proceed to the southward

> in order to make discovery of the continent [which was to be found south of the course taken by Wallis] until you arrive in the latitude of 40°, unless you sooner fall in with it : but not having discovered it, or any evident signs of it, in that run, to proceed in search of it to the westward, between the latitude before mentioned and the latitude of 35° until you discover it or fall in with the eastern side of the land discovered by Tasman and now called New Zealand. . . . If you should fail of discovering the continent . . . you will, upon falling in with New Zealand, carefully observe the latitude and longitude in which that land is situated, and explore as much of the coast [as circumstances allow].[2]

The observation of the transit of Venus was thus prefixed to the voyage the real objects of which were the discovery of the southern continent and the annexation of new lands to the British Empire. Cook was furnished with much information likely to be of use. He carried a copy of de Brosses' *Histoire des navigations aux terres Australes*, which contained some interesting observations on the southern continent and a strong plea for French action in that region. The arguments were repeated, with a different application, by

[1] The standard life of Cook is that of A. Kitson (1907). See also the valuable papers in *G.J.*, vol. lxxiii, pp. 97–122. There are many editions of Cook's *Voyages*. That used here is the octavo edition in seven volumes (1821). For the first voyage *Captain Cook's Journal during his First Voyage*, edited by Captain W. J. L. Wharton (1893), is a standard authority. See also *An Introduction to the Bibliography of Captain James Cook, R.N.*, by M. Holmes (1936), and the short but excellent biography, *Captain Cook*, by R. T. Gould (1935).

[2] Quoted by Professor J. Holland Rose in *G.J.*, vol. lxxiii, pp. 105, 106.

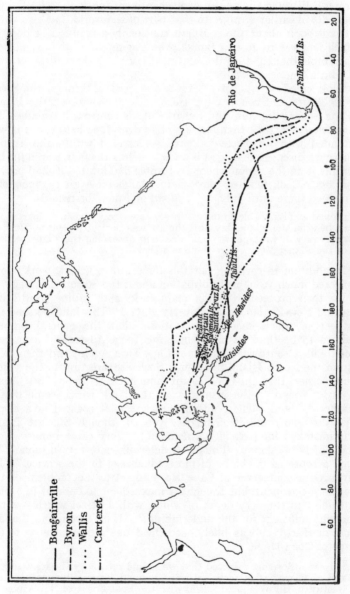

Bougainville
Byron
Wallis
Carteret

Rio de Janeiro

Falkland Is.

New Ireland
New Britain
Santa Cruz Is.
New Hebrides
Tahiti Is.
Louisiades

Fig. 19. THE AGE OF COOK—I

Callender in England in 1766. Further, Dalrymple, who was a strong believer in the reality of the continent, not only collected the accounts of earlier voyages to that part of the world, but also wrote a small book about the southern continent, a manuscript copy of which he gave to Joseph Banks, who accompanied the expedition. Dalrymple thought that the continent lay but a short distance west of South America.

Cook sailed on August 26, 1768, and passed through the Strait of Le Maire and round Cape Horn. He then crossed the Pacific to the Society Islands, and remarks of his course : " I made a far more westerly track than any ship had ever done before, yet it was attended with no discovery until we arrived within the Tropic, where we discovered several islands." Thus the first search for the continent, in the region where Dalrymple had located it, had proved fruitless. Cook reached the Society Islands on April 13, 1769, and remained there until July. " The 3rd of June," he records,

> proved as favourable to our purposes as we could wish. Not a cloud to be seen the whole day and the air was perfectly clear so that we had every advantage we could desire in observing the whole passage of the Planet Venus over the Sun's Disk.

In addition to carrying out this important scientific work, Cook collected much valuable information about the Society Islands.

He then proceeded to the main task, and, sailing southward, reached New Zealand near Poverty Bay. " This land became the subject of much eager conversation ; but the general opinion seemed to be that we had found the Terra Australis Incognita." Cook sailed southward as far as Cape Turn Again, and then went round the North Island in an anti-clockwise direction to the south-west corner, through Cook Strait, and back to Cape Turn Again in order to prove the insularity of the land, which some of the officers doubted. The South Island was next coasted in a clock-wise direction, and its insularity proved, though Stewart Island was mistaken for part of the mainland. Very careful charts were made of both islands. Cook now determined to return home " by such a route as might be of most advantage to the service." He favoured a course round Cape Horn to settle the problem of the southern continent, but thought it inexpedient to be kept in a high latitude " in the very depth of winter with a vessel which was not thought sufficient for the undertaking." This reason, and the fact that no discovery was likely, also ruled out a direct course to the Cape of Good Hope.

> It was therefore resolved that we should return by the East Indies, and that with this view we should, upon leaving the coast, steer westward, till we should fall in with the East Coast of New Holland, and then follow the direction of the coast to the northward till we should arrive at its northern extremity ; but if that should be found

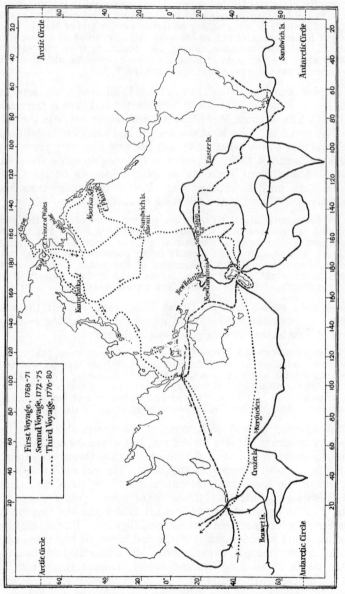

First Voyage, 1768-71
Second Voyage, 1772-75
Third Voyage, 1776-80

Arctic Circle

Antarctic Circle

Arctic Circle

Antarctic Circle

E. Cape
Prince of Wales
C. Prince of Wales

Montna St.
C. Prince

Kamchatka

Sandwich Is.
Hawaii

Easter Is.

Sandwich Is.

Society Is.

New Hebrides

New Caledonia

Crozet Is.
Kerguelen

Bouvet Is.

Fig. 20. The Age of Cook—II

impracticable it was further resolved that we should endeavour to fall in with the land, or islands said to have been discovered by Quiros. With this view, at break of day on Saturday the 31st of March, 1770, we got under sail, and put to sea with the advantage of a fresh gale at S.E. and clear weather, taking our departure from the eastern point which we had seen at noon on the 23rd and to which on this occasion, I gave the name of Cape Farewell.[1]

The plan was completely successful. Land was again seen on April 19. " I judged [it] to lie in latitude 38° and gave it the name of Point Hicks, because Mr Hicks, the first lieutenant, was the first who discovered it." No land was seen to the southward, and Cook wisely refused to say whether or not his new discovery joined up with Van Diemen's Land. Instead of delaying to settle the point he coasted northward, narrowly escaping shipwreck on the Great Barrier Reef, until he reached Cape York. His instructions had been fully carried out, as the following extract shows:

> As I was now about to quit the eastern coast of New Holland, which I had coasted from latitude 38° to this place, and which I am confident no European had seen before, I once more hoisted English colours, and though I had already taken possession of several particular parts, I now took possession of the whole Eastern coast, from latitude 38° to this place, in the right of His Majesty King George the Third, by the name of New South Wales.[2]

Cook then sailed through Torres Strait, and records the discovery with extreme modesty and generosity. Referring to some charts of New Guinea in De Bry's *Voyages*, he says:

> I always understood, before I had a sight of these maps, that it was unknown whether or no New Holland and New Guinea was one continued land, and so it is said in the very *History of Voyages* these maps are bound up in. However, we have now put this wholly out of dispute; but as I believe it was known before, but not publickly, I claim no other merit than the clearing up of a doubtful point.[3]

Cook returned by way of Batavia, where he was able to get the necessary repairs to his ship carried out, but where the crew suffered greatly from fever, and at length anchored in the Downs on July 13, 1771, after a most successful expedition. He had not settled the problem of the southern continent, nor had he, as is sometimes said, discovered Australia. There were minor points along his route, such as the insularity of Stewart Island and the location of Bass Strait, which required further investigation. But in addition to political and national results of the first order, he had made very substantial contributions to geography. He had settled the question of the insularity of New Zealand, which Tasman thought to be part of the southern continent. By his voyage southward from Tahiti he had very definitely limited the region in which such a

[1] *Voyages*, vol. ii, p. 22.   [2] *Ibid.*, vol. ii, p. 196.
[3] Kitson, *op. cit.*, p. 189.

continent might be found. He had connected up the work of Tasman in New Zealand with that of the Dutch explorers and Dampier on the north of Australia, and in so doing had added the east coast of that island continent to the map. He had also revived the knowledge of Torres Strait. To all this positive work must be added the construction of a number of very accurate charts, and —a fact of immense importance—the preservation of his crew from sickness. The unfortunate necessity of the call at Batavia raised the death-rate considerably : apart from this disaster Cook was able to report on his arrival in the East Indies : " I have the satisfaction to say that I have not lost one man by sickness during the whole voyage."

Mention has already been made of the French interest in the problem of the South Pacific, shown more particularly in the voyage of Bouvet and the work of De Brosses. In 1771 Yves-Joseph de Kerguelen-Trémarec undertook an expedition similar to that of Bouvet, in the hope of discovering Gonneville's Land. He found a large island lying to the south of Mauritius, which has since borne his name, but entirely mistook its nature and importance. " The lands which I have had the happiness to discover," he wrote,

> appear to form the central mass of the Antarctic continent . . . and the land which I have called South France is so situated as to command the route to India, the Moluccas, China, and the South Seas. . . . The latitude in which it lies promises all the crops of the Mother Country. . . . No doubt wood, minerals, diamonds, rubies, precious stones, and marble will be found.

A subsequent examination of his discovery in 1773 convinced Kerguelen-Trémarec that he had made a mistake ; he acknowledged it was not part of the southern continent, and appropriately renamed it " Land of Desolation."

In 1771 another voyage, from Mauritius, under the direction of Marion-Dufresne, resulted in the discovery of Marion Island and Crozet Islands. The French then visited Tasmania and New Zealand, where the commander and some of the crew were killed. Crozet, who now led the expedition, continued the voyage in the Pacific, without, however, adding to geographical knowledge.

The French voyages were interrupted by the second voyage of Cook, who did much to solve the problem which the French were trying to unravel, and did it with such success that the next French explorer, La Pérouse, generously declared that " Mr Cook has done so much that he has left me nothing to do but admire his work."

All reasonable doubts as to the existence of a southern continent were banished as the result of the second voyage of Cook. His instructions show the influence of the French voyages in the southern ocean :

> After leaving the Cape of Good Hope, I was to proceed to the southward, and endeavour to fall in with Cape Circumcision, which

was said by Monsieur Bouvet to lie in lat. 54° South, and in about 11° 20′ east longitude from Greenwich. If I discovered this cape, I was to satisfy myself whether it was a part of the continent, which had so much engaged the attention of geographers and former navigators, or a part of an island. If it proved to be the former, I was to employ myself diligently in exploring as great an extent of it as I could ; and to make such notations thereon, and observations of every kind, as might be useful to navigation or commerce, or tend to the promotion of natural knowledge. I was also directed to observe the genius, temper, disposition, and number, of the inhabitants, if there were any, and endeavour, by all proper means, to cultivate a friendship and alliance with them ; making them presents of such things as they might value ; inviting them to traffic, and showing them every kind of civility and regard. I was to continue to employ myself on this service, and making discoveries either eastward or westward, as my situation might render most eligible ; keeping in as high a latitude as I could, and prosecuting my discoveries as near to the South Pole as possible. . . . But if Cape Circumcision should prove to be part of an island only, or if I should not be able to find the said Cape, I was in the first case, to make the necessary survey of the island, and then to stand on to the southward, so long as I judged there was a likelihood of falling in with the continent ; which I was also to do in the latter case ; and then proceed to the eastward in further search of the said continent, as well as to make discoveries of such islands as might be situated in that unexplored part of the southern hemisphere ; keeping in high latitudes, and prosecuting my discoveries as above mentioned, as near the Pole as possible, until I had circumnavigated the globe ; after which I was to proceed to the Cape of Good Hope, and from thence to Spithead.[1]

The two ships, the *Resolution* and the *Adventure*, left Plymouth on July 13, 1772, and reached Table Bay on October 30. After a month's stay they began their search for Bouvet's cape, but could find neither continent nor island. For six weeks Cook cruised about in the Southern Ocean, crossing the Antarctic Circle on January 17, 1773, in longitude 39° 35′ E., and reaching latitude 67° 15′ S. before he decided to make for New Zealand. A further search for the continent to the east of New Zealand was equally fruitless, and Cook then sailed to Tahiti and the Friendly Islands. A third search was next made to the south of New Zealand, where the ships reached their southern limit, in the ice, in latitude 71° 10′ S., longitude 106° 54′ W. Cook's conclusions are interesting. " I will not say," he wrote,

that it is impossible anywhere to get farther to the south ; but attempting it would have been a dangerous and rash enterprise ; and which, I believe, no man in my situation would have thought of. It was, indeed, *my* opinion, as well as the opinion of most on board, that this ice extended quite to the pole, or, perhaps, joined on some land, to which it had been fixed from the earliest time ; and that it is here, that is to the south of this parallel, where all the ice we find scattered up and down to the north is first formed, and

[1] *Voyages*, vol. iii, pp. 24-25.

afterwards broken off by gales of wind, or other causes, and brought to the north by the currents, which are always found to set in that direction in high latitudes. As we drew near this ice some penguins were heard but none seen ; and but few other birds, or any other thing, that could induce us to think any land was near. And yet I think there must be some to the south behind this ice ; but if there is, it can afford no better retreat for birds, or any other animals, than the ice itself, with which it must be wholly covered.[1]

Cook sailed back to Easter Island, trying on the voyage to find the land said to have been discovered by Juan Fernandez in latitude 38° S., but without success. He discovered the Hood and Palliser groups, and then returned again to Tahiti. A large number of islands were next visited, and the New Hebrides thoroughly explored, before Cook sailed for New Zealand, passing in his course New Caledonia, where he examined the north-east coast, and Norfolk Island. From New Zealand the ships sailed across the Pacific, and saw no land until they approached Tierra del Fuego. A fourth search for the southern continent had thus produced no result. Still sailing eastward, Cook rediscovered South Georgia, saw the South Sandwich group, and arrived very near to the region in which Bouvet's cape was supposed to lie. From this point he turned northward for home. " I had now," he wrote,

made the circuit of the Southern Ocean in a high latitude, and traversed it in such a manner as to leave not the least room for the possibility of there being a continent, unless near the pole, and out of the reach of navigation. By twice visiting the tropical sea, I had not only settled the situation of some old discoveries, but made there many new ones, and left, I conceive, very little more to be done even in that part. Thus I flatter myself that the intention of the voyage has, in every respect, been fully answered ; the southern hemisphere sufficiently explored, and a final end put to the searching after a southern continent, which has, at times, ingrossed the attention of some of the maritime powers for near two centuries past, and been a favourite theory among the geographers of all ages.

That there may be a continent, or large tract of land, near the Pole, I will not deny ; on the contrary, I am of the opinion there is ; and it is probable that we have seen a part of it. The excessive cold, the many islands and vast floats of ice, all tend to prove that there must be land to the south ; and for my persuasion that this southern land must lie, or extend, farthest to the north opposite to the Southern Atlantic and Indian oceans I have already assigned some reasons ; [2] to which I may add the greater degree of cold experienced by us in these seas, than in the Southern Pacific Ocean under the same parallels of latitude. . . .[3]

It doth not become me to say how far the principal objects of our voyage have been obtained. Though it hath not abounded with remarkable events, nor been diversified by sudden transitions of fortune ; though my relation of it has been more employed in tracing our course by sea than in recording our operations on shore ; it is,

[1] *Voyages*, vol. iii, p. 270.   [2] See above, pp. 166–167.
[3] *Voyages*, vol. iv, p. 219.

perhaps, a circumstance from which the curious reader may infer, that the purposes for which we were sent into the southern hemisphere were diligently and effectually pursued. Had we found out a continent there, we might have been better enabled to gratify curiosity ; but we hope our not having found it, after all our persevering searches, will leave less room for future speculation about unknown worlds remaining to be explored. But whatever may be the public judgement about other matters, it is with real satisfaction and without claiming any merit but that of attention to my duty, that I can conclude this account with an observation which facts enable me to make, that our having discovered the possibility of preserving health amongst a numerous ship's company, for such a length of time, in such varieties of climate, and amidst such continued hardships and fatigues, will make this voyage remarkable in the opinion of every benevolent person, when the disputes about a Southern Continent shall have ceased to engage the attention and to divide the judgement of philosophers.[1]

The above extract indicates clearly the main results of the second voyage of James Cook. In addition to the discovery of many new islands in the Pacific Ocean, and the preservation of the health of his crew, he had shown that the southern continent, as then conceived, did not exist, and he had further suggested the existence of the Antarctic continent, of which nineteenth-century explorers were to prove the reality.

Cook's third voyage had for its object the solution of the other great geographical problem about which there was much speculation. The early attempts to find a north-west passage had ended in failure, but in 1745 the British Government offered a reward of £20,000 to any ship belonging to his Majesty's subjects which should discover a passage from Hudson Bay. A number of expeditions tried in vain to earn the reward,[2] so that the application of the Act was extended to cover warships and to make the search possible in regions other than Hudson Bay. Thus it came about that Cook was directed to search for the passage from the Pacific side. The object of the voyage was also political, for Cook was to take possession of lands not already discovered by other Powers, and to examine carefully " some islands said to have been lately seen by the French, in the latitude of 48° South, and about the meridian of Mauritius." [3] His orders in detail throw light on the current beliefs of the location of the passage. " Upon your arrival on the coast of New Albion," they read,

you are to put into the first convenient port to recruit your wood and water, and procure refreshments, and then to proceed northward along the coast, as far as the latitude of 65°, or farther, if you are not obstructed by lands or ice ; taking care not to lose any time in exploring rivers or inlets, or upon any other account, until you get into the before-mentioned latitude of 65°. . . . When you get that

[1] *Voyages*, vol. iv., pp. 266–267.   [2] See Chapter XII.
[3] See above, p. 165.

length, you are very carefully to search for, and to explore, such rivers or inlets as may appear to be of a considerable extent, and pointing towards Hudson's or Baffin's Bays ; and if from your own observations, or from any information you may receive from the natives, . . . there shall appear to be a certainty, or even a probability, of a water passage into the afore-mentioned bays, or either of them, you are, in such case, to use your utmost endeavours to pass through. . . .

In case you shall be satisfied that there is no passage through to the above-mentioned bays, sufficient for the purposes of navigation, you are, at the proper season of the year, to repair to the port of St Peter and St Paul in Kamchatka, or wherever else you shall judge more proper, in order to refresh your people and pass the winter ; and, in the spring of the ensuing year 1778, to proceed from thence to the northward, as far as, in your prudence, you may think proper, in further search of a north-east or north-west passage, from the Pacific Ocean into the Atlantic Ocean, or the North Sea : and if, from your own observation, or any information you may receive, there shall appear to be a probability of such passage, you are to proceed as above directed : and, having discovered such passage, or failed in the attempt, make the best of your way back to England, by such route as you may think best for the improvement of geography and navigation.[1]

Cook sailed from Plymouth on July 11, 1776, and duly examined the recent discoveries of the French. In contrast with Kerguelen-Trémarec's report, he records that his men found the land which the Frenchman had discovered "barren and desolate in the highest degree," and the surgeon declared that "perhaps no place hitherto discovered in either hemisphere, under the same parallel of latitude, affords so scanty a field for the naturalist as this barren spot." New Zealand was reached in February 1777, whence Cook sailed for Tahiti, making one or two minor discoveries on the voyage. At the beginning of December the ships left the Society Islands, and about a month later rediscovered the Sandwich Islands, whose location Cook rightly thought was one of great importance in the Pacific. At length, in March 1778, the coast of North America was reached, in latitude 44° 33' N., and thereafter was sighted in a number of places, including one, named Cape Flattery (48° 15' N.), of which Cook says : " It is in this very latitude that geographers have placed the pretended strait of Juan de Fuca. We saw nothing like it ; nor is there the least probability that ever any such thing existed." From Nootka Sound, called by Cook King George's Sound, in latitude 49° 33' N., the ships were obliged by unfavourable weather conditions to keep off the land, and it was not until they had arrived in the region already visited by the Russians that they made contact with it again. Prince William Sound was examined in the hope that it might be a " passage," but the search was abandoned because it " promised so little success " ; a more thorough

---

[1] *Voyages*, vol. v, pp. 33–34.

investigation of Cook's 'river' was also fruitless. Cook concluded that " the continent of North America extended farther to the west than, from the modern most reputable charts, we had reason to expect." He adds, with some justification:

> This made the existence of a passage into Baffin's or Hudson's Bays less probable, or, at least, showed it to be of greater extent. It was a satisfaction to me, however, to reflect that, if I had not examined this very considerable inlet, it would have been assumed, by speculative fabricators of geography, as a fact that it communicated with the sea to the north, or with Baffin's or Hudson's Bay to the east; and been marked, perhaps, on future maps of the world, with greater precision, and more certain signs of reality, than the invisible, because imaginary, Straits of de Fuca, and de Fonte.[1]

Cook continued to explore the coast as far as Cape Prince of Wales, the most westerly point of the continent, and then devoted some time to an examination of Bering Strait and the sea to the northward. Icy Cape and East Cape, two names given by Cook, roughly mark the limits of his voyage before the necessity of finding winter quarters obliged him to return to the southward. On arriving again at the Sandwich Islands, Cook discovered Hawaii, not seen on his outward journey, and here he met his death at the hands of the natives. The voyage was continued the next year by Captain Clerke, who visited Kamchatka and reached the high latitude of 70° 33', but was unable to solve the problem of the North-west Passage.

During the whole voyage the two ships between them lost only five men, of whom three had been ill at the start. Though the main purpose of the expedition was not fulfilled, much valuable work had been done in the region which Cook had been ordered to examine. It marks a fitting end to the career of a man universally acknowledged to have been the greatest explorer of his age. Stern, strict, yet just, and honest, Cook subjected his own body to the discipline which he expected and exacted from those under him. Utterly fearless, cheerful under the most depressing circumstances, and constantly occupied with some kind of work, Cook enjoyed the respect and sometimes the veneration of the native races of the Pacific and the regard of his own men. On his death consternation overtook the crews : they were silent and depressed, feeling that they had lost a father ; and with him went " the spirit of discovery, the decision, and the indomitable courage." [2]

Despite the thoroughness and the extent of his investigations, Cook had by no means solved all the geographical problems of the Pacific Ocean. So great, however, was his reputation that his suc-

---

[1] *Voyages*, vol. vi, p. 364. The 'voyage' of de Fonte was said to have been made in 1640. See Appendix.

[2] See *Zimmermann's Account of the Third Voyage of Captain Cook*, translated by U. Tewsley (1926), pp. 41–43, for a good and unbiased account of Cook's character.

cessors have received comparatively little attention, if they have not been altogether neglected.

The French expedition under François Galaup de La Pérouse, dispatched at the close of the War of American Independence, did much to fill in the blanks left by Cook, but actually accomplished far less than its promoters intended. Four spheres of activity were marked out for its commander. In the Southern Ocean he was to clear up the uncertainties of Bouvet's cape and to complete Cook's investigation of the South Sandwich group and South Georgia. In the tropics he was to continue the exploration of the islands lying between the Society group, New Zealand, Australia, and New Guinea, and to examine the Gulf of Carpentaria. Along the coast of Asia La Pérouse was to carry out his examination from China to Kamchatka, paying particular attention to the unsolved problems connected with the island of Yezo. On the opposite side of the Pacific he was to explore carefully the coast of America, with a view to the discovery of a passage through the continent to the Atlantic.

Two ships left Brest on August 1, 1785, and after sailing round Cape Horn touched at the coast of Chile, Easter Island, and the Sandwich Islands before beginning work on the North American coast. La Pérouse reached the coast near to Mount St Elias, and, having a high regard for the work of Cook, decided to explore it to the southward, along that portion of the mainland which Cook had either not seen or not thoroughly examined. Accordingly, he began his voyage to Monterey, investigating the broad features of the coast, from which he concluded that it was fringed by an archipelago, since known as Queen Charlotte Islands. Although he covered much ground already known, and failed to observe all the details of the coast, his carefully executed work was a valuable supplement to that of the Russians, Spaniards, and English.

La Pérouse now crossed the Pacific to the north of the Sandwich Islands, and reached Macao, whence he sailed for the Philippines, from which, on April 9, 1787, he began his work on the coast of Asia. His course lay past Formosa, the Lu-chu Islands, Quelpart Island, through Korea Strait and the Sea of Japan, to the Gulf of Tartary, separating Sakhalin from the mainland of Manchuria. He sailed up this strait until he reached its narrowest part, and then, returning southward, rounded the southern point of the island, and thus proved its separation from Yezo. La Pérouse then made his way through the Kurile Islands to Kamchatka, whence he sent his report home across Siberia.

La Pérouse now proceeded southward, and, after visiting Navigators' Islands and the Friendly Islands, put in to Port Jackson in January 1788. After a month's stay he set out on his last voyage, the details of which are unknown, save that his ships were wrecked off the island of Vanikoro, in the Santa Cruz group, and all hands were lost, either murdered by the natives or drowned. According to information sent home by La Pérouse from Australia, he intended to carry out the instructions relating to the islands in the tropics and the Gulf of Carpentaria, but it is not possible to say how much he achieved. But if he did less than Cook, he followed the main lines of scientific exploration which the latter had laid down. His crews were attended to with care, his naturalists were employed, where possible, to add to the knowledge of the lands of the Pacific, and his surveys, incomplete though they were, accurately represented many important geographical features, and are a worthy monument to an able and industrious French explorer.

The interest aroused by these discoveries in the Pacific gave a great impetus to the fur-trade, and from the year 1785 onward numbers of merchant vessels visited Nootka Sound and the neighbouring regions. It was only natural that some of them, often accidentally, made geographical discoveries of much importance. Portlock, Dixon, Meares, and Barclay were among the men who thus contributed to the detailed knowledge of the American coast, and the last-named is credited with the discovery of Juan de Fuca Strait and the strait separating Vancouver Island from the mainland. The Spaniards were also active, and not only sent expeditions to examine the coast near Nootka Sound and the Strait of Juan de Fuca, but organized a very important voyage under Malaspina to find a north-west passage on the south-west coast of Alaska. Malaspina spent more than four years in this enterprise, and made valuable additions to knowledge, not only in the north, but also on both coasts of South America and in the Philippine Islands.

The reports of Meares led to a general belief that a north-west passage might after all be found through Juan de Fuca Strait, and the English set about the preparation of a new expedition. But by this time the fears of the Spaniards led to their seizure of the English post at Nootka Sound, and war almost broke out between the two countries. Pitt insisted on restoration and reparation, and this involved the dispatch of an expedition under Captain George Vancouver [1] to the American coast. Thus the voyage had a double object, to effect a final settlement of the Nootka Sound dispute and to investigate the truth of the theories put forward by Meares. Vancouver was specially ordered to examine the coast between the latitudes of 60° and 30° N. for the purpose of

> acquiring accurate information with respect to the nature and extent of any water-communication which may tend, in any considerable

---

[1] The authority for this voyage is Vancouver's own record in *A Voyage of Discovery to the North Pacific Ocean and round the World* (3 vols., 1798). See also G. Godwin, *Vancouver* (1930), which deals fully with the most important period of Vancouver's career and prints some useful documents, and L. R. Boone, *Captain George Vancouver and his Work on the North-west Coast* (1934).

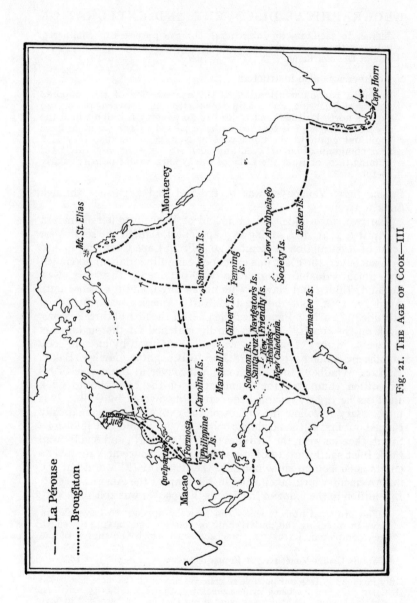

— La Pérouse
········ Broughton

Cape Horn

Monterey

Mt. St. Elias

Sandwich Is.

Easter Is.

Low Archipelago

Society Is.

Fanning Is.

Gilbert Is.

Marshall Is.

Kermadec Is.

Solomon Is.
Santa Cruz
Navigator's Is.
New Friendly Is.
Hebrides
New Caledonia.

Caroline Is.

Formosa

Philippine
Is.

Quelpart

Macao

Fig. 21. THE AGE OF COOK—III

degree, to facilitate an intercourse, for the purposes of commerce, between the north-west coast, and the country upon the opposite side of the continent.[1]

Vancouver was also instructed

to pay a particular attention to the examination of the supposed straits of Juan de Fuca, said to be situated between 48 and 49 degrees north latitude, and to lead to an opening through which the sloop *Washington* [2] is reputed to have passed in 1789, and to have come out again to the northward of Nootka. The discovery of a near communication between any such sea or strait, and any river running into, or from the Lake of the Woods, would be particularly useful.[3]

Failing here, Vancouver was to try and find a passage through Cook's 'river.'

The two ships under the command of Vancouver left Falmouth on April 1, 1791, and, sailing by Cape Town, sighted the south-west coast of Australia on September 26. From Cape Chatham, named by Vancouver, the coast was examined carefully for about 300 miles, and much valuable information was obtained. Tasmania, New Zealand, Tahiti, and Hawaii were next visited, and it was not until April 17, 1792, that the coast of North America was reached, in latitude 39° 20′ N. Vancouver then began the first of three seasons' work on the coast, " a survey hardly matched for thoroughness in the whole history of pioneer voyages." [4] Assisted by an able body of officers, among whom were Puget, Broughton, Mudge, Baker, Hanson, Whidbey, and Johnstone, Vancouver in the course of his expedition completed the examination of the coast up to Cook Inlet, as he rightly renamed the 'river' discovered by Cook. It is unnecessary to follow the details of the exploration systematically carried out first in the neighbourhood of Puget Sound and Johnstone Strait, then between the latitudes of 52° and 56° N., and finally from Cook Inlet southward to Chatham Strait. A glance at Vancouver's charts is enough to show not only the detail of the work, but the improvement which he effected in the map of the American coast. In addition to the fixing of the details, Vancouver was able to report:

The principal object which His Majesty appears to have had in view, in directing the undertaking of this voyage, having at length been completed, I trust the precision with which the survey of the

---

[1] Captain George Vancouver, *A Voyage of Discovery* . . . , vol. i, p. 18.
[2] Under the command of Robert Gray. Vancouver records, on meeting Gray in 1792 : " It is not possible to conceive anyone to be more astonished than Mr Gray, on his being made acquainted, that his authority had been quoted [by Meares], and the track pointed out that he had been said to have made in the sloop *Washington*. . . . He assured the officers that he had penetrated only 50 miles into the straits in question." (*Voyage of Discovery*, vol. i, p. 214.)
Gray subsequently rediscovered the mouth of the Columbia River.
[3] *Ibid.*, vol. i, p. 20.   [4] Heawood, *op. cit.*, p. 289.

coast of North-west America has been carried into effect, will remove every doubt, and set aside every opinion of a North-west Passage, or any water communication navigable for shipping, existing between the North Pacific and the interior of the American continent, within the limits of our researches.[1]

Vancouver returned to the Thames on October 20, 1795, and died in 1798. Brought up in the school of Cook, for whom he had a great respect, and living up to the best traditions of the British Navy, his work received comparatively little recognition, and he himself did nothing to gain notoriety. Hence the magnitude of his accomplishment passed almost unrecognized, and he has been all but forgotten. Yet his surveys have stood the test of time, and, like those of Cook, are not yet wholly superseded, and he must always remain one of the great figures in the history of the exploration of the Pacific.

Captain W. R. Broughton, who had sailed in one of Vancouver's ships, and had been sent home with dispatches in 1793, returned to the Pacific two years later, and in 1796 began an important series of surveys on the Asiatic side of the ocean. In the first year he followed the coast from Japan to the Southern Kuriles, discovering the strait to the south of Yezo (Tsugaru). In 1797 he sailed through the Sea of Japan, up the strait between Sakhalin and the mainland, and back along the coast of Asia to Quelpart Island. His voyage had not entirely cleared up the uncertainties which existed about this coast, but it had supplemented, in some important particulars, the work of La Pérouse.

Mention has already been made of the visit of La Pérouse to Port Jackson in January 1788. He was surprised to find there an English settlement, which had been established only a few weeks before his arrival. Its presence, however, had an important, if indirect, effect upon the progress of knowledge in the Pacific, and in particular in that part of the ocean where La Pérouse met his death. The discoveries thus made by ships returning from the first voyage to Australia with the settlers, or visiting Port Jackson subsequently, consisted mainly of islands hitherto unknown or of known islands whose position and outline was but imperfectly recorded. It was in this way that Captain Lever discovered Curtis and Macaulay Islands, in the Kermadec group. More important were the voyages of Captains Marshall and Gilbert, whose names are commemorated in the clusters of islands through which they sailed on an unusual course across the Pacific, and of Lieutenant Shortland, who did much work in the Solomon Islands, though he mistook some of the islands for a continuous land, to which he gave the name of New Georgia.

Among the other English voyages which close the work of the century may be mentioned that of Captain Hunter, whose surveys

[1] Vancouver, *op. cit.*, vol. iii, pp. 294–295.

on the coast of New South Wales continued those initiated by
Governor Phillip in 1788, and who also improved the knowledge of
the islands to the south of the Solomon group.   In the Low Archipelago Captain Edwards added a few islands to the map in 1792.
On the coast of Tasmania Lieutenant Bond surveyed a part of
D'Entrecasteaux Channel, while Captain John Hayes [1] visited and
mapped the same region in 1793.   In the same year Captain Mortlock
added a few islands to the Caroline group, and before the century
closed Fanning Island had been found and named after its discoverer, while the cruise of the *Duff* had greatly improved the
charting of a large number of islands from the Low Archipelago to
the Caroline Islands.

Meanwhile the French had dispatched an important expedition
under Bruni D'Entrecasteaux, with the object of finding the missing
ships of La Pérouse.   Two ships left Brest on September 28, 1791,
and in the course of their voyage across the Indian Ocean determined,
with close approximation to accuracy, the position of Amsterdam
Island.   They reached Tasmania on April 21, 1792, where some
surveys were carried out on the south-east coast, and sailed thence
to New Caledonia, the south-western coast of which was examined
in detail.   On their subsequent voyage to Amboina they visited
Bougainville Island, and passed through the strait between New
Britain and New Ireland.

Sailing again from the East Indies, D'Entrecasteaux took a course
round Australia, the south coast of which was charted as far as longitude 131° 30' E., when persistent easterly winds compelled him to
turn to the southward.   He thus again visited Tasmania before sailing for Tongatabu and the Friendly Islands.   From this group he
went to the northern portion of New Caledonia, Santa Cruz, and
the Solomon Islands.   Among these islands lying to the east of
New Guinea the French explorer did much useful work, and then
carried his surveys to the coast of New Guinea itself, entering the
bay named by him Huon Gulf, in honour of Huon de Kermadec,
commander of the second vessel, who had died at New Caledonia.
He next returned eastward, examining New Britain and greatly
improving the map of that island.   Shortly afterward D'Entrecasteaux died, and for all practical purposes the voyage came to
an end.   It had failed to find La Pérouse, but had done much to
fill in the details of that part of the ocean to which that commander had devoted the last part of his life.   Many of the charts,
particularly those of South Australia produced by Beautemps-
Beaupré, reached a high order of excellence, and in every way the
voyage marks a fitting conclusion to French enterprise in the South
Seas during the eighteenth century.

[1] Hayes followed very closely on the track of D'Entrecasteaux.   See Ida
Lee, *Commodore Sir John Hayes, his Voyage and Life* (1912).

TERRA AUSTRALIS AND THE PACIFIC OCEAN

The great work of exploration in the Pacific was now all but completed. In Australia there was still much to be done, for the interior of the country was almost entirely unknown, and even its coasts had not been fully explored. But its general outlines had been drawn with sufficient accuracy to make it clear that no new lands of any magnitude would be brought to light. Much the same might be said of New Guinea, where inland exploration had not yet begun. But the work of the future was essentially that of filling in the details ; the big discoveries in the ocean had come as a result of that continuous scientific exploration which had been so marked a feature of the last forty years of the eighteenth century.

CHAPTER X

ASIA, 1500–1800 [1]

I. SOUTHERN AND CENTRAL ASIA

THE opening up of Asia to Europeans came not as the result of the great land-journeys of men like Marco Polo, but in consequence of the discovery of the sea-route by the Portuguese. Yet the land connexion was not entirely lost, as the journeys made in the fifteenth century clearly prove. The sixteenth century opened with one of the most extensive journeys yet recorded, that of Ludovico di Varthema.[2] He was inspired by " the desire to behold the various kingdoms of the world which has urged on others," and determined, as he explains in the dedication of his book, " to ascertain the situations of places, the qualities of peoples, the diversities of animals, the varieties of the fruit-bearing and odoriferous trees of Egypt, Syria, Arabia Deserta and Felix, Persia, India, and Ethiopia." This formidable catalogue, however, fails to do justice to the extent of his travels. Toward the end of the year 1502 Varthema left Europe for Egypt, where he visited both Alexandria and Cairo. Thence he went to Beirut, Tripolis, Aleppo, and Damascus, where he joined an escort of a caravan bound for Medina and Mecca. He successfully accomplished the journey, and thus was the first European to visit the holy places. A more recent traveller in Arabia, Richard Burton, has paid tribute to the accuracy of his observations. Making his way to Jedda, Varthema embarked on a ship bound for Persia, and after touching at Jizan reached Aden, " the rendezvous for all ships which come from India Major and Minor, from Ethiopia, and from Persia." Here he was imprisoned, but managed to secure his release, and visited some of the interior parts of Arabia Felix, of which he has left an interesting account.

The port of Zeila, in North-east Africa, was next visited, and some information about the neighbouring country was obtained. The ship then sailed for India, taking Varthema first to Diu and after-

---

[1] There is no single work covering the whole of this period. Mr E. Heawood's *History of Geographical Discovery in the Seventeenth and Eighteenth Centuries* (1912) is invaluable. Other works dealing with particular journeys or areas are given in the footnotes below.

[2] See *The Travels of Ludovico di Varthema*, translated by J. W. Jones and edited by G. P. Badger (Hakluyt Society, first series, vol. xxxii). This work has recently (1929) been republished by the Argonaut Press, with an introduction by Sir Richard Temple. A popular account of Varthema's travels will be found in W. Boulting's *Four Pilgrims*.

178

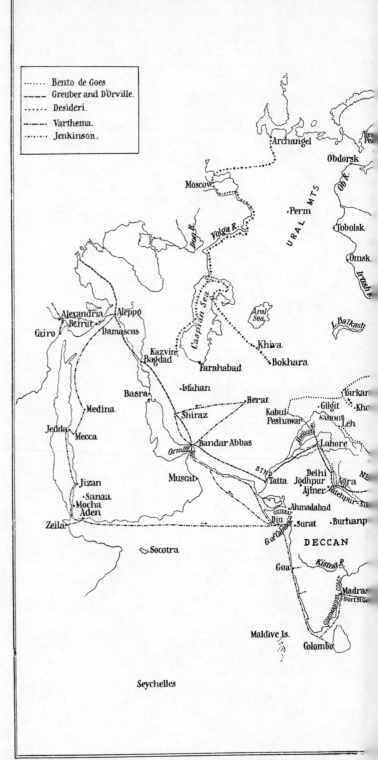

Fig. 22. ASIA, 1500–1800

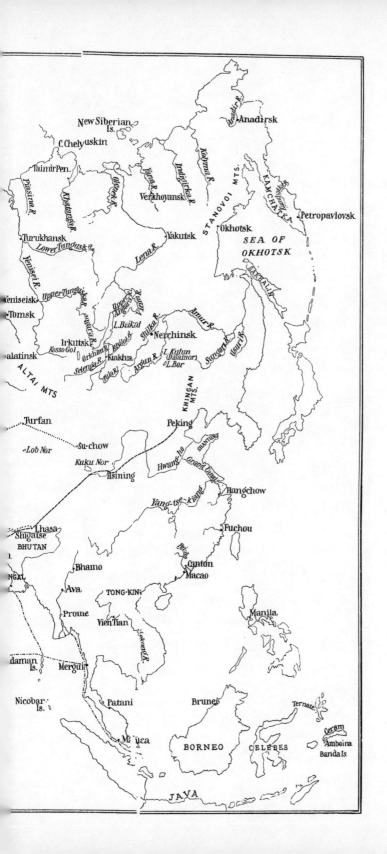

ward to Ormuz, whence the traveller made an excursion into Persia, reaching Herat, and returning to the coast by way of Shiraz. He went back to India, and spent some time on the west coast and in the Deccan. Subsequently he visited the Coromandel coast, Ceylon, and the East Indies, and then from India sailed home round the Cape of Good Hope. On this voyage a call was made at Mozambique, and perhaps at other islands of which Varthema has left an account.

The work of Ludovico di Varthema, first published in 1510, throws a valuable and interesting light on Asia, and in some respects anticipates the discoveries of the Portuguese. In Arabia and in the islands beyond Java Varthema was a real pioneer. He even heard of " some other races, who navigate by the said four or five stars opposite to ours " (*i.e.*, the Southern Cross), living to the South of Java, a reference which has been interpreted as indicating a report of Australia. At times, like all travellers, Varthema indulges in romance, and quite frequently shows great ignorance of the geography of places visited, but his book had a wide popularity, and remains a valuable record of one of the earliest adventurers of the great Age of Discovery.

While Varthema was thus travelling through Southern Asia Duarte Barbosa was collecting material for his *Book*, which was finished in 1516.[1] Barbosa was a Portuguese who went to India at the beginning of the sixteenth century. He acquired a good knowledge of the local languages, and travelled extensively in India and the adjacent seas. He went out by the Cape route, and has left a good account of a number of places on the east coast of Africa. Of Aden and Ormuz, both important trading-stations, he gives much interesting information. The western parts of India, from Gujerat to the southern extremity of the peninsula, are well and accurately described, but of the east coast he had less knowledge. He knew something of the islands as far as Sumatra, and may have visited Pegu, which he also describes ; of the countries of the Far East, however, Siam, China, and the islands beyond Sumatra, he had no personal knowledge, but relied on information obtained either from the newly arrived Portuguese explorers or from " trustworthy Moors and Heathen." Barbosa subsequently accompanied Magellan, who had married his sister, on his voyage to the Moluccas, and was killed a few days after the leader. As a descriptive writer Barbosa has a great value, especially because he has left an account of countries which had just come under the influence of the Portuguese.

This great area now thrown open to travellers of all kinds was visited by Mendez Pinto, who experienced many reversals of fortune between 1537 and 1558, when he finally returned to Spain. He

[1] See *The Book of Duarte Barbosa*, edited by M. L. Dames (2 vols., Hakluyt Society, second series, vols. xliv and xlix).

visited Abyssinia, Ormuz, India, Sumatra, China, Siam, Pegu, and Japan. Of the last three he left an account which was used by Purchas. His writing, however, is that of a mere adventurer, and its truthfulness has frequently been doubted, so that Astley called him 'Mendax' Pinto.

A further account of Pegu was given by Gasparo Balbi, who travelled overland by the caravan route, through Aleppo, Bagdad, and Ormuz, to India, in 1579, and reached Pegu in 1583. He spent over three years in the country, and was greatly impressed by the wealth of its king.

A Venetian merchant, Cæsar Frederick, claims to have "continually coasted and travelled, as it were, all the East Indies and many other countreys beyond the Indies" between 1563 and 1581. Like Balbi, he went by the overland route to India, where he visited the Portuguese trading-stations, and gathered some information about India and its inhabitants. Beyond India he describes Ceylon, Sumatra, the city of Malacca, "of marveilous great trade of all kind of merchandize," and the kingdom of Pegu, of which he has much of interest to relate. He also gives a list of the more important commodities which entered into the East Indian trade, and some useful advice both on the overland route and on the conduct expected of Europeans in the East.

The Venetians had long been interested in the Levant trade, and it was but natural that they should maintain that interest and extend it to the Far East: the Portuguese were obviously anxious to exploit their own particular discoveries to the full and preserve the monopoly of a new sea-route: but other nations, like the English, had only the alternatives of abstention from trade or the discovery of a new way to the East. They chose the latter, and tried, without success, to discover a north-east and a north-west passage. It was out of the search for the North-east Passage that the new route to the East evolved. Anthony Jenkinson, who had already spent a long time in the Levant, went to Russia in 1557, and from Moscow sailed down the Volga to the Caspian Sea, where he made a rough survey of the northern end. He then travelled eastward to Bokhara, where he arrived on December 23, 1558. Jenkinson spent three and a half months in the city, and returned to England through Russia. He went out again in 1561, and, following a route down the western shore of the Caspian Sea, reached Kazvin, the capital of Persia, in October 1562. His journeys did much to improve the knowledge of both Russia and the lands which lay beyond that country on the south-east. English trade by this route was, however, only partially successful, and came to an end in 1581.

The need for another route led to the journeys of Englishmen to the East by way of the Levant. Many others besides Jenkinson had traded in the lands round the Eastern Mediterranean, and among them John Newberry, who had reached Ormuz, and learned from Portuguese traders something of the route to India. In 1583 he and a number of others, including Ralph Fitch, sailed from London, and in due course reached Ormuz by way of Aleppo and Basra. Here the party were arrested and taken to Goa, where they secured their release and made their escape from the town. Three of them travelled across India to Fatehpur Sikri, where they separated, one remaining in the service of the Mogul emperor, a second setting out for home, and Fitch beginning a journey which took him to Bengal. Fitch subsequently visited Pegu and Malacca. He returned to India, missed a ship sailing for Europe, and, rather than delay, went to Ormuz, and by that route reached England in 1591.[1]

Fitch was not quite the first European of the new age to penetrate as far as Northern India, for he was anticipated by a Catholic priest, Pereira, in 1578, and by the first of the Jesuit missions to Akbar, in 1580. The Jesuits collected valuable information about the empire of Akbar,[2] and during their early relations with the Emperor were actuated solely by religious motives. They thus form yet another class in that miscellaneous collection of Europeans who opened up Asia during the sixteenth century.

As the sixteenth century drew to a close European visitors to the countries of Southern and Eastern Asia increased in number. The English arrived as competitors in 1592, to be followed, four years later, by the Dutch. Fortunately there remain two excellent accounts of the East just at that critical period when the control of its trade was passing from the Portuguese. First, both in time and importance, comes the work of Jan Huyghen van Linschoten, who sailed from Lisbon in 1583, and whose description of the voyage across the Atlantic has already been quoted.[3] Linschoten spent about five years in the East, and returned to give to his countrymen an excellent description of the lands that he had seen, and more particularly of the great trade of Goa and the other Portuguese factories of Southern India.[4]

A second account, differing in arrangement and in purpose, was that of Pedro Teixeira, who probably went out in 1587. He paid two visits to East Africa, visited Ceylon in 1588, and spent about four years at Ormuz, whence he travelled into Northern Persia. His next journey took him to Malacca, where he lived for two and a half years. In May 1600 he sailed for home, going first to Brunei,

---

[1] For Fitch see *Early Travels in India*, 1583-1619, edited by Sir William Foster (1921), pp. 1-47.
[2] See *Akbar and the Jesuits*, edited by C. H. Payne ("Broadway Travellers" series, 1926).
[3] See above, p. 68.
[4] See *The Voyage of John Huyghen van Linschoten to the East Indies*, edited by A. C. Burnell and P. A. Tiele (Hakluyt Society, first series, vols. lxx and lxxi).

then to Manila, and so across the Pacific Ocean to Mexico. Lisbon was reached in October 1601, but Teixeira was not content to remain, and went back by sea to Goa. He returned in 1604 by an overland route from Ormuz, through Basra, Bagdad, and Aleppo, to Italy, and then made his way across France to Antwerp, where he eventually died. Teixeira's *Travels*[1] relate almost solely to his last journey from India to Italy, but he also wrote two works on Persia, and he was an intelligent observer who might have written fully on the Portuguese empire. He knew the work of Linschoten, and this may explain some of his omissions.

Linschoten and Teixeira belong to the general class of travellers, whose object was very largely pure curiosity. There were many of them during the seventeenth and eighteenth centuries, and most add a little information that is worth preserving. Among the Frenchmen mention must be made of François Pyrard, of Laval, who sailed from Saint-Malo in 1601 and was wrecked on the Maldive Islands, where he remained until 1607. In 1608 he was at Goa, whence he made two voyages to the East, including Ceylon, Malacca, Ternate, and Banda, and to Diu. He gives a general account of many places in the Far East of which he had no personal knowledge, but his work is valuable for its picture of Goa, and for a long and accurate account of the Maldives. In particular he describes very well the atoll, which is a native term. Pyrard reached France again in 1611.[2]

Vincent Le Blanc was another early French traveller who spent a long period on his journeys, which included visits to Arabia, Pegu, Siam, and the East Indies. He is, however, but a poor narrator, and it has been suggested that some at least of his journeys were never made. More interesting are Jean Mocquet, whose account of Goa supplements that of Pyrard, and the Comte de Montfart, who made an overland journey to India in 1604.

A desire to travel took Pietro della Valle on an extensive tour of the East from 1614 to 1626. He first visited the countries of the Eastern Mediterranean and the Sinai peninsula, and then, using the well-known caravan-route, crossed from Aleppo to Bagdad. He visited Persia in 1616, knew the country well, and left a valuable description of it. He then went to India, arriving at Surat in 1623. Apart from one or two journeys into the interior, to towns like Ahmadabad, his travels were largely confined to the west coast ports. His return journey took him through Muscat, Basra, and Aleppo to Cyprus, Malta, and Sicily, and finally to Rome.[3]

[1] Edited by W. F. Sinclair (Hakluyt Society, second series, vol. ix).
[2] See *The Voyage of François Pyrard*, edited by A. Gray and H. C. Purvis (Hakluyt Society, first series, vols. lxxvi, lxxvii, and lxxx).
[3] See *The Travels of Pietro della Valle to India*, edited by E. Gray (Hakluyt Society, first series, vols. lxxxiv and lxxxv).

The last of the general travellers of the early period was Thomas Coryat, a man whose journeys were as extensive as his eccentricities were pronounced. After visiting a number of European countries Coryat went to the East in 1612, saw Egypt and Palestine, and then took the overland route from Aleppo to Persia and to India. He spent over fifteen months in the journey from Jerusalem to Agra, and later visited Ajmer and Surat. But, interesting as are his letters from India, they contain few valuable additions to knowledge. Coryat frequently quoted the classics, and still believed that the Indus river rose in the Caucasus Mountains.

A second class of traveller to the East, and more particularly to India, was composed of independent traders or the agents of the East India Company. Their number is large, and the information they give is both extensive and valuable. Though their chief concern was to promote trade, and their main anxiety was to follow closely the political events of India, their reports, often available only in manuscript, did much to improve the knowledge of India. John Mildenhall, a Levant merchant, reached India overland in 1603, and remained there for at least three years. He made a second journey about 1611, and died in India in 1614. William Hawkins, also a Levant merchant, went out in command of the East India Company's third expedition in 1607, but left the fleet at Surat and went to Agra, where he remained until 1611. Proceeding thence to Cambay, he joined a fleet bound for Sumatra, and subsequently returned with it, but died on the coast of Ireland in 1613. Much that Hawkins wrote is lost, but one of his works, a *Brief Discourse of the . . . Great Mogul*, gives a good picture of the Court of Jahangir.[1]

More valuable from a geographical point of view are the records of William Finch and John Jourdain, both of whom were in India during the residence of Hawkins at Agra. Of the first, Purchas declares that his work is " supplied in substance with more accurate observations of men, beasts, plants, cities, deserts, castles, buildings, regions, religions, than almost any other ; as also of waies, wares, warres." It was largely used by De Laet for his history of the Great Mogul. Finch landed at Surat in 1608, and remained there for two years, until Hawkins summoned him to Agra. He made several journeys from this latter place, the chief being to Lahore, whence he travelled overland to Bagdad, where he died. His accounts of certain routes, and especially those from Lahore to Kabul and to Kashmir and from Kabul to China, are of considerable value.[2]

John Jourdain was also living in India at this time. He went out with the fourth East Indian voyage in 1608, and by reason of

---

[1] See Foster, *op. cit.*, pp. 60–121.
[2] On Finch see Foster, *op. cit.*, pp. 122–187.

unfavourable winds touched at the Seychelles; he is the first Englishman to give any account of those islands. After calling at Socotra he went to Aden, "an uncomfortable cittie for within the walls there is not any greene thinge growinge, onely your delight must be in cragged rocks and decayed houses." A journey inland to Sanaa and back to the coast at Mocha gives Jourdain the title of the first Englishman to visit Yemen. India was reached in August 1609, and Jourdain remained at Surat until the end of December 1610, when he journeyed to Agra by way of Burhanpur. The return was made by a different route, through Jodhpur and Ahmadabad. Jourdain discovered the "Swally hole," a harbour near Surat afterward regularly used by the East India Company. In 1612 Jourdain went to Sumatra for the pepper trade, and afterward to Amboina and Ceram to buy cloves. To the latter island there came a Dutch ship in which "was an English sailer which had secreetlie brought a letter from Mr Adams . . . in which . . . there was a draught by him drawne of the countrye of Japan."[1] Jourdain went home to England, but returned again to the East Indies, where he was treacherously killed after surrendering to the Dutch. His *Journal*, only recently published,[2] is full of graphic details of the places which he visited.

Nicholas Withington,[3] who lived in various parts of India from 1612 to 1616, has left an account of his rather unfortunate career, which is, however, notable for a journey overland from Surat to Sind. The journey failed because the party were made prisoners, and some of them were killed, but Withington managed to get back safely. Of a more general character was the report of Sir Thomas Roe,[4] English Ambassador to the Mogul emperor. His work is well known for its valuable account of the Court and the general condition of India. He seems to have been indebted to Coryat for some of his information and for some details of the map of India which he assisted William Baffin to construct. Roe spent a period of three years at Court, and for part of the time had as his chaplain Edward Terry,[5] who also wrote about India, though he had seen very little of it.

One other Englishman in this early period deserves notice, though the account of his travels remained in manuscript until the present century. Peter Mundy spent about seven years (1628–34) in India as a servant of the East India Company. He covered the usual routes between Surat and Agra, both through Burhanpur and

[1] For Adams see above, p. 114.
[2] See *John Jourdain's Journal of a Voyage to the East Indies*, 1608–17, edited by Sir William Foster (Hakluyt Society, second series, vol. xvi).
[3] For Withington see Sir William Foster, *Early Travels in India*, pp. 188–233.
[4] For Roe see *The Embassy of Sir Thomas Roe*, edited by Sir William Foster (Hakluyt Society, second series, vols. i and ii).
[5] For Terry see Sir William Foster, *Early Travels in India*, pp. 288–332.

through Ajmer, and also visited Patna. His record is particularly notable for an account of the great famine of the year 1630.[1]

Of great interest and importance, as offering a different point of view; is the report of Francisco Pelsaert, who spent seven years (1620-27) in India and collected a great deal of information likely to be of use to the directors of the Dutch East India Company. Pelsaert visited Kashmir, and gathered some general facts about North-western India, but he knew little of the country at first hand. Such as he did know is described with great clarity, and for the purpose for which it was compiled his report is of the greatest value.[2] It appears to have been used in the work of De Laet, to which reference has already been made.

In the later years of the century two names deserve mention. Thomas Bowrey[3] landed at Fort St George in 1669, and remained in India for nineteen years. He collected information about Southern India, Bengal, Burma, and Sumatra, and drew a number of charts, including those of Ceylon and Tenasserim. William Hedges,[4] who belongs to the same period, left a *Diary* dealing largely with the affairs of the East India Company in Bengal.

As many of these travellers crossed overland to reach India or to return to Europe, they collected information about the countries through which they passed. Some, however, added to knowledge through being sent specifically to Persia. In the early years of the seventeenth century a number of Englishmen visited that country, and one of them, Thomas Herbert,[5] crossed it from Gombroon (Bandar Abbas) to Farahabad, on the Caspian Sea, returning through Kazvin. He collected much general information about Persia, and his book, based on a residence of over a year, was at once popular and authoritative. It was reissued, with many additions taken from later writers, several times during the century.

The embassy sent by the Duke of Holstein in 1633 included two men, J. A. de Mandelslo and A. Olearius, who made careful observations during their travels. The first collected information about the East in general, and the second wrote an account of Persia: both works were translated into English in 1662. A Russian embassy, which included in the party the Spaniard Cubero, also

[1] See *The Travels of Peter Mundy*, edited by Sir Richard Temple (Hakluyt Society, second series, vol. xxxv).
[2] See *Jahangir's India: The "Remonstrantie" of Francisco Pelsaert*, translated and edited by W. H. Moreland and P. Geyl (1925). Among the "various rarities" which the author recommended as likely to appeal to the leading men at Court were "one or two maps of the entire world."
[3] See *A Geographical Account of the Countries round the Bay of Bengal*, edited by Sir Richard Temple (Hakluyt Society, second series, vol. xii).
[4] See *The Diary of William Hedges*, edited by R. Barlow and Sir Henry Yule (Hakluyt Society, first series, vols. lxxiv, lxxv, and lxxviii).
[5] See *Thomas Herbert, Travels in Persia*, edited by Sir William Foster ("Broadway Travellers" series, 1928).

GEOGRAPHICAL DISCOVERY AND EXPLORATION

brought back information of countries far removed from Persia, since Cubero returned to Europe across the Pacific Ocean. There is also the Swedish embassy of 1683, which was accompanied by Kaempfer, a German naturalist. An interesting light is thrown on the importance with which Persia was regarded at this time by the fact that when the Ambassadors were at Isfahan they met representatives of Poland, Germany, France, Russia, Siam, and the Papacy, as well as messengers from Arabia and Central Asia. Kaempfer collected much information about Persia, and his work was rightly regarded as one of the most important on that country. He received considerable help from a Catholic priest who had lived at the Court for thirty years.

Kaempfer then joined the Dutch East India Company, and visited Ceylon, Sumatra, Java, and Siam before reaching Japan, where he lived for upward of two years. There he collected material for his *History of Japan*, which included a geographical description of the country based in part on the work of a Japanese geographer. Kaempfer returned to Europe in 1693, and died in 1716.[1]

During the second half of the seventeenth century a number of travellers visited parts of Southern and Eastern Asia. First among them was J. B. Tavernier. Of him Harris [2] declares:

He is more copious, and at the same time no less exact, than any of the authors who have attempted to point out the advantages derived from our commerce in the East, by which I mean in general the commerce of Europeans. We discover in his writings a greater compass of thought and a more masterly turn in his observations than in almost any other book of the kind, which is owing to his having considered these things over and over in consequence of the several voyages he made to the Indies.

His work is most valuable for its descriptions of routes and commodities of trade. It was based on the results of six journeys made between 1631 and 1668, in the course of which Tavernier visited Persia, India, and Java. He also described, from information which he collected, countries farther away, including Tong-king and Japan.

J. de Thévenot, like Tavernier, prepared for his Eastern travels by gaining a knowledge of European countries. In 1655 he made an extensive tour in the Eastern Mediterranean, which occupied him until 1659. Four years later he went overland to Persia, and spent five months at Isfahan. He subsequently lived for about a year in India. Though a good observer, more especially on the scientific side, Thévenot saw little more than the surface life of the lands through which he passed.

Another Frenchman, François Bernier, after visiting Syria,

[1] See E. Kaempfer, *The History of Japan* (Maclehose edition, 3 vols., 1906).
[2] *Navigantium atque Itinerantium Bibliotheca* (ed. 1764), vol. i, pp. 810–852.

186

Palestine, and Egypt, reached India about the end of 1658, and remained there until 1667, when he returned to France through Persia. There is much of very great interest in the account of Bernier's travels, particularly his descriptions of Agra and Delhi and his detailed account of Kashmir. Bernier also gives a brief summary of the geographical ideas of the Hindus. His work is characterized by thoroughness and clarity, and must always remain a valuable authority for the India of his time.

Yet another Frenchman, John Chardin, made two journeys to Persia and India between 1665 and 1677. He was a jeweller by profession, and travelled partly in the course of business. He settled in England in 1681, and a complete account of his travels appeared in 1711. His work is full, detailed, and accurate, and his account of Persia was highly regarded in England at the time of its publication.

The works of Tavernier, Bernier, and others are supplemented by the interesting letters of Dr John Fryer.[1] A surgeon in the service of the East India Company, he reached Madras in 1673, and later went by sea to Bombay, of which he has left a good description. He saw little of India, except for a short journey from Bombay up the Western Ghats, where he was much troubled by the difficulty of the road. He turned to England through Persia, where he spent the greater part of two years.

The countries lying between India and China [2] had been visited by many travellers from the time of Marco Polo onward, and some general information about them had been collected. This was supplemented by the traders of Portugal, Holland, and England who established posts in Burma and in Siam, and carried on a somewhat intermittent trade during the seventeenth century. In general, however, very little was known of the country apart from its coasts and its ports. A servant of the East India Company, Thomas Samuel, made a journey overland from Siam to Burma in 1618, and shortly afterward English traders were regularly found at Prome and Ava, and may even have reached Bhamo. The Dutch also established themselves in the interior during the early years of the century. It was not until the end of the eighteenth century, however, that any reliable information was obtained. In 1794 the mission of Captain Symes was dispatched to Ava. One of the party, Lieutenant Woods, made a survey of the Irrawaddy as far as Ava, while another member, Dr Buchanan, gathered much valuable information about the country. This expedition marks the beginning of the modern exploration of Burma.

---

[1] See *A New Account of East India and Persia*, edited by W. Crooke (Hakluyt Society, second series, vols. xix, xx, and xxxix).

[2] See Sir Hugh Clifford, *Further India* (1905), for the whole area, and J. Anderson, *English Intercourse with Siam in the Seventeenth Century* (1890).

In Siam the Dutch began their trade in 1602, but it was not particularly successful, and was subject to much fluctuation. The English too opened up commercial relations with Siam, through the port of Patani, in the Malay Peninsula, ten years later. But the greatest advance in knowledge was due to the Catholic missionaries from France, who reached Siam by crossing the isthmus of Tenasserim from Mergui in 1662. They were followed by ambassadors from Louis XIV, who took with them yet more priests. In one of these parties was M. de la Loubère, whose account of Siam, published in 1691, is one of the best of this early period.[1] Very little additional information was obtained during the eighteenth century.

In Indo-China the greatest advance was made by Dutch traders, who penetrated up the Mekong river to Vien Tian in 1641. This was a remarkable journey, but it was not repeated, and did not open up the country. Here also Catholic missionaries were active, but the geography of the country was so imperfectly known that D'Anville, on his map of Asia in 1755, marked a great desert extending from the Mekong river to the mountains of Annam.

Of China the Portuguese gained little real knowledge, and it is to the work of the missionaries that any advance was due. Dominicans entered the country in 1556, but had little success. They were followed by the Jesuits, who reached Macao in 1579. The Jesuits at once began to collect information about the country, and by 1601 had been so far successful in their general work that they were able to establish a mission at Peking. Its founder, Matteo Ricci, seems to have prepared a Chinese version of some European map, and to have used it successfully to further his religious ends.[2] Thus, with the spread of missionary activity with Peking as a centre, the Jesuits were able to gather much knowledge of the geography of China. The result was seen in Martini's *Novus Atlas Sinensis*, published in 1655.

In the same year two Dutch traders, Goyer and Keyser, acting on some information received a few years earlier from Martini, set out from Canton northward by the Pei river, crossed the divide to the Siang-kiang, and so reached the Yangtse-kiang. They then went up the Grand Canal to Peking. Eleven years later another trader, Hoorn, also reached Peking, travelling from Fuchow, on the coast, to Hang-chow by an inland route up the Min and down the Tsientang rivers. He then took the same route as the earlier

---

[1] E. Heawood, *Geographical Discovery in the Seventeenth and Eighteenth Centuries*, p. 68.

[2] On this map see J. F. Baddeley, " Father Matteo Ricci's Chinese World-maps, 1548–1608," in *G.J.*, vol. l, p. 254 ; E. Heawood, " The Relationships of the Ricci Maps," *loc. cit.*, p. 271 ; L. Giles, " Translations from the Chinese World Map of Father Ricci," in *G.J.*, vol. lii, p. 367, and vol. liii, p. 367. Reference should also be made to Professor W. E. Soothill's paper, " The Two Oldest Maps of China Extant," in *G.J.*, vol. lxix, p. 532.

traders to the capital. A third journey, by a Dominican, Navarette, was made from Macao to Peking through the provinces on the seaboard. Accounts of all these travellers were subsequently published, thus adding considerably to the knowledge gained by the missionaries. In 1676 there appeared Kircher's *China Illustrata*, which gave a good general account of China.

This same year was notable for the arrival in Peking of Nicolas Spafarik, who had crossed Manchuria, thus marking the beginning of that series of journeys which ultimately linked the knowledge of China to that of Russian Asia. It was followed by the dispatch of a Chinese embassy to the Russians, and with them went J. F. Gerbillon, a Jesuit priest. He crossed the arid country behind Peking, reached the Kerlun river about 80 miles above Lake Kulun, and arrived at Nerchinsk, on the Shilka river. The position of this place (latitude 51° 56′ N.) was determined with considerable accuracy. Gerbillon returned to China by much the same route, and subsequently travelled extensively in the valley of the Hwang-ho and on the north-west frontier. In 1698 he made a second journey to the north. From Peking he went to the north-east, into Manchuria and along the Khingan Mountains, which he crossed to Lake Bor. Thence he reached the Kerulen river, followed it to its northward bend, crossed over to the Tula river, and finally crossed a second divide to the Orkhon, where he met Russians and learned from them much about the geography of Southern Siberia. He made careful observations, and by his great journey linked up the Russian discoveries in the basin of the Amur and to the south of Lake Baikal with his own explorations in North China.

In China itself the Jesuits undertook the systematic survey of a large part of the country, extending their investigations to Manchuria in 1709, and finishing their work in 1715. Some additional details were obtained from the reports of missionaries and from Tibetans specially trained to collect information. The results are to be seen in the map of D'Anville published in 1735. The main features are remarkably accurate, and reflect the greatest credit on the Jesuits. On D'Anville's map the Hwang-ho is shown as following its old course to the south of the Shantung peninsula.

During this period a number of important journeys led to a much greater knowledge of Tibet and Central Asia.[1] The first was that of a ' lay ' Jesuit, Bento de Goes, who started from India with the object of ascertaining if China and Cathay were one and the same country. From Agra he went through Lahore and Peshawar to Kabul. He then crossed the Parwan Pass and the Pamirs to Yarkand, whence he reached Su-chow by way of the Turfan oasis. The journey took nearly five years, and Goes died before he reached

[1] See C. Wessels, S.J., *Early Jesuit Travellers in Central Asia* (1924), and Sir Thomas Holdich, *Tibet the Mysterious.*

China, but not before he had established communication with Ricci in Peking and had proved the identity of China and Cathay. " He was the first European of modern times to set foot on Chinese soil from the west and thus to assign to the country of legend and fable its true place on the map of the world." [1]

A second expedition went from India in 1624 to ascertain the truth of a report that Christians were living in Tibet. The journey was undertaken by Antonio de Andrade, who was "the first European to climb the [Himalaya], to discover one of the principal sources of the Ganges, and, starting from Hindostan, to penetrate into the unknown regions of Tibet." [2] From Delhi he went through Hardwar to Garhwal, and so to the sacred shrine of Badrinath at one of the sources of the Ganges. He crossed the Mana Pass and entered Tibet, reaching the town of Tsaparang, in the valley of the Upper Sutlej. He obtained permission to introduce Christian missionaries, and returned to Agra with much valuable information about Tibet. Andrade went back with other priests in 1625, and a regular mission was established in Tsaparang, which lasted for sixteen years.

From Tsaparang Francisco de Azevedo, in 1631, journeyed to Leh, and returned to India across the Rotang Pass, over which traders regularly travelled from Leh to Lahore. He thus opened up a vast area between the country discovered by Goes and that traversed by Andrade. A little earlier, in 1626, Stephen Cacella and John Cabral explored part of the Eastern Himalaya during their mission to Shigatse. They went out through Cooch Behar and Bhutan, and Cabral returned to India through Nepal. Both expeditions collected much geographical information about the Himalayas and Tibet, but some of it remained hidden among their reports until recent times.

Important as these journeys were, they are overshadowed by that of John Grueber and Albert D'Orville. Grueber was specially asked by Kircher, to whose *China Illustrata* reference has been made, to make notes on his journeys. He set out from Rome in 1656, and, contrary to the usual custom of the missionaries, went overland to Ormuz. After calling at Surat, where he spent ten months, Grueber reached Macao in July 1658, and shortly afterward went to Peking. He was then detailed to proceed to Rome, to transact certain business. The sea-route being then closed by the Dutch, and a route through Indo-China having been dismissed as impracticable, Grueber was directed to proceed through Tibet to India. He was accompanied by D'Orville, whose enthusiasm had earlier been roused by Martini's lectures on China.

The two men left China in April 1661, and in two months had reached the frontier at Hsining, beyond which the country was unknown. Their route lay by Kuku Nor, and thence in a general

[1] Wessels, *op. cit.*, p. 39.   [2] *Ibid.*, p. 43.

south-westerly direction to Lhasa, where they arrived on October 8. After a stay of about six weeks they continued their journey through Nepal to Agra, which was reached about the middle of March 1662. Grueber went on through Delhi and Lahore, down the Indus to Tatta, through Makran, Southern Persia, and Mesopotamia to Smyrna, and then to Rome, where he arrived in February 1664. Thus ended a remarkable journey, for, with the doubtful exception of Friar Odoric, Grueber was the first European to visit Lhasa. If his account of his travels contains but few descriptive passages it yet gives, with considerable accuracy, the position of a large number of places, and materially helped to improve the map of Asia.

Lhasa was reached, through Nepal, by two Capuchin missionaries in 1707, again by a Capuchin in 1709, and a fourth time, by Hippolyte Desideri, in 1716. This last visit was the outcome of a remarkable journey, undertaken with the object of re-establishing the mission of Tsaparang, which place was apparently confused with Lhasa. From Agra Desideri travelled through Lahore and over the Pir Panjal Pass to Srinagar, where he remained for six months. Thence he went on to Leh and along the high plain of Tibet, following in general the upper valleys of the Indus and the Brahmaputra. His journal is full of descriptions of great value and accuracy. From Lhasa his companion, Freyre, returned to India through Nepal; Desideri remained for a time in Lhasa, and later for nearly four years in a neighbouring province, until he too went back to India through Nepal in 1721. He compiled a geographical account of the country, full of accurate observations, which, however, remained in manuscript. For this, as well as for a remarkable journey, he deserves to rank high among the explorers : he has been called by Hedin " one of the most brilliant travellers who ever visited Tibet, and amongst the old ones, by far the most prominent and the most intelligent of all."

In 1724 a Dutchman, Samuel van de Putte, travelled through Persia to India, and thence through Lhasa to China. Unfortunately, he gave orders for his papers to be destroyed, so that his route cannot be traced. He was followed, in 1740, by Cassiano Belligati da Macerata, who reached Lhasa through Nepal. He has left an account of the missions in Tibet, as well as a detailed description of the people.

Under the guidance of Warren Hastings the English opened up diplomatic relations with Tibet in 1774, when George Bogle went to the country through Bhutan. He crossed the Brahmaputra to a place called Desheripge on the northern side, and there success-fully conducted his business, but he was unable to get permission for English merchants to pass through Bhutan. A number of missions followed during the period between 1775 and 1783, whereby the English knowledge of Bhutan and Tibet was greatly increased, but the departure of Warren Hastings put an end to expeditions of this kind, and no further progress was made during the remainder of the century.

In India itself a number of journeys by officers engaged on military or diplomatic missions paved the way for the first real survey of the country. The work of James Rennell [1] between 1763 and 1782 was in this respect of great importance. For part of the period he was engaged on the survey of Bengal, and, after 1773, in the preparation of the *Bengal Atlas*, which was first published in 1779. Colonel Call made a route survey in Southern India, while Colonel Pearce fixed the positions of a number of places between Calcutta and Madras. This and much other material was used in the preparation of Call's map, in 1787, but the map apparently has been lost. The next year, however, saw the publication of Rennell's *Memoir of a Map of Hindoostan*, which was accompanied by a map recognized to be the best available at the time. It was reissued several times, with additional information resulting from further route surveys, and remained the standard map of India until it was replaced by the productions of the Survey of India, begun under Lambton in 1800.

One other piece of exploration completes the work in Southern Asia during the eighteenth century. It too was a scientific expedition, undertaken by Carsten Niebuhr to Arabia. Niebuhr was the sole survivor of a party of five sent out by Frederick V of Denmark in 1761 with the double object, " to explore the most fertile part of Arabia known to Europe, and to collect there the best possible information about all the rest of the peninsula. Both tasks were carried out in a way which, when all circumstances are considered, is beyond criticism." [2] Niebuhr's *Description of Arabia* was a work of the highest value, and has probably never been surpassed as a description of Yemen.

II. Northern Asia

While the nations of Western Europe were filling in the details of the map of Southern and South-eastern Asia the Russians had crossed the continent and had planted themselves on the Pacific coast. At the end of the sixteenth century they had tightened their hold on the country immediately to the east of the Urals, and had gained a rough knowledge of its major features as far as the river Ob. The foundation of Tobolsk in 1587 marks at once the completion of the first stage of the military conquest of Siberia and

[1] See Sir Clements Markham, *Major James Rennell and the Rise of Modern English Geography* (1895).
[2] D. G. Hogarth, *The Penetration of Arabia*, p. 52.

the beginning of a continuous and successful penetration of that country by freebooters and fur-traders.

During the seventeenth century the advance across Siberia was made with astounding rapidity. Its success was in part due to the facilities offered by the river system of Northern Asia, but this fact must not be unduly stressed, and when allowance has been made for all of the natural advantages there stands to the credit of a host of unknown men an achievement which is a striking tribute to their courage and enterprise, and which was never equalled by any other European nation.

The river Ob was followed, and the town of Tomsk was founded in 1604. Six years later traders had reached the Yenisei, and by 1612 the Piasina was known. Finding it impossible to advance by sea from the Yenisei, the traders followed the Lower Tunguska to the Lena basin. Farther south the Upper Yenisei river formed a route which led to the Angara river, Lake Baikal, and the Lena basin. Thus the Lena had been reached in its upper and central regions: the founding of Yeniseisk in 1619 and of Yakutsk in 1632 was the natural sequence to this farther thrust to the eastward.

On the north coast the Lena delta was reached in 1617, and the Olenek river was discovered in the same year. In 1618 the coast was followed from the Lena to the Yana, and the latter was explored for some distance from its mouth.

From the centre of Yakutsk the Russian traders and soldiers pushed in all directions. By 1638 they had crossed the mountains to the east, and had reached the Sea of Okhotsk. In the north-east both the Indigirka and the Kolyma rivers had been discovered by 1644, and some portion of the northern coast eastward of the first river had been explored. In 1646 the Chukchees were first visited, and in the following year Deshnev accompanied a large but unsuccessful expedition to their country. In 1648 Deshnev sailed from the Kolyma river round the eastern extremity of Asia,[1] and although his ship was subsequently wrecked, he made his way overland to the site of the modern Anadirsk, which in turn became the centre of further exploration.

To the south-east the Russians pushed into the basin of the Amur[2] of which they first heard in 1636. Three years later they began their advance in the Vitim valley, east of Lake Baikal, and in 1643 undertook a more systematic exploration of the Amur. Although the expedition was badly organized, and committed unpardonable excesses, a party under Poyarkov succeeded in passing from the Aldan river to one of the tributaries of the Amur, and then followed

---

[1] This voyage of Deshnev is disputed. For the arguments against it see F. A. Golder, " Some Reasons for doubting Deshnev's Voyage," in *G.J.*, vol. xxxvi, p. 81.

[2] See E. G. Ravenstein, *The Russians on the Amur* (1861).

the latter to its mouth. In June 1646 Poyarkov was back again at Yakutsk. Others followed up the new discovery, and in 1649 a better route, by the Olekma river, was opened up by Khabarov.

Owing to the opposition both of the natives and of the Manchus, Khabarov had not been able to accomplish all he had intended. A further move was therefore prepared, but this time the Russian Government determined to act officially rather than trust to the vigorous brutality of adventurers. Between 1652 and 1658 parties under Stepanov and others were active in the Amur basin, and a number of Russian posts were established, but the increasing resistance of the Chinese compelled the Russians to withdraw in 1658.

Meanwhile, in 1652, an expedition from the Yenisei crossed Lake Baikal, and ascended the Selenga river and the Khilok to the divide between it and the Shilka. Two years later the Shilka was reached and followed to its mouth, thus opening up another route to the Amur river. A number of further expeditions were made in this region during the next twenty-five years, thereby giving the Russians increased knowledge of, and power over, the centre and north of the Amur basin.

The troubles with the Manchus, already mentioned, led to the dispatch of an envoy to Peking in 1653, but he was murdered before arriving at that city. In 1676, however, a Greek named Spafarik crossed Manchuria to Peking, but failed to effect permanent reconciliation between the Chinese and the Russians, who were forced to withdraw from the eastern part of the Amur basin. Another ambassador, a Dane named Ides, crossed Manchuria to Peking in 1692, and the account of his journey, subsequently translated into English, did much to improve the general knowledge of this part of the world and to give publicity to the Russian achievements. It was seized upon by Defoe, and used as the basis of some of the adventures recorded in the second part of *Robinson Crusoe*.

In the far north, at the end of the century, an expedition from Anadirsk pushed southward to the Kamchatka river, and the subjugation of the country followed. Early in the next century the most southerly point of the Kamchatka Peninsula was reached, and the Kurile Islands were sighted.

Thus at the end of a century of exploration the Russians had discovered most of the main geographical features of Northern Asia. They had, in 1696, made contact with the Jesuits in China, and had penetrated into the little-known north-east in the same year. It was a remarkable achievement, and if it was not strictly scientific, it at least compares favourably in extent and in accuracy with the work done by the French in North America during the same period.

During the first half of the eighteenth century the main problems of the geography of the north coast were solved. It was already known eastward from the Lena delta, but westward from that point to Novaya Zemlya it was unexplored. In 1701 some islands were reported to lie northward of the Yana river, but subsequent search failed to discover them, and doubts were cast on the original story. In 1734, however, exploration of the coast was undertaken systematically. One party began from Archangel and worked eastward. Their progress was not continuous, but in spite of difficulties and repeated failures the work went on, until by 1740 the Russians had reached the west coast of Taimir Peninsula. A second party set out from the Lena river in 1735, and, working westward, reached the Taimir Peninsula by 1740, but could make no headway in boats. The survey was therefore continued as far as the Yenisei by land, and in 1742 Chelyuskin reached the most northerly cape of Asia.

Eastward from the Lena a few journeys helped to improve the knowledge of the region. By sea the Russians had reached the Kolyma river by 1742, and one explorer had gone overland from that river to the Anadir. This latter region had been penetrated earlier in the century by a land expedition from Yakutsk.

In Siberia the Prussian naturalist Messerschmidt and the Swedes Tabbert and Renat undertook valuable explorations between 1720 and 1738. The first named explored parts of the Ob and Yenisei in 1721, and again in 1725 descended the Yenisei almost to its mouth, and penetrated as far eastward as the Dalai Nor, west of the Khingan Mountains. He was accompanied by Tabbert on his first visit to the Ob and Yenisei rivers. Renat travelled extensively in Central Asia between 1716 and 1733, perhaps reaching Lob Nor. He collected much information, and was able to map the region in a way never yet approached for general accuracy.[1]

In 1733 there began a series of journeys, assisted by the Russian Academy of Sciences, of which those of Bering, Chirikov, and Spangberg have already been considered.[2] They were all part of a large scheme to explore the unknown parts of Asia and the North Pacific. The naval officers were joined by members of the Academy. De la Croyère, an astronomer, visited Lake Baikal and the Upper Amur basin. The naturalist Gmelin and the historian Müller also explored the country east of Lake Baikal, while all three visited parts of the Lena basin. The aims of these men were purely scientific, and their journeys supplied, for the first time, " a basis for the mapping of Siberia in its broad outlines." [3] Their work was to some extent continued by Steller, whose researches have already been mentioned.

[1] See E. Heawood, *Geographical Discovery*, p. 375, for a reproduction of Renat's map.
[2] See Chapter IX. [3] Heawood, *op. cit.*, p. 202.

GEOGRAPHICAL DISCOVERY AND EXPLORATION

Scientific exploration in Russian Asia was resumed under the patronage of Catherine II, and a number of experts were sent out to examine the less-known parts of the Russian Empire. Between 1768 and 1774 P. S. Pallas covered a large piece of country between Southern Russia and the Upper Amur basin. In particular he examined the regions lying to the north of the Caspian Sea and the Ural and the Altai Mountains, and "made valuable observations in regard to the origin of mountain ranges."[1] In the same period S. G. Gmelin travelled extensively in the steppe region on both sides of the Caspian Sea and in Northern Persia.[2] After escaping several times from prison Gmelin died in confinement in the Caucasus. In this latter region J. A. Guldenstaedt carried out extensive explorations between 1769 and 1773. A fourth member of this illustrious band, J. P. Falk, examined parts of the Ob and Irtish basins in 1771 and the following year. The work of these men resulted in very little new discovery, although it was of great value in completing the detailed geography of some regions. It is to be compared with the scientific expeditions of Bering rather than with the pioneer journeys to which was due the opening up of Siberia.

[1] Heawood, *op. cit.*, p. 376.
[2] Earlier attempts to explore the steppe country and penetrate to Bokhara had been made between 1714 and 1717, but were ended by the annihilation of the Russian party by the Khan of Khiva.

CHAPTER XI

AFRICA, 1500–1788 [1]

THE exploration of Africa on a large scale begins in the year 1788, when the African Association was founded. Up to that date there was no progressive work carried out in the continent as a whole, and even in those areas where some advance was made it was comparatively small and unimportant. Various reasons account for this delay in the opening up of the continent. The great desert region on the north effectively shut off the Mediterranean nations from the interior, and the one route open to them, through Egypt, was partially closed by the Turks. The flat, unhealthy coastlands elsewhere took a heavy toll of European lives, and the lack of good rivers, navigable upward from the sea, made penetration of the inland districts almost impossible except on foot. To these geographical causes must be added some historical accidents. Africa lay on the route to the East. It was therefore in general an obstacle to be avoided if possible, and to be visited only when and where the difficulties of the sea-passage made such a course necessary. By comparison with the East and with the New World its economic resources, with the single exception of its 'black ivory,' were small and unattractive, and it offered no large field for trade, while in many parts fanatical Muslims made life impossible for Christians. Thus Africa was almost entirely neglected until some great geographical problem, like the question of the river Niger, or some human scandal, like the slave-trade, roused the nations of Europe.

During the period now under consideration exploration was carried out in five main areas. In Abyssinia, where Venetians had for some time possessed trading privileges; on the west coast; in the Congo valley; in South Africa; and in the Zambezi valley, where a little progress was made. In the first of these areas the embassy of Covilham resulted in a considerable extension of the knowledge of the Portuguese. Yet Venetians seem to have been well acquainted with the country many years earlier, and the map of Mauro, dating from the last years of the life of Henry the Navigator, marks the features of Abyssinia with surprising accuracy. This knowledge was, however, derived largely from native sources—that

---

[1] E. Heawood's *History of Geographical Discovery in the Seventeenth and Eighteenth Centuries* covers part of this period. Other works are given in the footnotes below.

is, from an Abyssinian visitor to Italy. It is none the less true that the Italians, as might almost be expected, had a better idea of the nature of North-east Africa than had the Portuguese.

Covilham's expedition of 1487 was followed by others sent from Portugal. Once established in the Indian Ocean, the Portuguese found it necessary to protect the trade-routes, and a friendly Abyssinia might help them to defeat the Turks. To the political and military expeditions of the sixteenth century were added those of the missionaries, whose activities began in 1557. It was one of these men, Pedro Paez, who, after an adventurous career, returned to Abyssinia in 1603, and ten years later visited the sources of the Blue Nile, at the same time discovering the correct reason for the Nile floods.

Another missionary, Antonio Fernandez, reached Fremona in 1604, and nine years later made an extensive journey into the Galla country, in order to try to open up a new route to Portugal, free from Turkish interference at Massaua.

A third Jesuit, Jerome Lobo, attempted to discover a way of reaching Abyssinia from Malindi. In the course of his journey he examined the east coast of Africa from the island of Pate to the Juba river, but the attempt to discover the new route failed, and he returned to India. He then went back to the Red Sea, crossed the Danakil country to Fremona, and from this centre visited many parts of Abyssinia, including Damot. These Jesuit missionaries gained much accurate knowlege of the country, as may be seen from the map of 1683 constructed by J. Ludolf.[1]

Abyssinia was reached from Egypt in 1699, when a party of missionaries, accompanied by Dr C. Poncet, made the journey from Cairo through Dongola and Sennar and across the Blue Nile to Gondar. Poncet wrote a good description of the outward journey, but his account of his stay in Abyssinia has been received with some suspicion. He returned to Europe by way of Massaua. A similar journey, along a slightly different route, was accomplished by another missionary, Theodore Krump, in 1700, by which year Abyssinia was better known than any other large area in Africa.

The expedition of James Bruce to the Blue Nile in 1768 drew the attention of Europe to these earlier exploits. From Egypt he reached the Red Sea at Kosseir, whence he sailed to Massaua, making a long *détour* to the north of that sea and calling at several ports on the Arabian coast, as far as the Straits of Bab-el-Mandeb. He then went inland from Massaua to Gondar, whence he reached the sources of the Blue Nile. His return was made through Egypt, across the Nubian Desert. Bruce made few real discoveries, and hardly gave due credit to the work of the Jesuits. He did some-

[1] For a reproduction of the map see Heawood, *op. cit.*, p. 147.

thing, however, to rouse interest in African exploration, and his lengthy narrative is a faithful record of a well-executed scientific expedition.

European contact with the west coast of Africa dates back to

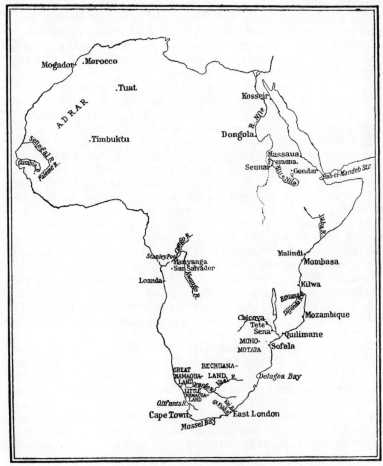

Fig. 23. AFRICA, 1500-1788

the Middle Ages, if one neglects the Carthaginian voyages, but no exploration of the country behind the coast was made until the time of Henry the Navigator. It is true that Genoese from the thirteenth century and Venetians from the century following had been interested in North African trade, and from them, as well as from Jews and Arabs, some knowledge of the interior filtered through

GEOGRAPHICAL DISCOVERY AND EXPLORATION

to Europe.[1] In 1447 a merchant named Malfante made a journey
to Tuat, a great centre for West African trade, and from a relative
of a leading trader in Timbuktu learned much of that city and the
Niger country generally.[2] A Florentine, who had travelled extensively in the Levant, seems to have reached Timbuktu from the
north about 1469, while the Portuguese, who had by this time
discovered the whole of the West African coast, opened up a trading-
station in Adrar ; from here they penetrated to Timbuktu in 1487,
and, farther south, were drawn into the interior of Benin once the
pepper trade assumed large dimensions.

In the sixteenth century the progress of commerce led to an
increasing knowledge of the coasts of West Africa, and other nations
appeared on the scene to share in the new riches thus disclosed ;
their contributions to geography, however, were very small.

The outstanding event of the century was the publication of the
Description of Africa, by Leo Africanus, who had travelled over the
greater part of Western Africa. His work is full of descriptive
passages of much value ; it was translated into most European
languages ; and it remained a great authority on the region down
to the beginning of modern exploration.[3]

In the seventeenth century the opening up of the interior proceeded very slowly. In 1618 a Frenchman, Paul Imbert, was
carried off from Morocco to Timbuktu, and subsequently described
his adventures as of great hardship and great importance. In
the same year the Englishman Thompson penetrated far up the
Gambia river, reaching, in 1619, a point about 400 miles from
the mouth. He was followed, in 1620, by Jobson, who was able in
part to fulfil his object of gaining some information about the trade
of Timbuktu.

While the Gambia remained the avenue of the English, the
French made use of the Senegal river. In 1637 an expedition had
ascended it for a considerable distance. Sixty years later André
Brue made two journeys up the river, and obtained information of
the gold region of Bambuk, in the Upper Senegal country, where
a French post was established near to the mouth of the Faleme river.
A further post on the Faleme itself was set up in 1715, and in the
following year Compagnon explored some of the country between
the Faleme and the Senegal above this point. The progress of the
French up to this date may be gauged from the accounts of Africa
given by J. B. Labat in his *Nouvelle relation de l'Afrique occidentale*,
published in 1728.

[1] See especially C. de la Roncière, *La Découverte de l'Afrique au moyen age*
(3 vols., 1924–27).
[2] " Sa relation du voyage est presque aussi détaillée sur les régions voisines
de Tombouctou que sur l'oasis du Touat " (Roncière, *op. cit.*, vol. i, p. 148).
[3] See *The History and Description of Africa . . .*, edited by R. Brown
(Hakluyt Society, first series, vols. xcii–xciv).

The English also had made some advance on the west coast. In 1723 Stibbs ascended the Gambia as far as the Barrakonda Falls. He concluded that the source of the river was not far off, and that it had no connexion with the Niger. Three years later Captain Smith made a survey of the river, while Captain Leach also compiled a good map in 1732. An account of the country was given in 1738 by Francis Moore, a servant of the Royal African Company, but there was little real knowledge of any part of West Africa outside these river valleys. West Africa had to wait for its exploration until the great journeys at the end of the century, undertaken to solve the problem of the Niger river.

In the Congo [1] region the Portuguese were active almost from the first discovery of the river by Diego Cam. Here, as in Abyssinia, Catholic priests took the lead, and in 1490 an expedition to the region reached the town later known as San Salvador, nearly 200 miles inland. The King and many of his people adopted the new religion, and the Christians rapidly gained a rough knowledge of the country, until their work was interrupted by the invasion of cannibals, called ' Jaggas,' in 1570. The invaders were defeated, but the Portuguese did not recover the ground lost until the seventeenth century. Grand projects, among them a journey from the Congo to Abyssinia, were planned, but came to nothing, and the general account of the country written by Lopez about 1578, while containing much accurate information, is full of exaggerated ideas which were clearly the result of little knowledge.

Meanwhile in Angola the Portuguese had made progress. They first visited the country in 1559, and fifteen years later made a settlement on the coast near Loanda. By the end of the century they were firmly established, and were pushing outward to Benguela. The transference of the bishop's seat from San Salvador to Loanda in the early years of the seventeenth century gave added importance to Angola, and in 1606 an attempt was made to open up a route to the Zambezi.

Before passing to the progress made in the seventeenth century reference must be made to the adventures of the Englishman Andrew Battell, who was shipwrecked off Brazil about the year 1589 and was carried by the Portuguese, as a prisoner, to Africa. He spent a number of years off the coast of Angola before he was given as a hostage to the savage ' Jaggas,' in whose company he travelled through parts of Southern Angola. He eventually got back to England, and was able to give some account of the region,

[1] See *The Strange Adventures of Andrew Battell of Leigh*, edited by E. G. Ravenstein (Hakluyt Society, second series, vol. vi). The volume contains, besides the account of Battell, a history of the Congo and Angola districts to the end of the seventeenth century and two very useful maps indicating the extent of exploration.

though, as might be expected, his journeys had little scientific value.

The extension of geographical knowledge in this region during the seventeenth century was due to the missionary activities of Capuchins, who first arrived in 1645, and seem to have penetrated as far as Manyanga, near the Falls of the Congo. In 1651 another expedition probably reached the country north of Stanley Pool, and although it is not possible to trace the routes of the priests with great accuracy, it seems likely that much ground was covered both to the north and to the east. The river Kwango was apparently discovered,[1] and many details between it and the coast were known when Dapper wrote his description of Africa in 1686. Practically no further advance was made in this region until the nineteenth century.

On the east coast of the continent the Portuguese also made considerable progress. Here their policy was directly affected, in the early years of exploitation, by the necessity of protecting the sea-route to India, and thus was related to the similar progress made in Abyssinia. By 1507 Kilwa and Mombasa, and the coast to the northward of the latter, were in Portuguese hands, as well as Sofala and Mozambique. This last became, in 1558, the chief African port, through which all coastal traffic was obliged to pass.

Along the coast the Portuguese naturally had trading relations with the natives, but they do not appear to have penetrated inland except by the Zambezi route. They tried first to establish a post on the river in 1513, and by 1531 had reached Sena. Within a few years they had established posts at Tete, far up the river, and at Quilimane on the coast, and by the middle of the century they had gained a large amount of knowledge about the Zambezi. The great incentive to penetration was the gold trade with the kingdom of Monomotapa, for which Tete was admirably situated. To the efforts of the traders were added those of Dominican missionaries, who arrived in 1577.

In the early years of the seventeenth century the Portuguese began the conquest of this native kingdom, and in 1616 Gaspar Bocarro made a journey from Chicova, on the Zambezi above Tete, to the coast at Kilwa, passing the southern end of Lake Nyasa and the rivers Lujenda and Rovuma. Six years later a plan was made to open up communication with Abyssinia by this newly discovered lake, but it came to nothing, and the Portuguese contented themselves with the extension of their influence inland by means of a system of overlordship which gave them control of the greater part of the country lying behind Sofala and extending up to the

---

[1] It was reached by a Dutchman, Jan van Herder, about the year 1660.

Zambezi.[1] No further progress in geographical. discovery was made until the expedition of Lacerda in 1798, but this belongs rather to the period of scientific exploration than to the age of the pioneers.[2]

In South Africa real exploration did not begin until the end of the seventeenth century. Table Bay was known to the Portuguese, and later became a port of call for English and Dutch traders to the East Indies, but no permanent settlement was made there until the Dutch occupied the site of Cape Town in 1652. Vague reports of a wealthy country to the north, and stories of the kingdom of Monomotapa, drew the Dutch northward. In 1660 an expedition in search of Monomotapa's kingdom penetrated a little beyond the Olifants river, and during the next two years further progress brought the Dutch into contact with the Bushmen. In 1668 Mossel Bay was reached, and in 1685 a party under Simon van der Stell discovered the district of Little Namaqualand, where copper was found. All these journeys were made in the immediate neighbourhood of the Cape peninsula : of South Africa as a whole little was known during the seventeenth century.

The next stage in exploration is marked by an expedition to Natal in 1705 and a second to Delagoa Bay in 1720. In both cases the Dutch went by sea to explore regions which seemed to offer better prospects for settlement. In 1736, however, a land expedition was made to the east, when the Dutch came in contact with the Bantu peoples of South Africa. Some of the party, including the leader Hübner, were killed by the natives, and though a few returned to Cape Town they had been unable to collect much geographical information. This defect was remedied by the expedition of Beutler in 1752, which followed, in general, the south coast, and penetrated for a short distance beyond the Kai river, to the northeast of the modern town of East London. A considerable area of the inland country was explored on the return journey.

The Orange River was first crossed in 1760, and in the following year a party penetrated far beyond the river into Great Namaqualand, thus opening up much of the country to the north of the Cape peninsula. Six years later R. J. Gordon reached the Orange River, near its junction with the Vaal, and in 1778 it was crossed in its lower course by W. Paterson. These two men accomplished much valuable geographical work in a number of journeys into the interior of the country. At the end of 1778 Paterson set out on an expedition to the east, and reached the Kafir country, beyond

[1] Efforts have been made to prove that the Portuguese had an extensive knowledge of Central Africa. The arguments, based largely on early maps, are not entirely convincing. See Sir H. H. Johnston in *G.J.*, vol. xlvii, p. 210, and E. Heawood, *ibid.*, p. 304. Defoe's Captain John Singleton describes an imaginary journey across Africa, and apparently a contemporary map was used for the general idea. See J. N. L. Baker, " The Geography of Daniel Defoe," in *Scottish Geographical Magazine*, vol. xlvii, p. 257.

[2] See below, Chapter XIV.

the Great Fish river, while in the following year the two men spent some time in the lower valley of the Orange River. The travels of Sparrman in the Kafir country and those of Le Vaillant both in the east and in the north belong to this period. Both were naturalists rather than geographers, and though their journeys were extensive, particularly those of Le Vaillant, they did not add greatly to geographical knowledge.

The century closed with two remarkable journeys into Great Namaqualand (in 1791 and 1792), in the course of which Walfish Bay was reached. At the end of the century the country up to the Orange River was thus known in its general outlines, and at a few points toward the west the limits of knowledge had passed beyond that river into the arid regions of South-west Africa.

CHAPTER XII

AMERICA, 1550–1800 [1]

DURING the seventeenth and eighteenth centuries the exploration of North America was carried out in five main areas. From the St Lawrence valley the French pushed across the continent to the foot of the Rocky Mountains and Hudson Bay, and down the Mississippi to the Gulf of Mexico. Along the Atlantic seaboard the English during the seventeenth century gradually extended their knowledge to the Appalachian Mountains, and in the following century reached the Mississippi. In the south, from their colony near the mouth of the Mississippi, the French carried exploration to the west of that river, and made contact with Spanish North America. The Spaniards themselves extended their knowledge from New Mexico to California, and explored parts of the arid South-western United States. In the Far North the English from Hudson Bay reached the Rockies and the Arctic Ocean, and one trader from Montreal crossed the continent to the Pacific.

I. The French from the St Lawrence Valley

Of all the nations engaged in opening up the continent the French accomplished most, and part of their success must be put down to the geographical advantages which they derived from using the St Lawrence valley as their starting-point. From this valley a large number of practicable routes ran in almost every direction. To the missionary priest, who looked on all the world as his parish, and to the trader ever searching for furs, as well as to the explorer anxious to extend the bounds of New France or merely interested in the solution of a geographical riddle, these natural advantages were too strong a temptation, and Frenchmen in Canada extended their influence and their knowledge at the expense of their strength.

French exploration from the St Lawrence falls broadly into three

---

[1] The literature for this period of discovery is voluminous. E. Heawood's *The History of Geographical Discovery in the Seventeenth and Eighteenth Centuries* (1912) is the standard work. Of a more detailed character are L. J. Burpee, *The Search for the Western Sea* (1908), N. M. Crouse, *In Quest of the Western Ocean* (1928), S. E. Dawson, *The St Lawrence Basin* (1905), and J. B. Brebner, *The Explorers of North America*, 1492–1806 (1933), all of which give good bibliographies. There is a useful short life of Champlain in the "Canadian Men of Action" series, by R. Flenley (1924), which also contains a bibliography giving the main original sources.

periods. When the first period opens nothing was known beyond the limits reached by Cartier half a century earlier.[1] During the first period, which extends to the year 1650, the most important figure is Samuel de Champlain. Born in 1567, Champlain had already visited the New World at the close of the sixteenth century, and his voyage to the West Indies and Mexico had given him some insight into the geography of that region. In 1603 he made a prospecting voyage up the St Lawrence, and in the following year examined the coast of Nova Scotia, the Bay of Fundy, and the mainland coast as far as the Kennebec river, passing farther southward, beyond Cape Cod, in 1605.

Champlain entered the St Lawrence again in 1608, from which year dates the city of Quebec. In order to obtain more information about possible routes to the South Sea, about which he had learned something on his earlier expedition, he joined an Indian war-party which went up the St Lawrence and Richelieu rivers, and reached the lake which now bears the name of the first white man who saw it.

Champlain made his second great journey in 1613. He had heard on his first visit to the St Lawrence of a sea to the north, the route to which lay up the Saguenay river, and also of a great inland sea, which he thought extended southward toward Florida, and to which there were routes by the St Lawrence itself and by the Ottawa. A Frenchman who had lived on the latter river now reported that the northern sea could be reached by the Ottawa river, and Champlain went to ascertain the truth of the report. He penetrated beyond the Chaudière Falls to Allumette Island, but, becoming aware of the inaccuracy of his information, returned to the St Lawrence.

Two years later, in 1615, he made his third and greatest journey. On this occasion he was accompanied by some Franciscan priests, one of whom, Le Caron, actually reached some points before Champlain. Following the Ottawa and Mattawa rivers, Lake Nipissing, and French river, the explorers reached Georgian Bay. Champlain went down the bay to the south-east, and, turning inland, crossed the modern Ontario by Lake Simcoe to the Bay of Quinté. He next went along the northern shore of Lake Ontario to its eastern end, where he crossed to the southern shore, and went inland to attack an Indian town near Lake Oneida. Thence he returned to Lake Ontario, made his way to Lake Simcoe, and back by his outward route to the Ottawa, and so to Quebec, where he arrived on July 11, 1616.

Champlain lived on in the service of French Canada for another nine years, but his work as an explorer was over. The discovery of Lakes Champlain, Nipissing, and Simcoe and the visits to Lakes

[1] See above, p. 117.

Huron and Ontario make a worthy record for one of Canada's greatest men. His administrative work, as well as his own enthusiasm for exploration, did much to make possible the discoveries of his successors.

Though his name is usually coupled with the discovery of two of the Great Lakes, Champlain was not the first Frenchman to sail on their waters. As early as 1611 a youth named Brulé had visited Lake Huron, and he had also reached Lake Ontario before Champlain in 1615. These were but incidents in a life of great adventure, which took Brulé through much of the modern Pennsylvania, down the Susquehanna river to Chesapeake Bay, into the country of the Seneca Indians, and, after 1621, to Lake Superior, before he was boiled and eaten by the Huron Indians.

In the year 1634 Jean Nicollet was specially commissioned by Champlain to find a passage to the South Sea, or, as it was more generally known, the " Sea of the West," about which there had been such persistent rumours. At this time there was no definite knowledge of the five Great Lakes, whose presence doubtless gave rise to the rumours, and it was Nicollet's task to clear up the mystery. From Lake Huron he passed inside the Manitoulin Islands to Sault Ste Marie, and thence into Lake Michigan and along its western coast to Green Bay. The Fox river was followed to the portage to the Wisconsin, and Nicollet thus reached the divide between the St Lawrence and the Mississippi. This last river was known to the Indians as " the Great Water," and Nicollet naturally concluded that he was but a short distance from the mysterious sea. His reports strengthened the belief that the Pacific Ocean was near to the St Lawrence valley and that he had thus found a new way to China and Japan.

The Jesuits now enter the field as explorers, and to their magnificent work is due the spread of French influence over a very wide area. Their journeys were numerous, and their reports are many and valuable, but much of their work was of too detailed a nature to permit of inclusion here. Two of their number, Brébeuf and Chaumonot, undertook a mission to the Neutral nation, in the course of which they were able to gather some vague information about Lake Erie (1640), but it was not until 1648 that the Niagara Falls were mentioned, and then only from report. In that year, however, Indian wars broke out, and put an end to further exploration. Thus the first period of discovery ended with at least some general knowledge of the five Great Lakes, reasonably full in the case of Ontario, Huron, and Michigan, but somewhat meagre in the case of the other two.

The signature of peace in 1653 brought with it the renewal of exploration, both by missionaries and by traders. The former greatly improved the knowledge of the country in the neighbourhood of their stations, which were always moving farther into the wilderness. The latter, and especially the *Coureurs de Bois*,[1] by their intimacy with the Indians picked up much useful geographical information. In 1658 two traders, Chouart and Radisson, made a journey to Georgian Bay by the well-known Ottawa route. They sailed over a large area of Lake Huron, and ultimately reached Green Bay, in Lake Michigan, where they spent the winter. In the spring of 1659 they passed up the Fox river to the Wisconsin, and visited the Mississippi, while at the end of the year, after examining the southern end of Lake Michigan, they went on to Lake Superior, and explored a great part of the modern state of Wisconsin. During these travels Radisson seems to have sighted the Missouri, or at least to have heard of it. He also heard of Hudson Bay, but did not visit it until a later date. There was much speculation as to the relationship between this sea of the north and the western sea, and it was to make discoveries in this region that the traders again set out in 1661. They coasted the southern shore of Lake Superior as far as the modern Ashland, where they spent the winter, and carried out some exploration in the interior. Beyond this their route is uncertain, but it is probable that they crossed the lake and reached Hudson Bay by a route through Lake Nipigon and Summit Lake.

Near Ashland, at La Pointe, Father Allouez established his mission of Saint-Esprit in 1665, and was able both to collect much information about the surrounding country and to carry out a careful piece of work on Lake Nipigon. Four years later he transferred his mission to the Fox river. He thus forms a link between the first real explorers on Lake Superior and the French agents in the Mississippi valley. His work is typical of many devoted priests who followed close behind the traders and filled in gaps in the knowledge of the country.

Three expeditions in the year 1669 added greatly to the knowledge of the Great Lake region. Joliet, who had been sent to find a copper-mine by Lake Superior, of which Champlain had heard years before, returned by a new route through Lake Huron and the Detroit river to Lake Erie. Thence he went up the Grand river and over to the site of the modern Hamilton, on Lake Ontario, where he met another party of Frenchmen, led by the missionaries De Casson and Galinée ; they had come up the St Lawrence, and had in the course of their journey heard of the Niagara Falls. The priests returned by the route by which Joliet had come, and their successful journey did much to encourage

---

[1] The real business of these men was not so much to trade themselves as to gather large bodies of Indians together and pilot them to Montreal. See Munro, " The Coureurs de Bois," in *Proceedings of the Massachusetts Historical Society*, vol. lvii, pp. 192–205.

exploration. With them had gone La Salle, who left the party at Hamilton, and in the course of his wanderings, the exact route of which is not known, probably discovered the Ohio river.

Late in 1672 Joliet, accompanied by Father Marquette, made another important journey. Reaching the Mississippi by Lake Michigan and the Fox-Wisconsin route, he followed that river down to its junction with the Arkansas, and returned to Lake Michigan by the Illinois river. He sailed up the lake to Sturgeon Bay, and passed again to the Fox river. In the course of a journey of nearly 3000 miles he had established beyond doubt the general outlines of the Mississippi. His work was completed by La Salle and Father Hennepin. These men reached the Niagara river in December 1678, and the priest has left the earliest description of the renowned falls. La Salle then sailed through the Great Lakes to the southern end of Lake Michigan, and up the river St Joseph to the Kankakee, a tributary of the Illinois. Leaving a party here to examine the Illinois river as far as the Mississippi, La Salle returned overland to Detroit, and eventually arrived in Montreal. When, however, he went back to the Illinois river he could not find his party, though he followed the river down to the Mississippi. He accordingly went up the Illinois, and reached Lake Michigan at the point where Chicago now stands.

Meanwhile Hennepin had undertaken a long journey, in the course of which he went down the Illinois to the Mississippi and up that river to the site of Minneapolis. He subsequently laid claim to far more extensive discoveries, which could not have been made in the time at his disposal.

In 1681 La Salle completed his earlier work by sailing down the Illinois and the Mississippi to the Gulf of Mexico. He took possession of the whole land for France, naming it Louisiana, and returned, with much difficulty, to Montreal. He then went to France, where he secured royal support for an expedition, by sea, to the mouth of the Mississippi, but he could not find the mouth, and was obliged to land among the lagoons of Texas. In the course of an overland march to the river he was murdered by some of his party, but the remnant, under Joutel, reached the Arkansas river, where they met an expedition which had come down the Mississippi in search of La Salle.

The death of La Salle removed the great figure of the second period of French exploration. His work, by which that of Champlain was completed, had proved the close connexion between the basins of the St Lawrence and Mississippi rivers.

Further exploration of the west was undertaken by Daniel de Greysolon, Sieur du Lhut, who went to the south shore of Lake Superior in 1678, and probably reached the St Croix river. In the course of a long life spent in these regions he gained a considerable, and generally accurate, knowledge of the country to the west of the Great Lakes.

In the east also extensive discoveries had been made. In 1672 Albanel, using the Saguenay river and Lake Mistassini, reached Hudson Bay, where he found the English in possession. Seven years later Joliet made a similar expedition, while in 1686 a war-party used a new route to the bay, by the Ottawa river and Lake Timiskaming. The knowledge thus acquired was turned to good account, and considerably increased, by the missionaries who followed the paths of the traders and soldiers, and the second period of exploration ended with some rough knowledge of the whole of America between the Ohio, the Mississippi, and the southern end of Hudson Bay.

The third period opened with the arrival of Jacques de Noyon on the Lake of the Woods in 1688, marking at once the continuation of the work of Du Lhut and the beginning of a still further expansion westward in search of the sea, which, like El Dorado, in South America, was moved farther away as exploration progressed. For a time, however, attention was directed to the Missouri river, where a number of French traders were established by 1708, mainly engaged in a search for minerals. The sea was relegated to the west of the Mississippi by the great French geographer Guillaume de L'Isle. There was, however, much confusion introduced into the maps of the period by the inventions of La Hontan, who described a great river flowing into the Mississippi from the west, and by attempts to connect the reports derived from Indian sources with known discoveries of openings in the west coast of America made by the Spaniards. Matters finally reached a head in 1720, when Father Charlevoix was specially commissioned to investigate the possibilities of making an expedition to the western sea. He returned to France declaring : " I saw only two practical routes to discover this sea : that the first was to ascend the Missouri whose source is certainly not far from the sea . . . that the second is to establish a mission with the Sioux. . . . The missionaries will have . . . all the information they wish." [1] The Regent decided on the latter plan, and in 1727 a mission was established on the Mississippi at Lake Pepin, but no progress was made with exploration.

The following year, however, Pierre Gaultier de Varennes, Sieur de la Vérendrye, who was in charge of a trading-post on Lake Nipigon, heard a story from an Indian which led him to conclude that it was a simple matter to reach this mysterious sea. After some preliminary negotiations he set out in 1731, and in the following year reached the Lake of the Woods. His son Pierre went still farther, and established Fort Maurepas on Lake Winnipeg, from which some knowledge was gained both of the extent of the lake to

[1] Quoted in N. M. Crouse, op. cit., p. 359.

the north and of the country to the south. The Red River was ascended to the mouth of the Assiniboine, and the latter followed to a point at which Fort La Reine was set up.[1]

From this fort La Vérendrye set out in October 1738 for the country of the Mandan Indians, on the Missouri, following not a river, as was usual, but an Indian trail. He did not remain long, but left behind two men, who got news of the sea from Indians, who promised to show them the way thither. Unfortunately, neither La Vérendrye nor his son, who actually returned to the Mandan Indians, could find guides, and the journey was not made. But Pierre and his brother visited the Mandans again in 1742, and undertook a long journey beyond their territory. Both their route and the place at which they turned back are unknown. They certainly reached the edge of the Rocky Mountains—possibly at the Big Horn Mountains—and may have penetrated much farther to the westward.

La Vérendrye died before he could make any further advance, and his sons were not allowed to continue the work. There was, however, one more expedition, the details of which are not known with certainty, but which seems to have reached the Rockies in 1751, making use of one of the branches of the Saskatchewan river. This marks the end of the third and final stage of French exploration, centring mainly round the figure of La Vérendrye. Within one hundred and fifty years the French from the St Lawrence had reached the Rockies on the west and the Gulf of Mexico on the south. Ever looking for the western sea, they had always failed to discover it, but the opening up of half a continent was a magnificent achievement and an ample reward for the failure to disclose a new route to China and the East.

II. The English from the East Coast

If French exploration had been undertaken by men whose names are well known in the history of geographical discovery and whose travels were on a considerable scale, it was far different with English exploration from the Atlantic seaboard, where hardly a name or an exploit stands out above the rest until after the year 1650. The arrival of Gosnold in Massachusetts Bay in 1602 marks the beginning of the exploration, which had for its object the search for a passage to the western sea. The coast of Maine was examined by Pring in the following year ; Waymouth explored the Penobscot river in 1605 ; and Pring, again looking for a route to " the other sea," continued his work on the coast of Maine in 1606. The next year saw the founding of a colony at Jamestown, Virginia, where Newport

[1] Near the modern Portage la Prairie.

went inland as far as the modern Richmond. The same year John Smith began his work in Virginia, penetrating into the interior by a tributary of the York river. Smith was captured by Indians, but said that his life was saved by the chief's daughter, and he returned with good news of the rich country occupied by the tribes. The following year he explored Chesapeake Bay, and learned from Indians of other tribes who lived " upon a great water beyond the mountains." Smith obtained a large amount of information about Virginia, which he embodied in a map and a history of the colony, but no serious attempt was made to penetrate beyond the mountains. In 1627 Fleete, from Virginia, claimed that he had many times " been within sight of the South sea," but his story is somewhat suspect, and his positive achievements were very small. The idea of an approach to the south sea was not, however, abandoned, and twenty-five years later Edward Williams wrote a pamphlet trying to prove that the journey was both short and easy.

Meanwhile English colonies had been established at many points along the seaboard from Florida to New Brunswick, and it was the slow movement of the frontier westward that brought about a gradual spread of geographical knowledge. A few bigger enter-prises were undertaken into the interior, as those of Dermer, who attempted to find a passage through the modern New York Harbour in 1620, of Yong, who went up the Delaware on a similar quest in 1633, and of an unknown Englishman who found his way, by the Kennebec, to Canada in 1640. The main work of the English during this period was to settle the coastal districts.

In the second half of the seventeenth century the English pioneers got beyond the Blue Ridge into the valleys of westward-flowing streams. Some still hoped to find a new route to Asia, others desired to investigate rumours of precious metals, and others again wished to engage in the very lucrative fur-trade : this last was by far the most powerful incentive to the westward movement.

In 1650 E. Bland, Captain A. Wood, and two others set out from Fort Henry on a journey of trade and discovery, and reached the Roanoke, at the site of the modern Clarksville. Their achievements were small, but they were the pioneers of a new age. The next advance was made by a German, John Lederer, who reached the summit of the Blue Ridge in 1669, and thought he saw the Atlantic Ocean from the top. The next year, with a companion named Harris, he set out from what is now Richmond, on the James river, and went due westward, until in about longitude 79° W. Harris then returned ; Lederer, however, continued to the south-west and reached a village of the Saura Indians, near the modern Winston. He returned by an unknown route. In August of the same year he set out again from a point near the modern Fredericksburg, and reached, and climbed, the Blue Ridge. Lederer " contributed much

212

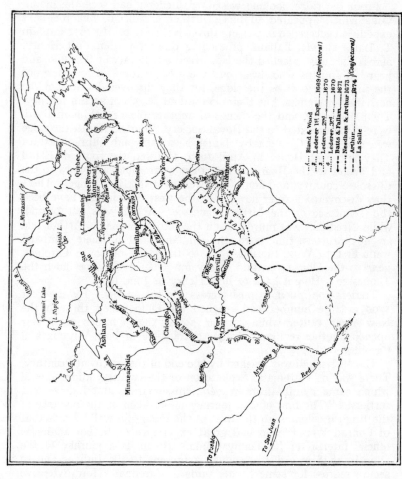

Fig. 24. North America, showing Explorations from the East Coast in the Seventeenth and Eighteenth Centuries

to the exploration of the piedmont and was the first white man to look into the valley of Virginia." [1]

From the ridge, looking westward, Lederer had seen the mountains which appeared to block further expansion, but the next expedition succeeded in passing through the ridge. In 1671 Captain T. Batts and R. Fallam, proceeding due west from Fort Henry, across the ridge, reached the New river, a tributary of the Ohio, and heard of Indians who dwelt on 'the great water.' They were not the first men to cross the ridge, for they discovered traces of the activities of traders, but theirs is the first record of such a journey. Their discovery, and the doings of another pioneer, William Byrd, were communicated to the Royal Society. Farther south the ridge was crossed in Carolina by James Needham and Gabriel Arthur. They left Fort Henry in April 1673, followed the route of Bland and Wood to the Roanoke, and then went south-westward to the Cherokee country, and finally due west over the Blue Ridge. There they discovered a river flowing to the west, which may have been the Tennessee or the Little Tennessee. Arthur was left behind, while Needham was murdered on the return journey. Arthur had an adventurous time with the Indians, and in their company went first to West Florida, then to the coast of South Carolina, next to the Ohio river, and finally for a short distance down the Tennessee. He got back to Fort Henry in June 1674.

Traders continued to push across the mountains. By the year 1700 a large number had reached the Ohio valley through the New river route, while farther south the journeys of Arthur opened another region to trade to colonists of both Virginia and Carolina.

The Mississippi was reached by the end of the eighteenth century. There was no systematic exploration of the country, knowledge of which came mainly from traders, missionaries, and independent settlers. "The first official journey undertaken at the instance of the English colonies, to the west of the mountain wall," [2] was that of Conrad Weiser, who had great experience of Indian affairs as official interpreter for Pennyslvania. He made a journey to the Ohio in 1748 in order to convey a present to the Indians and to secure redress for some border raids in Carolina. More extensive were the travels of the Irishman George Crogan, whose life-history is "an epitome of Indian relations with the whites, especially on the borders of Virginia and Pennsylvania and in the Ohio valley." He made allies of the Indians living near Lake Erie, he accompanied

[1] C. W. Alvord and L. Bidgood, *The First Exploration of the Trans-Alleghany Regions by the Virginians* (1912), p. 69. This work prints the original documents, and has been used for the account of English exploration.
[2] R. G. Thwaites, *Early Western Travels* (32 vols. 1904–7), preface to vol. i. This work is invaluable for the early history of exploration in the United States.

Weiser in 1748, he went the next year to the Ohio, to neutralize the influence of the French expedition of Céloron, and in 1750 and 1751 he was again travelling extensively in the Ohio valley. He took part in the victorious struggle with the French, visited Detroit on several occasions, and in 1765 so conducted affairs with the Indians that the Illinois river was opened to the English, and he himself gained some knowledge of the Wabash. In 1766 he visited Fort Chartres, on the Mississippi, and went down that river to New Orleans. Among other pioneers in these regions were the Moravian missionary C. F. Post and the fur-trader John Long, who gained an intimate knowledge of the Indians of Wisconsin.

Farther south Thomas Walker, of Virginia, made the important discovery of the Cumberland Gap in 1748, and two years later penetrated into the valley of the Kentucky river. Traders and settlers soon followed, and one, Daniel Boon, from Carolina, settled in the Kentucky valley. He was followed by John Floyd, who reached the country by the Ohio, and returned through the Cumberland Gap. Still farther to the south settlers entered the Tennessee valley, and pushed westward toward the Mississippi.[1]

At the end of the century two men, André Michaux and his son François-André, made a series of journeys, partly in this newly occupied country. The elder man was a botanist, and had travelled widely before reaching America. There his journeys took him to places as far apart as Hudson Bay and Florida. He explored the Carolina mountains in 1787, and was active in Kentucky in 1793. He began preparations for a large expedition to the Missouri, but it was never carried out. Michaux died in 1802, in Madagascar, when on his way to Australia. On several of these journeys François accompanied his father, and after his death returned to America to study its forests for the French Government. The elder Michaux

traversed nearly all the routes by which emigration was pouring into the Western country—the Wilderness road to Kentucky, the routes from North Carolina over the mountains to East Tennessee, the Wilderness Road of Tennessee, the paths thither to Louisville, and the Indian trails thence to the Illinois; as well as the river routes—the Mississippi, the Ohio, and the Cumberland.[2]

How rapidly the country was filling up may be gathered from a comparison of the journal of the father with the *Travels* of the son. Thus the elder Michaux records: " The 5th [September 1793] we passed a small settlement, looked upon as a town and called Paris, the capital of Bourbon county." [3] The younger man, writing about ten years later, found that it had one hundred and fifty houses,

---

[1] On the significance of the westward advance see the brilliant essays of Professor F. J. Turner in *The Frontier in American History* (1921).
[2] Thwaites, *op. cit.*, vol. iii, p. 18.   [3] *Ibid.*, vol. iii, p. 37.

half of which were of brick.[1] Similarly, Wheeling was "inhabited by about 12 families "[2] in 1793, but when the younger Michaux visited it he reported : " it consists of about seventy houses, built of wood. . . . From fifteen to twenty large shops, well stocked, supply the inhabitants twenty miles round with provisions."[3] The work of François is particularly valuable for its geographical descriptions and for the light it throws upon the influences of environment upon early settlement.

III. The French from Louisiana

At the close of the seventeenth century the French took up the exploration of the country round the mouth of the Mississippi. La Salle's unfortunate expedition, already mentioned, had penetrated some distance toward New Mexico in 1686 before the journey north-eastward in the following year. The remnants under Joutel met Henri de Tonti at the Arkansas. This man commanded a relief party, which went back to the settlement of St Louis, on the coast. Unable to find any survivors of the colony, he went to the Mississippi, reached the Arkansas, and ascended it as far as it was navigable. He then crossed to the Red River, and made a land-journey south-ward in search of the remnants of the colony. He was unable to find them, and his men refused to continue the search.

In 1697 the French again established themselves on the shores of the Gulf of Mexico, this time to the east of the Mississippi delta, near Mobile. In spite of much hardship and loss the colony sur-vived, and gradually other posts were established, the chief being New Orleans, founded in 1721. Reports of the presence of lead deposits took explorers far northward, to the St Francis river and the country of Western Tennessee, and by 1725 they had reached the Missouri in their search for furs. To the westward a trading-post was established near Pueblo in 1740, but had to be abandoned owing to the hostility of the Spaniards.

The French also made contact with the Spaniards through Texas. In 1714 Saint-Denis went up the Mississippi and Red rivers, and overland to the Spanish post of San Juan, on the Rio Grande. This expedition " established a road to the Spanish colonies in New Mexico, but beyond this it accomplished nothing in the way of discovery."[4] Four years later Bénard de la Harpe travelled up the Red River, with the object of establishing a trading-post in its upper reaches. War between France and Spain prevented the realization of La Harpe's plans, but he was able to add to the geographical knowledge of the Red and Arkansas rivers and to visit the Canadian river. Although La Harpe failed, others

---

[1] Thwaites, vol. iii, p. 199.   [2] *Ibid.*, vol. iii, p. 33.
[3] *Ibid.*, vol. iii, pp. 171, 172.   [4] Crouse, *op. cit.*, p. 329.

succeeded in making contact with the Spanish settlements, for the brothers Pierre and Paul Mallet reached Santa Fé from the Missouri river in 1739. This was, however, an isolated journey. The subsequent distractions of the French in other parts of the continent, and the permanent hostility of the Spaniards in Mexico, prevented the establishment of any legitimate trade between Mexico and Louisiana, and it was not until the nineteenth century, when Louisiana passed to the United States, that exploration was resumed in this region.

IV. THE SPANIARDS FROM MEXICO

A variety of causes brought about the renewal of Spanish exploration in North America after the first onrush of Cortes and Coronado. The stories which the first had verified, and which had deceived the second, were still current, and rumours of wealth in various kinds, such as fur, gold, and pearls, continued, at intervals, to spur on explorers. Missionaries too were very active, and to them no small part of the expansion of geographical knowledge was due. At the end of the period now under review political causes, and especially anxiety as to the movements of the French, English, and Russians, led to the dispatch of some Spanish exploring expeditions.

The Spanish expansion from Mexico followed four main lines. As already indicated, the coast of the Gulf of Mexico was explored by Pineda in 1519. After 1522 a number of expeditions were sent to the coast, but no settlements were made, doubtless because of the adverse conditions along the shore-line. To the north, however, following in the main the lines of the Coronado expedition, the Spaniards began the settlement of New Mexico. A number of exploring parties in the second half of the sixteenth century paved the way for the colonization of that country by Oñate in 1598.[1] Thence the Spaniards were drawn eastward by reports of Quivira, and in 1601 an expedition searched for it in vain. Other explorers reached the Jumano Indians, on the Upper Colorado river. Missionaries were active here after 1629, and in 1650 'pearls' were discovered in one of the rivers. This find led to another expedition into Western Texas in 1654.

Meanwhile an advance had been made from North-eastern Mexico. By 1565 the Spaniards had reached Monterey, and in 1583 Leon was founded. In 1590 they were settled in what is now Monclova. Never in any great numbers, and often opposed by Indians, the Spaniards were obliged to limit their activities to several small expeditions. They were, however, encouraged by reports of the silver deposit called La Sierra de la Plata, and were

[1] At least seven expeditions to New Mexico were made between 1568 and 1598.

anxious to establish connexion with Florida. In 1644 and again in 1648 efforts were made to discover this silver, but in 1650 the Governor was only able to report that he had

> made a beginning of northern discovery, whereby he has explored more than fifty leagues with the purpose of continuing till communication is established with La Florida, and has almost certain knowledge of the Sierra de la Plata, which he intends to reach, a feat which has so often been attempted by the governors of Nueva Vizcaya and Nuevo Leon, but which has been abandoned because of Indian troubles.[1]

In 1670 the missionaries began work in this frontier region, and shortly after reports came in of an important tribe known as the Texas, whose Great Lord did not permit foreign nations to enter his country. An expedition in 1684 reached the Nueces river, on a journey whose object was " the discovery of the Orient and the Kingdom of the Texas." The river in question seems to have been a tributary of the Colorado, on which the Spaniards built a fort.

Shortly after this news was received of the activities of the French, and a number of expeditions were sent out. In 1689 the Spaniards reached Matagorda Bay, on the Gulf coast of Texas, and in the following year established themselves at the westernmost village of the Texas, near the Neches river.

The fourth sphere of activity was in California. In 1604 Oñate reached the Colorado river, and followed it to its mouth : it is perhaps due to his report that there arose the curious belief that Lower California was an island. After this a large number of expeditions were made to Lower California and the gulf, but little progress was made until 1683. In that year Otondo founded a colony on the peninsula, but it only lasted for two years, and settlement was not permanently effected until 1697.

Further progress in exploration was due in large measure to the Jesuits. One of their number, Kühn,[2] explored Sonora, and in 1694 penetrated to the Gila river. He made several journeys to the river, and in 1698 reached the Gulf of California. Two years later, in an effort to solve the problem of the insularity of Lower California, he went to the Colorado river, and saw its mouth. Although he failed in his main purpose, his map was the first to establish the peninsular character of Lower California. He continued his explorations on the Colorado river in 1701, and again in 1702.

Shortly afterward the Pacific coast was reached by a number of expeditions. Salvatierra, from his station at Loreto, pushed inland, and sighted the Pacific, and the coastline was further examined by Ugarte in 1706 and Guillen in 1719. Two years later Ugarte made

---

[1] Quoted in H. E. Bolton, " The Spanish Occupation of Texas, 1519–1690," in the *South-western Historical Quarterly*, vol. xvi, pp. 1–26. This admirable summary has been used extensively for the account of Spanish activities in Texas. [2] On Kühn (or Kino) see H. E. Bolton, *Rim of Christendom* (1936).

a survey of the gulf shores northward from Loreto, and practically solved the problem of the insularity of Lower California. His results were confirmed by the work of Consag, who explored the Pacific coast in 1746, and, to some extent, by the journey of Wenzel in the north of the peninsula in 1756.

Further land exploration received great stimulus from the founding of settlements in Upper California. As early as 1603 Vizcaino had examined the coast, and had discovered the important harbour of Monterey. His work was not followed up for a century and a half,

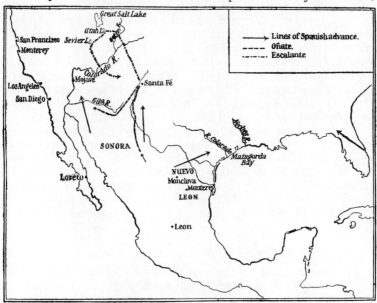

Fig. 25. SPANISH NORTH AMERICA, 1550-1800

until Gaspar de Portola was given command of a large expedition. It was divided into five parties, two of which went by land up the peninsula and three by sea. San Diego was reached by four of the parties, and from that point the journey by land was made first to Monterey and then to San Francisco. The crews suffered such hardships, through lack of supplies and scurvy, that it became clear to the Spaniards that an overland route must be discovered if their settlements at Monterey were to be maintained.

In this new discovery a Franciscan named Garcés played an important part. His missionary work made him familiar with the country of Northern Sonora, and in 1771 he went down the Gila to the Colorado, and all but reached the mouth of the latter. Three years later, accompanied by J. B. de Anza, he attempted to find a

219

suitable route to Upper California. The whole party crossed the Gila and the Colorado rivers, and reached the coast near the modern Los Angeles. On the return journey Garcés visited one of the Yuma tribes on the Colorado river. In the following year de Anza was again sent to California, to establish a Spanish post on San Francisco Bay. Garcés accompanied the expedition, but soon left it to explore the Colorado river up as far as Mojave and parts of the Colorado plateau south of the river.

Two other Franciscans, Escalante and Dominguez, tried to open up a route from Santa Fé to the west coast. They set out on July 29, 1776, and, taking a general north-westerly route, crossed the Colorado Plateau and the Green River, and finally reached a lake, which was probably Utah Lake. They collected much geographical information about the surrounding country, and heard of the Great Salt Lake to the north. The fathers were unable to learn anything about a route to the Pacific, and as winter was approaching decided to return to Santa Fé. Their homeward journey took them by Sevier Lake and over the Colorado in about latitude 37° N.

The friars failed in their main purpose, but they had discovered much new country, and "their journey constituted the most important exploration achieved before the beginning of the nineteenth century in the south-west of the modern United States." [1] It was not followed up, because the Spanish authorities, in their anxiety to establish contact with Upper California, regarded the exploration of the arid regions to the east as of secondary importance. [2]

V. THE ENGLISH FROM HUDSON BAY [3]

The country lying to the south and west of Hudson Bay was explored mainly by the English, whose attention had been drawn to the region in the course of their searches for a north-west passage. The adverse reports of Foxe and James, and the distractions of the Civil War, had put an end to activity on the shores of the bay, and it was not renewed until the *Nonsuch* was sent there to trade in 1668. A fort was subsequently established, known as Fort Rupert, or Rupert House, and in 1670 the Hudson's Bay Company received its charter.

It is largely to this trading company that the development of the west was due. The charter runs:

> Whereas our dear and entirely beloved Cousin, Prince Rupert, [and others] have at their own great charges undertaken an expedi-

---

[1] Heawood, *op. cit.*, p. 357.
[2] On Spanish expeditions in these regions see C. E. Chapman, *The Founding of Spanish California* (1916), and A. J. Denis, *Spanish Alta California* (1927).
[3] The main authority for this section is L. J. Burpee, *The Search for the Western Sea* (1908), a work of great value.

tion for Hudson's Bay . . . for the Discovery of a new Passage into the South Sea and for the finding some trade for Furs, Minerals, and other considerable Commodities, and by such their Undertaking have already made such Discoveries as do encourage them to proceed further . . . We give, grant, and confirm unto the said Governor and Company and their Successors the sole Trade and Commerce of all those Seas, Streights, Bays, Rivers, Lakes, Creeks, and Sounds in whatsoever Latitude they shall be that lie within the entrance of the Streights commonly called Hudson's Streights, together with all the Lands, Countries, and Territories upon the Coasts and Confines of the Seas, Bays, etc., aforesaid which are not now actually possessed by any of our Subjects or by the Subjects of any other Christian Prince or State.

Thus the great trading company was established to promote discovery as well as trade.

The first step was to place trading-posts round the shores of the bay, and by 1682 these had been established at the Rupert river, Albany river, Hayes Island, Port Nelson, and New Severn. For a long time the Company had to struggle with the French, who first led an expedition to the bay in 1686, and who for a time held all the posts except that at the Nelson river. The struggle was ended by the Treaty of Utrecht (1713), by which the territory of Hudson Bay was declared to be an English possession.

The exploration of the country followed two main lines. As the charter pointed out, the Company existed to solve the problem of the North-west Passage. There were complaints in England that this function was not fulfilled, and in 1742 Captain Middleton attempted to find a passage west of Southampton Island. In his voyage he discovered Wager Bay and Repulse Bay. Another expedition in 1746 investigated Chesterfield Inlet, while two further attempts to reach China through that opening, first in 1761 and again in 1790, only succeeded in penetrating a little beyond Baker Lake.

The most important journey of this century was that of Samuel Hearne, an employee of the Company, who set out in 1769 to find an exit from the bay on the west and to investigate Indian reports of the existence of copper-mines in the interior. Hearne did not get very far in 1769, owing to trouble with the Indians, but in the following year he tried again ; he again failed, but did explore the country behind the bay, south of Chesterfield Inlet, to about the longitude of Dubawnt Lake.

In December of 1770 he made his third attempt, and by keeping more to the west of his earlier routes reached the Coppermine river and followed it to the sea. On the return journey he discovered a large lake, which he called Athapuscow, and which some identify with Lake Athabaska, though, from the general direction of Hearne's route, it seems to be the Great Slave Lake. Hearne had a good knowledge of the lake, and brought back valuable information of the country in its immediate neighbourhood. His journey had resulted in the discovery, in outline, of a large area to the north-west of the bay, and in the fixing, somewhat inaccurately, of one point on the north coast of America. It did more than this, as he himself claimed. " Though my discoveries," he wrote,

> are not likely to prove of any material advantage to the nation at large, or indeed to the Hudson Bay Company, yet I have the pleasure to think I have fully complied with the orders of my masters and that it has put a final end to all disputes concerning a north-west Passage through Hudson Bay. It will also wipe off, in some measure, the ill-grounded aspersions of Dobbs, Ellis, Robson, and the American Traveller ; who have all taken much pains to condemn the conduct of the Hudson Bay Company as being averse from discoveries and from enlarging their trade.[1]

The remaining part of the story of the search for the North-west Passage falls in the history of Pacific exploration, and has already been dealt with. For the present purposes it will be sufficient to recall that Cook established a second known point on the north coast in Icy Cape, and that Vancouver and others carried out accurate surveys on the west coast.

Apart from the search for the North-west Passage, English exploration from Hudson Bay was almost accidental, arising in large measure out of the prosecution of the fur-trade. The earliest journey was that of Henry Kellsey, in 1691–92. He set out from Deering's Point, an unidentified locality, but perhaps on or about Split Lake, on the Nelson river, and travelled partly by canoe and partly on land in a general westerly direction. Although doubts have been cast on the authenticity of the journey, and it is now impossible to reconstruct its course,

> there is no question that from several points of view it was a notable achievement. It was the first serious attempt, indeed the first attempt of any kind, to explore the interior from Hudson Bay ; it foreshadowed the awakening of the Hudson's Bay Company from its comfortable sleep by the shores of the Bay, and the far sweep of its trading ventures throughout the length and breadth of the great west. Kellsey was the first white man, if we except the case of Radisson, to explore any portion of the north-west ; he was the first to visit one of the western tribes ; he was the first to see and hunt the buffalo.[2]

The next journey of exploration was that of Anthony Hendry, who left York Factory, at the mouth of the Hayes river, in June 1754. He went up the Hayes river, by means of several portages reached Oxford Lake, and thence, again using portages, passed to the north of Lake Winnipeg. From this point he went on to Moose Lake, whence he gained the Saskatchewan river. For some distance up the river he used a canoe, but later, on foot, explored a large stretch of country between the north and south branches

---

[1] Quoted in Crouse, *op. cit.*, p. 452.   [2] Burpee, *op. cit.*, p. 112.

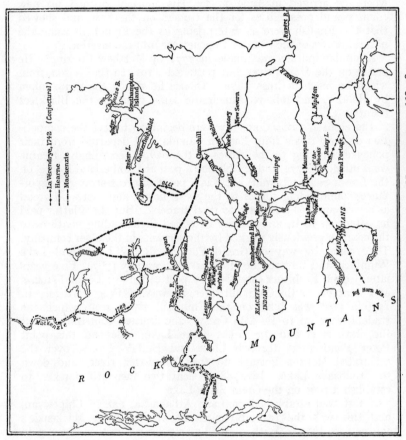

Fig. 26. NORTH AMERICA—WEST AND NORTH-WEST, 1668–1800

of the river, perhaps as far west as longitude 114° W. He spent the winter with the Blackfeet Indians, whose main strength lay beyond the Red Deer river, and it was down this river that Hendry returned to the South Saskatchewan, and so made his way to Hudson Bay, where he arrived in June 1755. His journey opened up new country and possibilities for the traders on the bay, and showed that the English were as enterprising as the French in using the natural routes of the country to penetrate into the interior.

A similar journey was made in 1772 by Matthew Cocking. He began on the Hayes river, but portaged across to the Nelson, from which he reached Cross Lake. Thence he struck the route taken by Hendry, and followed much the same track to the Blackfeet country.

The Hudson's Bay Company were beginning to feel the competition of their rivals from Eastern Canada, and departed from their policy of clinging to the shores of the bay. Accordingly, Hearne went inland in 1774, and established a post at Cumberland House, on the Lower Saskatchewan. It was a point of great strategic importance, commanding routes to the west, north, and east, and stood as a warning and a menace to rival traders. But these latter paid no attention to it, and rapidly extended their trading ventures to the country previously worked by the servants of the older company. They came by way of Grand Portage, Rainy Lake, and Lake Winnipeg, and they reached the Saskatchewan by 1767. Five years later Joseph Frobisher established a post called Cumberland House, and went on to the Churchill river, by way of Frog Portage. In 1776 a post was built on the Churchill river, from which the traders went up to Ile à la Crosse, and learned something about the Slave river and the Great Slave Lake. Beyond this point Peter Pond went through Clear and Buffalo Lakes, over the celebrated Methye Portage to the Clearwater river, and down to Athabaska Lake. In 1788 he sent two men still farther, to establish a post on the Great Slave Lake.

A fort was established on Lake Athabaska, named Chipewyan, and this was the real starting-point of Alexander Mackenzie's journey in 1789.[1] With a small party he set out on June 3 to discover if the reported water communication between the Great Slave Lake and the northern ocean existed. Sailing down the Slave river, and surviving the rapids in its course, he reached the Great Slave Lake, where he spent twenty days. Then began the important part of his exploration, for no one knew whither flowed the river which drained the lake. Some maps showed it as running into the Pacific Ocean, and it seems at least likely that Mackenzie

[1] On Mackenzie see M. S. Wade, *Mackenzie of Canada* (1927), and A. P. Woollacott, *Mackenzie and his Voyageurs* (1927), both of which contain useful references.

hoped that they were correctly drawn. He followed the course of the river until on July 10, when near the delta, he recorded that " it was evident that these waters emptied themselves into the Hyperborean Sea." When he reached what he called " the boundary " of the voyage he made an interesting remark. " My people," he wrote,

> could not at this time refrain from expressing real concern that they were obliged to return without reaching the sea ; indeed, the hope of attaining this object encouraged them to bear, without repining, the hardships of our unremitting voyage. For some time past their spirits were animated by the expectation that another day would bring them to the Mér d'Ouest ; and even in our present situation they declared their readiness to follow me wherever I should be pleased to lead them.[1]

The men at least had been deceived by the current beliefs of the geographers.

From Whale Island in the delta Mackenzie saw the Arctic Ocean. He was running short of food, he saw that progress was impossible, and there was nothing to be gained by delay. Accordingly, on July 16 he began his return journey, and reached Fort Chipewyan on September 12. His course from the fort and back again had occupied 102 days, and had covered 2990 miles. It was " one of the most remarkable exploits in the history of inland discovery, whether regarded in the light of the results achieved or of the time taken," [2] yet it brought Mackenzie little credit, and rarely finds a place among the great journeys of discovery.

Mackenzie returned to England to perfect his knowledge of surveying in preparation for a new expedition across the continent to the Pacific. In the meantime the activities of the free traders roused the Hudson's Bay Company, and they sent out Philip Turner to initiate a geographical survey. Turner was engaged on this task from 1790 to 1792, and as a result produced a very accurate map of the country from Cumberland House to the Great Slave Lake. The most striking features are the canoe route from Cumberland House to the Great Slave Lake and the outlines of Lake Athabaska. From the map itself one can gather which parts were surveyed by Turner and which were based on reports.

> He made a careful survey of the Saskatchewan up to the Forks and a short distance up the north branch to Hudson's House ; also of Sturgeon-Weir River and its connecting waterways to Frog portage ; of the upper waters of the Churchill to Methye . . . ; of the Clearwater River, and so much of the Athabaska as lies between the mouth of the Clearwater and Athabaska Lake ; of Athabaska Lake, Slave River, and a small portion of the south shore of Great Slave Lake. From Indian report he laid down the North Saskatchewan and indicated the South Saskatchewan ; laid down

---

[1] Quoted in Woollacott, *op. cit.*, p. 69.   [2] Burpee, *op. cit.*, p. 442.

Beaver River and the chain of lakes which empty into it from the westward ...; laid down Peace River and indicated the upper waters of the Athabaska.[1]

The work of survey in the far west was continued by Turner's successor, Fidler, and by his pupil, Thompson, but as both were still actively engaged at the end of the century an account of their explorations is postponed to a later chapter.[2]

The last great journey in Canada in the eighteenth century, excluding those of Fidler and Thompson, was that of Alexander Mackenzie in 1793. It is very probable that Mackenzie, while in England, had studied the history of exploration on the west coast of America, and in particular had read the report of Meares, and had heard of the voyage of the ship *Washington*.[3] He left England in 1792, and proceeded almost at once to Chipewyan. He proposed to use the Peace river, and to make his discoveries " across the mountains from the source of that river." He embarked on the Peace on October 12, and on November 1 built his winter quarters, Forks Fort, at the point where the Smoky river enters the main stream. Here he remained until May 9, 1793. During his stay he learned from Indians of the existence of a lake to the eastward, now known as the Lesser Slave Lake.

After continuing up the Peace river for an estimated distance of 148 miles Mackenzie reached the Peace River Cañon, which necessitated a twelve-mile portage. Beyond this the voyage was resumed until he " arrived at the fork, one branch running west-north-west and the other south-south-east." Of these rivers, now known respectively as the Finlay and the Parsnip, Mackenzie chose the latter after some hesitation, and against the wishes of his men and his own inclination. But he had been warned by Indians that the Finlay became " lost in various branches among the mountains," and wisely took their advice. On June 12 he reached the source of the Parsnip, in a small lake, and established its position as latitude 54° 24′ N., longitude 121° west of Greenwich. A short portage now took him to one of the headstreams of the Fraser river, and on June 17 he chronicled his arrival on the main stream. " At length," he wrote, " we enjoyed after all our toil and anxiety, the inexpressible satisfaction of finding ourselves on the bank of a navigable river on the west side of the first great range of mountains."

Mackenzie continued down the Fraser until he reached a point a little beyond the modern Quesnel, when he learned from Indians that it was almost impossible to proceed farther. He accordingly decided to strike westward. " The more I heard of the river," he wrote, " the more I was convinced it would not empty itself into the ocean to the north of what is called the river of the west." It

[1] Burpee, *op. cit.*, pp. 173–174.   [2] See Chapter XV.   [3] See Chapter IX.

would appear that Mackenzie, like explorers in the United States, was haunted by the belief in this mythical river, which entered the Pacific Ocean at various points, according to the fancy of the writer.[1]

Mackenzie returned up the Fraser river, perhaps to the Blackwater, perhaps beyond it, and then turned westward, following the general direction of that stream and crossing over to the Bellacoola river, which he followed to its mouth. He arrived there on July 20, and two days later reached the limit of his journey, in Dean Channel.

Before he left, he writes: " I now mixed up some vermilion in melted grease and inscribed in large characters on the southeast face of the rock on which we had slept, this brief memorial:
Alexander Mackenzie, from Canada by land, the twenty second of July 1793.' " The rock has recently been discovered and Mackenzie's inscription restored.

The return journey was made by the same route, and Forks Fort was reached on September 4. " Here," says Mackenzie,

> my voyages of discovery terminate. Their toils and dangers, their solitudes and sufferings, have not been exaggerated in my description. On the contrary, in many instances language has failed me in the attempt to describe them. I received, however, the reward of my labours, for they were crowned with success.[2]

This modest statement hardly does justice to a remarkable journey. It was the end of the first crossing of the continent since the days of Cabez de Vaca. The route lay through difficult country, yet in spite of all his anxieties Mackenzie found time to make and to record observations of his position which were reasonably accurate. He did not meet the Russian traders, as he thought he might, but he heard of the great ships of the white men, and missed, by a few weeks only, Vancouver's survey party. In addition to opening up a large area of hitherto unknown land, he pointed out its economic value and the need for new lines of communication.

> By opening this intercourse between the Atlantic and Pacific Oceans, and forming regular establishments through the interior, and at both extremes, as well as along the coasts and islands, the entire command of the fur trade of North America might be obtained, from latitude 48° north to the pole, except that portion of it which the Russians have in the Pacific. To this might be added the fishing in both seas, and the markets of the four quarters of the globe. Such would be the field for commercial enterprise, and incalculable would be the produce of it, when supported by the operations of that credit and capital which Great Britain so preeminently possesses.[3]

[1] For a view that the river is Cook's ' river ' or the Yukon see Wade, *op. cit.*, p. 157.
[2] A. Mackenzie, *Voyages from Montreal on the River St Lawrence through the Continent of North America to the Frozen and Pacific Oceans* (1801), p. 397.
[3] Mackenzie, *op. cit.*, pp. 407–408.

That was the conclusion of Mackenzie's *Voyages* : the project was in part realized by the fur-traders who followed in his tracks, and established themselves on the Pacific coast, but it had to wait for its complete development until the opening of the Canadian Pacific Railway in 1886, by which time a large and valuable part of the country to which Mackenzie referred had been definitely placed beyond the frontiers of Canada.

VI. SOUTH AMERICA [1]

From the time of the arrival of the Spaniards in the New World down to the end of the sixteenth century South America had been the scene of great discoveries. In the century which followed the discoveries are, by comparison, of a minor order, and of a more detailed character. In one respect, however, they may be compared with those of the pioneers, for they were made from the same three regions in which the earliest explorations had been undertaken.

From the Plate estuary the Catholic missionaries pushed inland, and established themselves in the interior. In 1623 one of their number reached the Guarani Indians, far up the Uraguay river, while three years later another missionary, Gonzales, explored part of the Sierra de Tape, in the basin of the Ybicuhy. Further progress on the confines of Portuguese territory was, however, impossible in the face of open hostility from bands of adventurers from São Paulo. At the end of the century a Jesuit priest journeyed to the country of the Chiquitos Indians, living to the east of the Upper Mamore, and founded several stations in their country.

In Brazil the slave-raiders and prospectors covered a vast area, but made no very substantial contributions to geographical knowledge. They reached the Uraguay basin, opened up the provinces of Minas Geraes, where Fernando Diaz discovered emeralds, and of Goyaz, where gold was found, and dissipated their energies in many regions in the western mountains. In the north-east the Jesuits, at the beginning of the century, did much useful work, while an adventurer named Soares, in the course of a search for El Dorado, explored the São Francisco river.

But interesting as these minor journeys were, they were of small consequence in comparison with the advances made during this century in the Amazon basin, both from the east and from the west. In the former case the Dutch had been very active in the delta of the Amazon, and at the beginning of the century had established posts on the left bank of the Xingú. They were reinforced by new settlers in 1616, while four years earlier the French had founded the post of St Louis on the island of Maranhão. This obvious threat

[1] On South America during this period see the work of Mr E. Heawood cited above, p. 205.

to the Portuguese led to the dispatch of an expedition from Pernambuco, and to the establishment of the Portuguese town of Pará. From 1616 to 1629 the Portuguese struggled to evict the intruders, but they were not left for long in undisputed possession of the Amazon.

In 1637 there arrived at Pará a party of seven men, including two Franciscan lay brothers. They had started out from Perú in search of gold, and had sailed down the Napo and the Amazon. It was this journey which stimulated the Portuguese to explore the great river, and an expedition was fitted out, under the command of Pedro Teixeira. The voyage began on July 25, 1637, and occupied ten months. An account derived from the chief pilot thus describes the journey:

> The journey up to the arrival at Quito lasted so long a time because they came very slowly discovering the rivers and noting the ports. The said chief pilot who has measured all the days-marches and distances, says that one could navigate the river upstream in two months. The whole of this river of the Amazons, in the islands, on the banks and the lands beyond, is peopled with Indians in such numbers that to signify its multitude, the chief pilot of this expedition, Bento de Acosta, a man experienced in these discoveries, who navigated the river and all those that enter into it, until the arrival at Quito, noting the land and observing its qualities that are so great and the Indians so numberless [says] that if a dart were to fall from the air, it would strike the head of an Indian and not fall on the ground. And not only the river of the Amazons is so thronged with people, but also the rivers which flow into it, in which the said pilot navigated for three or four days and says that each one of these rivers is a well-peopled kingdom, and the main river is an entire world greater than has been discovered up till now in all America.[1]

Teixeira went up the Amazon and the Napo, and finally up a tributary of the latter to Quito. His accomplishment roused the jealousy of the Spaniards, and they ordered that he should return by the same route and should take two Spanish Jesuits with him to make a survey of the river. The party set out on February 16, 1639, and reached Pará on December 12, without any outstanding adventures. One of the Jesuits, Cristoval de Acuña, wrote an account of this expedition, but its publication was suppressed by the Spaniards for political reasons.[2] It shows that the knowledge of the river and its tributaries, as well as of the Indians, was both extensive and, in the main, accurate.

A number of other journeys were made in this region from the east. The Tocantins river was ascended to the latitude of 6° S., an overland route from Maranhão to Pernambuco was opened up,

---

[1] Quoted by Rev. G. Edmundson in " The Voyage of Pedro Teixeira on the Amazon from Pará to Quito and back, 1637–39," in *Transactions of the Royal Historical Society*, fourth series, vol. iii (1920), p. 61.

[2] Portugal broke away from the Spanish union in 1640.

several expeditions were made up the Amazon to the Rio Negro, and a great amount of knowledge was acquired about the major features of North-eastern Brazil.

From Perú the missionaries pushed westward, and collected much information about the upper tributaries of the Amazon. In 1602 Jesuits went down the Napo to the valley of the Marañon, and several other journeys were made to this valley, where a mission was established in 1638. About the middle of the century another missionary, who was working in the Huallaga valley, opened up a route to Quito by the Marañon and the Napo. At the same time the Franciscans explored parts of the Huallaga, the Perene, and the Ucayali rivers, and both missionaries and lay adventurers reached the Madeira. In 1670 an expedition was sent to find an Inca kingdom supposed to exist to the south-east of Cuzco, and although the search was not successful, part of the Beni river was explored. About the same time the Jesuits began missionary work in the Guapay valley, and continued their activities during the remainder of the century.

Thus in many directions the missionaries were making numerous, if small, additions to the geographical knowledge of South America. But none did more than the Jesuit Samuel Fritz, who spent thirty-seven years among the Indians of the Amazon valley.[1] He began work among the Omaguas, who lived on the lower course of the river Napo, in 1686, and continued alone until serious illness compelled him to go down the river to Pará to seek medical help. Here he was arrested, and kept a prisoner for nearly two years. In 1691 he was allowed to go back, up the Amazon, to his mission, and in the following year he went to Lima, to report on the Portuguese encroachments on Spanish territory. Between 1693 and 1702 he was continuously engaged in missionary activity, moving about among the Indians and doing his best to protect them from Portuguese slave-raiders. From 1704 to 1713 he was superior of the whole mission, and spent much time visiting the Indians in the Marañon valley, where the last ten years of his life (1714–24) were devoted to work among the Xeberos.

The chief interest of Samuel Fritz lay in his Indian converts, " all his dear children," but he was able to collect much valuable geographical information, which he embodied in a map, first published in 1691 and reissued in 1707. His journey down the Amazon to Pará and back again, and his endless travels among the tribes living along the Marañon, fully qualified him for the task, while the excellence of the map is a striking tribute to his careful observation. He is typical of many devoted priests in South America and else-

[1] See *Journal of the Travels and Labours of Father Samuel Fritz in the River of the Amazons between* 1686 *and* 1723, translated by Rev. G. Edmundson (Hakluyt Society, second series, vol. li).

where, and, as his biographer remarks, " He was worthy of living for many centuries that he might complete the conversion of all the heathen of the Marañon."

The Portuguese slave-raids, which caused Fritz so much distress, extended also to the Rio Negro, and it was a desire to ascertain the conditions of the frontier zone that led to the first authentic journey from the Orinoco to the Amazon. This was made by Father Ramon, who started from a Spanish mission in Venezuela in 1744 and met Portuguese slave-traders at the junction of the Guaviare and the Upper Orinoco. In their company he went by the Cassiquiare to the Rio Negro.[1] Several other expeditions were also made to this region, including a Government expedition in 1756 and a futile search for El Dorado, while between 1775 and 1780 Antonio Santos crossed to the Rio Branco. But the real exploration of this country had to wait until the last year of the century, when Alexander von Humboldt began his epoch-making travels.

The scientific expedition of La Condamine to Perú in 1736 also resulted in some additional knowledge of the Amazon basin. The main object of the party was to measure an arc in Perú, and this was successfully completed by 1743. La Condamine then decided to return by the Amazon, and his voyage down the river " was of value as being the first descent of [that river] by a trained man of science." [2] Godin, another member of the party, also returned by that route in 1749, and his wife, who followed some twenty years later, had the misfortune to be stranded alone in the forests of the valley until the friendly help of Indians enabled her to reach Pará.

On the southern side of the Amazon basin the discovery of minerals in Matto Grosso in 1734 drew the attention of Portuguese adventurers to a little-known region, and one of their number, Manoel Felix de Lima, disappointed of his expectations of wealth, pushed westward on an exploring expedition. He reached the Guapore river, sailed down it to the Madeira, and ultimately arrived on the Amazon. In 1749 an expedition from Pará, under Francisco Leme, set out to repeat this journey in the reverse direction, and after great hardship successfully reached the Portuguese territory whence Manoel had set out in 1742.

Still farther southward, another Portuguese went down the Cuyabá river, from the town of that name, struck the Paraguay and ascended it to the divide between it and the Amazon, and finally made his way to the Tapajos, a tributary of the latter river.

In the Paraguay basin itself some very important work was undertaken during this century. In 1691 the Chiquitos Indians had been

---

[1] The junction of the Orinoco and the Amazon was known much earlier than this. See Edmundson, in *Transactions of the Royal Historical Society*, p. 64, quoted above, where he shows that an Englishman, Major John Scott, wrote an account of the Amazon valley about 1669.

[2] Heawood, *op. cit.*, p. 370.

visited, and several years later attempts were made to open up a route to their country first by the Paraguay and later by the Pilcomayo river. These efforts were almost crowned with success when, in 1721, parties from Tucuman and the Pilcomayo nearly met. The result of this activity, faithfully reflected in the maps of D'Anville, was a much-improved knowledge of the Chaco region, where a blank remained on the map a hundred years after the attempts of these missionaries had come to an end. Their efforts were renewed in 1741, but finally ceased with the expulsion of the Jesuits in 1767.

Shortly after this an exploration of the greatest importance was made by Captain Felix de Azara, who was originally sent out to delimit the boundary between Spanish and Portuguese territory. As there was some delay in beginning his official work, the Spanish officer made a number of independent journeys in the Paraguay-Paraná basin. He made a valuable topographical survey, and in addition contributed materially to the knowledge of the natural history of the region. After thirteen years' work in this area Azara was employed on the southern frontier of the Spanish settlements and in the region of the Lower Paraná before finally surveying the eastern border. His work ended in 1801, after he had accomplished more than any other single Spaniard in the work of geographical discovery in South America.

A few other journeys complete the story of the exploration of South America before the time of Humboldt. The travels of Ruiz, Pavon, and Dombey in the forest country to the east of Perú between 1781 and 1788, and the explorations among the many islands of the coast of Chile by J. de Moraleda y Montero between 1786 and 1796, were of a specialist character, and belong rather to the century which follows. Of a similar nature was the survey of the greater part of the west coast by the Frenchman Feuillée between 1707 and 1712. On the other side of the continent, in what was almost unknown Patagonia, Falkner traced the course of the Rio Negro in 1778, and four years later Viedma explored the Santa Cruz river.

Thus the century closed with no major region of South America entirely unknown, although in many places knowledge was, if not scanty, frequently very inaccurate.

PART II

THE NINETEENTH CENTURY AND AFTER

CHAPTER XIII

ASIA [1]

ALTHOUGH most parts of Asia had been visited before the beginning of the nineteenth century, there was still much exploration to be done before its geography could be fully known. Arabia, Indo-China, and Central Asia were almost complete blanks on the map, while even in countries like Siberia, China, and India, which had witnessed much activity in the seventeenth and eighteenth centuries, there were many unknown regions.

The period of exploration now under consideration falls broadly into two halves. During the first half of the century a number of pioneer journeys were made in almost every part of the continent, and these laid the foundation for the scientific work which followed after about the middle of the century. The great advances of Russia to the Amur in 1854, to the south of Orenburg after 1854, and to the Tian Shan in 1856 mark a turning-point in the exploration of Northern and Central Asia. Similarly, the journey of the brothers Schlagintweit indicates the beginning of the penetration of Central Asia from the Indian side. In Arabia the map of Ritter (1852) forms a suitable dividing point, while Yule's map of Burma (1855) and that of Parkes for Siam (1855) are indicative of significant stages on the road of discovery. The exploration of Japan, the scientific discovery of China, with which the name of Richthofen is so prominently associated, the accurate delineation of the features of Afghanistan and Persia, and the mapping of French Indo-China and Siam belong almost wholly to the second half of the century.

The exploration of the continent proceeded from so many scattered centres and was carried out under such differing circumstances that no description which is merely chronological will give the true picture of its development. The outstanding feature is the intense activity in Central Asia after 1855. By working round the

[1] On Asia as a whole see Sir Richard Temple, " On the Progress of our Geographical Knowledge of Asia during the Last Fifty Years (1830–1880)," in *Proc. R.G.S.*, new series, vol. iii, p. 610, and W. Barthold, *Die geographische und historische Erforschung des Orients mit besonderer Berücksichtigung der russischen Arbeiten* (1913).

continent from the north through the west and south to China and Japan one can close in Central Asia, and thus end the description with an account of that area, which for geographical and political reasons remained unknown until recent times.

I. NORTHERN ASIA [1]

As already explained, the Russians had gained a fair knowledge of the major features of Northern Asia during the seventeenth and eighteenth centuries, but they had been repulsed in their efforts to dominate the Amur basin. Almost as soon as the nineteenth century begins they renewed exploration in the Far East. The sea expeditions of Krusenstern in 1805 and Kotzebue in 1817 did much to clear up the remaining problems of the North Pacific, and added valuable information about Kamchatka and Sakhalin.[2] Similarly, the political mission of Golovkin to China in 1805 drew attention to the Amur region, although the proposals to attach scientific explorers to the mission were not carried out. But the most important work of the first half of the century was done in the north of the continent. In 1828 Erman examined the country between the north of the Urals and the mouth of the Ob, and continued his journey across the continent to Kamchatka. In 1829 Humboldt, who was accompanied by Rose and Ehrenberg, made his last scientific journey. It was remarkable for the ground it covered and for the acuteness of the conclusions which Humboldt formed rather than for any spectacular discovery. The party travelled out by way of Moscow, Perm, and Tobolsk to the Ob river, where they turned south to the Altai Mountains. The return route lay more to the south, through Omsk, down the Volga to the shores of the Caspian Sea, and finally up the Don to Moscow. The result of the journey was the publication of a brilliant though somewhat hasty account of the minerals and the geology of the region visited.

In 1830 important additions to knowledge were made by Fuss and Bunge, who crossed the Gobi Desert from Peking to Kiakhta, while two years later a Russian colonel, Ladijinski, engaged on a political mission, visited the Amur valley.

The most important exploration of the first half of the century was, however, that of Middendorf in Northern and Eastern Siberia. His object was to obtain a correct knowledge of the region between the Yenisei and Khatanga rivers, and as far north as the sea. He left Turukhansk on March 23, 1843, went down the frozen Yenisei, over the tundra to the Piasina river, and beyond to the basin of the Khatanga. His companion, Branth, remained on a

---

[1] On Northern Asia in general see L. Ravenau, " Travaux des Russes dans l'Asie septentrionale," in *Annales de géographie*, vol. vii, p. 351.
[2] For further details see below, pp. 447 and 448.

tributary of the latter river, while Middendorf went northward to the Taimir Peninsula, and reached the sea on August 12. He suffered extreme hardship through the failure of his supplies, but managed to struggle back, and was able to collect most valuable information about the conditions of animal and plant life in this desolate region.

Middendorf then undertook a journey across the continent, from Yakutsk to the Sea of Okhotsk, crossing the Stanovoi Mountains to Udsk. He continued his explorations into the basin of the Amur

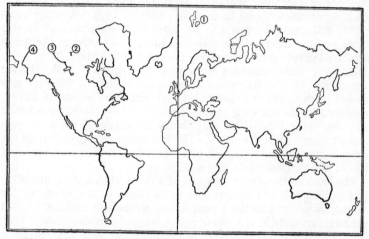

Fig. 27. OUTLINE SKETCH OF THE WORLD MAP OF J. CARY, 1801

Note the great improvement in the Pacific Ocean and Australasia, and the completion of the west coast of North America and the north coast of Asia. In the far north are Spitsbergen (1), the mouth of the Coppermine river (2), the delta of the Mackenzie river (3), and Icy Cape (4). A number of islands have been omitted.

as far as Lake Baikal. Again his observations were of the highest order, while his success, as well as his reports, once more attracted attention to the Amur river.

Another pioneer of the early period, A. Castrén, travelled over the length and breadth of Siberia between 1842 and 1849. His object was to study the aboriginal peoples, their language and customs, and his journeys took him from the Urals to the Yenisei and Lake Baikal. Similar motives inspired Ahlquist, who traversed Siberia between 1853 and 1858, and Radlov, who studied the peoples of the Altai regions about the year 1868.

When Muraviev became Governor of Eastern Siberia in 1847 a period of great activity began. The next year an unsuccessful attempt was made to explore the Amur river, but by 1850 the mouth had been reached, and in 1854 Muraviev led a military expedition down the river, and provided the material for the first modern account of it. Shortly before this, in 1846, the Imperial Geographical Society of St Petersburg was founded, and the efforts of this body were directed to this same region where the military authorities were active. The result was that from 1854 onward a very large number of expeditions were made in the trans-Baikal country. The astronomer L. A. Schwarz determined many positions east of Lake Baikal between 1849 and 1852. L. von Schrenck studied the natural history of the region round the mouth of the Amur in 1854, visited the island of Sakhalin in the following year, returned to the Amur and ascended the Usuri river for some distance, and was back again in Sakhalin in the early part of 1856. Another naturalist, Maksimovich, was also occupied from 1853 to 1856 in this same region. In 1855 the observations of Peschurov on the Amur furnished material for an entirely new map of the river.

In 1854 these scientists were reinforced by the East Siberian expedition of the Imperial Geographical Society. Schwarz was placed in charge of the expedition, and with some assistants was responsible for the mapping of the country. The geologist F. Schmidt and the naturalists Glehn and Radde were among the more prominent members of the party. The last made extensive travels not only in the Far East, but in other parts of Russia, and his work was of the greatest value to geographers.

The work of this expedition was of a detailed character, attention being given to the tributaries on both banks of the Amur, to the Angara river, and to the basins of the Vitim and Olekma. Other explorations outside the Amur region were also undertaken. Thus K. von Ditmar was engaged in Kamchatka from 1851 to 1855, while Schmidt in 1860, and Glehn in 1861, visited Sakhalin. In the same region, though unconnected with the work of the mission, Colonel Bugodorski's Boundary Commission of 1862 surveyed the Russo-Chinese frontier in accordance with the terms of the treaty of 1860. The result of all this work was a complete revision of the map, the determination of the position of many places and natural features, and considerable modification of the current ideas about Eastern Siberia.

Very shortly after further knowledge of the coastal regions came through the expedition of Prince Kropotkin in 1864 from the Argun river to the Sungari, across Northern Manchuria, while on the south coast of that country Timroth and Helmersen were carrying out geological investigations between 1862 and 1865.

The expedition of Staritski to the Pacific Ocean (1866–71) also resulted in more accurate knowledge of the coastline of Manchuria, Sakhalin, the Sea of Okhotsk, and Kamchatka. At the same time Lopatin was engaged in topographical and geological work in the northern part of the Vitim plateau in 1865, and, in the following year, along the Yenisei river to Turukhansk. He collected very full information, but his diaries were not published until the end of the century.

The explorations of Lopatin were supplemented by the important journeys of Chekanovski between 1873 and 1876. In all, three expeditions were made, first to the Lower Lena and Upper Tunguska valleys, then to the tundra of the Olenek, and finally to the mouth of the last-named river. Although the main object of the explorer was to study the geology of the country, he made a number of astronomical observations, and greatly improved the cartography of a little-known region. His exploits entitle him " to rank as a worthy successor of Middendorf who alone among men of science had traversed this region on his way to the distant north." [1]

Farther toward the west the great unknown region of Tobolsk was opened up by the expedition of Khandachevski in 1877–81. He followed the rivers Irtish and Ob from Tobolsk to Obdorsk, in the north of the province, ascended the Polui river, and returned almost due south across the country to Omsk. Western Siberia was also visited at this time by Adrianov, who carried out geographical and geological work in the Kuznetsk district, in the upper valley of the Yenisei (1880), while Lansdell, an English clergyman, travelled throughout the country by an unfrequented route, crossing from the Urals to Vladivostok. The main purpose of Lansdell was to visit prisons and hospitals, but he was able to give his countrymen some idea of the great progress which had been made by the Russians during the century.

Although much had been done, the Russians did not cease to explore the remoter parts of the country. Polyakov visited Sakhalin in 1881–82, and found large areas entirely unknown. He explored many parts of the island, and discovered the only accessible harbour on the coast, at the mouth of the Tym river. The French engineer Martin, who had gone to Eastern Siberia on business connected with the gold-mines in the Olekma valley, diverted his energies to exploration, and visited the country to the south-west of that valley. Later he went to the Stanovoi Mountains, but, finding he could not cross them near the source of the Aldan river, he followed them southward and reached the Amur, eventually returning to Irkutsk. This unofficial exploration was continued, in 1884, in the Amur basin. Martin travelled down the main river, and up its tributary the Usuri, and thence overland to Vladivostok. He kept a careful record of his routes, and was thus able to add something to the map of these regions.

In 1885 Bunge and Baron von Toll left Yakutsk and began the exploration of the Yana valley. They continued their journey to the north coast, and reached the New Siberian Islands. This region was again visited by Cherski in 1891. He began to explore the Kolyma,

[1] Sir R. Alcock, in Proc. R.G.S., old series, vol. xx, p. 418.

Indigirka, and Yana rivers, but he died before the task was complete. Cherski had rendered great service by his earlier geological surveys in the Lake Baikal area (1877–81), and by his death Russian science was deprived of a very able explorer. He was succeeded as leader of the northern expedition by Baron von Toll, who successfully completed the programme, covered more than 3000 miles of survey, stretching over fifty degrees of longitude, and returned with most valuable information.

Equally valuable was the work of Maydell, who had lived for twenty years in Siberia, and for ten years among the Yakuts in the extreme north-east of the country. His researches, published in 1893, did much to elucidate a very little-known part of the country. They were supplemented by the reports of the Jesup expedition (1900–1) to Northern Kamchatka, Anadir, and other parts of North-eastern Asia.

In 1895 two important expeditions were sent out. The first explored the lower course of the Yenisei, sailed round the Yamal Peninsula, examined Ob Bay, and proceeded up the Ob and Irtish to Tobolsk. The second, under Bogdanovich, went to the Stanovoi Mountains, to begin a systematic exploration of the country round the Sea of Okhotsk. Bogdanovich made important additions to the knowledge of the northern part of the range, examined the coastline from Petropavlovsk, in Kamchatka, to the mouth of the Amur, and extended his journey into the Liaotung peninsula. In addition to the discoveries already mentioned, he located new gold-fields in the mountains. A further expedition, in 1897, surveyed the shores of Lake Kosso-Gol, in Northern Mongolia, and explored the Munku-Sardyk Range, in the extreme south of Siberia.

The construction of the Siberian Railway, which was begun in 1891, led to much detailed geographical work along the whole route, which lies on the southern borders of Siberia. It is due to this fact, as well as to the desire to open up the mineral areas, that the exploration of Southern Siberia had progressed much farther than that of the north, where the geographical conditions render the country less suitable for settlement. Yet the important geographical expeditions of the present century have, almost without exception, been sent to Northern Siberia. In 1905 a party was dispatched to explore the Khatanga river. It accomplished much useful work in the upper part of the basin, and then followed the course of the river to the sea. Three years later another expedition, under Shitkov, was sent to the Yamal Peninsula, and produced an excellent account of part of a region which is still largely unknown. A third expedition, under Tolmachev, was sent to the north coast, in 1909, to ascertain the possibilities of commerce between the Pacific and the Kolyma river *via* Bering Strait and to survey parts of the coastline. Another party, sent at the same time, was instructed to survey the coast from the Lena to the Kolyma. Both expeditions were successful, the coasts were surveyed, and Tolmachev reported favourably on the possibility of trade.

In spite of the activity of a century there remain many unexplored parts of Northern Siberia. As late as 1926 S. Obruchev, in the course of exploring the Indigirka river, discovered a new mountain range in North-east Siberia, although its precise extent is not known.[1] Before the expedition it was supposed that the country to the east of the river was a vast lowland: now the map shows a second range lying within—*i.e.*, to the north of—the known arc formed of the Verkhoyansk Mountains and their easterly continuation. To this new range the name of Cherski has been given, in honour of the explorer to whose work reference has already been made

II. RUSSIAN SOUTH-WEST ASIA

The country lying between the Caspian Sea and the highlands of Central Asia stands in the same relationship, politically, to India and Persia as does the Amur basin to China. In both regions political questions drew Russian forces onward, although in both regions their advance was anticipated by geographers.

The exploration of the region now under consideration may be considered from two aspects. In the eastern part of the area the approach was toward Central Asia in its more limited sense, and ended when the exploration of the mountain region began. This is the shorter story, and will be dismissed briefly. The Russians had begun to explore the Altai Mountains in 1826, and soon after further information about this region came from the journey of Humboldt already mentioned. But its conquest really dates from the foundation of Sergiopol in 1831. Three years later Fedorov reached the Lepsa river, at its entrance into Lake Balkash. The district of Semiryechansk was surveyed by Schrenck and Karelin between 1840 and 1842, and ten years later explorers had reached Kuldja, in the upper valley of the Ili. Similar progress was made southward, and a fortress was built at Vyernyi in 1855. In the course of the next three years Russian surveys extended to the southern shore of Issyk Kul, and included the valley of the Chu. At this point the journeys of Semenov to the Tian Shan Mountains and of Golubev to Dzungaria mark the beginning of the exploration of Central Asia proper.

The other advance of the Russians was made by way of either the Caspian Sea or the Sea of Aral. In 1819 Muraviev surveyed the

[1] On this new discovery see *G.J.*, vol. lxx, p. 464. Much scientific work of a detailed character has been carried on recently by the Russians in Siberia, but it is chiefly connected with Polar research and is referred to at pp. 465, 466. But see V. A. Obruchev, "The Yablonovoi and Stanovoi Ranges in the Light of New Data," in *G.J.*, vol. lxxxvi, p. 422, and H. F. Smolka, *Forty Thousand against the Arctic* (1937).

Caspian Sea, and from the Bay of Balkhan proceeded to Khiva. This city was reached again by the Russians several times during the second decade of the century, and by the English in 1832 and again in 1839. In 1841 Lehmann visited Samarkand and the Zarafshan valley. Meanwhile renewed surveys had been carried out on the Caspian Sea in 1836, and much systematic work on the Sea of Aral was undertaken by Butakov in 1848. Soon after the Russians began the exploration of the Amu Darya and Syr Darya.

In 1854 the survey of the country round Orenburg commenced, and thereafter progress continued steadily toward the south-east, while between 1858 and 1860 attention was given to the Aral-Caspian depression and to further improvement in the map of the Caspian Sea. All this geographical activity was the prelude to vigorous political action in the following decade. Samarkand fell to the Russians in 1865, and Bokhara three years later. It was during this period that Butakov ascended the Syr Darya in a steamer as far as Chinaz, surveying its banks and determining a number of positions (1863). Between 1865 and 1868 C. V. Sturve fixed a large number of points, including Bokhara, Samarkand, and Turkestan. The Hungarian A. Vambéry also made his celebrated visit at this time. Although his object was not strictly scientific, and his disguise made it impracticable to take observations, his remarks on " Central Asia " were of considerable value. At the end of the decade two journeys were made between Khokand and the Issyk Kul, thus linking up the two areas where exploration had been most progressive.

From the year 1870 onward the Russians began to turn their attention to the steppe country east of the Caspian Sea. From Krasnovodsk two expeditions were sent out, one of which penetrated 360 miles to the north-east, while the other went nearly 200 miles due eastward. These were followed by the exploration of the dry bed of the Oxus and the country of the Turkomans in 1872. The next year Khiva fell to the Russians, and the task of investigating the problem of the Oxus was renewed. By 1875 the mapping of the old bed was complete, although a new survey in 1883 disclosed the fact that the Uzboi was probably not a former channel of the Amu Darya. By 1878 the Oxus was accurately known for over 500 miles from the Sea of Aral. Eight years later the Afghan Boundary Commission surveyed the frontier from the point where the territories of Russia, Afghanistan, and Persia meet to the Oxus, north-west of Balkh, and thence eastward along the river.

The advance eastward from the Caspian Sea was followed by a move toward the south, where the Tekkes were giving trouble to the Russians. An expedition was sent against them in 1879, and within two years they had been subjugated. In 1881 Lessar carried

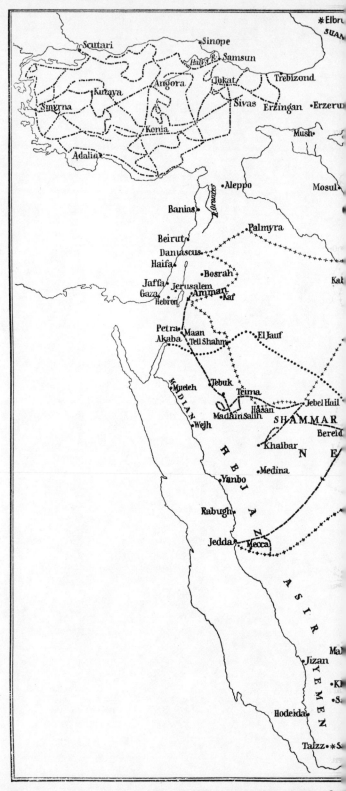

Fig. 28. SOUTH-WEST ASIA AFTER 1800

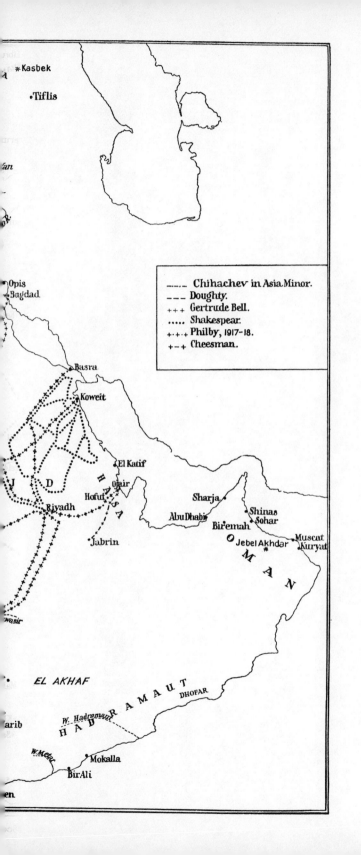

*Kasbek

•Tiflis

an

•Opis
•Bagdad

Chihachev in Asia Minor.
Doughty.
Gertrude Bell.
Shakespear.
Philby, 1917-18.
Cheesman.

•Basra

•Koweit

J   D   •El Katif
              Ojair
Hofuf•
•Riyadh

•Jabrin

Sharja•
AbuDhabi•   •Shinas
        Bir'emah •Sohar
        Jebel Akhdar •Muscat
              •Kuryat

wasir

EL AKHAF

Marib   W. Hadramaut   DHOFAR
        HADRAMAUT

W.Meifa •Mokalla
    •BirAli

en

the Russian surveys beyond the new frontier into Pers:a, and in the following year he surveyed the country in the valley of the Hari Rud, as far as Herat, a point which had already been reached from the Oxus in 1878. With this extension of geographical knowledge beyond Russian territory the exploration of South-western Asia was completed, although a considerable amount of detailed work remained to be done in Turkestan and the Kirghiz steppes, where the surveys had been undertaken in 1879.

A survey carried out in 1882 afforded a basis for the delineation of the frontier between Russia and Persia, while in 1886 the Russians extended their topographical work into the Merv region. In the same year Radde and Konshin explored the country between Askabad, Merv, and Meshed and along part of the Afghan frontier, while Schwarz commanded a party engaged in important topographical work in Eastern Bokhara. At the same time other surveyors were busy mapping parts of the Zarafshan valley and the western area of the Hissar Mountains, and in the course of a few years the whole of this region was well known.

III. South-west Asia

The southward advance of Russia against Persia during the first thirteen years of the nineteenth century led to the occupation of Georgia and, subsequently, to Russian exploration in the Caucasus. The war with Persia was renewed in 1826, and at its close two years later practically all the Caucasus became Russian territory. This gave rise to the first Russian explorations in the region and to those early surveys on the Caspian Sea which have already been mentioned.

The one man who did more than any other to improve knowledge of the Caucasian region was the Russian Abich, who spent thirty-three years (1844–77) in the study of its geology and topography. His work was supplemented by that of Russian officers, who, under General Khodzko, surveyed the Caucasian provinces and part of Armenia between 1847 and 1863. The latter produced a good general map of the lowland country, but left out a large number of important peaks in the Caucasus Mountains. During this period Radde, whose exploration in other parts of Russian Asia has already been mentioned, began his long connexion with the Caucasus districts ; by his travels, as well as by his organization of the Caucasian Museum at Tiflis, he added greatly to general knowledge of the region, and during the latter half of the century performed a work comparable only with that of Abich.[1]

A turning-point in the exploration of the Caucasus came with the journey of Mr Douglas W. Freshfield in 1868. " Before our journey," he wrote, " no great peak of the chain had ever been

[1] For a brief account of Radde's work see *G.J.*, vol. xxi, p. 563.

climbed and no pass over the range between Kasbek and Elbruz had ever been described, except from hearsay, in any book of travel." [1] In that year Freshfield, with two companions and an Alpine guide, climbed Kasbek and Elbruz peaks, and visited the more important valleys between them on the south side of the mountains, discovering a number of great peaks in the course of his journey. In the same year Favre began his geological researches in the central part of the range.

This phase of exploration, characterized by work among the mountain peaks, was not stopped by the new survey of the Caucasian provinces undertaken by the Russian Government in 1880. Between 1884 and 1887 M. de Déchy made a number of journeys, the last in company with Freshfield, while in each year between 1886 and 1891 separate expeditions attacked the lesser-known parts of the range. Among the last that of V. Sella is notable, not only for the magnificent photographic work accomplished, but also because he anticipated the Russian surveyors in parts of the Suanetian range.

Hitherto the main field of exploration had been in the Central Caucasus, although other areas were not neglected. Early in the present century the Russian topographers turned their attention to these little-known parts, and it may now be said that this region is well known.

While the Russian surveyors were gradually pushing toward Asia Minor and Armenia from the north-east a large number of explorers were entering that country from the west, and were making known to Western Europe the regions which once formed the heart of the classical world. The first scientific explorer in this region was Niebuhr, who crossed Asia Minor and travelled through Syria and Palestine, on his way to Arabia, in 1766. At the beginning of the nineteenth century W. M. Leake visited Asia Minor, and produced a map much in advance of previous compilations. He was followed, six years later, by J. M. Kinneir. The new information thus acquired was used by the English geographer Rennell in the compilation of a great work *The Comparative Geography of Western Asia*.

Captain Beaufort began a survey of the south coast in 1812, and this was extended to the west coast, by Captain Copeland and others, between 1834 and 1847. At the same time a number of important journeys had been made in the interior. Hamilton visited the valley of the Halys, and explored the country to the south of the Sea of Marmora. Ainsworth led an expedition organized by the Royal Geographical Society and the Society for Promoting Christian Knowledge to examine the land of the Nestorian Christians. The party left Scutari in September 1838, traversed the coastal regions toward Sinope, and then turned inland to Angora, where

[1] *The Exploration of the Caucasus* (2 vols., 1896), vol. i, p. 6.

they spent the winter. From Angora they crossed the whole country to the Euphrates. In 1839–40 Ainsworth made another journey through Asia Minor from Constantinople to Mosul.

British consular agents were also very active at this time. Brant, from Erzerum, visited the country to the west of Lake Van, Sutter covered a large area between Erzerum, Sivas, Samsun, and Trebizond, while Lord Pollington went from Erzerum through Mush to Aleppo.

In 1841 H. Kiepert first visited Asia Minor, and began to collect material for his monumental map. He used in addition information obtained by earlier travellers, and by the Germans Moltke and Fischer. The map first appeared between 1843 and 1846, but was revised from time to time, and for this purpose Kiepert made in all four journeys to Asia Minor prior to 1892. The map was unfinished when Kiepert died in 1899, but the work was completed by his son in the early years of the present century.

A large number of relatively small but important journeys continued to be made in this region, which attracted in particular many archæologists. Fellows in Lycia (1838–43), Barth in the south-west (1847) and in Central Asia Minor (1858), Wilson, Davis, and Bryce are some of the better-known travellers in the period of Kiepert's earlier activities. Ramsay, Hogarth, Munro, all primarily interested in archæology, may be mentioned as belonging to the later years of the nineteenth century.

Kiepert's researches in Asia Minor were only equalled by those of P. von Chihachev, who began his travels while *attaché* to the Russian Embassy at Constantinople in 1842–44, resumed them in 1848–53, during which time he traversed the country in six journeys, and returned a third time to Asia Minor and Armenia in 1853. His work was particularly valuable for the sciences of geology and botany. In Armenia the earlier researches of Abich have been supplemented by many other investigators, including Lynch, who made two journeys, in 1893 and in 1898.

In the present century A. Philippson, who has devoted much time to a study of Mediterranean lands, visited Asia Minor (1900–4), and added greatly to the knowledge of the geography of its western parts. Yet even now it is surprising how large an area remains imperfectly known. Although the country has been crossed in every direction, the amount of scientific survey work that has been accomplished is relatively very small.[1]

In Syria and Palestine [2] there have been many travellers throughout the period covered by this book, but until the second half of

[1] See H. Fischer, " Geschichte der Kartographie von Vorderasien," in *P.M.*, vol. lxvi (1920), pp. 82 *et seq.*
[2] Sir Charles Watson's *Fifty Years' Work in the Holy Land* (1915) gives a complete account of the activities of the Palestine Exploration Fund, and has been extensively used here.

the nineteenth century very little accurate information about the geography of the country was available. This is probably due to the fact that the attractions of some places were so strong that all travellers covered the same ground.

Nineteenth-century exploration begins here with the travels of Seetzen in 1805 and of Burckhardt in 1812, in both cases as a preliminary to work in Arabia. The first named collected much information that was new, and his travels roused considerable interest, but soon after the publication of the account of his journey disturbed political conditions made further exploration difficult. It did not, however, entirely cease, and in 1837 the German explorers Schubert and Roth were able to make valuable barometric observations on the Dead Sea.

But the turning-point in exploration is the journey of E. Robinson in 1838. He had been appointed Professor of Biblical Literature in the Union Theological Seminary of New York, and decided that he could not efficiently discharge his duties without visiting Palestine. He was accompanied by Dr E. Smith, who had lived for many years in Syria, and was able to supply him with much valuable information. The results of this journey are to be found in his *Biblical Researches in Palestine* (1841), which earned for its author the Patron's Medal of the Royal Geographical Society. Robinson returned to Palestine in 1852, and again added much to the knowledge of its geography.

Robinson's first journey was immediately followed by a number of small expeditions which had no connexion with his own work. Thus in 1841 Symonds carried out a triangulation from Jaffa to Jerusalem and the Dead Sea. In 1847 and again in 1848 the Jordan was traced from the Sea of Galilee to the Dead Sea, and in the latter year the Dead Sea itself was surveyed. In 1851–52, and in 1861–62, Lieutenant Van de Velde made extensive travels, as a result of which he was able to produce a much-improved map of Palestine. Other less scientific investigators, like Töbler, Guerin, Stanley, and Grove, kept alive the interest in Palestine, and added somewhat to the knowledge of its geography, while in Syria railway surveys from the mouth of the Orontes to Aleppo and the explorations of Wetzstein in the neighbourhood of Damascus (1858) supplied more accurate information for the map of those areas.

Real survey work in Palestine began with the dispatch of a party of Royal Engineers to Jerusalem in 1864, to prepare a map of the city and surrounding country in connexion with the provision of an improved water-supply. This small enterprise was a great success, and led to the formation of the " Palestine Exploration Fund, for the purpose of investigating the Archæology, Geography, Geology, and Natural History of Palestine." Thereafter scientific investigations in Palestine were carried out with a continuity and a vigour hitherto unknown. It is only necessary here to mention the more conspicuous geographical results. The first two years were devoted to a reconnaissance of the country from Damascus to Jerusalem, as a result of which

> accurate observations for time and latitude were taken at forty-nine points between Beirut and Hebron, and a line of azimuth was carried from Banias to Jerusalem. On these were based a series of maps, on the scale of one inch to the mile, of the backbone of the country from north to south, including the Sea of Galilee and the water-courses descending to its western shore.[1]

In 1869 an expedition was sent to Lebanon, and in the two following years the country west of the Dead Sea was explored. The topographical survey of Western Palestine occupied from 1871 to 1875, and, after a short interval, was resumed and completed in 1877. Four years later the survey of Eastern Palestine was begun under Captain C. R. Conder, who had been responsible for most of the earlier work, and this continued until 1882, when it was stopped by the Turkish authorities.[2]

The valley of Arabah, running southward from the Dead Sea, was surveyed by Professor Hull and Captain H. H. Kitchener in 1883–84, and the country east of the Jordan was again explored in the two following years. After this most of the expeditions were occupied with the archæology of the country until 1913, when the survey of Southern Palestine was undertaken.

In Syria less was accomplished, but the work of G. E. Post and West deserves mention, for they carried the surveys of Palestine into the Lebanon and Anti-Lebanon ranges, as well as adding much to botanical knowledge. The geological work of M. Blankenhorn (1893–1914) has also contributed greatly to the geographical knowledge of Syria and the bordering lands.

The great archæological wealth of Western Asia has always attracted explorers, and this is particularly true of Mesopotamia,[3] where, apart from the examination of the remains, little geographical work was accomplished during the nineteenth century. Along its eastern borders, where a survey party was engaged on work on the Turko-Persian frontier on the outbreak of the Great War,[4] a number of explorers, whose main sphere of activity was in Persia, added important details to the map : an account of their work is given later. But in the lowlands of the Tigris and Euphrates very little accurate geographical work was accomplished.

---

[1] Sir Charles Watson, *op. cit.*, p. 35. [2] See C. R. Conder, *Palestine* (1889).
[3] On Mesopotamia see H. V. Hilprecht, *Explorations in Bible Lands during the Nineteenth Century* (1903), and *Records of the Survey of India*, vol. xx, Part I (1925).
[4] This commission was finishing work which had been started as early as 1848. See *G.J.*, vol. lxvi, p. 227.

GEOGRAPHICAL DISCOVERY AND EXPLORATION

The first exploration of importance during the nineteenth century was that of C. J. Rich, who went out to India by way of Aleppo and Basra in 1807, and shortly afterward returned to Bagdad as Resident of the East India Company. In the course of nearly fourteen years spent in the country Rich was able to survey and describe the ruins of Babylon and Nineveh, to collect much general topographical information, and to make a survey of the Euphrates river for a short distance above Hit. Some of Rich's work was used by Rennell in his *Topography of Ancient Babylon*, while his surveys were incorporated in those of the Euphrates expedition of 1835–37.

A few details were added by Buckingham (1816), Porter (1818), and Mignan (1826), but the next large advance was made by the Euphrates expedition. Its objects were political and commercial, to open up railway or steamer communication with the Far East. This involved a survey of the northern part of Syria and of the rivers Euphrates and Tigris which was carried out by a party of fifteen officers, under the command of Colonel F. R. Chesney. They transported the parts of two iron steamers from the Syrian coast to the Euphrates, made a reconnaissance of Northern Syria, and began the descent of the Euphrates in March 1836. One ship was lost in a storm, but the other succeeded in completing the survey of the Euphrates, and ascended the Tigris to the rapids below Samarra. After this the breakdown of the remaining steamer and political complications brought operations to an end. Twelve maps, published in 1849, are the practical result of the expedition, and these remained for many parts the standard authorities for much of the region visited. In addition valuable archæological and descriptive works came from the pens of the leader and of the geologist W. F. Ainsworth.

This expedition was followed almost immediately by the valuable researches of H. C. Rawlinson. He had gone to Bombay in 1827, and seven years later found himself in Persia, where he travelled widely. He returned to India through Mesopotamia in 1838, and then went to Afghanistan. In 1843 he was appointed political Agent at Bagdad, and remained there until 1855. He made himself the foremost authority on geographical, political, and historical matters connected with the Near East, and was "the most commanding, and the best known, figure among English Orientalists."

During Rawlinson's tenure of office in Mesopotamia the French, under Botta and others, carried out valuable archæological researches in and near Mosul, where the Englishman A. H. Layard continued the work from 1847 to 1851. It was in this region that J. F. Jones collected his material for a map of the country between the Tigris and the Upper Zab (1852). To the southward, at the instigation of Rawlinson, a somewhat similar map was constructed for the region round Babylon, but the complete project of a map of Lower

Mesopotamia was not realized. The work came to an end in 1866, and five years later the results were published under the title of *Trigonometrical Survey of a Part of Mesopotamia [between 33½° and 32° N. Latitude]*.

Later archæological researches added fragments to the map, and a few more important journeys covered new ground. To the latter class belong those of Von Oppenheim in 1893. He began by taking an entirely new route from Damascus to Bagdad, through the middle of the Harra Desert, and then traversed the country between the Euphrates and the Upper Tigris. The results of Von Oppenheim were illustrated by an important map, compiled by Dr R. Kiepert, whose father had so distinguished himself in Asiatic researches. For the first time an attempt was made to combine all existing material available for the cartography of Syria and Mesopotamia.

Another valuable map, of smaller scope, but in greater detail, was that compiled by Sir William Willcocks and his staff in the course of their investigations into the irrigation projects on the Tigris and Euphrates between 1909 and 1911. The area covered did not extend much farther than 60 miles to the north, west, and south of Bagdad.

When the Great War broke out there was thus little precise information available, but the Survey of India took the matter in hand, and during the War, and after its conclusion, covered a great area. A triangulation was carried through Mesopotamia and connected with that of Egypt and of Palestine on the west and of Russia on the north, while in the country itself the surveys were extended beyond Mosul. It was a work of great difficulty and not infrequently of danger, but it was carried through successfully in accordance with the best traditions of a great body like the Survey of India.

To the west of Mesopotamia and to the east of Palestine lies the No Man's Land of the desert, prolonged southward into the peninsula of Arabia. Here, by contrast with all the parts of Western Asia so far considered, there are still vast areas unvisited by Europeans. There would seem to be some strong connexion between the aridity which characterizes this area and the absence of European explorers. Yet the whole explanation does not lie in that simple geographical fact, for religious and political fanaticism has helped to intensify the difficulties of environment.

Scientific exploration in Arabia[1] began in the later years of the eighteenth century, with the journey of Niebuhr, and has continued down to the present day. It can be divided conveniently into three main periods. The first ends with the publication of Ritter's map

[1] The standard work, on which this section is based, is D. G. Hogarth's *The Penetration of Arabia* (1904). Other authorities are quoted in the footnotes below.

of 1852, by which time much progress had been made in the country south of latitude 25° N. The second period may be marked by the publication of Hogarth's *Penetration of Arabia* in 1904, a date of convenience only, since no comprehensive work has since appeared on the history of the exploration of the country.

In the nineteenth century the first traveller of note was the Spaniard Domingo Badia y Leblich, who left Cadiz in 1803 and managed to reached Mecca. He fixed the position of Mecca by astronomical observations, described the roads from the coast to Mecca and Medina, and "can claim priority for his notes on the geology, botany, and meteorology of the Hejaz." [1] He was followed, in 1809, by the botanist Seetzen, who also reached Mecca, visited Sanaa and Aden, and returned to the interior with the object of crossing the country to the east, but was murdered before he had proceeded very far.

Increasing affronts in Palestine led to the Ottoman expedition to Arabia in 1811, and some of the Europeans who accompanied the expedition were able to add a little to the general knowledge of the country. Of outstanding importance was the work of J. L. Burckhardt, who had already travelled extensively in Syria and Nubia, and had discovered Petra, before he landed at Jedda in 1814. In due course he reached Mecca, and was able to explore some of the country to the northward. He left a most valuable description of the Holy City, its pilgrims and their ceremonies, and its trade, and he collected much general information about West Central Arabia. Burckhardt died at Cairo on his way back to England, but he had gathered material of the highest value, and the appearance of his *Journal* "may be said to have satisfied all the curiosity felt at the date of its publication concerning the Holy Cities and their neighbourhood by students of religion, politics, social custom, and local history, by topographers, and by economists and merchants." [2]

The country of Nejd, lying to the east of that small region seen by Burckhardt, had been visited, for a few days only, by Reinaud, who arrived from the Persian Gulf in 1799, and again by Rochwusky in 1818, but the first real information about it was due to an Englishman, Captain G. F. Sadlier. He was sent by the Government of India to co-operate with the Egyptian expedition, and landed at El Katif in June 1819, only to find that the Egyptians had gone. Determined to follow them, he crossed the country to Medina, and finally reached the Red Sea coast at Yanbo. He then went to Jedda, where he was detained for four months before he could resume his journey to India. Sadlier was the first to cross Arabia from east to west, and if, as was said, he passed through the country "like a bale of goods," he was yet able to give a description of

---

[1] Hogarth, *op. cit.*, p. 81.　　　[2] *Ibid.*, p. 91.

regions hitherto wholly unknown to Europeans, and the rough map that could be compiled from his observations more than compensated for the failure of his political mission.

The Egyptian expedition to Asir, the country lying to the south of Mecca, in 1832 and following years was, like the two earlier expeditions mentioned above, indirectly responsible for some geographical information about that area. At least six Europeans, of whom five were Frenchmen, accompanied the Egyptian army, and their plans and reports were of considerable value, since no other explorer visited the country during the century.

Still farther south, in Yemen, the advent of the Egyptians in 1826 was followed by that of European investigators. Some only reached the coastal towns, a few penetrated to Sanaa, and one, the French botanist P. E. Botta, climbed the summit of Mount Sabor. The longer journey of another Frenchman, L. Arnaud, from Sanaa to Marib in 1843, was productive of valuable archæological results, but added little to geographical knowledge.

Oman, the south-eastern corner of Arabia, was explored scientifically for the first time by Lieutenant James Wellsted, who had already served in the surveying ship *Palinurus* in Arabian waters. He was assisted for part of the time by another Englishman, Lieutenant Whitelock. Although neither man travelled very far, Wellsted was able to gather some useful knowledge of the fertile parts of Oman and to gaze upon the fringe of the desert, which he hoped to cross. To the south-west " vast plains of loose drift-sand, across which even the hardy Bedouin scarcely dares to venture, spread out as far as the eye could reach." In the north political disturbance put an end to all prospects of reaching Nejd, so that Wellsted returned to India in 1836 after a short but profitable stay in Oman.

The desert barrier which had frustrated Wellsted was turned by the Bavarian Wrede in 1843. He approached Hadramaut from the south coast, and reached the quicksands of El Ahkaf. Though doubt was thrown upon his reports, he seems to have been unjustly treated, and there is no reason to suspect the genuineness of his discoveries.

Hitherto very little attention had been paid to Northern Arabia, for, with the exception of a single journey of one of Seetzen's servants in 1808, the somewhat meagre exploration of the coast-lands of Midian by Rüppell in 1826, and the visit of the survey ship *Palinurus* in 1831, it was practically unvisited. Much importance, therefore, attaches to the journeys of G. A. Wallin, one of the ablest of Arabian explorers, who visited this region in 1845, and again in 1848. His mission was political, made in the service of Egypt, yet although he took no instruments, he accomplished important geographical work, and has been described as " a scientific explorer of the best modern type, thoroughly prepared, and determined to leave nothing

for the man who might come after him." [1] On his first journey
he crossed from Cairo to the south of the Dead Sea, and thence
travelled over the desert to Hail, the chief settlement of Jebel
Shammar. He returned by Mecca and Medina. In 1848 he
revisited Arabia, and from the coast of Midian crossed the country
by way of Teima and Hail to Meshed Ali, near to the Euphrates,
whence he reached Bagdad.

> He was the last of the original pioneers who, since Niebuhr, had
> been opening up Arabia, the last to force the barriers of a great
> unexplored region of the first importance. Since Wallin's time every
> European traveller who has made any considerable journey in the
> interior of the peninsula has touched or crossed . . . the track of a
> predecessor.[2]

It was this progress of the early explorers which Ritter recorded
on his map, published in 1852, which itself marks an epoch in the
growth of the knowledge of Arabian geography.

During the second period of exploration some additional knowledge in the north of the west coast came from R. F. Burton's
journey in 1877. Though he failed to find the goldfields which he
thought existed in Midian, he added materially to the geography
of the regions already seen in part by Rüppell and Wallin, explored
the western fringe of the peninsula north of Mueleh, and to the
south of that place ascended the rim of the plateau and gained
some impression of the interior. Farther southward, Burton's pilgrimage to Mecca and Medina, made in 1854, was not productive
of much that was new, although he was able to confirm the observations of earlier travellers, and in some respects to supplement their
information. Keane, who visited Medina in 1878, observed, as
Burton had done, the steady growth of the city, while the distinguished Dutch scholar, J. S. Hurgronje, was able to spend five
months in Mecca in 1885 and to gather most valuable information
about its inhabitants.

In the south-west much exploration was accomplished in the
second half of the century, and especially after the Turkish conquest
of 1872. Most of the explorers started from Aden, which had been
a British possession since 1839. Various routes inland to Ta'izz
and to Sanaa were taken by these explorers. To the former went
Zwemer, an American missionary, in 1894, while Manzoni (1877),
Deflers (1887), and Harris (1892) all reached Sanaa, and Manzoni
lived there for considerable periods. Farther toward the east
Millingen (1873), Deflers (1887), and H. Burckhardt (1890) penetrated the barren plateau, while the German archæologist E. Glaser
reached Khamr, to the north of Sanaa, in 1884, and brought back
valuable geographical information about the highlands of Yemen.
Even more extensive was the journey of Halévy, a French Jew,

---

[1] Hogarth, *op. cit.*, p. 161.   [2] *Ibid.*, p. 171.

in 1869–70. He set out from Aden, and, skirting the edge of the desert on the east, reached the distant Makhlaf, in Nejran. His main interest was in archæology, but he was able to give a general geographical account of much country hitherto entirely unvisited. His work was supplemented by a second journey of Glaser, in 1889. On this occasion he reached Marib, and obtained many copies of inscriptions, as well as material for a map.

On the south coast comparatively little progress was made during this period, and many of its features are still imperfectly known. Apart from coastal surveys, three important expeditions were made to the interior. In 1870 Captain S. B. Miles and W. M. Munzinger pushed inland from Bir Ali, and reached the Wady Mefat, but were unable to proceed farther, owing to the official position which Miles occupied at Aden. More than twenty years later, however, in 1893, the archæologist L. Hirsch went inland from Mokalla, reached the great Wady Hadramaut, and explored a large part of its upper course. The same year a party led by T. Bent, which included an Egyptian surveyor, was able to map this region. Although both parties visited unknown country, their contributions to geographical knowledge were comparatively small, since many of the major features of this region had already been ascertained by the Dutch scholar Van den Berg, who had cross-examined Arab immigrants to Java.

In Oman the journeys of Captain Miles extended the area of known ground already traversed by Wellsted and Whitelock. He visited the country lying to the south-east of Jebel Akhdar, and, by making a *détour*, struck the coast at Kuryat. In the north-west he reached Biremah, and gathered some general information about the country to the west. Miles arrived there in November 1875, and it was not visited again until 1901, when Zwemer crossed to it from the coast of the Persian Gulf. The latter, a missionary, made three journeys, in 1900 and 1901, in the northern projection of Oman, and was able to cross the country from Abu Dhabi to Sohar, and to visit Sharja and Shinas on its two coasts. From this region Major Percy Cox crossed the country to Muscat in May 1902, thus linking it up with the country already explored by Miles.[1]

Farther up the coast of the gulf lies the Hasa country, whence Sadlier had made his famous journey in 1819. It may have been visited by Palgrave in 1862, though a later explorer, Mr Philby, has cast doubts on his veracity.[2] It was certainly explored by Colonel L. Pelly, who went from Koweit inland to Riyadh in 1865, and returned to the coast at Ojair, passing through Hofuf on his

[1] On these journeys see *G.J.*, vol. xix, p. 54, and vol. xx, p. 452.
[2] See *G.J.*, vol. lv, p. 175 and pp. 189–191. Hogarth (*loc. cit.*, pp. 187–188) did not accept Mr Philby's statements in their entirety. *Cf.* also *The Penetration of Arabia*, pp. 249–250.

journey. Pelly travelled rapidly between these points, and, although provided with instruments, was unable to make much use of them. Yet he did supplement the information given by Sadlier and Palgrave.

The journey of W. G. Palgrave in 1862 was remarkable in many respects. He, like Wallin, approached Central Arabia from the north, and had a political mission to fulfil. Unlike that explorer, he did not produce many geographical results, for he admits that his interests did not lie in the direction of geography, and he was unable to make notes of his journey. If he accomplished all that he claimed to have done he crossed from Gaza to Hail, and continued through Central Arabia to the Persian Gulf at El Katif, but though his descriptions have at times some value, many places which he saw have since been revisited by more competent observers, and his work requires no further mention in this place.

In February 1864 there arrived at Teima from the north-west an Italian, C. Guarmani, who had come to buy horses for the rulers of France and Savoy. He remained to carry out some of the most important work that has been accomplished in Central Arabia. He was the first to visit " the ancient and famous oasis of Khaibar so entirely inhabited by blacks as to seem a bit of the Sudan," [1] and his subsequent journey to Jebel Shammar was productive of most valuable results. " From him we first learn of the large westward and south-westward extent of the oases and wells on which the Shammar depend," [2] while his compass bearings and other observations therein were so numerous that " he can claim the distinction not only of being the first to render scientific cartography of Central Arabia possible, but of having done more for the map-makers than any successor except Huber," [3] until quite recent times.

The next explorer, Charles Huber, also reached Central Arabia from the north, in 1878. From Damascus he travelled by Bosrah, Kaf, and El Jauf to Jebel Shammar. He was followed a few months later by W. S. Blunt, who was accompanied by his wife, Lady Anne, and who desired merely to see the people of Central Arabia. They too arrived at Jebel Shammar from the north, and have left a most valuable account of their journey. Huber again reached Hail in 1883, on this occasion in the company of J. Euting, who wished to carry out some archæological work. The journey was made inland from the west coast at Jedda, and ended with the murder of Huber in 1884. Nine years later the last explorer of this period, E. Nolde, again crossed from the north to Hail, and by taking a route which lay more to the eastward of those of his predecessors was able to cover some new ground. But his aims were not geographical, and his record is concerned mainly with politics, so that little new knowledge came from his adventure.

[1] Hogarth, op. cit., p. 267.   [2] Ibid., p. 268.   [3] Ibid., p. 270.

ASIA

There remain for consideration the travels of C. M. Doughty,[1] who was perhaps the greatest of Arabian explorers, and whose work *Arabia Deserta* is one of the classics of travel literature. During the months of May and June 1875 Doughty spent his time to the east of the river Jordan, vainly searching for means of getting farther. In November of the following year he succeeded in reaching Arabia, and remained in the country until August 1878. Passing through Tebuk and Madain Salih, he visited Teima, and reached Hail. Thence he went westward again to Khaibar, and eastward as far as Bereida, before striking south-westward across the country to Jedda. " No one has looked so narrowly at the land and the life of Arabia as Doughty, and no one has painted them in literature with a touch so sensitive, so sincere, and so sure." [2] The judgment of Hogarth may be confirmed by reading the somewhat difficult language of *Arabia Deserta*. Thus Doughty describes the nomad life with picturesque accuracy, following the tribesmen as they strike their tents, pack their goods, and move to the next camping-ground:

> After three days the Aarab removed south-eastward twelve miles, and pitched at the camping-ground Khussherkîsh. It was now the 22nd February, and we found here the rabîa, or new spring of sweet blossoming herbage. . . . The rabîa is the yearly refreshment, nay, the life, of the nomad's cattle. Delightful to the eye, in the desert land, was that poor faery garden of blossoms. When the Beduins saw me pensive, to admire the divine architecture of those living jewels, they thought it but childish fondness in the stranger. If I did but ask the names of the simples it was roughly answered, " The name of them all is el-usshb, ' the spring foliage,' very good for our small cattle and camels." [3]

The settled life of the oases, the nature of the ground, stray observations of apparently trifling matters, like the shape of a sand-dune or the origin of a belt of clay, and a multitude of details about the daily life of the country can be read of in Doughty's pages. Though later explorers may have added more scientific details, none has given a better picture of Arabia.

During the twentieth century some very important work has been carried out in Arabia. In the Hejaz there were, before the World War, two problems unsolved. Very little was known about the divide between the Red Sea drainage and that leading to the eastward ; and even the longitude of such prominent features as the stations and terminus of the Hejaz railway was unknown. The information collected by Colonel Lawrence and a number of military

[1] For a full account of this remarkable man see D. G. Hogarth, *The Life of Charles M. Doughty* (1928).
[2] Hogarth, *The Penetration of Arabia*, p. 274.
[3] *Travels in Arabia Deserta*, with an introduction by T. E. Lawrence (2 vols., 1921), vol. i, pp. 218–219.

expeditions went some way toward a solution of these questions, and a few points on the railway were determined. In addition

> two blocks of the Hejaz slope were explored pretty thoroughly. The one is a broad belt whose sea base stretches from Rabugh to Wejh . . . while it tapers slightly inland between a line drawn from Rabugh to a point about 35 miles north of Medina and another line drawn . . . from Wejh to Dizad. . . . The other block is smaller, being a triangle with apex at Akaba and base 50 miles in length on the railway from Maan to Tell Shahm.[1]

In a journey to Mecca, in 1925, Mr E. Rutter took a new route across the coastal plain, but the unfortunate loss of his compass and aneroid left him unable to make scientific observations.

In Asir, in 1918, British officers collected some general information, and this has been supplemented to a small extent by a more recent journey of Mrs Rosita Forbes.

In Yemen the French engineer Beneyton in 1909 carried out survey work to the east of Jizan in connexion with a proposed railway from Hodeida to Sanaa, while the two latter places were visited by Bury in 1912. Sanaa itself had been reached in the year before by Wavell. Here, as in Asir, a considerable amount of general information was collected during the World War.

In the south-east G. M. Lees, in the winter of 1925–26, was able to add to the geological and geographical knowledge of the coastal districts as far as the province of Dhofar.

It is, however, in Northern and Central Arabia that the most revolutionary changes in the map have been made. As early as 1909 two explorers were working in the north. A. Musil[2] made a number of journeys between 1908 and 1915 in the region between Basra, the Gulf of Akaba, and Aleppo. Some of this was unknown country, and some had not been visited since the days of Burton, but most of the secrets have since been revealed by other explorers. The second traveller, Captain Butler, with a brother-officer, crossed from Bagdad to Damascus in 1908, by way of El Jauf, which had not been previously reached from the east.

Shortly afterward D. Carruthers passed to the west of El Jauf in a journey from the Medina railway-line, near to the northern end of the Dead Sea, to Teima (1909), while Teima was almost reached by Gertrude Bell in her magnificent expedition of 1913–14. Miss Bell traversed the country east of the railway-line from Damascus to Hasan, near Teima, before she turned eastward to Hail. Her return route was again across country in a north-easterly direction to the

---

[1] D. G. Hogarth, " War and Discovery in Arabia," in *G.J.*, vol. lv, pp. 432–433. This valuable paper deals more particularly with Western Arabia, but also touches on Central and Southern Arabia.
[2] See A. Musil, *The Northern Hegâz* (1926), *Arabia Deserta* (1927), *The Middle Euphrates* (1927), *Palmyrena* (1928), *Northern Negd* (1928), and *The Manners and Customs of the Rwala Bedouins* (1928).

Euphrates, whence she made her way by Bagdad and Palmyra to Damascus. In all Miss Bell made many valuable additions to the knowledge of the country and its inhabitants in the course of her journey, which covered about 1500 miles.[1]

While Carruthers and Miss Bell were travelling in the north Captain W. H. I. Shakespear was improving the knowledge of the country behind Koweit, where he had gone as political Agent in 1909. A number of these preliminary journeys enabled him to establish good relations with the tribesmen of the interior, and facilitated his final achievement of crossing Arabia from Koweit to Egypt. In this he was brilliantly successful, covering about 1200 miles of unknown country. He kept a careful record of his route, and as he crossed the tracks of so many other explorers his observations " helped to pull these, in many cases, rough traverses into shape." [2]

Two other explorers before the War crossed the country visited by Shakespear. Colonel G. E. Leachman had explored a large area east of Basra in 1910, and in 1912 had travelled southward to the gulf coast at Ojair, while the Dane Raunkiaer had made an inland journey between Ojair and Koweit.

To all this exploration must be added the remarkable work of Mr H. St J. B. Philby. In 1917 he undertook a political mission to Riyadh, and in the course of it crossed the country from Ojair to Jedda, without, however, accomplishing his purpose. Accordingly, he went back to Basra, again reached Riyadh, and obtained permission to make a short journey southward to the Wady Dawasir. The results were of first-class importance, for Philby was the first Christian to penetrate so far southward in Nejd, and he was able to collect most valuable information both to dispel rumours of a well-populated area and to establish the facts of present-day conditions.[3]

Mr Philby, with Major A. L. Holt, undertook another expedition in 1920–22, crossing from Amman, on the Medina railway, by El Jauf, to Kabala, near to the Euphrates. This journey, taken in conjunction with the earlier and extensive surveys of Major Holt in connexion with a railway between Bagdad and Haifa, added much exact knowledge of Northern Arabia.

A final journey in the desert was that of Major R. E. Cheesman, who reached the unvisited oasis of Jabrin, on the fringe of the great southern desert, in 1923–24. In this exploration southward from Hofuf he covered 150 miles of unknown country, and as he made careful observations was able to fix the position of this oasis.[4]

[1] See D. G. Hogarth, " Gertrude Bell's Journey to Hayil," in *G.J.*, vol. lxx, p. 1.
[2] See D. Carruthers, "Captain Shakespear's Last Journey," in *G.J.*, vol. lix, p. 321.
[3] See H. St J. B. Philby, *The Heart of Arabia* (2 vols., 1922).
[4] See R. E. Cheesman, *Through Unknown Arabia* (1926).

GEOGRAPHICAL DISCOVERY AND EXPLORATION

Beyond lies the desert which has been crossed twice recently. Mr Bertram Thomas travelled from Dhofar, on the south coast, to Dohak, on the Persian Gulf, in 1931, and in the following year Mr Philby reached the Wady Dawasir from the Gulf of Bahrein. Thus the last great blank on the map of Arabia has been removed.[1]

IV. Persia, Afghanistan, and Baluchistan [2]

The expansion of Russia into Asia, which resulted in the exploration of the lowlands of Turkestan and the northern fringe of Persia and Afghanistan, was indirectly also responsible for much of the earlier exploration of those countries from the side of India. The main motive was political, due to fear of Russia, but just because of that fear statesmen in India were anxious to learn all they could about the country between themselves and their supposed enemies.

The two missions of Malcolm in 1800 and in 1810 were productive of the standard history of Persia, a work which remained authoritative for nearly a hundred years. Malcolm was accompanied by J. M. Kinneir, who travelled extensively in Persia, Kurdistan, Armenia, and Asia Minor, and produced *A Geographical Memoir of the Persian Empire*. J. J. Morier was another political servant whose journeys in Northern Persia and Armenia in 1808–9, and again between 1810 and 1816, covered a wide area.

While Persia was thus being examined Elphinstone was sent to Afghanistan. He got no farther than Peshawar, but he collected much valuable information, while one of his subordinates, Macartney, had been busily employed in examining the country from the Suleiman Mountains northward to Peshawar itself. Two years later, in 1810, Christie and Pottinger met with better success. They set out from Sonmiani, on the coast of Baluchistan, disguised as horse-dealers, and, passing through Bela and Kelat, reached Nushki, where they separated. Christie, following a northern route, made his way across the Helmand valley to Herat, and then turned westward into Persia, through Yezd to Isfahan. Pottinger went south of the

[1] See Bertram Thomas, *Arabia Felix* (1932), and *G.J.*, vol. lxxviii, p. 209; and H. St J. B. Philby, *The Empty Quarter* (1933), and *G.J.*, vol. lxxxi, p. 1.

[2] Curzon's *Persia and the Persian Question* (1892) gives a complete list of travellers to Persia up to 1891. The data used for his map of Persia (*Proc. R.G.S.*, new series, vol. xiv, p. 69) should also be consulted.
The following have also been used for this section:

SIR THOMAS HOLDICH, *The Gates of India* (1910).
—— *The Indian Borderland* (1901).
SIR GEORGE FORREST (ed.), *Selections from the Travels and Journals preserved in the Bombay Secretariat* (1906).
A brief account of the six journeys of Sir Percy Sykes, with a useful map, in the *Scottish Geographical Magazine*, vol. xxx, p. 169.
Records of the Survey of India, vol. xx (1925), Part II, which deals with Persian surveys during the War.

Seistan depression, passed through Kerman, and ultimately joined Christie at Isfahan. These journeys did much to reveal the essential geographical facts of Eastern Persia and Western Afghanistan.

In 1821 and subsequent years J. B. Fraser travelled extensively in the Persian country south of the Caspian Sea, while in 1830 Conolly rode from Tabriz to Herat, whence he crossed Afghanistan to Kandahar and entered India by the Bolan Pass. Another remarkable exploit was that of an American named Masson. From Tiflis he went to Tabriz and Teheran, thence to Resht, on the Caspian Sea, and finally to Herat through Meshed. From Herat he crossed to Kandahar, entered Sind, and collected information about the Indus valley while making his way to Peshawar. " On reaching Peshawar," the report reads, " Mr Masson seems to have passed a considerable time in wandering about between Peshawar, Ghazni, Jalalabad, Kabul, and Kandahar." Masson then entered the Punjab, went to Lahore, and again collected much useful information. He journeyed thence through Multan to Karachi, took ship for Muscat, and at length reached Bushire in 1830. There he made a report to the English Resident, Wilson, and this report, full of valuable details, was in due course forwarded to Bombay. Masson's career was by no means ended. He returned first to Baluchistan and later to Afghanistan, living in the latter country for about seven years.

> As an explorer in Afghanistan he stands alone. His work has never been equalled; but owing to the very unsatisfactory methods adopted by all explorers in those days for the recording of geographical observations it cannot be said that his contribution to exact geographical knowledge was commensurate with his extraordinary capacity as an observant traveller, or his remarkable industry.[1]

During this political penetration of Western Asia Moorcroft, who had already done valuable work in the Himalaya, set out to buy horses at Bokhara. He spent two years in Ladakh, and at length travelled to Kabul, whence he made the journey to Bokhara. He died on the way back to Herat, but not before he had sent to India his reports of Russian activity. He was followed by Alexander Burnes and James Gerard, who in various disguises also made the journey from Kabul to Bokhara (1832). On their return Gerard followed a route through Herat and Kandahar. Burnes went back to Afghanistan in 1835 as commercial Agent at Kabul, and took with him John Wood. The latter explored the Kabul river, crossed the Hindu Kush Mountains to the Oxus, and pushed up that river to one of its sources. He was able to gather valuable information about the country and its Kirghiz nomads.

[1] Sir Thomas Holdich, *The Gates of India* (1910), pp. 407–408. This work treats fully of Masson's career. *Cf.* C. Masson, *Narrative of Various Journeys in Balochistan, Afghanistan, the Panjab, and Kalat* . . . (4 vols., 1844).

Shortly after this the First Afghan War with England broke out, and J. S. Broadfoot, who accompanied the army, was able to explore a new route from the Indus at Dera Ismail Khan to Ghazni.

It was at this time that J. Abbott reached Khiva from Herat, by way of Merv, and that Stoddart and Conolly penetrated to Bokhara, where they were murdered. With these exploits Persian exploration as a political venture came to an end, although it was resumed in another form within a few years.

The middle years of the century are occupied by a few important travels, and by the beginnings of the survey of the Turco-Persian frontier from Mount Ararat to the Persian Gulf. Khanikov, a distinguished Russian officer, added greatly to the knowledge of Northern Persia by his explorations of 1858–59, when a very large area was covered and the position of over a hundred points was astronomically determined. At this time the work of Abich was directed to the north-western borders of Persia, while J. B. Taylor, British Consul at Diarbekir, made important discoveries in the region of the headwaters of the Tigris and the Euphrates, and was the first to describe the sources of the main branch of the first-named river. He renewed his explorations in 1866, making fresh discoveries in the country round Lake Van.

In Persia Captain C. Clarke travelled from Teheran to Herat, and from Teheran to Bushire, between 1857 and 1859. In Afghanistan Ferrier, some ten years earlier, had started from Herat for India, intending to travel through Balkh and Kabul, but, being unable to do this, had passed through the Hazara country to the west of Kabul, and had reached Ghur. He was sent back from Ghur, but had at least the satisfaction of exploring an entirely unknown region of Afghanistan.

The political mission led by Major-General Goldsmid during the years 1870–72 marks the beginning of a new phase in the exploration of Persia, inaugurating as it did the modern series of Boundary Commissions which have been so fruitful in geographical results. Actually two tasks were assigned to the mission, to settle a boundary in Seistan between Persia and Afghanistan and to fix the Perso-Makran frontier. In addition to carrying out the specific task allotted to them, the party collected much information about Persia. Major Euan Smith crossed the country from the Caspian Sea to Gwadar, and also examined the Seistan depression. Major D. B. St John covered the southern region between Shiraz and Gwadar, while Major B. Lovett devoted his attention to the Makran frontier regions. Of the main results St John wrote that

Khanikov's journey made a revolution in the prevailing ideas regarding the orography of eastern Persia, and the surveys of Major Lovett and myself have done as much for the south. Major Lovett's first journey in 1870–71 established the facts of a water-parting in Baluchistan, about 100 miles from the coast, dividing the Helmand valley from the oceanic basin ; and of a singular south-western deflection of the axes of the ranges south of Bampur. The following year we proved the continuity of the great plateau west of Sistan with the [mountains to the south of it] ; . . . further west we traced Khanikov's great central range west of Yezd, as far south as latitude 27° 30' ; and found the other minor ridges between Kerman and Shiraz to lie in the same uniform direction, a parallelism I had previously found to occur in the ranges on all the roads between Bushire and Shiraz, and that city and Isfahan.[1]

In the ten years immediately following this mission a number of important expeditions were active in Persia. In 1873 Colonel V. Baker and Lieutenant Gill explored new country north of Meshed and in the neighbourhood of the sources of the Atrak river. Napier visited part of the Elburz Mountains in 1874, and Tietze climbed the peak of Demavend. In 1875 Macgregor crossed from Bushire to within four miles of Herat, where he was turned back by the Afghans. Floyer, of the Persian Gulf Telegraph Department, penetrated the unexplored Bashakird country behind Jask in 1877, while Schindler travelled very extensively in Southern Persia between 1875 and 1879. In Northern Persia Lovett surveyed a route along the Elburz Mountains in 1881–82, embracing the country between Asterabad on the east and Teheran on the west.

Meanwhile important additions to knowledge had been made in Baluchistan and Afghanistan. In the year 1876 Colonel Macgregor stated that practically no new information about Afghanistan had been obtained since the year 1842. This defect was remedied by the surveyors attached to the British armies during the Afghan War which broke out in 1878. A vast amount of work was accomplished between the Bolan and Khyber Passes, and this was supplemented by the parties sent into Waziristan in 1881. In this progress (Sir) T. H. Holdich began a long and distinguished service on the North-west Frontier of India. In 1883 he was back again in Baluchistan, and in the following year served with the Russo-Afghan Boundary Commission to which reference has been made. Baluchistan claimed him again in 1889, when he surveyed the Zhob valley, while he also carried his explorations through Makran to Persia. The Perso-Baluch Boundary Commission, the surveyors entrusted with the execution of the Durand Agreement of 1893, and the Pamir Boundary Commission of 1895 all worked under the direction of Holdich, and when he left the frontier " there was hardly a corner of accessible ground on it that he had not seen." [2] By his own efforts and those of the surveyors under his command a vast area in Afghanistan

[1] *Eastern Persia*, edited by Sir Frederic Goldsmid (2 vols., 1876), vol. i, pp. 11–12. These volumes deal with the work of the Persian Boundary Commission.

[2] *G.J.*, vol. lxxv, p. 214. *Cf.* Sir Thomas Holdich, *The Indian Borderland* (1901).

and Baluchistan, as well as within the Indian frontier, was added to the well-known lands of the earth.

In Persia considerable progress has been made since Lovett traversed the Elburz Mountains. In the south-west Bell was active in 1884, while Yate, who was British Consul at Meshed, was able to collect additional general information about Seistan. In the west Lynch crossed Luristan in 1889, Vaughan travelled inland from Linga, on the Persian Gulf, almost to the Caspian Sea, in 1887–88, and performed a somewhat similar journey in 1890–91. Sawyer covered a very large area of new ground in the Bakhtiari country in 1890, while Maunsell and P. Galland have examined parts of Kurdistan.

Three names, however, stand out above the rest in the recent exploration of Persia. The French Scientific Mission under De Morgan in 1889–91, although not confining its attention to geographical exploration, was able to add considerably to the knowledge of Northern Persia, south of the Caspian Sea, and Kurdistan. In this same region A. F. Stahl made most valuable supplementary journeys in the years following 1895. Not only was much geological information obtained, but his extensive travels have resulted in many additions to the topographical maps.

Among the most important work is that of Sir Percy Sykes. He has lived for more than twenty years in the country, and has, excluding his journeys during the War, made six important expeditions. In 1893 he landed on the south-east shore of the Caspian, rode to Asterabad, and then travelled up the Atrak valley to Meshed. Thence Sykes crossed Persia to Kerman, Shiraz, and Bushire. In the course of this expedition across Central Persia some blank patches in the map were removed. The second journey, in 1893–94, which had for its object the exploration of Persian Baluchistan, began at Chahrar, on the south coast, and led the explorer northward into Sarhad. He climbed the volcanic peak of Koh-i-Taftan, and added greatly to the knowledge of a remote region of Persia. His return route lay across better-known country, through Kerman, Yezd, and Teheran to the Caspian Sea.

When he was appointed to the consulate in Kerman in 1894 Sykes began his third journey, covering a period of more than two years. Persia was reached from the Caspian Sea, and a new piece of country was explored on the route between Kashan and Yezd. South of Kerman, again, fresh discoveries were made. Sykes then served on the Perso-Baluch Boundary Commission, and after its termination was deputed to investigate a political dispute in the Karun valley.

The fourth journey covers the period from 1897 to 1901. It began with an exploration of unknown country in the north of Bashakird, during an expedition from Bandar Abbas to Chahrar.

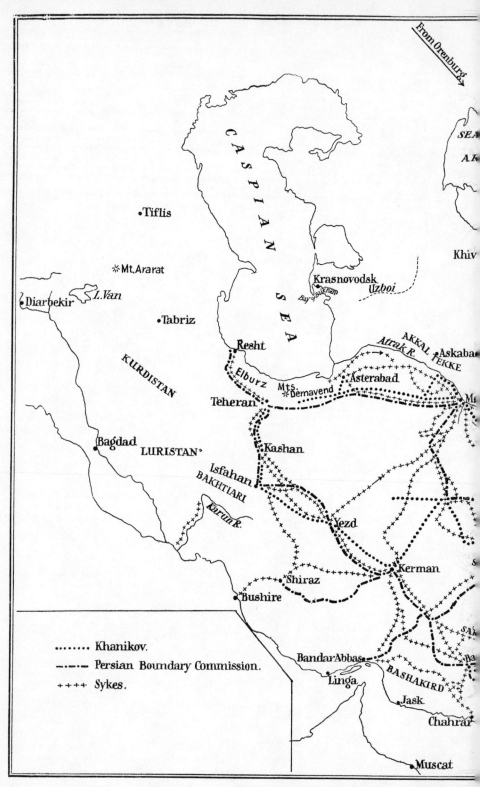

Fig. 29. PERSIA AND AFGHANISTAN AFTER 1800

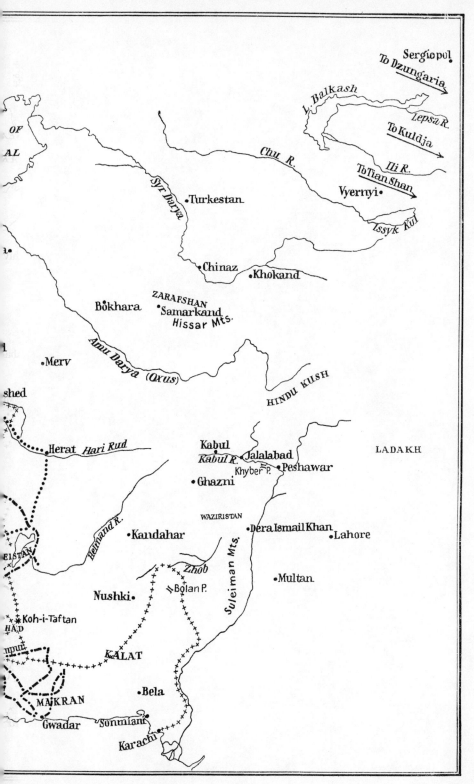

OF

AL

Sergiopol

To Dzungaria

L. Balkash

Lepsa R.

Chu R.

To Kuldja

Ili R.

To Tian Shan

Syr Darya

•Turkestan

Vyernyi•

Issyk Kul

1•

•Chinaz

•Khokand

ZARAFSHAN

Bokhara

•Samarkand

Hissar Mts.

1

Amu Darya (Oxus)

•Merv

HINDU KUSH

shed

LADAKH

•Herat Hari Rud

Kabul•

Kabul R. •Jalalabad

Khyber P. •Peshawar

•Ghazni

EISTAN

Helmand R.

WAZIRISTAN

•Kandahar

•Dera Ismail Khan

•Lahore

Zhob

•Multan

Nushki•

Bolan P.

Suleiman Mts.

•Koh-i-Taftan

HAD

mpur

KALAT

•Bela

MAKRAN

Gwadar Sonmiani•

Karachi

A further exploration of Seistan followed, when much country was surveyed by a Persian assistant. After a lengthy absence the party returned to Kerman, and undertook the exploration of another unknown region lying to the south-west of that town.

The fifth journey (1902–6) comprises two distinct explorations, first to the south-east of Kerman and then in the north-east, from Meshed, to which town Sykes had gone as Consul. The sixth journey (1906–10) was occupied with travel in the north-east, between Meshed and Asterabad.

During the World War Sir Percy Sykes again rendered invaluable service in Persia, and on these occasions Indian Survey officers were able to survey parts of the country. These activities covered six distinct areas : on the south coast a strip of country between Jask and Gwadar ; several routes between Kerman and Bandar Abbas ; a strip between Bushire, Shiraz, and Isfahan ; the valley of the Karun and South-west Persia ; a large area between Bagdad and the Caspian Sea, with projections on either side to Tabriz and Teheran ; and a great block of country immediately adjoining Afghanistan, and extending from the latitude of 31° N. to the Persian frontier. In spite of many difficulties considerable additions to geographical knowledge came as a result of these surveys.

V. India [1]

Although Rennell's map of India marked a great advance over all earlier efforts, there were still many parts of the country unknown at the beginning of the nineteenth century. The removal of these blank spaces has in large measure been due to the operations of the Survey of India, supplemented by the work of pioneer travellers, more especially in the Himalayan region.

The Great Trigonometrical Survey of India began operations on April 10, 1802, when a base-line was measured near Madras. Up to the year 1823 Lambton continued his work in peninsular India, and was able to correct serious errors in Rennell's map, but it was interrupted by his death in that year. It was not resumed until 1830, when George Everest, who substituted the ' gridiron ' system of chains of triangles for that employed by Lambton, was appointed Superintendent. Between 1845 and 1850 the main chain of triangles was run along the Indo-Gangetic plain, and at this time, or shortly after, the height of the main peaks of the Himalaya was ascertained. In 1855 triangulation was extended into Kashmir, and in 1913 was joined to that of the Russians.

[1] See especially Sir Clements Markham, *Memoir on the Indian Surveys* (2nd edition, 1878), and the continuation of the same by C. E. D. Black (1891), carrying the history to 1890. A useful summary account is in the *Imperial Gazetteer of India* (new edition, 1907), vol. iv, pp. 481–512.

Topographical surveys based on this triangulation have been carried on almost without interruption since 1800. By 1820 materials for a map of the country south of the Kistna river were available and some route-surveys had been made farther north. Political events on the north-east frontier led to a great extension of knowledge in that direction between 1825 and 1838, while in 1841 a map of Sind was compiled from the surveys of Burnes and others in the Indus valley. Under the direction of Sir Andrew Waugh (1843–61) greater progress in topographical surveys was made, the most notable being those of the country between the Indus and the Jhelum by Robinson (1851–59) and that of Kashmir by Montgomerie and his assistants (1855–64). This latter survey was carried into Gilgit by Tanner in 1879–80, after which that officer went to survey the eastern frontier of Nepal. Eastward of Kashmir the surveys were continued, and had reached the western frontiers of Nepal by 1887, while Ryall, who was in charge of the Kumaon and Garhwal survey, crossed into Tibet and lived for a few weeks in Hundes in 1877. At the same time progress had been made in Sikkim, but in Bhutan on the one side and in Nepal on the other very little information had been obtained. This condition remained until quite recent years, when the journeys of J. C. White (1906–8) and Major Bailey (1922) in Bhutan filled in a number of blank spaces : in Nepal practically the whole country was surveyed under the direction of Colonel M. O'C. Tandy in the years 1925–27.

While the survey had thus been making steady progress, and covering the whole country, a number of pioneers had been exploring the Himalaya. In the north-east Thomas Manning passed through Bhutan to Lhasa in 1811, and Pemberton led a mission to Bhutan in 1838, but neither acquired a great amount of information about the country. The Hungarian Csoma de Körös, who lived for nearly twenty years in Ladakh, Sikkim, and the southern confines of Tibet, devoted his life to a study of Tibetan literature, and in his day visited many unknown parts of the mountains.[1] Hooker, whose main object was botanical research, travelled in Sikkim and Eastern Nepal as well as in the Khasia Hills, between 1847 and 1850, and his *Himalayan Journals* throw much light on a little-known region, but a glance at the map which he produced is enough to show how scanty was the knowledge of this region by the middle of the century.[2]

The journey of Major Sherwill in the Sikkim Himalaya in 1853 and those of Blanford and Elwes in 1871 added to the knowledge of

---

[1] For an account of Csoma de Körös see " A Pilgrim Scholar," in Sir William Hunter's collected essays, published under the title of *The India of the Queen* (1903), p. 251.
[2] Hooker's work was published in 1854, and is illustrated by a map drawn by Petermann.

this country.   In 1871 the Donkia Pass was reached, three unmapped lakes were seen, and the routes from Sikkim to Tibet were examined. Further information was obtained from the various journeys of the Pundits [1] and from the searches for a solution to the Brahmaputra riddle.

Early in the century Wilcox and Griffiths had ascended the Lohit river in their exploration of the north-eastern frontier, and several expeditions had been made in this region subsequently.   Kishen Singh reached Sama, in Tibet, in 1882, and in 1886 Needham proved that the Brahmaputra did not flow into the Irrawaddy.   Yet the course of the Tsangpo in Tibet and that of the Brahmaputra in Assam had not been traced.   Williamson explored the Lohit in 1907–8, and definitely associated it with the Brahmaputra : in later years he worked in the Abor country, and accumulated much knowledge about it, but was murdered in 1911.   The punitive expedition sent to exact reparation and open up the country was able to carry out some survey work, but even then the problem was not settled, and in 1912, after the expedition had returned, Bethell expressed the definite opinion that the Dihang, the Tsangpo, and the Brahmaputra were not connected.   The problem was solved by Captain Morshead and Captain Bailey in 1913.   From the Dibang river they crossed to the Dihang, and followed it upward.   Although unable to keep to the river the whole way, their surveys left no doubt that the Dihang was continuous with the Tsangpo, which they reached and surveyed to Tsetang.   They mapped the Tsangpo for 380 miles, and filled in a large area south of the river which had never before been surveyed.

In the Himalayan regions west of Nepal the pioneer explorer was Webb, who was sent in 1808 to trace the Ganges to its source.   At the end of the eighteenth century several Englishmen had visited Kashmir, but there was some confusion as to the location of Srinagar and of the source of the Ganges.   Webb had been employed, in 1800, to survey the Ganges from Allahabad to Hardwar, and his second expedition was to complete the work already begun.   It succeeded in tracing the river upward from Hardwar to its glacier source at Gangotri, and fixed the position of Srinagar on the Alaknanda. Webb subsequently explored parts of Kumaon, where he continued the work of Hodgson, begun in 1815, while Hodgson himself was transferred to Garhwal.

Meanwhile, in 1812, Moorcroft and Hearsey had penetrated beyond the Himalaya, and had reached the Manasarowar Lakes : they returned through Nepal.   Moorcroft subsequently visited many parts of the Himalaya, including Ladakh and Kashmir, and was identified with that band of political explorers who collected information for the Government. of India.   Another of the band,

[1] See below, pp. 282–289.

Gerard, accompanied Burnes on his journey to Bokhara in 1831, and subsequently worked in the Kangra district of the Himalaya. Indeed, this period, from about 1830 to 1850, was one of considerable activity in the mountainous regions of North-west India. Vigne in Kashmir, Baron Hügel, and Csoma de Körös, all of different nationalities and with differing interests, visited the region. Cunningham, who had lived for eight years with the Sikhs, was sent to Ladakh in 1846 to fix the boundary, and was then instructed to " use his best endeavours to increase the bounds of our geographical knowledge." With Dr Thomson he reached Leh, and Thomson visited the Karakoram Pass.

Two brothers, H. and R. Strachey, are also numbered among the pioneers in the Himalaya. H. Strachey reached the Manasarowar Lakes in 1846. R. Strachey arrived there two years later, and in 1849 the two brothers carried out the long journey in Garhwal.[1] As a result of their efforts, and those of Cunningham and Thomson, a considerable amount of information about the Western Himalaya was acquired.

Very shortly after this the surveyors extended their work to the north-west : some account of that progress has already been given. It was supplemented by the information which came through the penetration of Central Asia, initiated by the brothers Schlagintweit. They, and men like Montgomerie and Godwin Austen, are the direct successors of the pioneers whose names have been given. In turn their work has been supplemented by a later body of explorers, who have given much attention to the smaller details. Many of the leaders of this new form of exploration, which can be dated from Younghusband's discovery of the Mustagh Pass in 1887, are still alive, and the names of Conway, Freshfield, Bruce, Norton, Longstaff, and Ryder are well known for their work in this respect. It is impossible to follow them into the recesses of the Himalaya, but mention must be made of the exploration of the Karakoram Himalaya, where recently most important work has been undertaken. Godwin Austen discovered the Baltoro Glacier in 1861. About thirty years later Sir Martin Conway began his exploration, and added to the knowledge of this region already acquired by Younghusband in several expeditions and by General Sir George Cockerill, who in turn had extended the area visited by Younghusband. This knowledge has gradually been enlarged by the work of Ferber (1902), Eckstein (1903), Longstaff (1909), the Duke of the Abruzzi (1909), the Workmans (1908 and 1911–12), and Sir Filippo de Filippi (1913), the last being assisted by Major H. Wood. The list of names is an indication of the intensity of modern exploration and its specialized nature. Finally, to complete the story, Major K. Mason

[1] The narrative of Sir Richard Strachey was not printed until 1900. It will be found, with a useful map, in *G.J.*, vol. xv.

ASIA

led an expedition to the Shaksgam valley and the Aghil Ranges in 1926.[1] His exploration of a wide belt of country on the divide between the drainage to the Indian Ocean and that to Central Asia had important results. He has shown conclusively that the so-called Karakoram Range does not exist, that the pass of the same name is not in the range which is called Karakoram, and that the country beyond the Shaksgam river (a tributary of the Yarkand) exhibits the same series of parallel ranges as is found on the Indian side of that river.[2]

VI. SOUTH-EAST ASIA [3]

The scientific exploration of Burma came to an abrupt end after the mission of Symes to Ava in 1798, and was not renewed until the first Burmese war of 1826 directed attention to a country which was virtually unknown. From the north-east of India surveys were being pushed eastward, and the Government recognized that some steps were necessary to gain information about this unexplored country. The first of the new expeditions was that of Lieutenant R. B. Pemberton, who in 1830 went overland from Manipur to Kindat and the valley of the Chindwin, which he followed to its junction with the Irrawaddy. By the latter river he made his way to Ava, where a British Resident was living. In the following year Dr D. Richardson performed a journey in the reverse direction, travelling from Ava to Shwebo, and thence to the Chindwin valley and Kindat. Here he met another officer, who had crossed from Manipur by a route different from that taken by Pemberton.

Farther southward, the Arakan Yoma had been crossed by a military party, using the An Pass, in 1826, and had been examined in greater detail by Captain White and by Pemberton in 1830. The knowledge thus acquired, both of this region and of that to the north, was collected by Pemberton in a report to the Indian Government in 1835. He was able to give a description of the country separating Burma from India, and, from information derived from natives, to furnish some account of Burma itself.

Shortly after the first exploration of the Irrawaddy above Ava was undertaken, when Captain S. F. Hannay went with a mission to investigate a tribal quarrel. He reached Katha on December 13,

[1] On this expedition, and for the details of the exploration in this region, see Major K. Mason, " The Exploration of the Shaksgam Valley and Aghil Ranges " (*Records of the Survey of India*, vol. xxii, 1928).
[2] On the exploration of the Himalaya generally see Sir Francis Younghusband, " The Exploration of the Himalaya," in the *Journal of the East India Association*, vol. xviii, pp. 157–172. Much detailed work is still being done in the Himalaya, full details of which are recorded annually in *The Himalayan Journal*, which was first published in 1929.
[3] On this section see Sir Hugh Clifford, *Further India* (1905). This work contains a useful bibliography.

1835, and, a week later, arrived at Bhamo. Large boats were at first employed, but after travelling for 400 miles it was found necessary to exchange them for smaller craft. On the last day of the year Hannay reached the mouth of the Mogaung river, and took astronomical observations, which were, however, inaccurate. Mogaung itself was entered shortly after, and from that town Hannay set out northward for the amber-mines of the Hukawng valley. He spent some time in their neighbourhood, but the miners distrusted his Burmese escort, and he was therefore not able to see very much. He returned by the same route to Ava, arriving there on May 1, 1836. Hannay's journey was important both for the information he collected and for the fact that white men were once more able to penetrate into the heart of the country. His observations in the Hukawng valley improved the knowledge of the upper course of the Chindwin, thus supplementing the work of Wilcox on the Assam frontier in 1825–28 and that of Pemberton lower down the valley. Hannay also helped to solve the mystery of the Tsangpo (Brahmaputra) river, which some thought found its exit by the Irrawaddy. Hannay's records showed that this theory was probably incorrect, although the question was not settled for some years.[1]

Wilcox in his Assam surveys had determined the western sources of the Irrawaddy, and his work was connected up with that of Hannay by Griffiths and Bayfield, who made journeys across from Assam to the Hukawng valley in 1837.

Meanwhile important advances had been made in the south-east. Toward the end of 1829 Dr Richardson left Moulmein, went up the Salween, and, by using various tributary valleys, reached the Me Ping river. He arrived at Lampun in the middle of January, but was unable to get permission to proceed farther. In 1834 he again reached this town, and was able to go beyond it to Chieng Mai, being the first European to penetrate so far from the Bay of Bengal.

Chieng Mai was again visited by Captain W. C. McLeod, in 1837. He had taken a more southerly route than Richardson, and hoped to be able to penetrate as far as China. He succeeded in reaching Chieng Kong, on the Mekong river, but there he waited in vain for permission to enter Yunnan. Meanwhile Richardson, who had travelled part of the way with McLeod, was covering new ground in the Salween valley, which he explored for a long distance. He then crossed westward through the mountains to Ava, where he arrived in May 1837. Although the main object of both these journeys was to open up the country to traders, McLeod and Richardson had accomplished much valuable geographical exploration.

Richardson's was the first journey ever made by a European from Moulmein to Mandalay, and in the course of it he had explored the

[1] See above, p. 263.

hitherto unknown country of the Karins, and the Shan States lying between that country and Ava. It served to link up the British possessions in lower Burma with the region already explored further to the north and west. At the same time McLeod's journey had added to the map many details of the eastern Shan States between the Salween and the Mekong.[1]

In December 1838 Richardson began another journey, from Moulmein, by way of Kanburi, to Bangkok. Although the geographical results were small, its interest lies in the fact that it marked the end of the first phase of Burmese exploration. The withdrawal of the British Resident from Ava, consequent upon the revolution of 1837, of necessity brought exploration to an end, and it was not resumed until after the war of 1852.

The Second Burmese War added the province of Pegu to the Indian Empire, and made further exploration possible. How much had already been achieved was set out by Colonel H. Yule in a map of Burma, which embodied the results of the expeditions already mentioned and of surveys made by two officers who accompanied the new Governor to Ava in 1855. In Burma proper " the interior towns and districts " below Ava were inaccurately represented, being based on native information; " the country lying between the Salween and the Me-ping river is a blank, as is also the large tract north of the Chieng Mai." [2] Other important blanks were in the north and west, between the Arakan Yoma and the Chindwin, and between the Chindwin and Irrawaddy rivers.

The expedition of E. O'Riley from Toungoo to the Karin country in 1856 helped to remove part of one of the blank areas. The Pegu survey had already begun, but all the work was rejected and a new survey started in 1860 by Captain Fitzroy.[3]

While the survey of Burma was progressing steadily Captain E. B. Sladen attempted to open up the old trade-route to Yunnan. He left Mandalay in January 1868, and ascended the Irrawaddy in a river-steamer to Bhamo. During this journey his assistant, Bowers, charted the river. Beyond Bhamo he followed the Taiping valley, and reached Teng-yueh (Momein), beyond which town he thought it inexpedient to venture. Sladen came to many wrong conclusions as the result of this journey. He assumed that beyond Teng-yueh the way to Yunnan was easy, and he believed that the Tsangpo and the Irrawaddy were the same river. Yet the journey was not entirely fruitless, and some valuable surveys were made of many parts of the route. In this remote region T. T. Cooper tried to cross from China to the Irrawaddy in 1868. From Hankow he travelled to Batang, on the frontier of Tibet (latitude 30° N.), and thence reached the upper waters of the Mekong; but was

[1] Clifford, *op. cit.*, p. 273.
[2] *Ibid.*, p. 275. The map will be found in *J.R.G.S.*, vol. xxvii, p. 54.
[3] Markham, *Memoir on the Indian Surveys* (2nd edition), p. 168.

prevented from going to Ta-li-fu. In another attempt, from Assam, in 1869, he went up the Brahmaputra and Lohit rivers, only to be turned back from Tibet. The object of these journeys was finally accomplished by A. R. Margary in 1874. He started from Shanghai, went up the Yangtse river, and across to Yunnan and Ta-li-fu, eventually reaching Teng-yueh early in January 1875. He proceeded thence to Bhamo, met the English mission which he was to guide back to China, and on January 23 began the return journey. He was murdered when just within the Chinese frontier, and the mission was obliged to retire. By this remarkable exploit, however, the limits reached by Garnier,[1] at Ta-li-fu, and that of Sladen, at Teng-yueh, had been connected, and the first journey by a European from Shanghai to Bhamo had been accomplished.

A new mission to investigate the circumstances of this disaster left Hankow in November 1875, and from the surveys of E. C. Baber, who accompanied it, the necessary geographical records, which had been expected, but not realized from Margary's journey, were now obtained. Baber pointed out the great difficulties of this route for the purposes of trade.

A number of journeys were now made from China to Burma. McCarthy reached Bhamo through Yunnan and Ta-li-fu in August 1877 ; Cameron arrived by the same route shortly after ; Captain W. J. Gill, " from a pure love of Geography and Science, and entirely at his own expense," [2] concluded an extensive and important journey in Southern China by reaching Batang, whence he travelled to Ta-li-fu and Bhamo ; and the Austrian Count Bela Szechenyi, who, like Gill, had done much valuable work in China, came through Ta-li-fu to Bhamo in 1880. The next year another Chinese traveller, A. Colquhoun, made the journey from Ta-li-fu to Bhamo by what was now a well-known route.

The Third Burmese War of 1885 led to the cessation of exploration for a short time, but ultimately the many parties sent to put down guerrilla bands traversed the length and breadth of the country, and solved its geographical riddles. Of the larger exploits mention must be made of the journey of J. F. Needham in 1885–86. He started from Assam, and went up the Lohit river to within a mile of Rima, in Tibet, and put an end to the dispute as to the identity of the Tsangpo and the Irrawaddy.[3] The sources of the latter river were not, however, definitely known. Native explorers had been sent to locate them in 1879, and in 1884–85 Colonel R. G. Woodthorpe and Major R. C. Macgregor visited the upper tributaries, while the expedition of Prince Henry of Orleans in 1895 crossed all the tribu-

---

[1] See below, p. 272.   [2] *Proc. R.G.S.*, old series, vol. xxii, p. 271.
[3] This was virtually settled after the journey of Pundit A-K. See p. 289, and General Walker's paper "The Lu River of Tibet," in *Proc. R.G.S.*, new series, vol. ix, p. 352.

ASIA

taries in its journey from the Mekong to the Brahmaputra. The Prince collected much information about the Salween and Irrawaddy rivers, definitely established the fact that the first does, and the second does not, originate in Tibet, and so solved the problem that had perplexed geographers throughout the century.[1]

Exploration in Siam progressed very slowly until the year 1881, when J. McCarthy began his work. The country had been reached at many points both by the English from Burma and by the French from the east, but the knowledge thus acquired was comparatively small. Richardson crossed the difficult mountains which separate Moulmein from Kanburi in 1839, but gave little scientific information about the route. Thirteen years later Bishop Pallegoix made use of such facts as the missionaries had gathered to write an account of Siam which, under the circumstances, was very good. Yet the small amount of progress was revealed by Parkes in his paper to the Royal Geographical Society in 1855. The map which accompanied it was based on primitive surveys, and embodied the work of American missionaries. Actually it dealt only with the lower parts of the valleys of the Menam and Mekong, although the knowledge of the Catholic missionaries covered a wider area.[2]

In addition to missionaries, traders and officials added scraps of information, while the French botanist Henri Muhot, who went to Indo-China in 1858, made an important journey up the Menam, and continued overland to Korat, Chaiapun, and Pak Lay, on the Mekong. He subsequently reached Luang Prabang, where he died. This journey, together with his earlier explorations on the Mekong and in the neighbourhood of Tonlé Sap, entitles Muhot to be regarded as the first important explorer in the interior of Siam. Shortly afterward the splendid work of the French on the Mekong dwarfed that of the earlier explorers, but it belongs to the story of French Indo-China, and is dealt with later.

In Siam the journey of Sir Robert Schomburgk, in 1860, up the Menam and the Me Ping rivers to Chieng Mai, thence to Moulmein and Kanburi, and finally back to Bangkok, was the only notable achieve-

[1] Two recent journeys have added to knowledge of this remote region. See J. W. and C. J. Gregory, " The Alps of Chinese Tibet and their Geographical Relations," in *G.J.*, vol. lxi, p. 153, and F. Kingdon Ward, " From the Yangtze to the Irrawaddy," in *G.J.*, vol. lxii, p. 6 ; and for a fuller account J. W. and C. J. Gregory, *To the Alps of Chinese Tibet* (1923), and F. Kingdon Ward, *The Mystery Rivers of Tibet* (1923). Mr Kingdon Ward has continued his work in this border region. See especially " Explorations in South-eastern Tibet," in *G.J.*, vol. lxvii, p. 97 ; " Explorations on the Burma-Tibet Frontier," in *G.J.*, vol. lxxx, p. 465 ; and " The Himalaya East of the Tsangpo," in *G.J.*, vol. lxxxiv, p. 369. In the last paper he put forward arguments in favour of an extension of the Himalaya eastward into China ; on this question see the opposite view of D. N. Wadia in *Himalayan Journal*, vol. viii, p. 63.
[2] Parkes' map will be found in *J.R.G.S.*, vol. xxvi, p. 71.

ment before the surveys of James McCarthy in 1881. McCarthy spent ten years in the service of the King of Siam, and did much valuable work, especially in the northern parts of the kingdom, so that by 1890 its major features were well known. His first task was to connect Rahang to the surveys already made on the Burmese frontier. A short visit to the Malay Peninsula interrupted his work, but it was resumed in 1884, when he began a journey into Northern Siam. Proceeding from Bangkok to Korat, and thence to the Mekong at Nong Kai, McCarthy crossed to the mountainous country north of the Mekong, and explored a considerable area. He then returned to Nong Kai, followed the Mekong to Luang Prabang, and returned again to Pak Lay, whence he crossed to the Menam, and by that river reached Bangkok.

In another expedition, begun at the end of 1884, to the Menam river, above its junction with the Me Ping, McCarthy carried exploration far beyond the point reached in the previous year. He examined the country round the headwaters of the Song-ma, while Collins, another member of the party, explored the Nam-hu, a tributary of the Mekong, almost to its source. Both these rivers lie in what is now French territory.

During 1887 and 1888 McCarthy was engaged on railway surveys between Bangkok and Korat, and Ayuthia and Chieng Mai, after the completion of which he spent much time in the north and west of the kingdom, where the Anglo-Siamese Boundary Commission of 1889–90 practically completed survey work by delimiting the boundary between Burma and Siam. At the close of 1893 McCarthy's long service came to an end: he was able to produce a map of Siam far in advance of all previous efforts.[1] The northern part of the kingdom was now well known, although to the east of the Lower Menam there were still some blank areas. Even here, however, all places of real importance had been visited and their positions fixed.[2]

To McCarthy is due the formation of a Survey Department in Siam. It was established in 1885, and has continued ever since to map parts of the country. A cadastral survey was begun in 1896, while by 1910 about 75,000 square miles of the country had been topographically mapped.[3]

In what is now French Indo-China exploration began with the journey of Muhot in 1858, though his more important work was accomplished in Siam; it was not until 1866 that real progress was

[1] See J. McCarthy, *Surveying and Exploring in Siam* (1900), with map.
[2] Clifford, *op. cit.*, p. 321.
[3] The area surveyed topographically by modern methods, up to September 30, 1927, represents 24·8 per cent. of the total area of the kingdom. It lies mainly in the southern part. (*Report on the Operations of the Royal Survey Department for* 1926–27 (1929).)

made. In that year the French Government decided to send an expedition to explore the valley of the Mekong. It was placed under the command of Doudart de Lagrée, with Francis Garnier as second in command. The geographical work was entrusted to Garnier, who

> was instructed to determine the precise position of all points of importance, to make a map of the country traversed, to take soundings and ascertain the navigability of the rivers, to note the means of navigation employed by the various native tribes, and to compare the advantages presented by the river and the neighbouring land-routes.[1]

The party left Saigon on June 5, 1866, and proceeded up the Mekong river to Pnom-Penh, where some time was spent in an investigation of the ancient Khmer civilization and the ruins of Angkor. Continuing up the river, they used gun-boats as far as Kratie, and native vessels beyond, but they found the ascent difficult and dangerous on account of the river floods, and were obliged to admit that this route could not be used for trade with China. By July 21 they had reached Stung-treng, where the Se-khong enters the main river from the mountains of Annam. The tributary was examined by De Lagrée as far as Siempang.

The explorers then followed the main river to Bassac, which became the centre for a number of expeditions. Garnier visited the Boloven plateau, explored the Se-don river in search of silver-mines, and then went down the Mekong to Stung-treng. De Lagrée circled the plateau, following the valley of the Se-don and crossing the divide to that of the Se-khong, by which he returned to Bassac.

Bassac was left on Christmas Day, and the party continued up the Mekong to the Se-mun, which they followed to the town of Ubun. From this point Garnier made a journey overland to Pnom-Penh, through Siemreap, near Tonlé Sap. By this traverse, covering over 1000 miles, Garnier was able to fill in a great blank in the maps.

While Garnier was thus employed another of the party, De la Porte, surveyed the Mekong from the mouth of the Se-mun to Kemmarat, while De Lagrée reached the same point by an overland journey. The leader then made a short expedition up the Se Bang Hien before taking the whole party up the main stream.

Garnier joined his companions on March 6 at Uthen, and twenty days later the expedition reached Nong Kai. Continuing up the river, the Frenchmen arrived at Chieng Kan, where, on April 12, they heard of another exploring party, and shortly afterward met a Dutchman, Duyshart, in the employ of the Siamese Government, who had crossed from Chieng Mai to a point on the Mekong 200 miles above Luang Prabang.

[1] Clifford, *op. cit.*, p. 144.

At the end of April the Frenchmen were at Luang Prabang, and at the beginning of June had reached Chieng Kong, which became the starting-point for a number of local expeditions. Shortly afterward the rapids compelled them to abandon the river. They struggled on through the difficult country to the west of the river, making frequent visits to its bank, crossed it at Chieng Hung, and struck out toward the north-east, finally reaching Yunnan on December 21. De Lagrée was too ill to complete the journey to Ta-li-fu, but Garnier accomplished it successfully, only to be turned back on reaching the city. Finding it impossible to revisit the Mekong, Garnier crossed to the Yangtse-kiang, and by that river made his way back to the sea, and finally to Saigon. De Lagrée died before the expedition had finished his task. His wise leadership " had contributed enormously to the success of the expedition,"[1] although a great part of the work was undertaken by his lieutenant. If they had failed to reach the sources of the Mekong, and to open up a trade-route to China by its valley, the French explorers had accomplished a great work.

A detailed survey of the Mekong had been made from Pnom Penh to a point a day's march above the rapid of Tang He, and the river had been frequently visited between that place and Chieng Hung. Most of the large tributaries below Luang Prabang had been explored in detail. A vast area in Laos and the Shan States, where no white man had hitherto set foot, had been carefully examined ; China had been reached from the south ; much of Yunnan had been explored and surveyed for the first time, and finally, in circumstances of great difficulty, Ta-li-fu had been visited. In addition to this much information had been collected concerning not only the geography, but the social, commercial, and political condition, of the countries traversed. Facts bearing upon the history and upon the difficult ethnological problems of this part of Asia had been assiduously noted and recorded, the whole being subsequently embodied by Garnier in his elaborate *Publication Officielle*.[2]

In the course of the next twenty-five years scientific exploration in the French territory was carried out with such vigour that by the end of the century practically the whole country had been examined. This result was partly due to a few individual journeys, of which that of Harmand into the hilly country west of Khong between 1875 and 1877 is the most conspicuous, but it was mainly due to the work of Auguste Pavie and his forty assistants, who were working in the field between 1879 and 1895. It is unnecessary to follow their journeys in detail. Pavie began in 1879 with a survey in Southern Siam. Between 1880 and 1885 a number of journeys were made in Cambodia and in Siam, while between 1886 and 1888 an exploration was made up the Mekong and over to Tong-king. Between 1889 and 1891 the Mission Pavie was engaged in a large

---

[1] Clifford, *op. cit.*, p. 251.   [2] *Ibid.*, pp. 253–254.

number of operations in Siam, Tong-king, Laos, Yunnan, Annam, and Cambodia, while in the last period, from 1892 to 1895, when Pavie was French Minister at Bangkok, the boundary between Siam and French territory was delimited, and much useful work was accomplished by the Anglo-French Mekong expedition. How great was the transformation may be seen by comparing the map of French Indo-China by Dutreuil de Rhins, published in 1881, with that of the Mission Pavie issued in 1902.[1]

Since the conclusion of the Mission Pavie the work of exploration has been carried out by the Service Géographique de l'Indo-Chine, which was established in 1899.[2]

The Malay Peninsula remained an unknown land until the last quarter of the nineteenth century, with the exception of the Kra Isthmus, which had been crossed by Richardson and Tremenheere in 1839. But with the beginning of a close political relationship between Great Britain and the states of the peninsula, which dates from the appointment of a Resident in Perak in 1874, and with the journeys of prospectors a few years later, the whole situation was completely changed. The explorations of Bozzolo in Patani in 1880–83, and the survey of the Perak river in the year 1883 by McCarthy, mark the beginning of exploration in the north, while farther southward the peninsula was crossed a number of times and by various routes from the west coast to the many tributaries of the Pahang river. In the last decade of the century the prospectors opened up much country from Kedah to the Patani river, while Bailey explored the mountains between the Galas and the Jelei rivers in 1892, and Sir Hugh Clifford and his subordinates mapped a large area in Trengganu in 1895. The work of systematic survey is now being undertaken by the Federated Malay States Survey Department, and although some of the forested areas are still unexplored, it may be said that no new features of major importance are likely to be revealed.

VII. China and Japan [3]

During the eighteenth century the surveys of the Jesuits had produced a reasonably accurate map of China, and very little improvement was effected until the second half of the nineteenth

[1] See D. Aïtoff, " L'Œuvre de M. Pavie en Indo-Chine," in *La Géographie*, vol. vii, p. 77, where the maps referred to are given. The itineraries of Pavie and his assistants are given on a map in vol. i of the *Report* of the Mission.

[2] See Rouget, " Étude sur la cartographie de l'Indo-Chine française," in *Annales de géographie*, vol. xv, p. 26, for a detailed account of the work up to 1906.

[3] See E. Tiessen, *China, das Reich der achtzehn Provinzen*, Part I, " Die allgemeine Geographie des Landes " (" Bibliothek der Länderkunde "), Chapters I and II.

century. In the interval China was not unvisited, but it would be true to say that few travellers penetrated very far. Klaproth, from Russian Asia, reached Peking, and was able to improve the knowledge of the Liaotung peninsula. Lord Macartney visited the capital on an unsuccessful trade mission in 1793, and a second English party in 1816 had also failed to gain permission for freedom of trade. A few years later the Russians again reached Peking.

The efforts of diplomatists and trade envoys failed to penetrate Chinese reserve : yet during this early period some missionaries were able to move freely about the country and collect fragments of knowledge, and none gained greater fame than the Lazarists Gabet and Huc. They were sent to carry on new work in Mongolia, and accidentally performed a remarkable journey to Lhasa between 1843 and 1846. There seems no reason to doubt the authenticity of this journey, the account of which was written by Huc. The descriptions are, however, unreliable in detail.[1]

The so-called ' Opium ' War with England opened up a little of the country to foreigners, and one Englishman, Robert Fortune, was able to travel in the coast provinces and learn something about Chinese tea-gardens (1848–56), while in 1858 Lockhart, who lived on the Yangtse-kiang, collected useful information about the country in general. At the same time events were happening which made possible the real exploration of the country.

The *Arrow* incident of 1856 led to the Second Chinese War of 1857–60. A British squadron of fifteen gun-boats was sent to China under Captain Sherard Osborn, and two of these ascended the Yangtse for 600 miles, reaching Hankow. This feat made it possible for the British to insist that the river should be opened to trade, while the final settlement of 1860 confirmed the general trading privileges granted by the earlier treaty of 1842.

Exploration of the interior followed almost at once, and was mainly the work of British subjects. Michie went from Tiensin to Moukden in 1861, Blakiston and others traced the Yangtse for 1800 miles, Morrison followed the Grand Canal, Richards and Slossin were engaged in the country round Peking, Dickson, Beach, and others made a journey of over 700 miles between Canton and Hankow, and Legge, supplementing the earlier work of McCleverty in 1859, ascended the Tung-kiang, in Kwang-tung. It was a remarkable indication of a radical change in the affairs of China that so many journeys should have been made in a single year. Nor were they isolated ventures, for the pressure was maintained. In 1862 the Lazarist missionary David began a long series of journeys, mainly in Northern China. For three years, while engaged in his official duties, he collected zoological specimens in North China

[1] See Huc and Gabet, *Travels in Tartary, Thibet, and China*, edited by P. Pelliot (2 vols., 1928, " Broadway Travellers " series).

and Manchuria, and after 1865 devoted himself entirely to scientific work. In 1866 he extended his travels into Mongolia, and between 1868 and 1870 he journeyed up the Yangtse-kiang, beyond the Chinese frontier. David continued his work in Northern China until 1874.

David's explorations coincide with a number of very important journeys in China. In 1863 Pumpelly, an American, began those travels which furnished the first material for a geological map of the country. In the following year Bastian passed through North China and Mongolia on his way from Japan to Europe. The missionary Williamson visited Manchuria three times between 1864 and 1867, and found it " a country of much interest and great promise, and not that barren, bleak, and lawless country generally supposed." In 1866 he paid a visit to Shansi.

While Williamson was in Manchuria Ney Elias began his brilliant career by making a careful exploration of the Tsientang river in 1867. In the next year he travelled from Shanghai along the Grand Canal to Kaifeng, and investigated the new course of the Yellow River from that point to its mouth, collecting much useful information about its change of course. In 1870 he surveyed the old channel of the river. Two years later Elias set out from China, and crossed Mongolia. He was able to take many astronomical observations on his journey, and thus add greatly to its scientific value.

A three years' residence at Hankow enabled Oxenham to gather much information about the floods of the Yangtse-kiang, which at this time was receiving considerable attention. In 1867 Swinhoe, a British Consul, led a trade-mission up the river, and took with him two surveyors, who did excellent work. The party reached Chung-king, beyond which they reported that there was no hope of steam navigation. The next year T. T. Cooper went up the river, and reached the town of Ta-tsien-lu. He was turned back by the frontier authorities at Batang. In 1870 he attempted to reach China from Assam, but failed to do so, owing to his sudden illness.

In 1868 Fritsche, the Director of the Peking Observatory, crossed Mongolia to Nerchinsk to inspect the meteorological station there. He was able to collect some information about Mongolia, which he characterized as " steppe-like, thinly populated, with lakes and rivers gradually drying up." In the following year J. Markham travelled in the Shantung peninsula, a region hitherto little visited.

All these exploits, falling within a period of about ten years, had greatly increased the knowledge of China. They were, however, made to appear of little importance by the splendid work of Baron F. von Richthofen, who had gone to the East with a commercial mission in 1860, visiting among other places Japan and Formosa. His travels in China began at Shanghai in September 1868 and ended at that city in May 1872. During this period he made seven expeditions into the interior, of which the third (1869), through Shantung and Southern Manchuria, the fifth (1870), through Central China from Canton to Peking, and the last (1871–72), in the north and west, from Chihli to Szechwan, are the most important. Richthofen's very valuable contributions to the geology and physical geography of China were published in his monumental work *China* ; his *Atlas of China* marked a great advance on all previous cartographical representations of that country.

In 1870 an expedition sent out by the Imperial Russian Geographical Society, and led by the Archimandrite Palladius, crossed the whole of Manchuria in a journey of about 1000 miles through one of the least-known parts of China, while at the other extreme a merchant of Hankow, named Dupuis, went from Hong-Kong to the Songkoi river, in Tong-king, which he ascended as far as Lao-kai.

This latter journey serves to introduce a series of explorations in the remote parts of South-western China which profoundly modified existing ideas as to the country.[1] Gill's expedition, from Cheng-tu, in Szechwan, across the south-eastern corner of Tibet to Ta-li-fu, and thence to Bhamo, in 1877, was followed by that of McCarthy, who turned southward from the Yangtse at Chung-king, journeyed through the centre of Kwei-chow into Yunnan, and from Ta-li-fu made his way to Bhamo. In the same year (1877) E. C. Baber set out from Chung-king, and, proceeding first to Cheng-tu, followed a course roughly parallel to, but farther to the west than, that of McCarthy, and also reached Ta-li-fu. Szechenyi, who had already tried to cross Mongolia from North-west China, traversed Yunnan in 1880, approaching it from the north, while Colquhoun approached it from the east, in 1881, and surveyed a route from Wuchow, on the Si-kiang, to Ta-li-fu, through almost unknown country.

While the south-west was being opened up two other travellers were filling in details. In the south G. J. Morrison made two journeys into the interior, the first from Hankow to Canton through the mineral areas of Southern Hunan and the second from Chin-kiang, near the mouth of the Yangtse, to Tiensin. The town of Hang-chung was the starting-point for the Russian expedition under Sosnovski which had for its objects the discovery of the best road from the Semipalatinsk area to China and the investigation of trade prospects. The Russians left in January 1875, travelled north-westward through Lan-chow and An-hsi-chow, and then crossed Mongolia to the upper valley of the Irtish.

The west of China now began to receive more attention. Hosie reached Szechwan in 1882 as British Agent in Western China, and began a long career of great service in the country. In the next three years he travelled extensively in Szechwan, and beyond it to Yunnan on the south. Hosie's reports on the country, although primarily concerned with its economic aspect, were of great value.

[1] Some of these expeditions have already been referred to. See above, p. 268.

ASIA

During the next twenty years the greater part of the energy of explorers was devoted to Western China, and especially to the south-west. In Szechwan Miss Bird undertook a journey in the north and central parts in 1896, regions which had been crossed by Pratt, whose main work, in 1889 and in 1890, lay in Western Szechwan. The journey of Prince Henry of Orleans has already been mentioned [1]: in the same region of the south-west Major Davies began the surveys of Yunnan in 1895, and was assisted in 1898 and the following year by Captain C. H. D. Ryder. Their journey started at Bhamo, and their surveys covered a large area to the north, west, and south of Yunnan. Their work was of a very high order, and after it there was some reality in a map of Yunnan, which had hitherto been crossed only by a number of route surveys.[2] Working in the same region, although quite independently, was Dr R. L. Jack, who was examining the country for minerals at the instigation of the Chinese Government. A similar mission was undertaken, in 1898–99, by Leclère, which also added a little to the knowledge of Yunnan. Even after those efforts a number of blanks remained on the map, some of which were filled in by A. F. Legendre, who carried out much useful work in Western Szechwan and to the north-west of Yunnan (1910–11), and explored the almost unknown valley of the Ya-kong, a tributary of the Yangtse-kiang.

Belonging to a different category are the expeditions of Bonin (1895), Futterer (1898), and d'Ollone (1906). The first was a circuit of China beginning at Tong-king, passing up the western frontier to the Ordos region, and thence to Peking. Its results supplemented many of the details already discovered by others. That of Futterer was part of a large expedition across Central Asia. He reached the Chinese province of Kansu, having come from Kashgar, over the Gobi Desert, and proceeded to make a careful survey of Eastern Tibet before crossing the Tsin-ling Mountains to Hankow. The whole route in the unexplored country was mapped, both topographically and geologically. This same region was visited by Filchner and the geologist Tafel in 1905 and succeeding years. The main object was to explore the upper course of the Hwang-ho and the country southward to Szechwan. They carried out a most successful piece of work, first on the border between Shensi and Shansi, then between Lan-chow and the western border of Kansu, and finally beyond the border, where they covered much new ground.

The third expedition referred to above was that of Captain d'Ollone, who in some respects repeated in 1906 what Bonin had attempted ten years earlier. He traversed the frontier from

[1] See above, p. 268. The Prince began his journey at Hanoi, and intended to complete the earlier work of Garnier on the Mekong river. For an account of the expedition see *G.J.*, vol. viii, p. 566.
[2] For Ryder's map see *G.J.*, vol. xxii, p. 236.

Yunnan to the Upper Hwang-ho, and was able to confirm some of the discoveries which the German explorers had made.[1]

Most exploration since the days of Richthofen had taken place in the west and south-west of China, and other parts had been somewhat neglected. In Manchuria the journey of Wylie, through the centre of the country, in 1892, was not productive of important results. But toward the end of the nineteenth century the Russians turned their attention to Northern Manchuria, in connexion with railway surveys, while Hosie collected many useful facts about it in the same way as he had done earlier in the west. The impact of Russia and Japan, and the light thrown on the country during the Russo-Japanese War, much increased knowledge of its geography.[2]

On the southern borders, in Northern and in Central China, there was also much work carried out during the early years of the present century. Much of this was of a very detailed character, and space will not permit of more than a reference to nearly twenty explorers who were engaged at this time. Among them were Captain Wingate [3] and E. Teichman ; the latter was able to improve the maps of Kansu and Shensi in the course of a number of journeys before and after 1916.

Exploration is not over in China. In the tangled mass of mountains of the south-west Mr Kingdon Ward has combined a search for rare plants with geographical exploration, and his work in this region is not yet completed. He has, however, succeeded in elucidating the problem of the rivers of South-east Asia, and the award to him of the Founder's Medal of the Royal Geographical Society in 1930 is a just tribute to one who has done excellent work in a region where English geographers of an earlier period, Margary, Gill, Baber, and many others, did much pioneer work.[4]

At the beginning of the nineteenth century Japan was practically unknown to Europeans. Yet even at this time, before the Japanese people had begun to copy the ways of the West, some geographical work was accomplished by one of themselves, for the country was surveyed along the whole length of its coastline between 1800 and 1817, and an area of 137,000 square miles was covered.[5] The Dutch attempted to open up trade with the country in 1823, and sent an expedition for that purpose which included the naturalist Dr P. F. von Siebold. During his seven years' residence at Nagasaki Siebold collected much information of a general character about Japan. His work remained authoritative for about thirty years.

[1] For a recent expedition on the borders of Szechwan and Tibet see E. Teichman, in *G.J.*, vol. lxix, p. 1.

[2] For some recent exploration of Manchuria (1913–15) see Captain A. de C. Sowerby, " The Exploration of Manchuria," in *G.J.*, vol. liv, p. 73.

[3] See Wingate, " Nine Years' Survey and Exploration in Northern and Central China," in *G.J.*, vol. xxix, p. 174.   [4] See above, p 269, note 1.

[5] On this remarkable survey see E. B. Knobel, " Inō Chūkei and the First Survey of Japan," in *G.J.*, vol. xlii, p. 246.

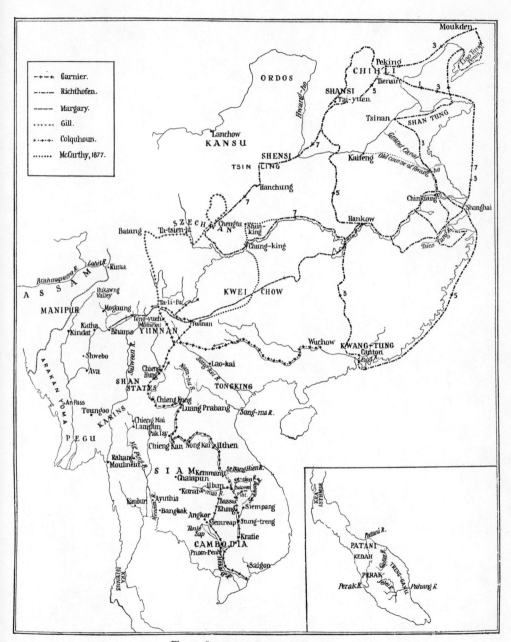

Fig. 30. SOUTH-EASTERN ASIA AFTER 1800

ASIA

The American expedition of Perry, in 1853, led to the opening up of Japan to traders of all nations. R. Alcock went there in 1858 to represent the interests of Great Britain, but on his arrival he found himself in an unknown land. Surveys had been made on many parts of the coast, but knowledge of the interior was restricted to a few towns and routes. Alcock was able to make a number of journeys inland, in the island of Nippon, and to give the world the fruits of his labours in a classical work, *The Capital of the Tycoon*.

Another Englishman, Blakiston, made a journey on shore round the island of Yezo in 1871, while in that year the British Admiralty surveyed the coasts of the island. In the same decade the island was again visited, by Miss Bird, who also travelled in unknown parts of Nippon.

Although a number of other visitors, both before and after Miss Bird, have made small contributions to the knowledge of Japan, it is to two German scholars that most scientific advance was due before the Japanese themselves began systematically to map the country. J. J. Rein went to Japan in 1874 with an expedition sent by the Prussian Minister of Commerce, the main object of which was to study the trade and industries of Japan. He was able to travel extensively through Nippon, Shikoku, and Kiushiu, and as a result to publish most valuable accounts of Japan.

Even more extensive were the journeys of Naumann, who directed the geological survey of Japan for ten years (1875–85). Like Rein, he made long journeys in the larger islands, especially in Northern Nippon, and was able to make large contributions to the physical geography of the country.

The primary triangulation of Japan was begun in 1882 and completed in 1921. All parts of the Japanese Empire—that is, Japan proper, Korea, and Formosa—have now been surveyed and mapped.

VIII. Central Asia [1]

The exploration in Central Asia is largely due to the Russians, who approached it over the Tian Shan, the Pamirs, and Mongolia, and to the English, who came from India, over the Karakoram group of

[1] See the following works:

J. Deniker, "Les Explorations Russes en Asie Centrale (1871–95)," in *Annales de géographie*, vol. vi, p. 408 (with a useful map).
Lord Curzon, "The Pamirs and the Source of the Oxus," in *G.J.*, vol. viii, p. 15 *et seq.*
M. Friederichsen, "Morphologie des Tiën-schan," in *Zeitschrift der Gesellschaft für Erdkunde zu Berlin*, vol. xxxiv, p. 1 (with a useful map showing routes of explorers).
Sir Thomas Holdich, *Tibet the Mysterious*.
F. von Hellwald, *The Russians in Central Asia* (English translation (1894), by Lieutenant-Colonel T. Wirgman).

mountains or the plateau of Tibet. It begins with the journey of Semenov in the Tian Shan and that of Schlagintweit to Yarkand in 1857. During the nineteenth century its characteristic feature is to be found rather in the large number of expeditions than in the outstanding importance of any one. Yet an important exception to this statement must be made. One name, that of the Russian Prjevalsky, stands out conspicuously. From the beginning of his work in 1871 to his death in 1888, at the commencement of his fifth journey, a great change had been made in the map of Central Asia. His career requires separate consideration, and may well mark the turning-point in the history of exploration in this area. This will therefore be considered in three stages, before, during, and after the work of Prjevalsky.

During the first period advances were made in four directions. The Russians began the exploration of the Tian Shan range, the English reached the Pamirs, Indian surveyors began the exploration of Tibet, and a small amount of work was accomplished in Mongolia.

In the Tian Shan the first important exploration was that of Semenov in 1857. This able Russian officer had consulted Humboldt about the problems of the geography of Central Asia, and was anxious to confirm or to disprove the suggested volcanic composition of the Tian Shan. He approached the region from the eastern side of Lake Balkash, crossed the Ala Tau to Issyk Kul, and penetrated to Khan Tengri, in the main range. He was able to determine many positions, to collect much information about the physical geography of the region, and, as he thought, to prove that Humboldt's theory was wrong.

Valikhanov, who followed the track of Semenov, in 1858, turned to the south-west after rounding Issyk Kul, and, crossing the Naryn valley and a number of other parallel valleys to the southward, reached a route leading to Kashgar.

Four years later a third expedition explored the country at the western end of Issyk Kul, and made a circuit of Son Kul. This route was next used by Osten-Saken, who crossed over the whole range, following a more westerly line to Kashgar than that taken by Valikhanov.

Two lines of advance had now been followed, to the east and to the west of Issyk Kul. The two were united by Severtsov. He had already, in 1864, continued the geological researches of Semenov, and had surveyed the mountainous country between the Chu river and the Syr Darya. A number of heights had been determined, and the separate identity of the Kara Tau range had been established. In 1868 Severtsov turned his attention to the eastern part of the Tian Shan, and explored the country partly along the general line of Osten-Saken, partly to the south of Issyk Kul, by a route

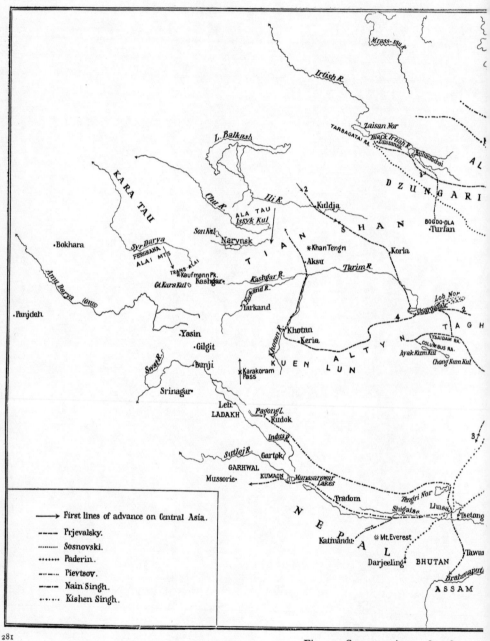

Fig. 32. CENTRAL ASIA, 1857–84

First lines of advance on Central Asia.

- - - - Prjevalsky.
.... Sosnovski.
+++++ Paderin.
-..-..- Pievtsov.
-.-.-. Nain Singh.
..+..+.. Kishen Singh.

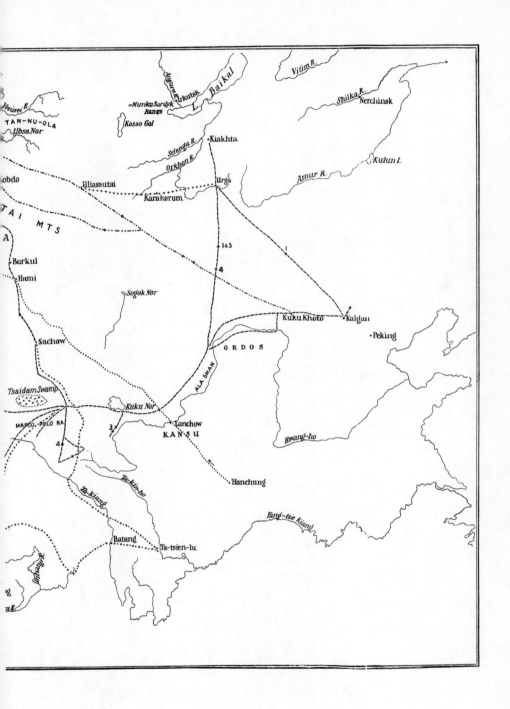

parallel to but north of that of Valikhanov, and partly to the east of Issyk Kul.

Severtsov was followed by Von Kaulbars, who linked up all the areas hitherto explored in the Central Tian Shan, from the region where Severtsov had worked in 1864 to the route followed by Osten-Saken to Kashgar; from that route by Valikhanov's track to the eastward; and from that line farther eastward to the point reached by Semenov.

The last of the Russian expeditions falling within this first period is that of Fedchenko (1871), who skirted the Ala Tau highlands, and from the Ferghana turned southward across the Alai Mountains to the edge of the Trans-Alai range. Here he named the highest peak Mount Kaufmann, in honour of his Commander-in-Chief. Although he did not reach the Pamirs, at the close of this period the Russians were rapidly closing in on the 'roof of the world.'

Meanwhile they had been anticipated by explorers from India. The pioneers were the brothers Schlagintweit, who crossed the Karakoram Pass and

traversed a diversified and broken plateau of about 16,500 feet average above the sea, and of about 100 miles in breadth from south to north, when, reaching a depression extending from west to east, they found, between it and the low country of Khotan, another parallel east and west range, one of the heights of which they determined to be from 19,000 to 20,000 feet above the sea.[1]

This mountain range was identified with the Kuen Lun, and was thought to confirm Humboldt's general theory as to the separate identity of that chain. Two of the brothers, Hermann and Robert, reached Khotan, but could not get as far as Yarkand: the third, Adolph, who had followed a more westerly route, did reach Yarkand, and went on until within sight of Kashgar, where he was murdered, in August 1857.

The operations of the Survey of India had at this time extended to Kashmir, and one of its officers, W. H. Johnson, journeyed from Leh to Khotan in 1865. He spent sixteen days in the town, and was able to determine its position (latitude 37° 8' N., longitude 79° 25' E.).

Another member of the Survey, Mirza Shuja, one of the so-called 'Pundits,' who was known as 'the Mirza,' reached the Oxus in 1868, discovered Chakmak Kul (where he turned toward the north-east), and made his way to Kashgar. In the same year Hayward set out from Peshawar, and, travelling through Leh, reached Yarkand, where his main work began. He was able to trace the general line of the Karakash and Yarkand rivers and to reach Kashgar. The results of his journey, as shown in the map he produced, were of great importance. Hayward set out on another expedition in 1870.

[1] *Proc. R.G.S.*, old series, vol. ii, p. 301.

He met with many obstructions from local rulers, and generously took all responsibility for his journey, electing to go in a private capacity rather than as an official representative of the Royal Geographical Society. He left Gilgit in July 1870, " in the hope of being able to penetrate to the Pamir steppe and the sources of the Oxus," but was murdered at the beginning of August ; the results of his journey were lost.

Yet in the year 1870 great progress was made in exploration from India. R. B. Shaw, who had reached Yarkand and Kashgar in 1869, accompanied Forsyth on a mission to the latter town in 1870. Working with this party were two Indian assistants, one of whom went by Gilgit, Yasin, Sarhad, and Tashkurghan to Yarkand, while the second reached Yarkand by a track a little farther to the north-ward. Shaw and Forsyth also took different routes, and were thus able to collect much valuable information about the country to the south-west of the Kuen Lun Mountains, and to make good the loss occasioned by the murder of Hayward. They were ably assisted by Dr Cayley, political Resident in Ladakh, who accompanied them to the foot of the Kuen Lun ranges. Thus the first period closed with a number of important routes through the country to the north-west of India well known, while explorers had reached the Pamirs and had made contact with the Russians in Kashgar.

The difficulties of exploring a country where the suspicion and hostility of the inhabitants and their rulers intensified the natural obstacles had been realized by Montgomerie, and he therefore decided to employ Indians to explore these inaccessible regions. It is to their magnificent work that a great amount of the accurate knowledge of Tibet is due. The first attempt to penetrate Tibet from Kumaon in 1864 failed, but in the following year Nain Singh reached the Tsangpo from Nepal, and, joining a caravan, arrived in Lhasa in January 1866. He returned to India through Tradom and by the Manasarowar Lakes, Kumaon, and Garhwal to Mussorie. The results of the journey were of the greatest importance. Latitude observations had been taken at a number of places, " an elaborate route survey extending over 1200 miles, defining the road from Katmandu to Tradom and the whole of the great Tibetan road from Lhasa to Gartok," had been made, and the course of the Brahmaputra had been fixed " from its source near Manasarowar to the point where it is joined by the stream on which Lhasa stands." Observations of the temperature of the air and boiling-water were made by which the height of thirty-three points was determined, and some idea of the climatic conditions was obtained. In addition a vast amount of general information was collected. When it is realized that most of the work was done secretly it will be seen how successful the expedition had been, and Captain Montgomerie in no way exaggerated when he said, in the formal report, that the work was

" on the whole well done " and " the results are highly creditable to the Pandit." [1]

The object of the next journey, in 1867, was to connect up the surveys made in Ladakh with the newly explored country in the neighbourhood of the Manasarowar Lakes, to obtain information about the upper courses of the Indus and Sutlej rivers, and to investigate reports of gold- and salt-mines near to Gartok. The expedition was a complete success ; 850 miles of route survey, with 190 latitude observations at 75 stations, served as the basis for a map covering about 18,000 square miles.

The third journey, undertaken by Kalian Singh, was to Rudok, beyond the Upper Indus valley, and the country to the eastward. It began from the west, and ended at Shigatse, on the road to Lhasa. From information he was able to collect from other sources, as well as from his own observations, this Pundit made valuable contributions to geography. At the same time another explorer was working in the country behind Mount Everest. One result of these exploits was to show " how very far behind, or north of the great peaks, the Himalayan watershed lies, and what a great breadth the highest parts of the range cover."

Thus at the end of the first period of Central Asian exploration some progress had been made in Western and Southern Tibet and the holy city of Lhasa had been reached for the second time in the century.

In the fourth region, Mongolia, very little advance was made before 1871. The eastern and northern borders had been touched by the Russians in their Amur expeditions of 1857 and subsequent years ; Fritsche had, as already related, crossed the Gobi Desert from Peking ; and in 1868 another Russian party travelled from Peking to the country north of the Altai. In the west Radlov had visited Kobdo in 1870. But very little was known of this region when Prjevalsky began his first journey.

In 1871 Prjevalsky set out from Kiakhta, and, travelling through Urga, reached the Gobi Desert, which he crossed to Kalgan. Thence he made a journey into North-eastern Mongolia and back to Kalgan. An excursion to the Ordos country followed, after which he returned to Peking. He left this city again in March 1872, travelled through Kansu, and, taking approximately the route of Gabet and Huc, reached Kuku Nor on October 14. " In all my life," he said, " I have never beheld such a beautiful lake as this. . . . Its salt waters are a magnificent deep blue, and in the month of October the snow-

[1] The official accounts of this and other similar journeys between 1865 and 1892 will be found in *Records of the Survey of India*, vol. viii (2 parts, 1915). A useful summary of these two volumes will be found, with additional matter, in Major K. Mason's " Kishen Singh and the Indian Explorers," in *G.J.*, vol. lxii, p. 429.

clad mountains surrounding it formed a frame of sparkling white to the picture." Prjevalsky continued his journey to the Tsaidam country, " one vast marsh, its perfectly plane surface covered with salt and reeds showing that, at some not far distant period, it has formed the bed of an immense lake." He found it necessary to correct some of the inaccurate or exaggerated reports of Huc. Prjevalsky reached one of the headstreams of the Yangtse-kiang, and hoped to be able to go on to Lhasa, but lack of resources compelled him to return. He went back to Kuku Nor, skirted the Ala Shan, and struck northward across the Gobi Desert, in its widest part, to Urga. He had been within 500 miles of Lhasa, and had visited a great area of unknown country. " Among the results of this expedition, besides rich collections of the flora and fauna of the countries visited, and a detailed route survey, was the discovery of a moist, mountainous region in Kansu, to the north of the Upper Hwang-ho and east of lake Kuku Nor, well wooded and abundantly supplied with rainfall, though isolated by arid tracts." [1]

Between the first and second journeys of Prjevalsky a little progress was made in Central Asia, almost all of which was due to Indian and English explorers. In Mongolia Ney Elias, who wished to identify the ancient site of Karakorum, set out from Peking in the summer of 1872, and crossed the Gobi Desert to Uliassutai, travelling over 2000 miles and taking a large number of astronomical observations. In the following year the Russian Paderin, whose object was similar to that of Elias, explored a part of Northern Mongolia and added to the knowledge of the upper courses of the Orkhon and Selenga rivers. At the same time Fritsche crossed Eastern Mongolia, and spent some time in an examination of its south-eastern districts, while on a journey to Nerchinsk. With one exception all other exploration during this interval in Prjevalsky's work originated in India. In 1872 the Russian Sosnovski accompanied an expedition to the Black Irtish river and Dzungaria, which greatly improved the map of those regions.

In 1871 an Indian explorer, Hari Ram, made his way from Darjeeling, through Sikkim, to Shigatse, and returned to the north of Mount Everest and through Nepal. Once again the watershed was found to lie " far behind or north of the lofty peaks that are visible from Hindustan." Valuable information was obtained about the upper valley of the Arun river, and altogether the journey " opened out the geography of nearly 30,000 square miles of what had hitherto been in many portions *terra incognita* and in others nearly so." As Montgomerie, now a major, wrote, " His [Ram's] work I think will prove a valuable addition to the trans-frontier geography of India." Even more valuable was the journey of

---

[1] E. D. Morgan, " Prjevalsky's Journeys and Discoveries in Central Asia," in *Proc. R.G.S.*, new series, vol. ix, p. 214.

Kishen Singh,[1] who started from Kumaon in 1871, and made a route survey from Shigatse to the great lake, Tengri Nor, lying to the north of Lhasa. He continued his journey through the capital, crossed the Brahmaputra, and returned to Shigatse. " The route survey," Montgomerie reported,

> extends over 320 miles of what has hitherto been veritable *terra incognita*. Latitude observations were taken at ten places, and heights by observations of the boiling-point and of the aneroid at twenty-four places. The geography of an area of about 12,000 square miles has been elucidated, and one northern tributary of the Upper Brahmaputra has been thoroughly explored, thus giving us some idea as to how far back the northern watershed of this great river lies.[2]

Hari Ram made another important journey in 1873, starting from Kumaon and reaching Tradom. He returned through Nepal. But, valuable as this work was, it was surpassed by that of Nain Singh, who had already made the famous journey to Lhasa. With three servants he left Leh on July 15, 1874. He travelled through Western Tibet parallel to, but north of, the Brahmaputra river to Tengri Nor, turned south to Lhasa, and entered the capital on November 18. He sent back his reports from Lhasa to Ladakh, and himself undertook a further exploration to the south of the capital, ultimately reaching Assam in March 1875. The results of his journey were of the greatest importance, and are thus described in the official report:

> In addition to the general information acquired, the Pundit has made a very careful and well-executed route survey of the whole line of country traversed, viz. 1013 miles from Lukung (at the west end of Pangong Lake) to Lhasa, and 306 miles from Lhasa to Oialguri. Of this total distance of 1319 miles, throughout which his pacings and bearings were carefully recorded, about 1200 miles lie through country which has never previously been explored. Numerous lakes, some of enormous size, and some rivers, have been discovered; the existence of a vast snowy range lying parallel to and north of the Brahmaputra river has been clearly demonstrated, and the positions of several of its peaks have been laid down, and their heights approximately determined.
>
> The Brahmaputra has been followed for a distance of thirty miles in a portion of its course, and 50 miles lower down than the lowest point hitherto determined; and as its approximate course for another 100 miles has been laid down, the absolutely unknown portion of that mighty river's course remaining has been very materially reduced. The route between Lhasa and Assam *via* Tawang, of which next to nothing has hitherto been known, has been carefully surveyed.[3]

Additional information about the climate of Tibet was obtained.

This was the last journey of Nain Singh, the first of the Pundits,

---

[1] Known as A-K.
[2] *Records of the Survey of India*, vol. viii, Part I, p. 140.   [3] *Ibid.*, p. 179.

for his health had broken down, and he was anxious to retire. He was rewarded with a village in Rohilkand, with a revenue of Rs. 1000, and was afterward made a Companion of the Indian Empire. As Lord Salisbury wrote, " the successful travels of the Pundit . . . have for many years attracted attention not only in England but among geographers all over Europe." [1]

Further light was thrown on the Brahmaputra problem by the journey of Lala in 1875-76. From Darjeeling he went to the Brahmaputra at Shigatse, travelled along it for about fifty miles, until the road left the river, and after a *détour* to the south joined it again and followed it for another sixty miles to Tsetang, where he turned southward because further progress was impracticable without an armed escort. He reached Bhutan, but was arrested and sent off to Lhasa. A fortunate ' informality' in a document led to his release by a subordinate official before he reached the capital, and he was able to return to Shigatse, and so to reach India.

While progress was thus being made in South-eastern and Southern Tibet important new information had been obtained in the north-west of India. Thus Haider Shah travelled from Peshawar to Faizabad through Chitral in 1870 ; made a route survey from Kabul to Bokhara in 1872 ; and reached the Oxus from Faizabad in the following year.

In 1873 Sir Douglas Forsyth led a semi-political mission to Kashgar. It included Captain H. Trotter, in charge of the survey, Captain Biddulph, Lieutenant Gordon, and Dr Stoliczka. These men added greatly to the knowledge of the Pamir region, and their work " constituted the first serious British contribution to the scientific knowledge " of this part of the world.[2] In addition Indian surveyors who accompanied the party collected much information. Abdul Subhan did valuable work on the Oxus river, and Kishen Singh returned to India from Yarkand, through Khotan and Western Tibet, to Leh, supplementing very considerably the knowledge which had been obtained by Shaw in 1870. Another Pundit, Ata Mahomed, reached Yarkand through Chitral in 1874, and in 1876 " followed the wild gorges of the Indus, tracing its course up from the plains to Bunji, after which he explored Yasin." [3]

Prjevalsky began his second journey in 1876, by which time some progress had been made all round the fringes of Central Asia. On this occasion his object was to reach Lhasa from the north. The journey began at Kuldja, in the upper valley of the Ili, and the route lay over the Tian Shan Mountains to the Tarim river, and thence by its valley to Lob Nor. The Altyn Tagh range was discovered, and efforts were made to find a way through, without

[1] Mason, *op. cit.*, p. 438.   [2] Curzon, *op. cit.*, p. 253.
[3] Mason, *op. cit.*, p. 435.

success, "owing to deep winter which set in and want of time." Yet enough was done to establish the main features of the country. " We succeeded," Prjevalsky wrote,

in exploring these mountains, that is to say their northern slopes, over an extent of 300 versts [198 miles] east of Chargalak. Throughout the whole of this distance the Altyn-Tagh serves to buttress a lofty plateau overhanging the Lob-Nor desert, and most probably forming the northern limit of the Tibetan highlands; at least that is what the inhabitants gave us to understand, one and all assuring us that the south-western prolongations of the Altyn-Tagh continued to margin the desert uninterruptedly as far as the towns of Keria and Khotan. According to the same informants this range stretches a long way in an easterly direction, but where it terminates none could say.[1]

After making this discovery, the most important of his expedition, Prjevalsky returned to Kuldja.

Between 1876 and 1879, when Prjevalsky began his third journey, a very great advance was made in Central Asia, especially by Russian explorers. In the Tian Shan region Stolicza and Trotter, members of Forsyth's expedition, crossed the Pamirs to the Oxus, descended the river to its lowland valley, and reached Panjdeh, on the borders of Afghanistan, in 1874. Sosnovski, who had explored the Black Irtish and parts of Dzungaria in 1872, now entered China by a route roughly identical with that of Prjevalsky, and from Hang-chung crossed the desert to Dzungaria. This journey resulted in the first modern account of Hami and the first extensive traverse of Dzungaria. Romanovski and Mouchketov carried out a large amount of detailed work, between 1874 and 1880, in the whole area of the western mountains, from the Alai and the northern side of the Pamirs, through the Ala Tau and the Tian Shan, to the Tarbagatai range. The first devoted his attention to surveys scattered throughout the region indicated, while the second confined himself to the Central Tian Shan, the geology of which he examined very carefully. Still farther to the north-east Pievtsov made two expeditions, in 1876 and 1878–79, to the country north-east of the Altai and in Dzungaria. On the first he crossed Dzungaria by the Urungu river, and reached Bogdo-ola, the culminating point of the Eastern Tian Shan. On the second he crossed from the north of the Altai to Kuku Khoto, on the borders of Mongolia, returned to the north-west of Mongolia, and completed the route of Paderin (1872) beyond Uliassutai by a line of march which lay to the north of his outward track. Kropotkin in 1876 crossed the Tian Shan from the Ferghana to Kashgar, and traversed the whole of the lower country at its foot, as far as Korla. Some members of the party went farther, to Bagrash Kul, while on the return a new

[1] Colonel N. M. Prjevalsky, *From Kulja across the Tian Shan to Lob-Nor*, translated by E. D. Morgan (1879), pp. 80–81.

route over the range from Ak-su was discovered. In the same year Potanin made the first of his important travels, in North-western Mongolia and Eastern Dzungaria. From the north of Dzungaria he crossed the Altai to Kobdo, and recrossed the (Mongolian) Altai to Barkul and Hami. After a short stay there he crossed the Altai for the third time, to Uliassutai, whence he travelled to Kosso Gol. Turning here to the westward, he skirted the southern side of the Tan-nu-ola to Ubsa Nor and Kobdo. It was a valuable expedition, crossing the routes of Pievtsov, linking up his explorations with those of Sosnovski, and covering much unknown country.

The last of the journeys that fall within this period were made by the botanist Regel in 1876–77 and 1878–79. He covered a great part of the Northern Tian Shan area, east of Issyk Kul, and extended his investigations far to the eastward, being the first scientific explorer to reach Turfan.

In the Pamir region also some progress was made. A Russian party, which included Prince Witgenstein and Kostenko, who acted as geographer, crossed the Alai in 1876. The main body did not go farther, but the two members named proceeded southward to the Great Kara Kul, and the Prince was the first European in modern times to see its waters. Both men penetrated a little distance to the south of the lake. The following year Severtsov led a party across the Trans-Alai, to explore the country between that range and the Great Kara Kul. In 1878 they went to the southward of the lake, and carried their surveys to a point eastward of Yeshil Kul, on one of the headstreams of the Oxus, where Trotter had also been surveying four years earlier. In the same year Mouchketov investigated the geology of part of the country traversed by this expedition. Its results were important, for it

> solved the main questions relating to the geography of the Pamir and its orographical peculiarities. Instead of its being a high desert plateau, intersected by few and insignificant ranges, as was believed by some, even after the English and Russian surveys of 1873–6, the expedition found a system of high valleys—not a line of valleys extending from east to west, between comparatively low ranges, as had been supposed by Fedchenko, but a network of valleys, intersected at different angles by the ranges which form the vast mountain masses.[1]

Although this result had been proclaimed abroad in 1880, the old opinion remained, and drew a protest from Curzon in 1895. " Correctly described," he wrote,

> a Pamir in theory, and each Pamir in fact, is . . . neither a plain, nor a down, nor a steppe, nor a plateau, but a mountain valley of glacial formation, differing only from the adjacent or other mountain valleys in its superior altitude, and in the greater degree to which

[1] *Proc. R.G.S.*, new series, vol. ii, pp. 505–506.

ASI A

its trough has been filled up by glacial detritus and alluvium, and
has therefore approximated in appearance to a plain owing to the
inability of the central stream to scour for itself a deeper channel.[1]

From India, also, a certain amount of progress was made. The
work of the Pundits continued without interruption. In the north-
west one of these men explored Swat and "traced the Kandia
tributary of the Indus to its confluence with the latter river near
its great southerly bend."[2] At the other end of the frontier Nem
Singh set out from Darjeeling "to trace the Tsangpo river from
Tsetang downwards as far as he was able." He followed it for
287 miles, to Gyala, and from his reports it seemed highly probable
that the Tsangpo discharged by the Dihang river into the Brahmaputra of Assam. But the greatest exploit was that of Kishen Singh,
who began his last journey in 1878. From Darjeeling he went to
Lhasa, and then travelled across the width of Tibet to the northward, crossed the Altyn Tagh, and reached Sa-chow, a point also
on the route of Prjevalsky's third journey. That marked his
northern limit, but instead of returning the same way Kishen
Singh crossed Eastern Tibet to the Chinese town of Ta-tsien-lu,
whence he journeyed through Batang to Sama. Here he was
refused passage into Assam, so he turned northward, made a great
bend round the Brahmaputra river, and reached it at Tsetang.
He was now in well-known country, and was able to cross into
India, arriving at Darjeeling on November 12, 1882.[3] It is impossible in a short space to do justice to this achievement. Not only
was a vast area of entirely unknown country crossed by the Pundit,
but he found time to collect an amazingly complete amount of
general information, such as temperatures, wind directions, population figures, and details about trade. In a single journey he had
linked areas where the British were active to those reached by the
Russians, while his visit to Ta-tsien-lu connected up Indian and
Chinese route traverses, and he was able to accomplish the task in
which Gill and others had failed. It was a magnificent end to the
career of a great explorer.

The exploration of Mongolia continued during this period, but
was related to journeys in other parts of the region which have
already been considered.

Thus when Prjevalsky began his third journey, which in point
of time overlapped with that of Kishen Singh, a considerable
change had taken place in the map of Central Asia. He set out
from Zaissansk in 1879, crossed Dzungaria to Hami, and, continuing
to the southward, intended to travel through Tibet to Lhasa. He
made his way over the Altyn Tagh and to the east of Tsaidam,

[1] Curzon, *op. cit.*, p. 31. [2] Mason, *op. cit.*, p. 435.
[3] Mason says he "reached India in 1884" (*op. cit.*, p. 439). The date here
given is taken from *Records of the Survey of India*, vol. viii, Part II, p. 287.

and finally crossed the Tangla range to a village within 170 miles of Lhasa. Here he waited for permission to proceed, but as this was refused he was obliged to return. Instead of traversing the Gobi by his outward route he turned eastward, skirted the Hwang-ho, and then crossed the desert to Kyakhta, as on his first journey. He was the first European to penetrate Northern Tibet, and his was the first general account of the country which was made public. In addition to the valuable information thus acquired, some additional knowledge of the Chinese border resulted from his return journey.

Comparatively little was done between the third and the fourth expedition of Prjevalsky. Potanin, on his second journey in 1879, explored the Tan-nu-ola range and the country round Kosso Gol, thus completing his earlier work. Unfortunately, the results of the exploration were lost in a fire at Irkutsk in 1880. In the Pamirs Regel carried out botanical researches among the western borders. In Mongolia and in the Tibetan borderlands the expedition of Szechenyi has already been mentioned.[1] Eutioughin crossed the north-eastern part from Dolon Nor, by a route to the west of the Great Khingan Mountains, to Lake Kulun in 1882, while in the same year Vanin made the journey between Dolon Nor and Urga. In Tibet a little information came through a native of Sikkim, named Kinthup, who went with a lama to carry out further exploration on the Brahmaputra, but was sold into slavery, and only escaped after four years, to return to India in 1884. He confirmed the belief, which was almost a certainty after Kishen Singh's last journey, that the Brahmaputra, the Dihang, and the Tsangpo were all one river.

The object of Prjevalsky's fourth journey (1883-84) was to make a more thorough examination of Tibet and Eastern Turkestan. He set out from Urga, crossed the Gobi to the Ala Shan, reached the upper valley of the Blue River (Di-chu), but found he could not cross it, and returned to explore the country in which the Hwang-ho rises. Proceeding thence south of Tsaidam, and north of a series of ranges to which he gave the names of Marco Polo, Columbus, and Moscow, he reached the " Valley of the Winds," which he explored. Retracing his steps, he turned northward and crossed the Altyn Tagh to Lob Nor. From this point he travelled westward at the foot of the Altyn Tagh, but his efforts to penetrate southward to Tibet were frustrated by the Chinese. At length he reached Khotan, where he turned northward, crossed the Takla Makan to Ak-su, and went over the Tian Shan to Issyk Kul. One of the most important results of this expedition was the elucidation of the relief of Northern Tibet. " The famous Kuen Lun," wrote Prjevalsky,

that backbone of Asia, as Baron Richthofen calls it, before our last journey was entirely unknown through 12° of longitude, from the

---

[1] See above, p. 276.

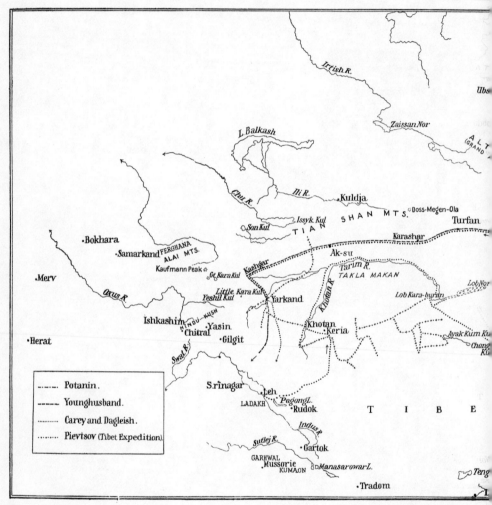

Fig. 32. CENTRAL ASIA, 1885–88

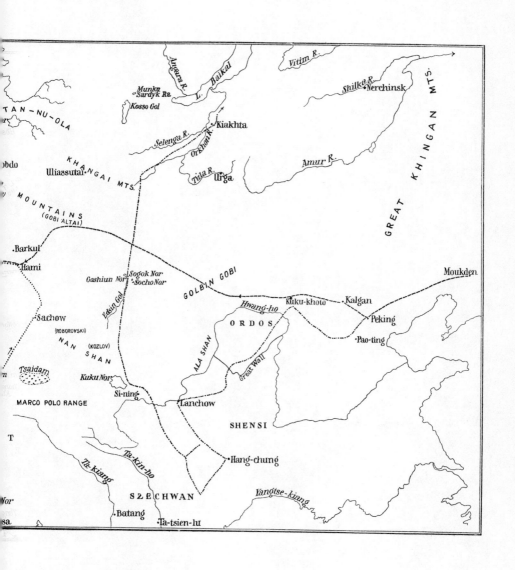

TAN-NU-OLA

Angara R.

L. Baikal

Vitim R.

Munku
Sardyk Ra.

Shilka R.
Nerchinsk

Kosso Gol

obdo

Selenga R.
Kiakhta

KHANGAI MTS.

Orkhon R.

Uliassutai

Tula R.

Amur R.

Urga

GREAT KHINGAN MTS.

MOUNTAINS
(GOBI ALTAI)

Barkul

Hami

GOLBIN GOBI

Moukden

Gashiun Nor.
Sogok Nor
Socho Nor

Ezsin Gol

Hwang-ho

Kuku-khoto

Kalgan

Sachow

(ROBOROVSKI)

ORDOS

Peking

NAN
SHAN

(KOZLOV)

ALA SHAN

Pao-ting

Tsaidam

Kuku Nor

Great Wall

Si-ning

MARCO POLO RANGE

Lanchow

SHENSI

T

Ta-kin-ho

Ta-kiang

Hang-chung

Nor

SZECHWAN

Yangtse-kiang

sa

Batang

Ta-tsien-lu

meridian of Naijin-gol in Tsaidam to that of Keria in Eastern Turkestan. We have now passed along this unknown belt of the most ancient ranges of Asia, and have in some measure elucidated its topography. We find the principal chain forms an arc, the eastern and western extremities of which lie in the same parallel of 36°, whilst the northern periphery touch 38° N. latitude. A line drawn to the westward of this in about the 87th meridian of east longitude (from Greenwich) at the point where the still more northerly Altyn-tagh chain separates from the main range would serve to define approximately the centre of the Kuen Luen, its eastern limit being, according to [Richthofen] the 104th degree of east longitude, where the system is characterised by a ramification into parallel chains. The chief of these, the Kuen Lun proper, serves as a gigantic buttress to the highlands of Northern Tibet, facing on the north the desert and saline plains of Tsaidam ; while on the east it cuts off the upper basin of the Hwangho and continues far into China.[1]

Prjevalsky intended to lead a fifth expedition in 1888, but died before it started. His work in Central Asia was, however, continued by those who had accompanied him on his earlier journeys, and served to fill in the details of the general outline which he had traced. His explorations embraced the whole region from the Tian Shan to Mongolia, and from the Amur basin to Northern Tibet. When he died the map of Central Asia was being rapidly completed, and for his own share in that process he will always be remembered as one of the greatest explorers of the nineteenth century.

Between 1884 and 1888 considerable progress was made in all regions. In the west Klements continued the work of earlier explorers in the country south of Tan-nu-ola in 1885–86, and in 1886 Ignatiev and Krassnov carried out valuable geological and topographical investigations in the Tian Shan, to the south-east of Issyk Kul. In the Pamirs the Russian expedition of 1883 explored the country in all directions from Kara Kul, and " contributed to Pamir cartography more accurate and detailed information than any preceding or subsequent expedition." [2] The naturalist Grum-Grijimailo made four expeditions into the Pamir country between 1884 and 1887, and linked up the region explored by Fedchenko in the Alai with that covered by other explorers to the south-west of Issyk Kul. In 1885 Ney Elias was sent by the Government of India on a mission to Chinese Turkestan, and was ordered to collect information about the Afghan districts of the Upper Oxus. He took an entirely new route, from east to west, across the Pamirs, travelling from Kashgar to Herat, where he met the Afghan Boundary Commission. " His journey added greatly to the geographical and political knowledge in possession of the Indian Government, and has contributed substantial additions to all subsequent maps." [3] In the next year an English mission to

[1] *Royal Geographical Society : Supplementary Papers*, vol. iii, p. 58.
[2] Curzon, *op. cit.*, p. 259. [3] *Ibid.*, p. 254.

Chitral, which "had explored the southern slopes and valleys of the Hindu Kush," visited part of the Oxus valley, and produced "the first scientific report of the main course of that river from its glacial source to the great bend at Ishkashim." [1]   In 1886 Bonvalot, Capus, and Pepin left Merv with the intention of going to Afghanistan, but, not receiving the necessary permission, travelled to Samarkand, and prepared to cross the Pamirs to India.   They succeeded in their project, and were thus the first to cross the Pamirs from the Ferghana to Chitral.

In the east Ressin made a traverse of the Eastern Gobi Desert, between the Great Wall and Tsitsihar, on the borders of Manchuria, in 1887, and in the same year the brothers Garnak carried out important work on the western side of the Great Khingan Mountains.

Connecting the two areas, east and west, were three important expeditions.   The first, under Potanin, started from Peking, crossed the Ordos to Lan-chow, and penetrated to Northern Szechwan, where one member of the party remained to study the people and the flora.   Potanin returned through Kansu to Kuku Nor, whence he followed a new route northward over the Gobi Desert, through Sogok Nor, and across the Altai Mountains.

In 1885–86 A. D. Carey, an Indian Civil Servant, and A. Dagleish crossed Northern Tibet from Leh to Keria, turned westward to Khotan, and made a complete circuit of the Tarim basin, following the Khotan and Tarim rivers to Lob Nor.

The third journey was that of Younghusband, from Manchuria to India.   With a friend, H. E. M. James, of the Indian Civil Service, he arrived in Manchuria in 1886.   Some time was spent in exploring that country, and then the party turned westward on their long march.   From Peking and Kalgan they crossed north of the bend of the Hwang-ho, and, following a route parallel to that of Pievtsov in 1878, reached the Altai.   They then turned south to Hami, skirted the base of the Tian Shan to Kashgar, travelled to Yarkand, and crossed to India by the Mustagh Pass, which they discovered.   A somewhat similar route was taken by Colonel M. S. Bell.   He had left Younghusband at Peking, and travelled through Southern Shensi to Lan-chow, expecting to meet him again at Hami.   Failing in this, he reached India alone a short time before Younghusband. [2]

The last period of Central Asian exploration begins with the Tibetan Expedition of the Russian Government in 1888, under the leadership of Pievtsov.   It supplemented in many respects the fourth journey of Prjevalsky.   The work was entrusted to a large party, including the geologist Bogdanovich, and Kozlov and

[1] Curzon, *op. cit.*, p. 254.
[2] See *Proc. R.G.S.*, new series, vol. xii, p. 57, for Bell's journey, and *The Heart of a Continent* (1896) for that of Younghusband.

Roborovski, who had served under Prjevalsky. They crossed the Tian Shan and skirted the Takla Makan to the foot of the Kuen Lun range. Here a number of surveys were made to the southward, covering a large area between Khotan and Lob Nor, and extending southward to the Kuen Lun. The main object of the expedition, to reach Lhasa by a more direct route than those attempted by Prjevalsky, was not accomplished, but 5000 miles of topographical survey were made, and a large collection of geological, botanical, and zoological specimens was obtained. Kozlov and Roborovski returned in 1893, and made another highly important expedition, connecting the Tian Shan and Lob Nor with the mountains of Nan Shan, and reaching Kuku Nor.[1] Perhaps the greatest contribution to geography which they made was to explore the Nan Shan Mountains, in which they worked independently, Kozlov devoting his attention to the eastern part, while Roborovski worked in the west. The expedition returned to Russia by Hami.

So large was the number of other explorers in Central Asia at this time, that it is only possible to refer to a few of them. In the Tian Shan the brothers Grum-Grijimailo made important discoveries in 1889 and 1890. The area covered stretched from the Tian Shan and Altai ranges to Lob Nor and Western China. " In their journey over the Tian Shan they abandoned the ordinary caravan road and travelled along the northern flanks of the range." They discovered a new mountain mass, the Doss-megen-ola, and a part of Turfan which lay below sea-level.

In the Pamir country Younghusband and Bower from the English side, and Grombchevski from Russia, were very active exploring the less-known regions, partly from political motives. The rivalry between Great Britain and Russia, of which this exploration is a symptom, led ultimately to the Pamir Boundary Commission of 1895, which fixed the Russian and British frontier and gave a small piece of the Pamirs to Afghanistan as a ' buffer ' between the two larger Powers. The operations in connexion with the boundary demarcation virtually completed the exploration of the country. Of the later expeditions in this region and the adjoining mountain areas mention should be made of that of Lipski to the Hissar Mountains in 1896 and those of Merzbacher, who visited the Central and Eastern Tian Shan in 1902–3 and again in 1907–8, and made a detailed study of their geology and land-forms. Another explorer, Olufsen, in two expeditions (1896 and 1899) examined parts of the Pamir region. He surveyed the country round Yeshil Kul, crossed some hitherto unvisited areas between the Pamir river and the Oxus, and, in his second expedition, visited the Southern Pamir region and some of the upper valleys of the Hindu Kush. In addition to improvements in the cartography of

[1] See *G.J.*, vol. viii, p. 196, and vol. xi, p. 546.

the region, Olufsen obtained valuable ethnological results from these two journeys.

In Mongolia very considerable progress has been made during the last forty years. It is only possible here to mention a few of the more important expeditions. In 1892 Radlov and Klements explored a large part of the valley of the Orkhon, in Northern Mongolia. In the same year Obruchev began a series of brilliant journeys in Eastern, Central, and South-eastern Mongolia. He crossed from Kyakhta to Peking, traversed the Ordos region to the foot of the Ala Shan, surveyed the Hwang-ho to Lan-chow, and explored a considerable area of the Nan Shan Mountains. He then crossed the Gobi, to the south-eastern extremity of the Altai, and returned to Su-chow to explore the central Nan Shan range. His impression of Central Mongolia is of interest. "Central Mongolia," he said,

> completely deceived my expectation.... Instead of the sand deserts of our maps, I found broad ridges and rocky hills, mostly very low and much disintegrated, but certainly not sandy plains. There is very little sand indeed, and the loess, contrary to Richthofen's opinion, is wanting here as well. Broad valleys and shallow depressions occupy the spaces between the ridges, and everywhere there is vegetation. It is not a desert, but a steppe, and the poorest parts of the Golbin Gobi are oases in comparison with the true deserts of the left banks of the Edzin-gol.[1]

Klements returned to Northern Mongolia in 1894, and in that and in the following year explored the Khangai Mountains and parts of the Gobi Altai. At the same time Strelbitzki made a long journey from Urga to Vladivostok by the Kerulen river, and across the Great Khingan Mountains to Tsitsihar. The researches of Pozdneiev (1874–93) in Northern Mongolia, between Urga and Kobdo, although directly concerned with historical and linguistic studies, helped to throw light on a region which was at that time very imperfectly known. In 1895 Chaffanjon, who had made some important corrections to the map of the Great Khingan Mountains and Northern Manchuria, crossed Mongolia from the south-west to the north-east, and added somewhat to the knowledge of the Altai Mountains.

At the end of the century Kozlov began a series of explorations in the Altai regions, which extended from the little-known country of the Great Altai, in and round the Kobdo district, to the Gobi Altai. Subsequently he crossed the country, in one of its least-known parts, to Gashiun Nor, reached Tsaidam, and examined the upper course of the Yangtse-kiang. He returned over the Gobi to Kyakhta, where he arrived at the end of 1901.[2] In 1907 he went back to Mongolia, to explore those parts not yet visited by Europeans,

---

[1] *G.J.*, vol. v, p. 263.　　　[2] *Ibid.*, vol. xix, p. 576.

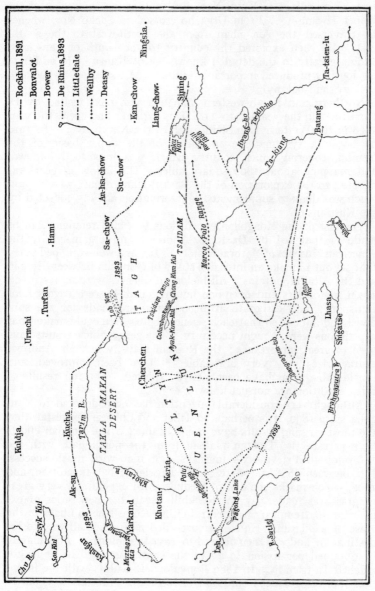

Fig. 33. CENTRAL ASIA, 1889–99

Rockhill, 1891
Bonvalot
Bower
De Rhins, 1893
Littledale
Wellby
Deasy

Kan-chow.
Liang-chow.
Ninşia.

Ning-hsia.
Sining
Si-chow.
An-hsi-chow.
Ta-tsien-lu
Batang
Ta-Kiang
Hoang-ho
Tarldu-ho
Koko
Nor 1888
Kaku
Nor
Sa-chow
Marco Polo Range
TSAIDAM
Tsaidam Range
Columbus Range
Ayak-Kum-Kul Chong Kum Kul
Lob Nor
1893
TAGH
Turfan
Hami
Urmchi
Kuldja
Tangri
Nor
Lhasa
Shigatse
Braqmaputra R.
Tengri-num-ts
ALTYN
UEN
LU
Cherchen
TAKLA MAKAN DESERT
Tarim R.
Khotan R.
Ak-su.
Kucha.
Keria
Polu
Langha
Pangong Lake
Leh
1895
R. Sutlej
Kashgar
Yarkand
Raskam R.
Muztag
Ata
1893
Chu R.
Issyk Kul
Son Kul

to take soundings of Kuku Nor, and to examine the region of the Upper Hwang-ho. From Urga he crossed to Socho Nor, whence he traversed the Ala Shan from the north-west to the south-east. He then explored the country to the south of Lan-chow, adding greatly to the detailed knowledge of Kansu.[1] In addition, his journey produced important results for the sciences of geology, zoology, and botany.

Northern and North-western Mongolia was next visited by D. Carruthers in the years 1910–11. This explorer had spent the year 1908 in the Western Tian Shan south of the Naryn river. In 1910 he began a systematic examination of the upper basin of the Yenisei, covering much country which was imperfectly known, and mapping about 1800 square miles. The following year was devoted to the exploration of the Barkul-Hami group, where again much was done to supplement the information already collected by the Russians.

The last of the Mongolian expeditions to which reference can be made is that led by Dr R. C. Andrews and organized by the American Museum of Natural History. It was a well-equipped party that set out to make an intensive study of Mongolia between Kalgan and the Altai Mountains. All biological sciences were represented ; seven motor-cars and over one hundred camels were engaged for transport ; and elaborate arrangements were made for the sub-division of labour so that each science represented could make what expeditions were thought necessary. The geographical results have been of great importance ; the Russian maps, which Dr Andrews characterizes as " very unreliable," [2] have been improved, and considerable areas have been newly explored. The full results of this expedition are not yet known.

Although very considerable attention has been devoted to Mongolia since 1890, it is perhaps in Tibet and Chinese Turkestan that the most striking results have been obtained. The Russian efforts to penetrate the Tibetan plateau from the north had, with the exception of Prjevalsky's journeys, not met with much success. But between 1888, the date of the Russian Tibet expedition, and 1908, which marks the end of Hedin's third expedition, very great progress was made. W. W. Rockhill began the new series of ex-plorations, attempting to penetrate from Kuku Nor to Lhasa in the guise of a pilgrim. He so far succeeded as to get half-way to his destination, and was then obliged to leave the country. Fortunately he obtained permission to go to the south-east, and he at length reached Ta-tsien-lu. In 1889 Bonvalot left Kuldja with the inten-tion of crossing Tibet from Lob Nor to Batang. He also was partly successful, and his route from Lob Nor to Tengri Nor covered entirely new ground. But he too was not allowed to go to Lhasa,

[1] See *G.J.*, vol. xxxv, p. 288.   [2] *Ibid.*, vol. lxix, p. 6.

and, like Rockhill, proceeded to Ta-tsien-lu. Rockhill made a second attempt in 1891–92. From Kalgan he crossed Mongolia to Tsaidam, whence he made a great sweep to the south-west, and turned north of Tengri Nor. His nearest point to Lhasa was Namru-tso, but again he failed to get permission to proceed, and crossed South-eastern Tibet to Batang. On his journey he had seen the sources of the Yangtse-kiang, and had collected much valuable information, more especially relating to the religious and social life of the Tibetans.

Meanwhile Captain H. Bower had left Leh in April 1891 with the object of crossising Tibet north of the route taken by Nain Singh in 1874. He was completely successful, passed north of Tengri Nor, and reached China in about latitude 30° N. In the course of his journey of 3000 miles he added greatly to the accurate knowledge of Northern Tibet, and traversed at least 800 miles of country never before touched by any explorer.

The pilgrimage of Baza-Bacha to Tibet in 1891–94, during which he succeeded in reaching Lhasa, has little of geographical interest, and the journey of Potanin, on the Tibetan borderlands (1892–94), while adding to knowledge of Szechwan, came to a premature end through the death of the explorer's wife. Tragedy also marked the expedition of Dutreuil de Rhins and Grenard. From Khotan they went south-eastward to Polu, traced the upper reaches of the Keria river, and then traversed an unknown region east of Ladakh to Leh. They returned to Yarkand by the Karakoram route, and in July 1893 began a second journey in Tibet. Starting from Cherchen, they endeavoured to cross Tibet to Lhasa. They successfully accomplished a great part of the journey, crossed Bower's route in about latitude 33°, and penetrated to the south of Tengri Nor, when they were refused permission to enter Lhasa. They therefore began a return journey to Si-ning, on the borders of Kansu, but De Rhins was murdered long before that city was reached : Grenard and the other members of the party escaped with difficulty. Yet the expedition did valuable work. It supplemented in many ways the information obtained by Bonvalot, threw much new light on the lake region of Tibet to the east of Ladakh, and filled in many broad features in the northern part of the country.

The English explorer Littledale, in the course of a transcontinental journey, made important additions to knowledge in Turkestan in 1893. His route lay through Samarkand, Kashgar, Ak-su, and Korla, to Lob Nor. He next went to Sa-chow by an entirely new track, and thence to Kuku Nor, also across unknown country. Beyond this point his route lay through Lan-chow to Peking. Littledale returned in 1895 to make a journey into Tibet. He again crossed the continent, travelling through Constantinople, Poti, Baku, Merv, Bokhara, Khokand, and Kashgar. Thence he went by Khotan to

Cherchen, where he began his journey southward into Tibet. He penetrated to within forty-three miles of Lhasa, and then turned westward, finally reaching Leh. He had thus made a traverse of Tibet between the routes of Bonvalot and Pievtsov.

While Littledale was engaged in his Tibetan exploit Sven Hedin began the first of a series of very important expeditions. He abandoned all intention of crossing Tibet to Lhasa, a city which exerted an influence on Tibetan exploration out of all proportion to its importance, and devoted his attention to Northern Tibet and the Tarim basin. He tried unsuccessfully to climb Muztag Ata, a peak of over 24,000 feet in the Pamirs, crossed the desert between the Yarkand and the Khotan rivers, discovered buried cities in the Takla Makan, and then proceeded to Lob Nor. Here he carried out important topographical work, and discovered that the 'lake' had changed even since the time of Prjevalsky. He then travelled through Cherchen to Keria, and returned by way of Tsaidam to Kuku Nor, across the Ala Shan and Ordos to Kalgan. Thence his route lay over the Gobi to Siberia.

Two other explorers helped to fill in the blank spaces in Tibet while Hedin was making his archæological discoveries in Turkestan. In 1896 Captain M. S. Wellby and Lieutenant Malcolm crossed the country from Leh to Kuku Nor, proceeded along the Hwang-ho, and ended their journey at Peking. In the same year Captain H. H. P. Deasy began a series of expeditions which had for their object the careful survey of as many unknown areas in Tibet as circumstances allowed. Deasy continued his work until 1899, during which time he explored part of the Upper Yarkand valley and a large area to the south of the Kuen Lun and east of Pagong Lake and Rudok.

The journey of Futterer and Holderer has already been mentioned so far as it related to China. In crossing Central Asia from Kashgar to the Upper Hwang-ho they made valuable additions to knowledge, more especially in the valley of the Tarim river, the Eastern Tian Shan, and the Gobi Desert between the Hami oasis and the Great Wall of China. Another explorer, Bonin, has also been mentioned for his work in China. In 1896 he had, in the course of that work, visited Kansu. Three years later he left Peking, to follow the silk route between China and Europe. He navigated the Hwang-ho in its upper course to Ningsia, whence he crossed the Ala Shan by a new route to Liang-chow, in Kansu, and proceeded thence to Kuku Nor. He made some additions to the knowledge of the Nan Shan, followed the foot of the Altyn Tagh to the Tarim valley (where he met Sven Hedin), and finally crossed the Tian Shan by a new track to Urmchi. Beyond this he passed through Kuldja and Samarkand to the Caspian Sea.

When Bonin met Hedin the latter was engaged on his second Asiatic expedition (1899–1902). It was devoted to Chinese Turkestan

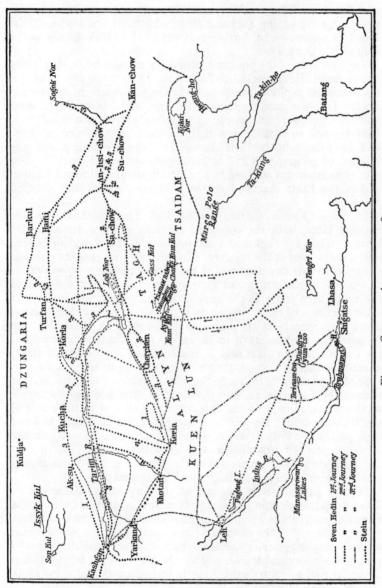

Fig. 34. CENTRAL ASIA AFTER 1899

Kuldja·

Issyk Kul

Son Kul

Sogok Nor

Barkul

DZUNGARIA

Turfan

Kucha

Ak-su

Korla

Lob Nor

Tarim R.

Keria

An-hsi-chow

Hami

Sa-chow

Su-chow

Kan-chow

Kitah Nor

Hoang-ho

Ta-hin-ho

Batang

Ta-kiang

Marco Polo Range

T A G - H

Gass Kul

Cherchen

Mum Kul

Ayik

Kum-chong

Kumkul

TSAIDAM

Tengri Nor

A L T Y N

Samanskoe

T A N

Lhasa

Shigatse

Kashgar

Yarkand

Khotan

K U E N   L U N

Brahmaputra R.

Pang-kong-tso

Tari-nan-bso

Panggra-yum-tso

Pagong L.

Indus R.

Leh

Manasarowar
Lakes

Sven Hedin   1st Journey
    ,,   ,,   2nd Journey
    ,,   ,,   3rd Journey
Stein

and Northern Tibet, and its most important geographical results were a survey of the Yarkand river, additional knowledge of the Lob Nor region, and a further removal of the blank spaces in the map of Northern Tibet.

The first year of the present century was marked by the beginning of Sir Aurel Stein's work in Turkestan. The main object of this distinguished explorer has been archæological research, but he has always taken trained surveyors with him, and has produced most valuable topographical maps. The important archæological finds have thrown an entirely new light on the history of Central Asia, and have brought to their discoverer " the admiration and the interest of geographers and archæologists the world over." [1] The first expedition was confined to a relatively small area round Khotan and in the Takla Makan, but was productive of valuable detailed maps.

In 1903 Captain C. G. Rawling and Lieutenant Hargreaves entered Tibet, with the object of continuing the work begun by Deasy. They accomplished a detailed survey of a considerable area in the north-west of the country. In the following year the political situation led to the dispatch of the Younghusband expedition to Lhasa. This had important geographical results, not confined to the route from India to the capital of Tibet. Captain Ryder and other members of the survey party were able to survey the Brahmaputra from Shigatse to its source, to do the same for the Sutlej from its source to the borders of India, and to map the Gartok branch of the Indus. Thus a great area in Southern and South-western Tibet, amounting to about 40,000 square miles, was accurately known.

Shortly afterward, in 1906, the blank spaces were still further reduced by Sven Hedin, who devoted his third journey of 1906–8 to the region lying between Shigatse and Leh and to the north of the Brahmaputra. He produced maps of the area, which had not been previously visited, and revealed the existence of a large range of mountains lying parallel to the Himalaya on the Tibetan side. He elucidated many points about the country of the Manasarowar Lakes, and filled in a very large blank on the map.

Hedin's expedition is the last of the large-scale discoveries in Tibet. Much valuable knowledge of a smaller area came from the recent expeditions to Mount Everest. Though they ended in failure to reach the top of the mountain, they established a new record for altitude climbing, immortalized the names of those gallant men who perished, Mallory and Irvine, and provided a wealth of topographical detail, as well as contributing greatly to the solution of some problems of physical geography.

[1] Lord Ronaldshay in *G.J.*, vol. lxv, p. 499. The valuable paper by Sir Aurel Stein in *G.J.*, vol. lxv, p. 377 *et seq.*, should be consulted for this aspect of the subject.

ASIA

There remain three expeditions to Turkestan, undertaken by Pelliot and Stein. The first began work at Kashgar in 1906, and produced a route survey of over 1000 miles. But his main object was to find traces of pre-Muslim Buddhism in Kashgaria, and his expedition need not be further considered.

Stein's second expedition, 1906-8, covered a much greater area than the first, and took him from the Lob Nor region to the west of China. His main object again was archæological research, but his party carried out important surveys extending from Yarkand to the Nan Shan range.

The third expedition of Stein, in 1913-16, began with some fresh exploration in the mountainous country to the north-west of India. From Kashgar he took an unfrequented route to Khotan, whence he proceeded to Lob Nor and beyond to the borders of China. He returned along the northern edge of the basin, and in 1914-15 made important surveys in Turfan. Stein returned to Kashgar in the summer of 1915, and then left for an expedition to Seistan. Thus the journey embraced the whole of Central Asia between the Tian Shan ranges on the north and the Kuen Lun on the south, from the Pamirs to China. The geographical results are of the greatest importance, for from the maps produced, as well as from the weighty volumes in which the results have been described, a picture of Inner Asia can be drawn which leaves but few empty spaces.[1] With this great expedition the long series of travels which has been recorded since 1857 may fittingly be closed.

[1] The geographical results of Sir Aurel Stein's three expeditions are dealt with in his *Memoir on Maps of Chinese Turkestan and Kansu* (1923).

CHAPTER XIV

AFRICA [1]

THE modern exploration of Africa begins with the foundation of the African Association in 1788. The main object of this society was to promote the discovery of Africa, but it had, as a secondary project, the advancement of British trade and political authority in the unknown continent. The task before the Association was formidable, because in 1788 very little was known about the interior of the continent. A narrow strip in North-west Africa, a small piece of territory between the Senegal and the Gambia, parts of the west coast south of the Congo mouth, the Cape Province south of the Orange River, a narrow strip up the Zambezi River, and a larger region covering Egypt and Abyssinia north of the Blue Nile represented the total known area in 1788.

The exploration of Africa falls broadly into three periods. From 1788 to 1849 the problem of the Niger attracted most attention : elsewhere, as in the north-east, there was considerable activity, especially toward the end of this first period. In 1849 Livingstone began his explorations, and in the following year Barth set out for the Sahara. These two journeys mark a turning-point in the exploration of the country, and begin the period of discovery in Central Africa and in the Sahara and Sudan. With the conclusion of Stanley's work in 1889 this second period comes to an end, for by that date the main problems of African geography had been solved. From 1890 to the present day has been occupied with filling in the details in those areas whose features had been sketched in outline before that date, and by removing or reducing those

[1] See the following works :

A. SUPAN, "Ein Jahrhundert der Afrikaforschung," in *P.M.*, vol. xxxiv (1888), p. 161, with a very useful series of maps.
SIR HARRY JOHNSTON, *The Nile Quest* (1903).
—— *The Colonisation of Africa* (2nd edition, 1913). This contains a useful chapter on " Great Explorers."
J. S. KELTIE, *The Partition of Africa* (2nd edition, 1895).
R. BROWN, *The Story of Africa and its Explorers* (4 vols.)—a good popular account, the first volume of which appeared in 1892.
A. SILVA WHITE, *The Development of Africa* (2nd edition, 1892). This contains a summary of exploration to that date, based on Supan's article quoted above.
F. R. CANA, " Problems in Exploration : Africa," in *G.J.*, vol. xxxviii, p. 457, and " The Sahara in 1915," in *G.J.*, vol. xlvi, p. 333.
J. BATALHA-REIS, " Recent Portuguese Explorations in Africa," in *Proc. R.G.S.*, new series, vol. xi (1889), p. 686.

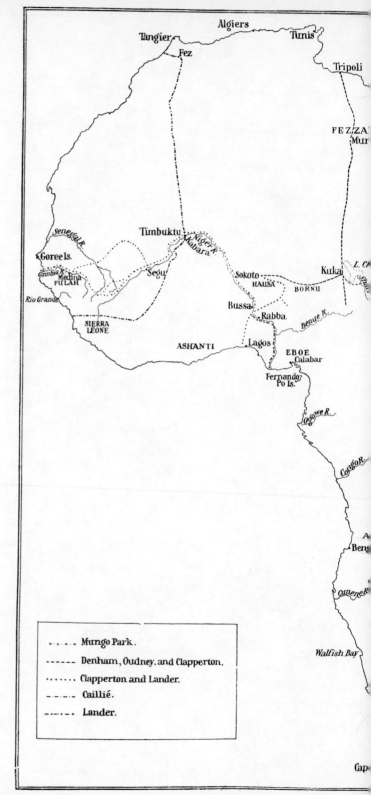

Fig. 35. AFRICA, 1788–1849

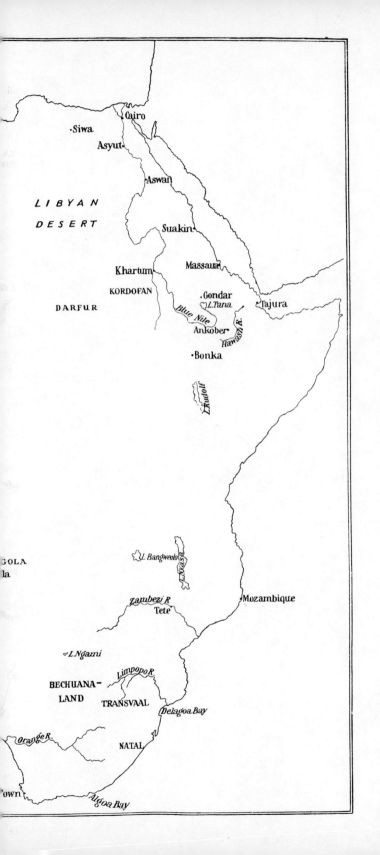

·Siwa

Cairo

Asyut·

·Aswan

LIBYAN

DESERT

Suakin·

Khartum

Massaua·

KORDOFAN

·Gondar

DARFUR

L.Tana

·Tajura

Blue Nile

Ankober·

Hawash R.

·Bonka

L.Rudolf

GOLA

la

L. Bangweolo

L.Nyasa

·Mozambique

Zambezi R.

Tete·

⌐L.Ngami

Limpopo R.

BECHUANA-
LAND

TRANSVAAL

·Delagoa Bay

Orange R.

NATAL

·own

Algoa Bay

AFRICA

blank spaces which still remained on the map in 1889. The Sahara Desert, Southern Abyssinia and the north-east corner of Africa, and the Nile-Congo divide are the areas in which most important discoveries were made during this last period. Elsewhere ceaseless political activity is reflected in many important journeys of scientific exploration and in boundary surveys, which are particularly important during the present century.

I. NORTH-WEST AFRICA AND THE NIGER PROBLEM, 1788–1848 [1]

The first task to which the African Association turned was the discovery of the river Niger, about which there was great confusion. Some idea of current theories may be gained from the pages of the Annual Register, which stated, in 1758 :

> The river Senega or Senegal is one of those channels of the river Niger by which it is supposed to discharge its waters into the Atlantic Ocean. The river Niger, according to the best maps, rises in the east of Africa, and, after a course of 300 miles nearly due west, divides into three branches the most northerly of which is the Senegal, as above, the middle is the Gambia or Gambra, and the most southern the Rio Grande.

It must be admitted that more competent writers in 1788 did not hold such preposterous views, but at best their ideas were based on theory or the writings of Leo Africanus. No one knew where the Niger rose, in which direction it flowed, or where it entered the sea.

The African Association sent out John Ledyard to Egypt in 1788, with the object of crossing the desert to the Niger. He died in Cairo before anything was done. At the same time Lucas was sent to penetrate the desert from the north, but all he could do was to collect some information about trade-routes across the Sahara. Hornemann next tried the Egyptian route in 1789, reached Murzuk, but was diverted to Tripoli. Setting out thence on a second attempt, he undoubtedly crossed the desert, but died on the Niger, and no definite news has ever been received of his accomplishments. Houghton was the next victim to the fanaticism of Northern Africa. He attempted the Gambia route, followed the general course of that river to Medina, and struck eastward to the Faleme, a tributary of the Senegal. Still moving eastward, he sent back his last message : " Major Houghton's compliments to Dr Laidley ; is in good health, on the way to Timbuktu ; robbed of all his goods by Fenda Bukar's son." He was murdered shortly afterward.

Thus four attempts, two from Egypt, one from Tripoli, and one from the Gambia, had failed. The fifth expedition was made by a

[1] On this section see especially J. Thomson, *Mungo Park and the Niger* (1890).

young Scotch doctor, Mungo Park, who had returned from a voyage to Sumatra in 1793. His orders were plain and concise. " I was directed," he wrote,

> on my arrival in Africa to pass on to the river Niger either by way of Bambouk, or by such other route as should be found most convenient. That I should ascertain the course, and, if possible, the rise and termination of that river. That I should use my utmost exertions to visit the principal towns or cities in its neighbourhood, particularly Timbuktu and Hausa ; and that I should be afterwards at liberty to return to Europe either by way of the Gambia, or by such other route, as, under all the then existing circumstances of my situation and prospects, should appear to me to be most advisable.[1]

Park reached the Gambia on June 21, 1795, and early in July was at the last outpost of European traders up the river. After much delay he continued his march eastward and beyond the Faleme river, until on July 20, 1796, he records :

> Looking forwards I saw with infinite pleasure the great object of my mission ; the long sought for, majestic Niger, glittering to the morning sun, as broad as the Thames at Westminster, and flowing slowly to the eastward. . . . The circumstance of the Niger's flowing to the east did not, however, excite my surprise ; for although I had left Europe in great hesitation on this subject, and rather believed that it ran in the contrary direction, I had made such frequent inquiries during my progress concerning this river, and received from Negroes of different nations such clear and decisive assurances that its general course was towards the rising sun as scarce left any doubt on my mind.[2]

Park reached the Niger at Segu, and followed it for a short distance, but, to quote his words,

> worn down by sickness, exhausted with hunger and fatigue, half-naked, and without any article of value by which I might procure provisions, clothes, or lodging, I began to reflect seriously on my situation.

His reflections led him to observe that the rainy season had arrived, when the ground was flooded and travel difficult, that he had little chance of " subsisting by charity in a country where Moors have such influence," and that to advance was to place himself " more and more within the power of those merciless fanatics." Nor could he gather much information about the Niger. " All the natives with whom I conversed," he wrote,

> seemed to be entirely ignorant. Their commercial pursuits seldom induce them to travel further than the cities of Timbuktu and Hausa ; and they pay but little attention to the course of rivers or the geography of countries. It is, however, highly probable that the Niger affords a safe and easy communication between very remote nations.[3]

[1] Mungo Park, *Travels in the Interior Districts of Africa* (1799), p. 3.
[2] *Ibid.*, pp. 194-195.   [3] *Ibid.*, p. 214.

As to the termination of the river, all Park could gather was that it ran " to the world's end."

Park left the Niger for his homeward journey on July 30, 1796, but was obliged to rest on the way to recover from sickness. He was thus able to make some observations of interest. " When the wind sets in from the north-east," he wrote,

> it produces a wonderful change in the face of the country. The grass soon becomes dry and withered ; the rivers subside very rapidly ; and many of the trees shed their leaves. About this period is commonly felt the *harmattan*, a dry and parching wind blowing from the north-east and accompanied by a thick haze through which the sun appears of a dull red colour. This wind in passing over the great desert of Sahara acquires a very strong attraction for humidity and parches up everything exposed to its current. . . . The air during the rainy season is so loaded with moisture that clothes, shoes, trunks, and everything that is not close to the fire become damp and mouldy ; and the inhabitants may be said to live in a sort of vapour bath : but this dry wind braces up the solids, which were before relaxed, gives a cheerful flow of spirits, and is even pleasant to respiration. Its ill effects are that it produces chaps in the lips, and affects many of the natives with sore eyes.[1]

During his period of convalescence at Kumalia Park made good use of his opportunity to collect information about the country and its inhabitants. On April 19 he set out for the coast, and on arrival there sailed to the West Indies, ultimately reaching Falmouth on December 22, 1797, after an absence from England of two years and seven months.

Park had at least settled one point about the Niger : it flowed to the eastward. But as to its termination, the old controversies revived. Rennell, the ablest geographer in England at the time, believed that it ended somewhere in the middle of Africa, in a great swamp. Park himself thought it was identical with the Congo. Others guessed that it turned southward and entered the Gulf of Guinea.[2]

Park went out again in January 1805,[3] with instructions " to pursue the course of this river to the utmost possible distance to which it can be traced " and to return either by a new route to the Atlantic or " by marching upon Cairo by taking the route leading to Tripoli." It would appear that Lord Camden, who drew up the instructions, held the same belief as Rennell. The expedition reached Goree Roads at the end of March, was delayed at the last trading-post until May, and then began to move slowly to the eastward. It was hampered by its own size, for Park had with him about forty Europeans, mostly soldiers, and a number of asses for transport. It set out just as the rainy season was beginning, and soon the men

[1] Mungo Park, *Travels in the Interior Districts of Africa* (1799), p. 259.
[2] See the authorities quoted in Supan, *op. cit.*, p. 166, and J. McQueen, *A Geographical and Commercial View of Northern Central Africa* (1821).
[3] See *The Journal of a Mission to the Interior of Africa* (1815).

began to fall out through illness, until by July Park recorded : " All the people either sick or in a state of great debility except one." The Niger was sighted on August 18, but of the " thirty-four soldiers and four carpenters who left the Gambia only six soldiers and one carpenter reached the Niger." The river was again followed for a short distance, and then Park stopped to convert a native boat into a suitable vessel for the purpose of ascertaining whither the river flowed. On November 19 the small party set sail on H.M. schooner *Joliba*. At the Bussa Rapids all were drowned, either accidentally or in their efforts to escape from the attacks of natives.

Thus ended the short but brilliant career of Mungo Park. In two heroic journeys he had accomplished more in the way of practical discovery than any man in Africa for one hundred and fifty years, and if he had failed to solve the problems of the Niger he had at least reduced the possibilities of error. He had heard from a native guide that the Niger did bend to the southward, and this information in due course reached England.

In 1815 a triple advance on the Niger was planned. Burckhardt was to cross from Egypt, Nicholls from Calabar, and Röntgen from Morocco ; the whole plan, however, failed. In the following year Tuckey was sent to the Congo to prove, if possible, its connexion with the Niger, but this was not the sole object of the journey. In his instructions it was pointed out: " That a river of such magnitude as the Zaire [*i.e.*, Congo], and offering so many peculiarities, should not be known with any degree of certainty, beyond, if as far as, 200 miles from its mouth, is incompatible with the present advanced state of geographical science," and he was ordered to remedy the defect. He ascended the river for a short distance, but failed in the main object. He himself and a large number of his party died either before or immediately after leaving the river.

While Tuckey explored the Congo Peddie and Campbell set out from the west coast. The latter reached the Fulah country, but died on the return journey, while Peddie did not even live to see that region. Three years later, in 1818, Ritchie and Lyon started from Tripoli. Ritchie died a short distance beyond Murzuk, but Lyon succeeded in exploring parts of Fezzan, until lack of resources compelled him to return. Thus at the end of thirty years of effort the problems of the Niger were still unsolved.

Very shortly after this Denham, Clapperton, and Oudney set out from Tripoli, and, following a route roughly along the 15th meridian east of Greenwich, reached Bornu ; they were the first Europeans after Hornemann to cross the desert and the first to see Lake Chad. It was on February 4, 1823, that Denham records : " The great Lake Chad, glowing with the golden rays of the sun in its strength, appeared to be within a mile of the spot on which we stood. My heart bounded within me at the prospect, for I believed this lake to be the key to the great object of our search." [1]

Oudney died in the Hausa country, but Clapperton went on to Sokoto, while Denham reached the Shari, and rejoined Clapperton at Kuka. The two men returned together to Tripoli, and reached England in 1825. " Although we have not been able to solve that interesting problem, to which the discovery of Mungo Park gave rise," Denham wrote, " I hope I may be allowed to say that we have very considerably enlarged the boundaries of our geographical knowledge of Africa." This was a modest claim for men who had crossed the Sahara, discovered Lake Chad, travelled for over 700 miles of longitude in the centre of the continent, and proved that the Niger had no connexion with the lake of their discovery.

In 1825 Clapperton landed on the Guinea coast near to Lagos, and attempted, by yet another route, to solve the Niger problem. He reached the river at Bussa, and pushed on to Sokoto. Here he too fell a victim to climate and disease, and the only surviving member of the party, Richard Lander, was left to find his way back to the coast as best he could. Indeed, it seemed as if the geographical and political conditions of West Africa formed an obstacle that no amount of courage or resource could overcome, and for a time efforts to solve the problem ceased.

Meanwhile a number of small expeditions had been made in various parts of North-west Africa. Political troubles led to the dispatch of James and Bowditch to Ashanti in 1817, and Bowditch made the most of his small opportunities to study the country and the people. In the next year Mollieu discovered the sources of the Gambia, the Rio Grande, and the Senegal, while Gray and Dochard covered Mungo Park's routes in the Gambia basin. Major Laing located the sources of the Niger in 1822, although he was not able to reach them, and three years later made his way from Tripoli to Timbuktu, where he remained for a month. He was the first explorer of modern times to reach the city, but he paid for the honour with his life, for he was murdered shortly after leaving it on his return journey across the desert.

The most picturesque figure of this intermediate period is René Caillié. He had accompanied the expedition of Gray in 1818, and in 1824 went to live with the natives of the Senegal to learn their language. Three years later he set out from Sierra Leone, reached the Niger, and followed it to Kabara, the port of Timbuktu. Thence he went to the mysterious city, saw something of its real character, and crossed the Sahara to Morocco, reaching the coast west of Fez. For this journey he was rewarded by the Geographical Society of Paris, founded in 1821.

---

[1] *Narrative of Travels and Discoveries in Northern and Central Africa* (3rd edition, 2 vols., 1828), vol. i, p. 182.

The Niger problem was now somewhat nearer a solution. The sources of the river were known to be within a short distance of the Atlantic seaboard; its course to Bussa was approximately traced; and there was definite knowledge of the country east of Sokoto. Its termination was settled in 1830 by Richard Lander and his brother. They started from the Guinea coast, and, travelling overland, reached Bussa. Thence they sailed down the Niger to the sea, and put an end to all further controversy. Lander received the Royal Premium from the Royal Geographical Society, just founded in London, and that society absorbed the older African Association. Thus in more than one way Lander's voyage marks the end of a chapter in the history of geographical discovery.

During this first period of African exploration little further progress was made in the Niger region. An expedition to the Niger in 1832 failed to reach Rabba, though one of its members, Laird, ascended the Benue for a short distance. The next year the brothers Lander were more successful, but though they penetrated to Rabba they could get no farther. At the same time the party ascended the Benue for about 100 miles. In 1832 C. H. Coulthurst went from Fernando Po to Calabar, and pushed up the Calabar river to the Eboe country, where his progress came to an end; with it ceased all activity in this region until 1840, when Beecroft went up the Niger to within thirty miles of Bussa. The next year a big effort was made to open up trade with the interior, but it ended in dismal failure.

Meanwhile most important events had been taking place in the north. In 1830 the French began their conquest of Algeria. Between 1839 and 1843 most of the Tell and high plateau had been conquered; war was carried into Morocco between 1843 and 1847; and in 1848 Algeria was declared to be part of France. Thus a large region was opened to European influences, a field for geographical research was prepared, and a valuable base for the exploration of the Sahara was established. The country was thrown open to European scientists, and a great impetus was given to the study of African geography. Among the early visitors were Berbrugger, an archæologist and ethnologist of distinction, who went to Algeria in 1835, and died in Algiers, after long service, in 1869; Von Puekler-Muscau, who travelled both in Tunis and in Algeria; Wagner, an anthropologist and geologist (1836–38); Bradshaw (1845–47); and J. W. von Müller, who also visited Morocco, as well as travelling extensively in the New World. One Englishman, Davidson, tried to cross the Western Sahara from Tangier, but lost his life in the attempt (1836).

Two other journeys which ultimately had close relationship with the exploration of North-west Africa may be mentioned here. In 1844–45 Barth traversed the fringe of the desert from Tunis to Egypt, and in 1845 Richardson reached Murzuk from Tripoli. Both men were soon to be associated in one of the greatest explorations in the whole of African history.

II. North-east Africa, 1788–1848

The main features of North-east Africa were known in broad outline before the year 1788, but there were still regions which were unvisited or little known, and a very small amount of scientific exploration had been carried out. The period opens with the remarkable journey of W. G. Browne to the oasis of Siwa (1792) and, more important, to Darfur (1793). He reached this country, not without difficulty, by the regular caravan-route from Asyut, and returned the same way, having barely escaped with his life. During his stay in the country he was able to collect much valuable information, and his work remained authoritative for over a century.

The most important factors in the opening up of the Nile valley were, however, not the single journeys of men like Browne or Bruce [1] (whose travels had inspired Browne), but the Napoleonic invasion of 1798 and the later rule of Mohammed Ali. The French not only directed the attention of Europe to Egypt and its archæological remains, but were themselves active in collecting and in disseminating information. The *Atlas of Egypt*, published in Paris in 1807, accurately represented the Nile as far as Aswan.

Out of the political chaos which followed the withdrawal of the French and the British there arose the strong power of Mohammed Ali (1805–48), which reduced Egypt to order and spread her conquests as far south as Kordofan. European explorers were quick to take advantage of their opportunity, and visited the country in large numbers. Seetzen (1810) and Burckhardt (1812, 1814–17) are among the general class of traveller. The latter visited Cairo in 1812, and crossed the Nubian Desert to Suakin. Returning from Arabia, he prepared to start from the Nile valley for the Niger, but died at Cairo. Ehrenberg travelled in Libya in 1820, while Caillaud and Letorzec not only visited the oases of the Libyan Desert, and extended their travels into Nubia, but accompanied the Egyptian expedition which resulted in the founding of Khartum in 1823, and reached the Blue Nile. This same expedition gave an opportunity to Rüppell to visit Darfur in 1824.

On the White Nile definite, if spasmodic, progress was made. In 1827 Linant de Bellefonds ascended the river to the latitude of 13° 6′ N., and came to the conclusion that its source must be in some lake in about the latitude of 7° N. Twelve years later an Egyptian expedition, which was accompanied by Thibaut, reached a point in about latitude 6° 30′ N., and in 1841 a second expedition, with which went D'Arnaud and Werne, penetrated as far as about the latitude

[1] See above, p. 198.

of 4° 42′ N. Thus De Bellefonds was proved wrong so far as his location of the sources of the Nile was concerned : as to their general nature, all the information available seemed to be in his favour.

A number of other travellers visited Egypt, and penetrated to Kordofan, at this time, but their contributions to knowledge were small. An exception must be made, however, in the case of John Petherick, who reached Kordofan in 1848, and lived there subsequently for a long period. His more important work belongs to the years following 1848, and will be dealt with later.

The year 1830 marks an important turning-point in the history of discovery in Abyssinia. Up to that time the only journey of note was that of Salt in 1810, and this had furnished some general knowledge of the north of the country, but for that south and east of Lake Tana information was vague and unsatisfactory. These gaps were filled in, to some extent, between 1830 and 1848. Rüppell landed at Massaua in September 1831, and devoted the next two years to work in the country north and east of Lake Tana, while Ferret and Galinier covered the region between Hamasen and Gondar. Combes and Tamisier (1835–36), after travelling from Massaua to Lake Tana, explored the country to the south-east of the lake, and extended their journey to Ankober, while the country between that town and the Gulf of Tajura was examined by Lefebvre (1839–42). Thus considerable new information was obtained for the eastern edge of the highlands.

The small advances thus made were greatly extended by C. T. Beke and the brothers d'Abbadie. The first-named landed at Tajura in November 1840, and left Massaua in May 1843. He carried out a series of thermometric levels across nearly seven degrees of longitude from Tajura, and fixed by astronomical observation the latitude of upward of seventy places. He roughly mapped the watershed between the Nile and the Hawash, constructed a sketch-map of the plateau of Gojjam, and was the first traveller since Bruce to describe the sources of the Blue Nile, the course of which he approximately determined. He also collected information about the country to the south of the Abbai (Blue Nile), while on his homeward journey to Massaua he made valuable additions to the knowledge of Abyssinia. In all, his maps covered about 70,000 square miles.[1] For part of the time Beke was accompanied by the German missionary Krapf, destined to reach fame shortly afterward in East Africa.

Even more extensive and more valuable was the work of A. T. d'Abbadie and his brother, who lived in Abyssinia for twelve years (1837–48), and made a traverse of it from north to south, from Massaua to Bonka (north of Lake Rudolf), in the Kaffa country. They contributed more than any other explorer to the accurate knowledge of the country. A geodetic survey was attempted, and

[1] Roberts, *op. cit.*, p. 280 ; *J.R.G.S.*, vol. xiv, p. cxvi.

the results were remarkably accurate. The Red Sea was connected by a series of triangles to the Kaffa country, and the position of about nine hundred points was fixed.

The political rivalry between France and England, which extended to the missionaries working in Northern Abyssinia, was responsible for some small amount of exploration at this time, and as an outcome of this rivalry Harris conducted a successful expedition in 1841, with the object of opening up trade with the interior. He made a route map from Tajura to Ankober, and was the first to fix precisely the longitude of the latter town.

With the work of Beke, Harris, and d'Abbadie the first period of Abyssinian exploration comes to an end. It had been marked by much progress in the mountain regions of the country, but had left the east and south-east almost untouched.

III. CENTRAL AND SOUTH AFRICA, 1788–1848

Progress during this period was very slow, especially in Central Africa. The travels of naturalists in South Africa have already been mentioned:[1] to these should be added one exploit of importance, that of Barrow, who went to the Cape as private secretary to Lord Macartney in 1797, travelled about the country, and produced a map of South Africa much in advance of previous attempts.

A number of relatively unimportant journeys followed. In 1801 Truter and Sommervill went beyond the Orange River into Bechuanaland, and penetrated nearly as far as Lake Ngami. Two years later Lichtenstein explored parts of Bushmanland and Bechuanaland to the north of the confluence of the Orange and the Vaal rivers. Burchell's travels in the Transvaal and on the borders of Bechuanaland (1810–12) were of greater value to zoologists than to geographers, but the missionary Campbell (c. 1812) performed a valuable work in laying down the course of the Orange River with reasonable exactness and in discovering the source of the Limpopo. Captain Owen, who commanded a survey party from 1822 to 1826, delineated many features of the east and west coasts with great accuracy, and especially added to the knowledge of Delagoa Bay and its neighbourhood. He also began the scientific exploration of the Zambezi, but unhappily all Europeans engaged in the enterprise died.

The Boer Trek, which began in 1833, and the foundation of the Cape of Good Hope Association for Exploring Central Africa[2] marked a turning-point in the history of exploration, for not only did these events lead to an extension of European influence, but they

[1] See Chapter XI.
[2] On this interesting society see *J.R.G.S.*, vol. iv, pp. 362–374, and vol. vi, pp. 394–413. The results of Smith's expedition were published in Sir Andrew Smith's *Illustrations of the Zoology of South Africa* (1849).

ensured systematic exploration, which had hitherto been lacking. In 1834 Smith reached the Southern Tropic and explored the upper valley of the Limpopo ; two years later Harris, who afterward took part in the exploration of Abyssinia, visited Bechuanaland; and in 1836–37 Alexander crossed Namaqualand in the course of an overland journey from Cape Town to Walfish Bay. Others in the meanwhile had been filling in details within the region already known in outline. Among them were Cowie and Green, who undertook a journey in Natal in 1829, and Wahlberg, who explored the country north of Natal to the Limpopo between 1841 and 1844.

It was at this period that Livingstone arrived in South Africa. He left Algoa Bay in May 1841, to join the band of missionaries working in Bechuanaland. Almost immediately he began his exploratory travels, although at this period they were conducted solely with the idea of extending the mission field. In this way he linked his own efforts to those of his father-in-law, Moffat, who more than any other missionary enlarged the bounds of knowledge on the borders of the Kalahari Desert. This useful work was Livingstone's preparation for his greater journeys of exploration, which began in 1849, and led him to the Zambezi country.

Until the time of Livingstone's first journey knowledge of Central Africa was remarkably inaccurate. The Portuguese had done little to open up the country over which they exercised some political influence, and even such small efforts as had been made do not appear to have been generally known. The first and most important of these which falls within the present period was that of Lacerda in 1798.[1] Lacerda heard that an expedition was proposed "with a view of establishing land communication between the eastern and the western coasts of Africa, and of cutting off the long and perilous passage round the Cape of Good Hope." He proceeded to offer some advice on the subject, and enlarged upon the advantages which would follow. It would extend Portuguese influence, bind together scattered possessions, open a new trade-route and so increase revenue, and check the English, who "require careful watching, or our want of energy will enable them to extend themselves northward." Further, since nothing was known of the upper course and the source of the Zambezi, it was possible that it was connected with the Cunene, "the most important stream between the Zaire and the Cape of Good Hope," which Lacerda had explored in 1787. "Should this conjecture prove correct," wrote Lacerda,

and should the line be opened by Government, it will carry to Benguela cargoes landed by ships from Asia, and thus Mozambique

---

[1] On this expedition see *The Lands of Cazembe* (Royal Geographical Society publication, 1873). The volume also contains particulars of the journeys of the "*pombeiros* "—*i.e.*, native travelling traders—and of Monteiro and Gamitto.

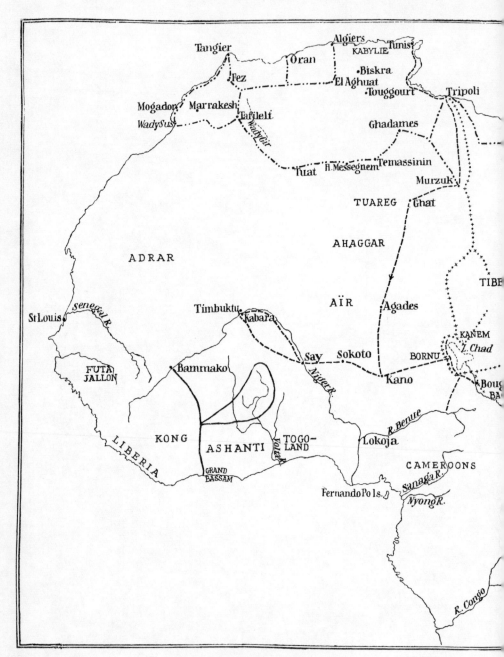

Fig. 36. NORTH AFRICA, 1849–89

Note that Barth's homeward route across the Sahara is almost the same as that shown for Nachtigal between Lake Chad and Murzuk
The route of Rohlfs from Aujila to Kufra has been omitted.

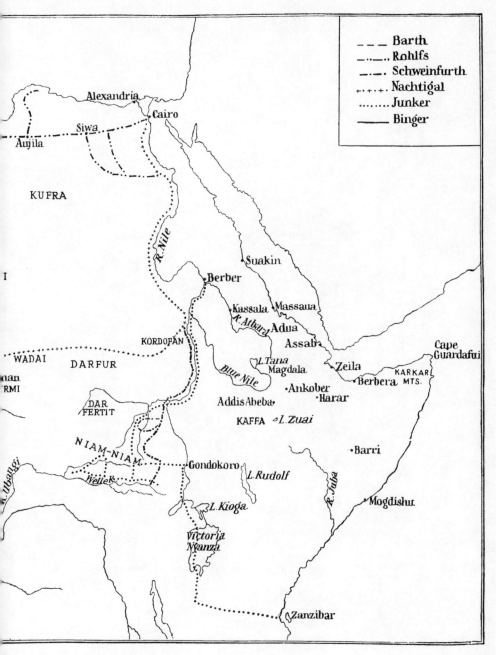

Barth
Rohlfs
Schweinfurth
Nachtigal
Junker
Binger

Alexandria

Cairo

Siwa

Aujila

KUFRA

R. Nile

Suakin

Berber

Kassala   Massaua

R. Atbara   Adua

KORDOFAN   Assab

WADAI   DARFUR   L. Tana   Zeila   Cape Guardafui
         Blue Nile   Magdala   KARKAR
man   Berbera MTS.
RMI   Ankober

DAR
FERTIT   Addis Abeba   Harar

KAFFA   L. Zuai

NIAM-NIAM   Barri

W. Ubangi   Gondokoro   L. Rudolf   R. Juba

Welle   L. Kioga   Mogdishu

Victoria
Nyanza

Zanzibar

as well as Benguela will become an emporium second to none. The inter-coastal and overland route once practicable, native guides will be forthcoming, and nothing will be easier than the exploration of the stream above mentioned.

Lacerda was given the command of an expedition to solve these geographical problems and open up the country of Cazembe to Portuguese traders. He relied to some extent on information about Cazembe derived from a Portuguese named Pereira, who visited it in 1796 and reported favourably on the prospects of trade. Lacerda left the Zambezi on July 3, 1798, and travelled northward between Lake Nyasa and Lake Bangweolo without seeing either, although from the remarks in his diary he seems to have known of their existence. He reached the Cazembe country in October, but died there. The party returned, under the command of the chaplain, after a stay of nine months in Cazembe, and were back at Tete in November 1799. The expedition failed to accomplish its main purpose, but it did advance geographical knowledge. Unfortunately its results were not generally known, and by the time of Livingstone's first journey were entirely forgotten.

Two other exploits of the Portuguese belong to this early period, though neither is of great importance. In 1802 two Portuguese traders set out from Angola and crossed to the Cazembe country, whence they reached the Zambezi. Their reports were rather confused, but they at least confirmed the possibility of an overland route. In 1831 part of this journey was performed in the reverse direction by Major Monteiro and Captain Gamitto. They left Tete in June of that year, passed through the Cazembe country in November, and returned shortly afterward. Monteiro added little to what Lacerda had discovered, although he succeeded in drawing general attention to a little-known region.

One other isolated expedition in Central Africa was that of Bowditch, who visited the Gabun region in 1817, and made valuable additions to the map of a small area in the Ogowe valley.

IV. NORTH-WEST AFRICA, 1849–89

Exploration in North Africa during the forty years now under consideration followed four well-marked phases. From the year of Barth's journey in 1849 to the end of the period explorers were gradually closing in on the Sahara Desert, without, however, effecting the conquest of that region ; this process includes the exploration of the neighbouring lands on the north, west, and south of the desert. The outstanding figures are Barth, who began the task, Rohlfs, and Binger, with whom the period ends. A second feature is the connexion established between exploration in the Nile Valley and that on the borders of North-west África : here the greatest explorers worked from the east toward the Congo or Lake Chad. The conspicuous figures are Schweinfurth, Nachtigal, and Junker. The third feature is the rather slow progress in North-east Africa, where hardly a name stands out above the rest. Finally there is the prosecution of the Nile quest, associated from the Egyptian side with the name of Sir Samuel Baker ; this feature, however, belongs so closely to the exploration of Central Africa that it will be dealt with in that section.

Exploration in North-west Africa begins with the English " mixed scientific and commercial " expedition to the Sudan under Richardson, who was accompanied by Barth and Overweg : it was joined later by Vogel. The party left Tunis in December 1849, but their real exploration began at Tripoli, whence they set out in February of the following year. Their route lay through Murzuk, Ghat, and Agades, across the desert, after which they separated, Barth going to Kano and then to Kuka, where he arranged to meet the others, who had taken a more easterly route. Richardson unfortunately died on the journey, and Barth assumed command. He was able to investigate Lake Chad, of which he gives a good account. " The character of the Tsad," he wrote,

> is evidently that of an immense lagoon, changing its border every month, and therefore incapable of being mapped with accuracy. Indeed, when I saw to-day [April 24, 1851] the nature of these swampy lowlands surrounding the lake or lagoon I immediately became aware that it would be quite impossible to survey its shores even if the state of the countries around should allow us to enter upon such an undertaking. The only thing possible would be on the one side to fix the furthest limits reached at times by the inundation of the lagoon, and on the other to determine the extent of the navigable water.[1]

Barth and Overweg then turned south to Yola, the chief town of Adamawa, where the Benue river was examined.

> The principal river, the Benue, flowed here from east to west, in a broad, majestic course, through an entirely open country, from which only here and there detached mountains stand forth. . . . I had now, with my own eyes, clearly established the direction and nature of this mighty river ; and to an unprejudiced mind there could no longer be any doubt that this river joins the majestic watercourse explored by [Allen, Laird, and Oldfield].[2]

Barth was unable to go beyond Yola, and so retraced his steps. Overweg in the meanwhile had examined Lake Chad. Barth was disappointed at this turn of events, since he had been " intensely desirous " of penetrating farther south. However, he decided to

[1] H. Barth, *Travels and Discoveries in North and Central Africa*, 1849–55 (5 vols., 1859), vol. ii, p. 322. This work gives the whole account of the expedition : it is particularly valuable in its historical aspects.
[2] *Ibid.*, vol. ii, pp. 466, 468. This expedition of 1832 is referred to above, p. 308.

try to reach " the regions south of Baghirmi " after making an expedition to the north of the lake. He accomplished this latter task, and in February 1852 set out for Baghirmi. He reached the Shari river at Bougoman, and returned to Bornu, where he met Overweg. Soon afterward Overweg died. Barth then undertook a long and successful journey to Timbuktu by way of Sokoto and Say, on the Niger. On the outward route he went overland from Say: on his return he sailed down the Niger to that town. He made his way back to Bornu, and there met Vogel, who had been sent out by the British Government.

Vogel proceeded to complete the work which Barth had begun to the south of Lake Chad, and intended to cross Africa to the Nile. He reached Wadai, where he was murdered. No less than seven expeditions went in search of him, but only one successfully penetrated the region, and its leader, Beurmann, suffered the same fate as Vogel in 1863.

Barth returned across the desert to Murzuk and Tripoli, and reached England in the autumn of 1855, after a long and splendid work in North Africa. " Extending over a tract of country of twenty-four degrees from north to south," he wrote,

and twenty degrees from east to west, in the broadest part of the continent of Africa, my travels necessarily comprise subjects of great interest and diversity. After having traversed vast deserts of the most barren soil, and scenes of the most frightful desolation, I met with fertile lands irrigated by large navigable rivers and extensive central lakes, ornamented with the finest timber, and producing various species of grain, rice, sesamum, ground-nuts, in unlimited abundance, the sugar cane, etc., together with cotton and indigo, the most valuable commodities of trade. The whole of Central Africa, from Baghirmi to the east as far as Timbuktu to the west, . . . abounds in these products. The natives of these regions not only weave their own cotton, but dye their home-made shirts with their own indigo. The river, the far-famed Niger, which gives access to these regions by means of its eastern branch, the Benue, which I discovered, affords an uninterrupted navigable sheet of water for more than six hundred miles into the very heart of the country. Its western branch is obstructed by rapids at a distance of about three hundred and fifty miles from the coast; but even at this point it is probably not impassable in the present state of navigation, while, higher up, the river opens an immense highroad for nearly one thousand miles into the very heart of Western Africa, so rich in every kind of produce.[1]

Barth's own estimate of his success was modest.

In this enterprise [of reaching Timbuktu and exploring parts of the Niger river remaining unknown through Mungo Park's death] I succeeded to my utmost expectation and not only made known the whole of that vast region which, even to the Arab merchants in general, had remained more unknown than any other part of Africa,

[1] Barth, *op. cit.*, vol. i, pp. xx–xxi.

but I succeeded also in establishing friendly relations with all the most powerful chiefs along the river up to that mysterious city [Timbuktu] itself. . . . No doubt even in the track which I myself pursued I have left a good deal for my successors in this career to improve upon ; but I have the satisfaction to feel that I have opened to the view of the scientific public of Europe a most extensive tract of the secluded African world, and not only made it tolerably known, but rendered the opening of a regular intercourse between Europeans and these regions possible.[1]

The verdict of another great African explorer may suitably close this account of Barth's journey. " Never before," wrote Thomson, " had such a rich harvest of geographical, historical, ethnographical, and philological facts been gathered in the African field of research." [2]

The process of closing in on the Sahara from the north begins with the French conquest of Algeria already mentioned. It was continued by the capture of the oasis of Zaatcha (near Biskra) in 1849, the expedition against El Aghuat in 1852, the occupation of Touggourt in 1854, and the decisive campaign in Kabylie three years later whereby the French secured their rear from attack. In 1870 they proceeded successfully against the Wady Gir. This progress brought with it increasing knowledge of the Algerian fringe of the Sahara.

Meanwhile its conquest had been begun by explorers. In 1850 Panet attempted to reach Timbuktu from Senegal, but was diverted from his goal, and was murdered on the way to Morocco. Nine years later (1859–61) Duveyrier explored the Algerian fringe and the Ghat-Murzuk route. In 1860 Vincent reached Adral from St Louis. Shortly afterward the French gained further knowledge through the story which Mordokhai Abi-Serur told to the Consul at Mogador. He had lived at Timbuktu from 1860 to 1862, and had travelled between that town and Morocco for some years.

The greatest advance at this period was, however, made by G. Rohlfs, who began his African career in the French Foreign Legion in 1855, and ended it as German Consul at Zanzibar in 1885. His travels embraced a wide area and a long period of time. In 1862 he left Tangier in disguise, visited Fez and Morocco, followed the coast to the Wady Sus, and there turned eastward to Tafilelt, which he was the first European to visit after Caillié. The next year he attempted to cross the desert to Timbuktu, but failed. In 1864 he again visited Tafilelt, and thence proceeded to Tuat, which had never been visited by a European ; his return journey was made by Ghadames to Tripoli. In 1865 he went back to Tripoli and projected a journey to Ahaggar ; as this proved impracticable he went to Murzuk, whence he crossed the desert to Bornu, reached the Benue, and sailed down it and the Niger. The years 1867 and 1868

[1] Barth, *op. cit.*, vol. v, pp. 453–454.
[2] J. Thomson, in *Mungo Park and the Niger*, p. 298.

were spent in Abyssinia. In 1869 Rohlfs travelled from Tripoli to Siwa and Alexandria. He returned to the Libyan Desert in 1874 with an important expedition to Siwa. In 1878 he again visited Tripoli, in company with Strecker, with the object of reaching Wadai, but only succeeded in penetrating to the oases of Kufra. This was the last important expedition of Rohlfs, who was hardly a scientific traveller in the strict sense of the term, but who revealed many entirely unknown parts of Africa in the course of his sixteen years of exploration.[1]

In 1871 French explorations were resumed when Soleillet, aiming at Timbuktu, succeeded only in reaching the Algerian fringe. Three years later Joubert and Dourneaux-Dupéré, whose object was the same, were murdered near to Ghadames, while in 1877 E. von Bary, from Tripoli, attempted to reach Timbuktu through Aïr, and met a like fate.

From Morocco H. O. Lenz followed a well-used caravan-route, and successfully reached Timbuktu in July 1880. He was able to remain for twenty days, during which time he gathered valuable information about the city. As a result of his journey knowledge of the geology of the Sahara was considerably improved. About the same time Schaudt (1879–82) explored the Moroccan Sahara.

In 1880 French projects for a railway across the desert had advanced so far that Flatters was sent to survey a route from Algeria to the Niger. In that year he only penetrated a little distance beyond Temassinin, but he returned in 1881, and crossed the Tropic of Cancer, only to be murdered in the Tuareg country.[2] The next year Foureau led an expedition to Hassi Messegnem, and in 1885 Palat advanced from Oran, but was murdered in Tuat. The last expedition within this period, in 1889, was that of Douls, who was also murdered on the way to Timbuktu. In the next decade the French undertook the military conquest of the Sahara, and with it greatly increased geographical knowledge.

Part at least of the French success in penetrating the Sahara from the north at the end of the last century was due to their advance to the Niger from Senegal, which began in 1859. The pioneer work of exploration in Futa Jallon was undertaken by Lambert. He was followed by Mage, whose instructions were quite definite. " Votre mission consiste à explorer la ligne qui joint nos établissements du haut Sénégal avec le haut Niger et spéciale-ment avec Bammako, qui paraît le point le plus rapproché en aval

---

[1] The more important works of Rohlfs are *Reise durch Marokko* (1868), *Von Tripolis nach Alexandrien* (1871), *Mein erster Aufenthalt in Marokko* (1873), *Quer durch Afrika* (1875), and *Expedition zur Erforschung der Libyschen Wüste Kufra* (1875).

[2] On this and subsequent missions up to 1904 see P. Leroy-Beaulieu, *Le Sahara, le Soudan et les chemins de fer transsahariens* (1904) (with a useful map).

duquel le Niger ne présente peut-être plus d'obstacles sérieux à la navigation." [1] In spite of the successful explorations of Mage in the upper valley of the Niger he was unable to carry out his instructions, and after 1865 attempts to reach the Niger ceased for eleven years.

The proposal to build a railway to the Niger led to renewed exploration in 1879. Two years later Galliéni began to move eastward, and although he was at first unsuccessful, the French persisted, and reached Bammako on February 1, 1883. The final move in this direction was the building of two vessels on the Niger, in which Caron sailed from Bammako to Kabara in 1887.

In the country round the shores of the Gulf of Guinea comparatively little was done to follow up the discoveries of Lander and the pioneers on the Niger. W. B. Baikie led an expedition to the Niger in 1854, in order to open up the trade of the region and, if possible, to co-operate with Barth. He sailed up the Benue for over 300 miles, and definitely established the fact that it was the same river as that discovered by Barth, but he never made contact with that explorer. A second expedition reached Lokoja in 1857, but British Governments were not interested in the Niger, and such traders as frequented its waters were not concerned with exploration. Thus apart from a few isolated ventures no progress was made. Burton, already famous for journeys in Arabia and East Africa, was sent to Fernando Po as Consul in 1861, and took the opportunity to explore a small area in the Cameroons Mountains. Anderson, in 1868, added a little to the knowledge of Liberia, one of the unfrequented regions of the west coast. Reade visited Ashanti in 1872, and again in the following year, when the Ashanti War afforded the British an opportunity of penetrating the country. But Reade was pessimistic about West African exploration. " The days of discovery in this part of Africa are over," he wrote; "the Niger has gone out of fashion and the present generation has been interested only in the story of the Nile." [2] Accordingly the important discoveries were made by the French and the Germans, both keenly interested, for political reasons, in West Africa.

Bonnat penetrated to the Gold Coast hinterland in 1875, exploring the Volta river. Flegel, who began his work as an explorer in the Cameroons in 1879, turned his attention to the Niger in the following year, and examined the eastern half of its course. In 1883 and 1884 he visited Adamawa, and discovered the sources of the Benue river, but was unable to carry out his project of crossing the unknown region between the Benue and the Congo.

Flegel was only one of the many German explorers sent out to Africa by the German African Society. An explanation of this

[1] Quoted in Rambaud, *La France coloniale*, p. 174.
[2] Quoted in Brown, *op. cit.*, vol. i, p. 312.

activity is to be found partly in the outburst of German nationalism which followed the Franco-German War and partly in the political scramble for Africa at this time. Yet it would not be fair to overlook the fact that Germans had, throughout the century, been interested in geographical exploration, and the exploits of Barth, Rohlfs, and Nachtigal, to mention only three names, show that their interest was not solely due to the chances of territorial expansion. In 1886 they made their first advance into the interior of Togoland. In the following year the penetration of the Cameroons was undertaken, by Kund and Tappenbeck, and in 1888 the former surveyed the upper courses of the Sanaga and Nyong. Krause explored the Volta river, on the Togo frontier, in 1886, and Von François and Wolf began their valuable work in that colony in the next year. It was only the Royal Niger Company's expedition to Sokoto in 1885 that prevented the Lower Niger valley from falling into the hands of Germany.[1]

From a geographical point of view, however, the most important work was that of the Frenchman Binger in 1887 and succeeding years. His first efforts were devoted to the unknown country lying to the south of the bend of the Niger. Before his journey it was supposed that the valley of the Niger was very wide. Binger showed that, on the contrary, it was quite narrow, and that the Volta river rose near to the course of the Niger. He also proved that the great range of mountains shown on many maps as running across the country at about the latitude of $10°$ N. had no existence. Binger's later work was equally important, but falls within the last period of African discovery.

One other journey, remarkable for its accomplishment rather than for any geographical results which followed, was that of Matteucci and Massari, who crossed Africa in 1882, from Suakin to the Niger through Kordofan, Wadai, Bornu, and Kano.

Meanwhile explorers in the Nile valley had been gradually pushing westward into the Bahr-el-Ghazal region. Part of this exploration belongs to the story of the Nile quest, but part is an attempt to discover the unknown regions between Lake Chad and the Nile valley, where Vogel had perished. In 1860 Miani and Antinori travelled along the shores of the Bahr-el-Ghazal and the Dur, and this same country was visited by Lejean and Peney in the following year. Petherick, in the course of a number of journeys made between 1848 and 1863, penetrated to the Niam-niam district, to the north of the Welle river, and Piaggia lived there for a year

---

[1] The German explorers very thoroughly and systematically examined their own political possessions in Africa. For an account of this work during the nineteenth century see A. Schenck, " Die Afrikaforschung seit dem Jahre 1884 und ihr gegenwärtiger Stand," in *Geographische Zeitschrift*, vol. iv (1898), pp. 336 *et seq.*

in 1864. At the same time T. von Heuglin and Steudner pushed beyond the Bahr-el-Ghazal and reached Dar Fertit. This led up to the very important journey of G. Schweinfurth in 1868–71. This distinguished German botanist had already explored the coasts of the Red Sea and crossed through the north of Abyssinia to Khartum (1863–66). While at Khartum he had "collected a variety of information about the ivory expeditions undertaken by the merchants of that place to the country about the sources of the Nile." Returning to Egypt in 1868, he sailed from Suez to Suakin, whence he travelled to Khartum. There he began his most important work in 1869.[1] His main objects were to investigate the botany of those equatorial districts which are traversed by the western affluents of the Upper Nile and to show the importance of those western affluents, which he considered had been minimized by Speke and Baker, who had recently discovered the course of the Nile from the lakes to Gondokoro. Further, there was a geographical mystery awaiting solution.

> It was in December 1868, just before starting from Khartum, that I received the first intelligence of a people called the Monbutto, who were said to dwell to the south of the Niam-niam. . . . [This intelligence] had the intrinsic merit of enlarging the domain of geographical knowledge by some matters of fact which it was reserved for me individually to confirm by my own observation. It laid down as facts, first, that to the south of the Niam-niam territory there is a river flowing towards the west; secondly, that this river is not a tributary to the Nile; and, thirdly, that its banks are populated by a race quite distinct from the ordinary negro race.[2]

Schweinfurth successfully carried out his exploration, penetrated to the Niam-niam country, and proved the truth of the report he had heard at Khartum. "At length," he wrote,

> the attainment of my cherished hopes seemed close at hand. The prospect was held out that on the 19th of March [1870] we might expect to arrive at the Welle. The way to the river led us due south, and we went onwards through almost uninterrupted groves of plantains, from which the huts, constructed of bark and rotang very skilfully sewn together, ever and again peeped out. A march of scarcely two leagues brought us to the bank of the noble river, which rolled its deep dark flood majestically to the west. For me it was a thrilling moment that can never fade from my memory. My sensations must have been like Mungo Park's on the 20th of July, 1796, when for the first time he planted his feet upon the shore of the mysterious Niger, and answered once for all the great geographical question of his day—as to whether its waters rolled to the east or to the west. Here, then, I was upon the very bank of the river, attesting the western flow of the water, about which the contradictions and inconsistencies of the Nubians had kept up my un-

---

[1] The record of this journey is Schweinfurth's *The Heart of Africa* (English translation, 2 vols., 1873).
[2] Schweinfurth, *op. cit.* (3rd edition), vol. ii, p. 33.

flagging interest. . . . If the river should flow to the east, why then it solved the problem, hitherto inexplicable, of the fullness of the water in Lake Mwootan [*i.e.*, Albert] ; [1] but if, as was far more likely, it should go towards the west, then beyond a doubt it was independent altogether of the Nile system. A moment more, and the question was set at rest. Westerly was the direction of the stream, which consequently did not belong to the Nile.[2]

But a further problem arose. If this stream was not part of the Nile system, whither did it flow ? Schweinfurth answered it wrongly, but his error was due to lack of information in Central Africa.

The probability that the Keebaly [*i.e.*, the upper course of the Welle] and the Welle are identical with the upper course of the Shari appears to become at once almost a positive certainty when we ask the counter-question, " If this is not the Shari, whence does the Shari come ? " All that we know and all that we do not know about the north and north-western districts conspire to satisfy us that in that direction there is neither a sufficient reservoir, nor an adequate space, for the development of a network of streams large enough to form a river which is half a mile broad at its mouth and which fills a lake as large as the whole of Belgium.[3]

In an earlier passage Schweinfurth remarks :

If the Welle flows neither into the Shari nor yet into the Ghazal, it could only be a tributary to the ample waters of the Benue, which Barth found at Yola on the 18th of July, 1851, to be 1200 feet in width, with an average depth of eleven feet, and a periodic difference of 50 feet between its highest and lowest level. But then there would still remain the question as to what, in that case, must be the origin of the Shari, and whence it comes. There would seem to be no room left for the stream at all.[4]

But the real value of Schweinfurth's expedition was not in propounding theories of drainage nor in solving puzzles, but in giving a most graphic and excellent picture of the country through which he travelled, and his descriptions can be read with profit to-day. There is not space to do justice to this side of his work, but one quotaton will suffice to show its character. It relates to the country of the " Monbutto," in the Welle region.

The Monbutto land greets us as an Eden upon earth. Unnumbered groves of plantains bedeck the gently-heaving soil ; oil-palms, incomparable in beauty, and other monarchs of the stately woods, rise up and spread their glory over the favoured scene ; along the streams there is a bright expanse of charming verdure, whilst a grateful shadow ever overhangs the domes of the idyllic huts. The general altitude of the soil ranges from 2500 to 2800 feet above the level of the sea ; it consists of alternate depressions, along which the rivulets make their way, and gentle elevations, which gradually rise till they are some hundred feet above the beds of the streams below.

[1] Discovered by Baker in 1864 ; see below, section vi.
[2] Schweinfurth, *op. cit.*, vol. i, p. 264.
[3] *Ibid.*, vol. ii, p. 96.   [4] *Ibid.*, vol. i, p. 269.

Upon the whole the soil may be described as far more diversified in character than what is observed in the eastern parts of Niam-niam land. Like that, it is rich in springs, wherever there are depressions ; it has a network of *desaguaderos* associated with the watercourses, and justifies the comparison that has already been suggested between the entire land and a well-soaked sponge, which yields countless streams to the pressure of the land. Belonging to one of the most recent formations, and still in process of construction, the ferruginous swamp-ore is found very widely diffused over the Monbutto country, and indeed extends considerably farther to the south, so that the red earth appears to be nearly universal over the greater part of the highlands of Central Africa. The denser population has involved, as might be expected, more frequent clearances for the sake of establishing plantain-groves, and promoting the culture of maize and sugar-canes, but even here in the deeper valleys trees grow to such a prodigious height, and exhibit such an enormous girth, that they could not be surpassed by any that could be found throughout the entire Nile region of the north. Beneath the imposing shelter of these giants other forms grow up and, rising one above another, stand in mingled confusion. In its external and general aspect the country corresponds with the description which Speke has given of Uganda ; but the customs of the inhabitants of that land, their difference of race, and their seclusion from all intercourse with commercial nations stamp them as being of a type which is of a very contrasted character.[1]

Schweinfurth's work was supplemented and extended in important respects by two other great African explorers. G. Nachtigal set out from Tripoli in February 1869 for Murzuk, whence he made a journey into the Tibesti country. He travelled across the Sahara a second time in 1870, and took a new route to Kuka. There he began important explorations, visiting Kanem, to the north of Lake Chad and Baghirmi, to the south-east, and it was not until March 1873 that he set out on his return march. Then, instead of recrossing the desert to the north, he attempted the task which had baffled Vogel and his successors, and travelled through Wadai and Darfur to Kordofan and thence to Cairo, where he arrived in November 1874. The results of this journey were published in *Sahara und Sudan*, the third volume of which appeared after the author's death.

Nachtigal added greatly to geographical knowledge. He was the first European who penetrated the Eastern Sahara to Tibesti ; he was the first to connect that area of exploration, with which the name of Barth is associated, with the region of the Nile. Further, by his lengthy stay in the neighbourhood of Lake Chad he was able to put forward some new theories as to the Welle river discovered by Schweinfurth. He believed that the Shari was of limited extent and that the Welle was identical with the Benue.

The second explorer was W. Junker, who travelled in Africa between 1879 and 1886, and added very important details to the

[1] Schweinfurth, *op. cit.*, vol. ii, pp. 37–38.

region visited by Schweinfurth, and .to others which were beyond the limits of that explorer.[1] In particular he succeeded in making very complete investigations into the question of the Welle river. Of this river Schweinfurth had seen little. Junker not only reached it at many points, but he paid special attention to its upper course and that of its tributaries. Further, Junker became involved in the troubled political conditions which followed the Mahdist revolt, and found his route to the north completely blocked. Hence he returned up the Nile from Lado, crossed Lake Albert, and finally reached Zanzibar. Junker's researches in the Welle region, together with Grenfell's ascent of the Ubangi in 1885,[2] left little doubt that the two rivers were the same, and part of the Congo system, a position which had never been suspected by either Schweinfurth or Nachtigal. He was also able to correct a number of earlier travellers who had visited this region, notably Miani and Potagos, the latter of whom reached the Congo basin from the Bahr-el-Ghazal in 1877.

V. NORTH-EAST AFRICA, 1849–89

The exploration of North-eastern Africa progressed little during this period, for although many journeys were made in this part of Africa, they resulted in the filling in of small details rather than in the solution of any geographical problems, and at the end of the period Somaliland and South-eastern Abyssinia were still very imperfectly known.

In the north, between Suakin and Massaua, on the Red Sea, and Berber and Khartum, a number of journeys added a few new routes, and completed the examination of the lower course of the Atbara. Among the explorers were the missionary Sapeto (1851), whose sphere of labour was round Massaua, Hamilton (1854), Munzinger (1855), Baker (1861), Von Heuglin (between Suakin and Berber), and Hilderbrandt. Most of the explorers confined themselves to small deviations from regular tracks. Thus several routes from Suakin to Berber were traced ; a broad belt of country was covered between Kassala, on the Atbara, and Massaua ; small deviations from the route between Kassala and Suakin were made ; and the valley of the Atbara, below Kassala, was followed.

In Northern Abyssinia, again, there were many travellers who added to the work already accomplished. In the earlier part of the period Dufton, Von Heuglin, Steudner, and Lejean traversed the country between Lake Tana and Massaua. The British expedition to Abyssinia (1867–68) resulted in new information about the

[1] See Junker's *Travels in Africa*, translated by A. H. Keane (3 vols., 1890–92). A brief account will be found in *Proc. R.G.S.*, new series, vol. ix, p. 400 *et seq.*

[2] See below, p. 342.

323

country between Magdala and Massaua, while Rohlfs, who accompanied it, visited the country again in 1880–81, and took a course roughly parallel to, but to the west of, that of the English. Similarly, Munzinger, by his journeys to the north-west of Adua, Stecker, to the south of that town and between it and Lake Tana, and Raffray, to the east of the lake, added some precise information to the general knowledge of the country.

In the south of Abyssinia the expedition of Burton and Speke in 1855 added one detail of importance, for the former was the first European to reach Harar. Ten years later Von der Decken, who had already spent five years in the exploration of Eastern Africa, lost his life in an attempt to explore the river Juba. Between 1876 and 1881 Cecchi and Chiarini crossed Southern Abyssinia from Ankober, and added much to the knowledge of the Kaffa country in the south-west, while Giulietti (1881) explored the region between Zeila, on the coast, and Harar and that round Assab, and Antonelli crossed from the last-named town to Ankober (1883). Stecker in 1883 penetrated to the south of Addis Abeba and rediscovered Lake Zuai, and Bianchi added to the knowledge of the country west of Ankober in 1884.

In the borderlands to the south, however, very little progress was made, except for some exploration in the vicinity of Cape Guardafui, where Miles (1871) and Graves (1879) were active.[1] In 1877 the Frenchman Révoil attempted to follow the route of Von der Decken, but found it impossible, and confined himself to an examination of some parts of the Somaliland coast. In a second visit, made in 1878, Révoil was able to see a little of the country near Cape Guardafui, but, his object being the promotion of commerce, he did not gain much precise information. He returned to the country again in 1880, with a scientific mission sent by the French Ministry of Public Instruction, and made several attempts to explore the north-eastern corner of Africa, but he was unable to do more than visit the mountainous country of Karkar. He collected much information about neighbouring districts, roughly fixed the position of a number of places, and greatly improved the map of the whole region.

Southern Somaliland was visited in 1884–85 by an English expedition, which included the brothers James, and Aylmer. They intended to cross from Mogdishu to Berbera, but only reached Barri, a town 215 miles from their starting-point. Their journey covered about 400 miles, through country which was almost unknown.

[1] For a brief summary up to 1884 see E. G. Ravenstein, "Somal and Gallaland," in *Proc. R.G.S.*, new series, vol. vi, p. 255.

AFRICA

VI. CENTRAL AFRICA, 1849–89

Great as had been the advance in North Africa during this period, it was hardly equal to that made in Central Africa, where the whole map was transformed, and such a wealth of knowledge accumulated that it caused nothing less than a revolution in geography.

The first great problem awaiting solution was that of the sources of the Nile. The information collected in Egypt and the Sudan had confirmed the classical tradition of a lake source, but its location was a matter of difficulty. In 1848 Rebmann discovered the snow-covered mountain of Kilimanjaro, and in the following year Krapf saw Mount Kenya, but the reports of these disinterested missionaries were not always believed. They were, however, confirmed by Von der Decken in 1860.

Meanwhile the second great step toward a solution of the Nile problem had been taken.[1] Burton, after his Harar expedition, had served in the Crimean War, and on his return to England "determined to follow none but the career of an explorer." The news of Livingstone's discoveries in the southern parts of Central Africa, and the interest aroused by the reports of Rebmann and Krapf, led Burton to propose an expedition " primarily for the purpose of ascertaining the limits of the Sea of Ujiji[2] [*i.e.*, Lake Tanganyika], and secondarily to determine the exportable produce of the interior and the ethnography of its tribes." The Royal Geographical Society accepted the offer, and laid down his instructions as follows:

> The great object of the expedition is to penetrate inland from Kilwa or some other place on the east coast of Africa, and make the best of your way to the reputed lake Nyasa. . . . Having obtained all the information you require in this quarter, you are to proceed northward toward the range of mountains marked upon our maps as containing the probable source of [the Nile], which it will be your next great object to discover ; . . . you will be at liberty to return to England by descending the Nile . . . or you may return by the route by which you advanced or otherwise, always having regard to the means at your disposal.[3]

Burton, who was accompanied by J. H. Speke, was not able to leave the coast until August 1857. After an exhausting march the two men reached Lake Tanganyika on February 13, 1858. Both explorers were ill, but Speke was able to see something of the northern part of the lake, and both made a short voyage from Ujiji. They were informed that a river entered the lake from the north, but Burton later denied this, and much confusion resulted. They could not prolong their stay, and were obliged to abandon an attempt to reach Lake Nyasa. On the return journey Speke left Burton in

[1] See Sir Harry Johnson, *The Nile Quest, passim.*
[2] Reported by the missionaries and thought to be of immense size.
[3] *J.R.G.S.*, vol. xxix, p. 5.

Tabora and struck northward, discovering the Victoria Nyanza, about which they had gained some knowledge from the Arab traders. Speke was convinced that he had found the source of the Nile: Burton subsequently disputed this, and even asserted that Speke had not discovered a lake, but merely a " lake region." Both men reached Zanzibar in March 1859, but Speke was the first to arrive in England and to give an account of the expedition. It was left for Burton to supplement the topographical and general descriptions of Speke, in a valuable report.[1]

Speke was now given command of a second expedition, and with J. A. Grant left England in April 1860, " avowedly for the purpose of establishing the truth of [his] assertion that the Victoria Nyanza ... would eventually prove to be the source of the Nile." [2] In due course he made his way inland from the coast to one of the rivers flowing into Lake Victoria, marched round on the western side of the lake, and saw the Ripon Falls. He summarized the results as follows:

> The expedition had now performed its functions. I saw that old father Nile without any doubt rises in the Victoria Nyanza, and, as I had foretold, that lake is the great source of the ... river. ... I mourned, however, when I thought how much I had lost by the delays in the journey having deprived me of the pleasure of going to look at the north-east corner of the Nyanza to see what connection there was, by the strait so often spoken of, with it and the other lake, where the Waganda went to get their salt, and from which another river flowed to the north. ... But I felt I ought to be content ... for I had seen full half of the lake, and had information given me of the other half, by means of which I knew all about the lake, as far, at least, as the chief objects of geographical importance were concerned.
>
> Comparative information assured me that there was as much water on the eastern side of the lake as there is on the western—if anything rather more. The most remote waters or top head of the Nile is the southern end of the lake, situated close on the third degree of south latitude, which gives to the Nile the surprising length, in direct measurement, rolling over thirty-four degrees of latitude, of above 2300 miles. ... Now from this southern point, round by the west, to where the *great* Nile stream issues, there is only one feeder of any importance ... whilst from the southernmost point, round by the east, to the strait, there are no rivers at all of any importance [according to the reports of Arabs]. There remains to be disposed of the "salt lake" [which may be the same as one reported by Krapf]. In no view that can be taken of it, however, does this unsettled matter touch the established fact that the head of the Nile is in 3° south latitude, where, in the year 1858, I discovered the head of the Victoria Nyanza to be. I now christened the "stones" Ripon Falls ... and the arm of water from which the Nile issued Napoleon Channel.[3]

[1] See *J.R.G.S.*, vol. xxix.
[2] See J. H. Speke, *Journal of the Discovery of the Source of the Nile* (1863), p. 1.   [3] Speke, *op. cit.*, pp. 467–469.

Speke and Grant did not follow the exact course of the Nile, and so missed its entrance into Lake Albert, but they heard of this other lake, and when they met Baker lower down, at Gondokoro, they passed on their information to him. The two men returned to

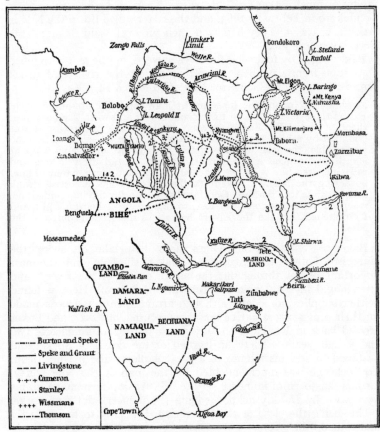

Fig. 37. CENTRAL AND SOUTH AFRICA, 1849–89

The routes of Speke and Grant to Tabora and of Stanley to Lake Victoria are not shown.
They are practically identical with that of Burton and Speke.

England in 1863, having fully carried out their mission: their work, however, was almost entirely unrewarded.

Meanwhile Baker had completed the discovery from the Nile valley upward toward the source. As already indicated, traders had long been active in the Upper Nile region, and two, Petherick and Miani, had collected much information about the country. Neither had, however, reached either of the lakes which fed the

327

Nile. When Speke and Grant set out on their final expedition it was arranged that a supporting party should advance from Egypt and meet them. Petherick undertook to do this, but for various reasons was unable to carry out his promise, and the task was taken up by Samuel Baker and his wife. They met the explorers at Gondokoro in February 1863, and the latter sailed down the Nile in Baker's boats. " They had won their victory," said Baker; " my work lay before me."

Baker began by following the river upward, but he met with much opposition from slave-dealers, so that he left the river and struck across country to the Somerset Nile. On March 14, 1864,

> at about 12 [noon] the long-sought lake suddenly presented itself. Far as the eye could reach to the south-west and west, the boundless sheet of water lay like a mirror ; while to the north-west it was bounded by a high range of mountains. . . . On all sides, where land was visible, the lake was completely shut in by mountains. We at length commenced a precipitous descent . . . and after a long and toilsome, step-like walk, we reached the flat and large extent of land bordering the lake. . . . Went to the water's edge directly ; drank a long draught ; thanked God most sincerely for having guided me, when all hope of success was lost, to this much wished-for end : and I christened the lake the Albert Nyanza as the second source of the Nile.[1]

Baker coasted along the eastern shore of the lake, discovered the Murchison Falls, " the greatest waterfall of the Nile [and] the most important object throughout the entire course of the river," and after long delays was able to return to Gondokoro. Here he found neither supplies nor boats, although arrangements had been made for their provision ; a native craft was secured, however, and Baker arrived back in Khartum on May 5, 1865, after an absence of two and a half years. There he learned of the death of Speke, and hastened to add his tribute to a great explorer and a true friend. To Speke he was much indebted for the map of the Nile valley, " which has been of immense service." [2] Again, he summed up his own work by frankly acknowledging the pioneer efforts of Speke. " This being the close of the expedition, I wish it to be distinctly understood," he wrote,

> how thoroughly I support the credit of Speke and Grant for their discovery of the first and most elevated source of the Nile in the great Victoria Nyanza. Although I call the river between the two lakes the " Somerset," as it was named by Speke upon the map he gave to me, I must repeat that it is positively the Victoria Nile, and the name " Somerset " is only used to distinguish it, in my description, from the entire Nile that issues from the Albert Nyanza. Whether the volume of water added by the latter lake be greater

[1] Quoted from Baker's *Journal* in T. D. Murray and A. S. White, *Sir Samuel Baker : a Memoir* (1895), p. 90.
[2] *Ibid.*, p. 97.

AFRICA

than that supplied by the Victoria, the fact remains unaltered : the Victoria is the highest and first discovered source ; the Albert is the second source, but the entire reservoir of the Nile waters.

He then proceeds to explain that he uses the word 'source' to indicate the " reservoir as a head or main starting-point of the river," and that, although this might not be technically correct, it was more appropriate than trying to fix upon any individual stream.[1]

Baker modestly concealed, in this generous tribute to a friend, the achievements of his own successful expedition. He had, however, been unable to explore Lake Albert fully, for, had he done so, he would have discovered that it was not the second source of the Nile, but that it received its waters from another lake still farther to the south. It was left to H. M. Stanley to clear up the doubtful points. Before, however, the full significance of the discovery can be appreciated it is necessary to look at the work of other explorers in Central Africa.

A new epoch in the history of Central Africa opened with the first discovery of Livingstone in 1849. On June 1 in that year he set out, accompanied by Oswell and Murray, to satisfy a long-cherished ambition of finding Lake Ngami. He crossed the Kalahari Desert, and records that

> on the 1st of August 1849 we went down to the broad part [of the lake] and, for the first time, this fine-looking sheet of water was beheld by Europeans. ... It is shallow, for I subsequently saw a native punting his canoe over 7 or 8 miles of the north-east end ; it can never, therefore, be of much value as a commercial highway. In fact, during the months preceding the annual supply of water from the north the lake is so shallow that it is with difficulty cattle can approach the water through the boggy, reedy banks. These are low on all sides, but on the west there is a space devoid of trees, showing that the waters have retired thence at no very ancient date. This is another of the proofs of desiccation met with so abundantly throughout the whole country.[2]

Livingstone and Oswell revisited Lake Ngami in 1850, and in the following year, while exploring to the northward, made a second valuable discovery, the Zambezi river. " This," said Livingstone,

> was a most important point, for that river was not previously known to exist there at all. The Portuguese maps all represent it as rising far to the east of where we now were ; and if ever anything like a chain of trading stations had existed across the country between the latitudes of 12° and 18° south, this magnificent portion of the river must have been known before.[3]

[1] *The Albert N'Yanza, Great Basin of the Nile, and Explorations of the Nile Sources*, edition of 1870, pp. 460–461.
[2] D. Livingstone, *Missionary Travels and Researches in South Africa* (1857), pp. 65–66.   [3] *Ibid.*, p. 90.

Livingstone now returned to his mission station, but found his work seriously impaired by Boer raids. He therefore went to Cape Town, whence he sent his family to England, and where he learned some astronomy, preparatory to further explorations in the north. With his second visit to the Zambezi, in 1853, Livingstone's most important work as an African explorer began.

Livingstone went up the Liambai, the main Zambezi stream, crossed to the Congo basin, and reached the west coast at Loanda. After a short rest he returned to the Zambezi, discovered the Victoria Falls, and followed the general course of the river to the east coast, at Quilimane, where he arrived in May 1856. He was able to collect some general information about Lake Nyasa. The journey had resulted in the revelation of an entirely unknown part of Africa : yet to Livingstone this discovery was " a matter for congratulation only in so far as it opens up a prospect for the elevation of the inhabitants." " I view," he said, " the end of the geographical feat as the beginning of missionary enterprise." [1]

The results of the journey can best be expressed in Livingstone's words :

> Most geographers are aware that, before the discovery of Lake Ngami, and the well-watered country in which the Makololo dwell, the idea prevailed that a large part of the interior of Africa consisted of sandy deserts, into which rivers ran and were lost. During my journey in 1852–6, from sea to sea, across the south inter-tropical part of the continent, it was found to be a well-watered country, with large tracts of fine fertile soil covered with forest, and beautiful grassy valleys, occupied by a considerable population ; and one of the most wonderful waterfalls in the world was brought to light. The peculiar form of the continent was than ascertained to be an elevated plateau, somewhat depressed in the centre, and with fissures in the sides by which the rivers escaped to the sea ; and this great fact in physical geography can never be referred to without calling to mind the remarkable hypothesis by which the distinguished President of the Royal Geographical Society (Sir Roderick I. Murchison) clearly indicated this peculiarity before it was verified by actual observation of the altitudes of the country and the courses of the rivers. [As a result of this journey, and of the work of others like Barth, Speke, and Baker] the fabulous torrid zone, of parched and burning sand, was now proved to be a well-watered region resembling North America in its freshwater lakes, and India in its hot humid lowlands, jungles, ghauts, and cool highland plains. [2]

Livingstone began his second journey in 1858. He had been appointed Consul for the Zambezi, and he took with him a number of men who were to assist in the exploration and exploitation of the

[1] D. Livingstone, *Missionary Travels and Researches in South Africa* (1857), p. 673.
[2] D. and C. Livingstone, *Narrative of an Expedition to the Zambesi and its Tributaries* (1865), p. 5.

country, the most important being John Kirk. "In our expedition," wrote Livingstone,

the chief object in view was not to discover objects of nine days' wonder, to gaze and be gazed at by barbarians; but to note the climate, the natural productions, the local diseases, the natives, and their relation to the rest of the world; all which were observed with that peculiar interest, which, as regards the future, the first white man cannot but feel in a continent whose history is only just beginning.[1]

Several journeys were made up and down the Zambezi and the Shiré rivers, during which Lake Shirwa was discovered, and finally, Livingstone reported,

we discovered Lake Nyasa, a little before noon of the 16th September, 1859. Its southern end is in 14° 25' S. latitude, and 35° 30' E. longitude. At this point the valley is about twelve miles wide. There are hills on both sides of the lake, but the haze from burning grass prevented us at the time from seeing far.[2]

In another connexion Livingstone added: "The direction in which it lies is as near as possible due north and south. Nothing of the great bend to the west, shown in all the previous maps, could be detected."[3] This was not strictly a discovery, for the lake was at least known to the Portuguese: but, as may be gathered from Livingstone's remarks, the knowledge was far from accurate. Lake Nyasa was reached, farther north, by A. Roscher a few months after Livingstone's visit. Roscher had crossed from Kilwa, and was thus able to supplement the work of Von der Decken and of Livingstone: shortly afterward "he lost his life in his zeal for exploration."

Early in 1861 Livingstone attempted to reach the lake from the east coast, by using the Rovuma river, reported to be "infinitely superior to the Zambezi, in the absence of any bar at its mouth, in its greater volume of water, and in the beauty of the adjacent lands."[4] After ascending the river for some distance the attempt to cross the country was abandoned. Livingstone returned to the Zambezi, revisited Lake Nyasa, and explored and mapped a considerable part of its west coast. He then went down the Zambezi, and sailed for Zanzibar and Bombay.

The expedition was not entirely a happy one, and although much valuable geographical work had been accomplished, the results went rather to supplement what was already known than to open up new regions. The difficulties of penetrating the country from the coasts were serious, and were fully appreciated by Livingstone. "Some parts of the continent," he wrote,

[1] D. and C. Livingstone, *Narrative of an Expedition to the Zambesi and its Tributaries* (1865), p. 6. [2] *Ibid.*, p. 123.
[3] *Ibid.*, p. 369. [4] *Ibid.*, p. 430.

have been said to resemble an inverted dinner plate. This portion [*i.e.*, the region round Lake Nyasa] seems more of the shape, if shape it has, of a wide-awake hat, with the crown a little depressed. The altitude of the brim in some parts is considerable ; in others, as at Tete and the bottom of Murchison's cataracts [it is very small].   So long as African rivers remain in what we may call the brim, they present no obstructions, but no sooner do they emerge from the higher lands than their utility is impaired by cataracts.   The low-lying belt is very irregular.   At times sloping up in the manner of the rim of an inverted dinner plate, while in other cases, a high ridge rises near the sea, to be succeeded by a lower district inland before we reach the central plateau.   The breadth of the low land is some-times as much as three hundred miles, and that breadth determines the limits of navigation from the seaward.[1]

Livingstone noticed that beyond the rivers flowing into Lake Nyasa the drainage was toward the centre of the continent.

The course of the Kasai . . . and its feeders was to the north-east, or somewhat in the same direction [as the drainage west of Nyasa]. Whether the water thus drained off finds its way out by the Congo or by the Nile has not yet been ascertained.[2]

Thus he considered a possible source of the Nile to exist in about the latitude of 10° S.   His third journey was to throw more light on the problem, although not to find a solution to it.

In the Congo basin and on the west coast of Central Africa a considerable amount of exploration had been accomplished before Livingstone's third journey.   Ladislaus Magyar, who went to the Kalahari desert in 1847, began his romantic travels in the Congo basin two years later.   He passed inland, from Benguela to the kingdom of Bihé, married the daughter of an African chief, and wandered eastward to the valley of the Upper Zambezi and into the Congo basin.   In these journeys Magyar saw much country that was quite unknown, but the geographical information he obtained was wholly disproportionate to the area covered.

In 1853 Silva Porto began his trans-African journey from Benguela to the mouth of the Rovuma river.   He crossed the country of the Congo-Zambezi divide, passed south of Lake Nyasa without seeing it, and then traversed the country south of the Rovuma.   Welwitsch, a naturalist, made a journey across Angola in 1853, and began the scientific exploration of that country.   In the following year Leal discovered the mouth of the Cunene.   In 1858 Bastian explored the Lower Congo, while Serval Griffon du Bellay in 1862, and Labingot and Touchard in 1864, began the investigation of the Ogowe river, in Gabun.   It was in this latter region that P. du Chaillu carried out his remarkable travels, beginning in 1850 and extending to 1865. His father had been a trader on the Gabun river.   He himself reached one of the headstreams of the Ogowe in 1850, travelled

---

[1] *Zambesi*, pp. 532–533.   [2] *Ibid.*, p. 532.

through Southern Gabun in 1856, and in 1858 explored some of the shorter rivers entering the coast to the south of the Ogowe. These early journeys, however, were productive of many adventures, but of little geographical information. In 1863–65 Du Chaillu did most valuable work, travelling inland from the Gabun to the Kambo river, fixing a number of points, and visiting regions hitherto entirely unknown.

Although there had been much exploration, the great problems of Central Africa were still unsolved when Livingstone began his last expedition in 1866. He arrived at Zanzibar on January 28, proceeded to the Rovuma river, and followed that valley inland, ultimately reaching Lake Nyasa. He went round the southern end of the lake, turned northward, and on April 1, 1867, reached the southern end of Lake Tanganyika, the northern part of which had already been discovered by Burton and Speke. Livingstone was the first to give the true orientation to this lake.

The next important discovery was made on November 8, 1867, when Livingstone saw Lake Mweru. " The northern shore," he wrote,

has a fine sweep like an unbent bow, and round the western end flows the water that makes the Lualaba, which, before it enters Mweru, is the Luapula, and that again (if the most intelligent reports speak true) is the Chambezi before it enters Lake Bangweolo.[1]

Livingstone spent some time travelling about to the south of Lake Mweru, and visited the lake on a second occasion before making his next discovery, Lake Bangweolo, which he first saw on July 18, 1868. He then decided to go north to Ujiji, on Lake Tanganyika, for letters, and reached that place in March of the following year. He left again on July 12, recrossed the lake, and travelled north-westward until, after many *détours*, he came to the Lualaba river in March 1871. He had been inclined to believe that this river was part of the Nile, but as he gained more information he was less certain, and prepared himself " to find it after all the Congo." Indeed, Livingstone had been collecting so much information that he was doubtful what to believe. At one time he thought Lake Tanganyika was " an expansion of the Nile " and sent its waters northward to the lake discovered by Baker (Lake Albert).[2] Now, on his return from the Lualaba, he suggested that the

Longumba is the outlet of Tanganyika : it becomes the Luassé further down, and then the Luamo before it joins the Lualaba : the country slopes that way, but I was too ill to examine its source.[3]

Livingstone again crossed Lake Tanganyika, reached Ujiji on October 23, and five days later met H. M. Stanley, who had been

[1] *The Last Journals of David Livingstone in Central Africa*, edited by H. Walker (2 vols., 1874), vol. i, p. 243.
[2] *Last Journals*, vol. i, pp. 284–285.　　　　[3] *Ibid.*, vol. ii, p. 154.

sent out, as Livingstone put it, " to obtain accurate information about Dr Livingstone if living, and if dead to bring home my bones."[1] Stanley brought a letter from the Royal Geographical Society suggesting the advisability of exploring the north end of Lake Tanganyika, and Livingstone and Stanley proceeded to carry out this suggestion. They proved that the small river at the end of the lake flowed into it, and so disposed of one theory as to the source of the Nile. But Livingstone was not content : he accompanied Stanley part of the way back to the coast, but refused to go home until he had solved the mystery. On May 31, 1872, he wrote :

> In reference to this Nile source I have been kept in perpetual doubt and perplexity. I know too much to be positive. Great Lualaba . . . may turn out to be the Congo and Nile, a shorter river after all—the fountains flowing north and south seem in favour of its being the Nile. Great westing is in favour of the Congo. It would be comfortable to be positive like Baker. " Every drop from the passing shower to the roaring mountain torrent must fall into Albert Lake, a giant at its birth." How soothing to be positive ! [2]

After waiting for stores to be sent up from the coast Livingstone turned southward again, intent on discovering the source of the Nile, which he thought he would find near Lake Bangweolo. Increasing illness hampered the progress of his party, but he reached the shores of the lake. There, on the night of April 30, 1873, he died. Almost his last remark was : " How many days is it to the Luapula ? " To the end the search had kept him going : but for years it had sapped his strength, and he died, a prematurely old man, without the satisfaction of finding a solution. Yet Livingstone must always remain one of the greatest figures in African exploration. His positive accomplishments were of supreme importance, for he revolutionized the map of Africa. Brave in danger, patient in all kinds of adversity, he was incurably obstinate ; his last journey, after leaving Stanley, was almost a waste of time, and undoubtedly hastened his end. He is remembered now for his qualities as a man almost more than for his achievements as an explorer ; and no one has more happily described his real worth than Lord Curzon, whose judgment is this :

> His was the type of character and career that will always remain an inspiration for our race. Born with no social advantages, possessing no prospects, backed by no powerful influence, this invincible Scotsman hewed his way through the world, and carved his name deep in the history of mankind, until in the end he was carried to his grave in Westminster Abbey amid the sorrowing admiration of an entire people, and bequeathed a name which has been, and will ever be, a light to his countrymen. How did he do it ? By boldness of conception, by fertility and courage in execution, by a noble

---

[1] *Last Journals*, vol. ii, p. 156.
[2] *Ibid.*, pp. 193–194. Stanley believed, with Livingstone, that the Nile sources might be found far to the south. See the interesting map in *How I found Livingstone* (1872), p. 449.

endurance in suffering and disappointment, by self-sacrifice 'unto death, he wrested triumph even from failure, and in the darkness never failed to see the dawn. His spirit hovers over Central Africa, just as that of Cecil Rhodes, of many of whose ideals he was the unconscious parent, broods over the South African regions that bear his name. And, though Africa has changed since Livingstone's day beyond all human recognition ; though settled territories and demarcated frontiers have taken the place of lawlessness and inter-tribal warfare ; though geographical problems which he went down to the grave without having solved are now among the common-places of school primers ; though exploration has given way to peaceful evolution, and railways have replaced the tortuous crawl of the caravan ; though Africa is no longer merely a European interest, but has almost become a European possession ;—yet the work of Livingstone still stands forth in monumental grandeur among the achievements of human energy, and the spirit of Livingstone will continue to inspire a generation that knew him not, but will never cease to revere his name.[1]

Two relief expeditions were sent out from England to help Livingstone. On the west coast Grandy was to ascend the Congo, but he only reached San Salvador, where he died. V. L. Cameron, however, had better fortune on the east coast. He soon heard of the death of Livingstone, but decided to push on. He reached Lake Tanganyika, and explored it, mapping the greater part of its outline for the first time ; and he discovered the Lukuga river, and although he did not follow it throughout its course, he believed that it was the outlet of the lake. He then continued across Africa toward the south-west, and reached the coast of Benguela. He had made some observations on the Lualaba river, and came to the conclusion that it was part of the Congo system. He thought that the Welle might be a tributary of the Lualaba, or, if not, of the Ogowe or the Benue.

The work of the earlier Nile explorers and of Livingstone and Cameron was in large measure completed by H. M. Stanley's expedition of 1874–77. His first important task, the circumnavigation of Lake Victoria, began on March 8, 1875. Within the month Stanley had settled some of the problems of the Nile. " From the 17th of January, 1875, up to the 7th of April, 1876," he wrote,

we had been engaged in tracing the extreme southern sources of the Nile, from the marshy plains and cultivated uplands where they are born, down to the mighty reservoir called the Victoria Nyanza. We had circumnavigated the entire expanse ; penetrated to every bay, inlet, and creek ; become acquainted with almost every variety of wild human nature . . . we had travelled hundreds of miles to and fro on foot along the northern coast of the Victorian Sea, and, finally, had explored with a large force the strange countries lying between the two lakes Muta Nzigé [i.e., Edward] and the Victoria, and had been permitted to gaze upon the arm of the lake named by me "Beatrice Gulf," and to drink of its sweet waters. We had then returned from farther quest in that direction . . . and had struck

[1] G.J., vol. xli (1913), p. 423.

south from the Katonga lagoon down to the Alexandra Nile [*i.e.*, the Kagera], the principal affluent of the Victoria Lake, which drains nearly all the waters from the west and south-west. We had made a patient survey of over one-half of its course and then owing to want of the means to feed the rapacity of the tribes [and to reluctance to force a way through] we had been compelled, on the 7th of April, to bid adieu to the lands which supply the Nile, and to turn our faces towards the Tanganyika. . . . I have not ventured beyond the limits assigned to me, viz. the exploration of the southern sources of the Nile, and the solution of the problem left unsolved by Speke and Grant—Is the Victoria Nyanza one lake or does it consist of five lakes as reported by Livingstone, Burton, and others ? This problem has been satisfactorily solved, and Speke has now the full glory of having discovered the largest inland sea on the continent of Africa, also its principal affluent, as well as the outlet. I must also give him credit for having understood the geography of the countries he travelled through better than any of those who so persistently assailed his hypothesis, and I here record my admiration of the geographical genius that from mere native report sketched with such a masterly hand the bold outlines of the Victoria Nyanza.[1]

Stanley began the second phase of his exploring work when he set sail on Lake Tanganyika on June 11, 1876. At the end of July he had completed the task he had set himself. Again he may tell his own story:

> On the 28th [July] we skirted the low land which lies at the foot of the western mountains, and by noon had arrived at the little cove in Masansi, near the Rubumba or the Luvumba river, at which Livingstone and I terminated our exploration of the northern shores of Lake Tanganyika in 1871. I had thus circumnavigated Lake Tanganyika from Ujiji up the eastern coast, along the northern head, and down the western coast as far as Rubumba river in 1871, and in June-July 1876 had sailed south from Ujiji along the eastern coast to the extreme south end of the lake, round each inlet of the south, and up the western coast to Panza Point, in Ubwari, round the shores of Burton Gulf, and to Rubumba river. The north end of the lake was located by Livingstone in south latitude 3° 18' ; the extreme south end I discovered to be in south latitude 8° 47', which gives it a length of 329 geographical miles. Its breadth varies from ten to forty-five miles, averaging about twenty-eight miles, and its superficial area covers a space of 9240 square miles.[2]

Stanley also examined the Lukuga outlet, and came to the conclusion that Cameron had been mistaken : the lake only overflowed through that channel when it was exceptionally high.

From Lake Tanganyika Stanley followed the valley of the Luama river down to the junction of that stream with what he called the Livingstone, what Livingstone called the Lualaba, and what is the Congo. " My task," he wrote, " was to follow it [the Congo] to the Ocean." He had reached the country where Livingstone had turned back in 1871, through disgust with the Arabs, and where

---

[1] H. M. Stanley, *Through the Dark Continent* (1878), vol. i, pp. 480–482.
[2] *Ibid.*, vol. ii, p. 60.

Cameron had turned south-westward in 1874 through the hostility of those same people. Stanley, with an armed force numbering 152 persons, succeeded where the others had failed. He marched to the Lualaba, which he reached in latitude 3° 35′ S., longitude 25° 49′ E. "The name Lualaba terminates here," he wrote. " I mean to speak of it henceforth as the Livingstone."

There is no need to follow Stanley in his successful journey down the river to the Atlantic. On August 9, 1877, he reached Boma, on the "999th day from the date of our departure from Zanzibar." Thus ended one of the most remarkable expeditions in the whole history of exploration. If it be objected that Stanley reaped the fruits of other men's labours, it should not be overlooked that he accomplished a vast amount of pioneer work and that he succeeded in finding solutions to problems which had baffled his predecessors.

The fate of Livingstone and the astonishing success of Stanley roused Europe to the importance of African exploration, and henceforth discoveries followed one another in bewildering numbers. It will be convenient first to dispose of the quest for the Nile sources.

Baker returned to the Nile in 1869, when, in the service of the Khedíve of Egypt, he was given command of an expedition to conquer the country south of Gondokoro and to suppress the slave-trade. Baker's work was of a preparatory nature, and although it brought with it increased knowledge of parts of the Nile, it did not result in any startling discoveries. Baker was succeeded by Gordon, and under his authority· several important events took place. The Nile itself was surveyed up to Lake Albert; Chaillé-Long definitely established the connexion between the Victoria and Albert Lakes by the Somerset Nile, and added to the knowledge of Lake Kioga, about which there was already some information (1874); and Gessi (1876) and Mason (1877) sailed round Lake Albert, although neither saw the river which enters its southern end. Missionaries, sent to Uganda at the suggestion of Stanley, reached that country by the White Nile, and one, R. W. Felkin, who had made that journey returned with C. T. Wilson, who had gone to Uganda from Zanzibar. Stanley himself had met E. Linant de Bellefonds in Uganda, and the latter had returned down the Nile, but was murdered before reaching Egypt. All this work in the valley of the White Nile was rapidly increasing geographical knowledge.

One man in particular added greatly to the romance of Nile exploration, as well as to its completion. The German Jew E. Schnitzer, who is known to history as Emin Pasha, took service with the Egyptian Government under Gordon. From 1877 to 1888 he lived in the Upper Nile country. He travelled through the

337

regions round Lake Albert, although he never saw the Ruwenzori range ; he discovered the Semliki river, which enters the lake at its southern end, but never traced it very far to the south ; and he did much useful work on the Nile-Congo divide. The results of his explorations were brought to England by Junker.[1]

The withdrawal of the missionaries from Uganda in 1885, and the death of Gordon in Khartum in the same year, resulted in the isolation of Emin Pasha. Various relief parties were organized, and one, under Stanley, finally solved the problem of the Nile. He approached the region through the Congo forests, discovered the Ruwenzori Mountains, traced the Semliki river to the Edward Lake, explored the latter (which he had already discovered on his earlier journey), and escorted Emin to the east coast. It was a magnificent end to his career as an explorer. " The main facts regarding the sources of the Nile were finally revealed by him, and nothing was left for future explorers but to fill in the details." [2]

In the eastern portion of Central Africa considerable progress was made after the second expedition of Livingstone and the journey of Roscher already mentioned. The Livingstone search expedition commanded by Lieutenant Young in 1867 reached the southern end of Lake Nyasa, and collected information disproving that the great missionary explorer was dead : its successful accomplishment of the task in the short space of eight months reflects much credit on the commander.

Missionaries, who arrived in Nyasaland in 1875, took up the task of exploration, and their efforts were supplemented by Consuls Elton and O'Neill and the engineer Stewart, a servant of the African Lakes Company. Elton proved that Lake Nyasa extended farther north than had hitherto been supposed, and also explored the Livingstone Mountains. He died on an overland journey to Zanzibar. O'Neill, who succeeded him, added much to the knowledge of the country between Lake Nyasa and the coast in the course of a number of overland journeys. Stewart meanwhile did much to improve the map of the lake itself : he established a number of positions, supplemented the work of Thomson in the north, and completed the exploration of the eastern shores of the lake (1882). To all this must be added the inconspicuous but extremely useful work of the missionaries.[3] The period closed with the important discovery of the navigability of the Chinde river in 1889 by D. J. Rankin. The fact that this mouth of the Zambezi " possessed a bar shorter and safer and simpler than that of any other outlet

[1] See Sir Harry Johnston, *The Nile Quest*, p. 250 *et seq.*
[2] Sir William Garstin, " Fifty Years of Nile Exploration," in *G. J.*, vol. xxxiii, p. 117 *et seq.* This is a very useful article.
[3] Among them was Chauncy Maples, whose work extended from 1877 to 1895. See E. Maples, *Chauncy Maples, a Sketch of his Life* (1897).

of the Zambesi" was of the greatest political importance for the development of the interior.[1]

Farther north little was done between the discoveries of Krapf and Rebmann and the first East African journey of J. Thomson, except that Von der Decken carried out a thorough exploration of the region round Kilimanjaro in 1861–62 and that Sir John Kirk virtually established a British protectorate over Zanzibar. The country had also been crossed several times, notably by Burton, Speke, Stanley, and Cameron, in the course of longer African journeys.

In 1878 the Royal Geographical Society sent out an expedition to explore the country between Dar-es-Salaam and Lake Nyasa in order to find out a practicable route to the interior. The expedition was entrusted to Keith Johnston, who unfortunately died soon after leaving the coast. The command then fell on Joseph Thomson, a young man, twenty years of age.[2] He led the party with conspicuous success, crossed to the northern end of Lake Nyasa, explored the wholly unknown country between that Lake and Lake Tanganyika, and discovered Lake Rukwa. He next proceeded up the west coast of Lake Tanganyika to the Lukuga outlet, which he found " a swift resistless current," establishing the fact that it was the outlet of the lake and that, if Stanley had been correct, changes had taken place since his visit.[3] After a short journey to Ujiji, where he met the missionary Hore, Thomson recrossed to the western side and attempted to reach the Congo, but was frustrated by the opposition of the natives. He accordingly returned to the lake, sailed down its eastern shore, and from the south end crossed north-eastward to Tabora, whence he returned to the coast. He had covered much entirely unknown country, and had subjected the whole area to a scientific study which marked him out as one of the great African explorers.

In 1881 Thomson returned to the Rovuma river for the purpose of examining a report of Livingstone that there was coal to be found there. The journey was in one respect a failure, for the coal proved to be bituminous shale, and although a substance like anthracite was discovered it was found to leave more than 50 per cent. ash. Yet Thomson was able to add to the knowledge of the geology and geography of the region and to increase his own reputation as a careful explorer.

Thomson's third East African expedition had for its object the opening up of a new route to Uganda from the coast in the neighbourhood of Zanzibar. Here some preliminary work had been done by Von der Decken, by the missionaries New and Wakefield, and by the recent journeys of Fischer. The last named had reached

[1] See Sir Harry Johnston, *British Central Africa* (1897), p. 79.
[2] See J. B. Thomson, *Joseph Thomson, African Explorer* (1897).
[3] The facts about the Lukuga were ascertained by Hore in April 1879.

Kilimanjaro in 1882, and had penetrated as far as the Great Rift Valley, where he discovered Lake Naivasha.

While Fischer was in the interior Thomson started from Mombasa, in March 1883. He pushed inland to "the majestic mass of Kilimanjaro," and then, turning toward the north, followed much the same route as Fischer to the Rift Valley. Passing beyond Lake Naivasha, he made a *détour* to Mount Kenya, and there discovered Lake Baringo, another Rift Valley lake. Here he turned westward, and finally south-westward, to strike the northern shore of Victoria Nyanza near to Napoleon Gulf. The return journey was made by way of Mount Elgon, Lake Baringo, and a route somewhat more to the east of that taken on the way out. Thomson had successfully crossed the land of the Masai, the fierce warriors who barred the way to Uganda, had made most valuable observations of the country through which he had passed, and had added some important details to the map.

A few other expeditions complete the story, in outline, of the exploration of East Africa up to the year 1889. German scientific investigation in what is now called Tanganyika Territory[1] began with the expedition of 1880, when Böhm, Kaiser, and Reichard began a systematic examination of the country between Zanzibar and the eastern edge of the Congo basin. Reichard, who spent a number of years in East Africa, went as far as the copper country of Katanga.

Lieutenant Giraud also crossed to the Congo region from Dar-es-Salaam, reaching the northern end of Lake Nyasa and visiting Lake Bangweolo, where he was able to make some important corrections to Livingstone's map. Owing to the desertion of his carriers he was obliged to give up his projected crossing of the continent and to return to Lake Nyasa and the Zambezi (1883).

Fischer, in 1885–86, continued his explorations southward from Masailand, and connected up the northern route with the more southerly lines to Lake Victoria and Tabora, while in 1885 Count Teleki, who started from Zanzibar, pushed inland to Kilimanjaro, and then, continuing to the northward, made the very important discoveries of Lakes Rudolf and Stefanie.

About the year 1884 the Germans became increasingly active, but their objects were, for the moment, almost entirely political. Indirectly, however, their actions had important geographical consequences, for in the years immediately following 1889 the English began the occupation of Uganda and Kenya, and both countries were more systematically explored.

There remains for consideration the geographical work which had been carried out from the west coast and in the Congo region since Livingstone's last expedition. First, to the north of the Congo,

[1] For convenience this name is used instead of German East Africa.

Güssfeldt led an expedition to the Loango coast in 1873–76, and, without covering much ground, obtained valuable scientific results, paying particular attention to meteorology, anthropology, and natural history. Marche and the Marquis de Compiègne followed up the earlier explorers on the Ogowe, and penetrated beyond the Falls of Bone, the limit of European advance up to this date. Their work was in turn supplemented by the extensive and important journeys of De Brazza in 1875 and succeeding years. He explored the Ogowe for the greater part of its course, discovered a number of the northern affluents of the Congo, and reached that stream at Brazzaville and at Bolobo. He also crossed the country between the mouth of the Kuilu river and Brazzaville. His visit of 1879 marks the definite establishment of French power in this region. This was followed up by the French West African Mission of 1883–85, when the Ogowe was surveyed, as well as many parts of the adjoining country. The positions of a number of places were established, and political and economic results of the greatest importance followed.

In the Congo valley very great progress in exploration was made between 1875 and 1887. In the first year Pogge [1] crossed from the west coast to Muata Yamvo, revealing much unknown country in between the river-courses. He was followed by Schütt (1877–79), who also penetrated inland as far as the Chikapa, one of the tributaries of the Kasai river. H. M. Stanley returned to the Congo in 1879 on a political mission, and during his stay in the country discovered, in 1883, the lakes Tumba and Leopold II. With his arrival, and the backing of Leopold II of Belgium, exploration proceeded rapidly. Büchner in 1879 crossed the country from Loanda, roughly along the parallel of 10° S., as far as the meridian of 20° E., where he turned north-eastward to Muata Yamvo. He fixed the latitude of sixty-seven points, made a careful survey of his route, and added to the knowledge of the peoples of the region. Two men, however, rank above the others in the exploration of the Congo at this time. First is H. von Wissmann, who began work with Pogge in 1880, and in the course of six years made three journeys of great importance. In 1880–83 he started from Loanda, went inland as far as Malange and Kimbandu, and then struck first northward along the Chikapa and then across the tributaries of the Kasai and Congo to the Congo itself at Nyangwe. He thus followed a route roughly parallel to, but north of, that of Cameron. He then continued his journey to Lake Tanganyika, crossed to Ujiji, and travelled by Tabora and a route nearly coinciding with the modern railway to the east coast.

In 1884–85 he made a second journey, again starting from Loanda, travelling eastward to Malange, and then turning to the north-east.

[1] Pogge, Schütt, Büchner, and Von Wissmann all originally went out at the instigation of the German African Association.

On this occasion he joined his earlier route at Ginambanza, having crossed a great many of the western affluents of the Kasai. He then returned down the Kasai.

The third expedition of Von Wissmann led to much fuller knowledge of the Kasai. He started up the Congo in 1886, and on March 22 began the exploration of the Kasai with Grenfell. Early in April Von Wissmann met his friend and former colleague L. Wolf, and learned of the exploration of the Sankuru river which the latter had carried out after Von Wissmann had returned from his second expedition. Wolf died shortly afterward, in Dahomey, and although some of his results were embodied in the work of Von Wissmann, some at least were lost.

After meeting Wolf at the mouth of the Lulua Von Wissmann went up to the falls named after himself on the Kasai, returned to the Lulua and ascended that river, and finally crossed to Nyangwe on the Congo. Thence, following his earlier route, he reached Lake Tanganyika, sailed to its southern end, crossed the country to Lake Nyasa, navigated its entire length, reached the Zambezi by the Shiré river, and finally arrived at Quilimane. Thus for the second time in seven years Von Wissmann had crossed the continent.

Von Wissmann had been assisted by a number of other Germans in the service of the Congo state, notably by Von François and Müller. At the same time Von Mechow had mapped the middle course of the Kwango in 1880, and Kund and Tappenbeck, in 1884, had travelled southward from Stanley Pool, and then, turning toward the east, had crossed all the rivers from the Kwango to the Kasai, and penetrated some distance beyond the latter. Büttner had also made an important journey inland, to the east of San Salvador.

The work of these able German officers was supplemented by that of the Protestant missionaries, of whom only Comber and Grenfell can be mentioned. The former, in 1879-80, explored the country immediately to the south of the Congo in his many efforts to reach Leopoldville. To Grenfell, however, must be given credit for some of the most important explorations ever made in the Congo basin. If Von Wissmann discovered the Kasai and Wolf the Sankuru, Grenfell was the first to reconnoitre most of the other navigable tributaries of the Congo.[1] Between 1884 and 1886 he explored the Ubangi, the Mongala, and other rivers entering the right bank of the Congo, as far as the Aruwimi, as well as the Lulanga and the Lomami. In 1885 he ascended the Ubangi to the Zongo Falls, and as a result it became almost certain that the Ubangi and the Welle were one river.

[1] Sir Harry Johnston, *George Grenfell and the Congo* (2 vols, 1908), vol. i, p. 4. For an admirable illustration of the work of Grenfell, Von Wissman, and the other explorers here mentioned see the maps on pp. 130 and 131 of that book.

The work of Grenfell, which was continued for a long period after 1889, and of Von Wissmann entirely revolutionized the knowledge of the Congo basin. Before their journeys the great Kasai system was almost unknown, and it was assumed that most of the rivers which travellers had crossed about the latitude of 8° S., or even beyond that parallel, flowed into the main Congo. The explorations of Von Wissmann and Grenfell revealed the Congo system as it is known to-day.

To complete the outlines of the geography of the region Van Gèle in 1887 ascended the Ubangi, and proved conclusively that it was identical with the river seen by Schweinfurth and Junker.

There remain for consideration a number of expeditions, connected for the most part with the southern part of the Congo region and with South Africa. In 1877 the Portuguese were aroused by Stanley's success, and sent two expeditions to the west coast. Serpa Pinto crossed the continent from Benguela to Natal, tracing part of the Kwando, and traversing the eastern part of Bechuana-land. He explored much unknown country, and added to the knowledge of the river-system to the south-east of Bihé. In the same year Capello and Ivens struck north from Bihé, and examined part of the Kwango and a large area in the north of Angola. In 1884–85 the same travellers crossed the continent from Mossamedes to the mouth of the Zambezi. They explored a considerable part of Southern Angola, reached the Katanga district and what is now Northern Rhodesia, and then turned southward, to strike the Zambezi at the mouth of the Kafue river.

The missionary F. S. Arnot, who was looking for healthy places in which to establish stations, travelled from Natal in 1884, crossed the Zambezi above the Victoria Falls, followed the river to Lialui, and finally traversed the country to the north-west as far as the plateau on which Bihé stands. His journey supplemented in some respects those of the Portuguese scientific explorers, and marks the end of Central African exploration during this period.

VII. SOUTH AFRICA, 1849–89

Something has already been said of exploration in South Africa in connexion with Livingstone's expedition to Lake Ngami in 1849. His subsequent journeys in Central Africa, and the romance and novelty of travel in that region, have robbed that lake of the interest which it once had, for in the middle of the century it was an object of great attraction. F. Galton and K. J. Andersson attempted to reach it in 1850 from Walfish Bay, but only penetrated a little beyond the Etosha Pan. Andersson, however, remained behind when Galton returned to England, and actually reached Lake Ngami, and journeyed for sixty miles beyond the lake to the northward

(1853). In 1857 Hahn and Green followed a route roughly parallel to that of Galton, but were not able to cross Ovamboland. Two years later, however, Andersson reached the Okovango river, in about latitude 17° 31′ S., longitude 19° E., and explored it for a distance of about 100 miles. He thought it was a tributary of the Zambezi.

This country was reached from the south by the trader and hunter J. Chapman, who travelled extensively in Eastern Bechuanaland between 1849 and 1855, and by Baines and Chapman in 1861.

Meanwhile a little advance had been made on the east coast, where Gassiott travelled from Durban to the upper waters of the Limpopo, and although he said that his visit was never intended " to be one of geographical research," he was able to add to the knowledge of a little-known region. Four years later Montanha and Teixeira, starting from the coast at Inhambane, also reached the Limpopo, and passed beyond it into the north of the Transvaal. In 1868 Erskine reached the Olifants river, followed it to the Limpopo, and traced the latter to its mouth. In 1870 the Limpopo was made still better known through the exploration of Elton.

The survey of the greater part of the course of the Orange River by Moffat in 1856 marks the beginning of an advance into the regions lying east of Bechuanaland. Between 1864 and 1866 the zoologist Fritsch examined the Orange Free State and Bechuanaland, and collected much interesting information about their inhabitants. Mauch, in 1860, discovered gold at Tati (in the south-west of Southern Rhodesia), and Baines followed him shortly after, and spent seven years in the country exploring for that metal : at the same time Mohr travelled through Rhodesia to the Zambezi. Mauch next turned to the south-east, and in 1872 saw the ruins of Zimbabwe, discovered in 1868 by A. Renders.

Three lengthy journeys complete the story of the general exploration of South Africa. The long sojourn of A. Anderson in Bechuanaland between 1864 and 1880 added much to the knowledge of the eastern part of that land and of the Kalahari Desert. Between 1872 and 1879 the Bohemian doctor Holub, in his journeys to study ethnology and natural history, travelled through the Transvaal and Southern Rhodesia, and collected much useful information. During this period, from 1872 to 1892, F. C. Selous, in the course of his hunting trips, crossed and recrossed the country between Lake Ngami and the Zambezi, and passed beyond the Zambezi in 1887 and 1888 ; he devoted most of his attention to Mashonaland, and in 1891 travelled thence to the east coast at Beira.[1] Of this region of Matabeleland and Mashonaland W. M. Kerr furnished the first detailed account after his journey throughout the country in 1884.

The German colony of South-West Africa was the scene of much

[1] For a map showing the country covered by Selous see *G.J.*, vol. i, p. 384.

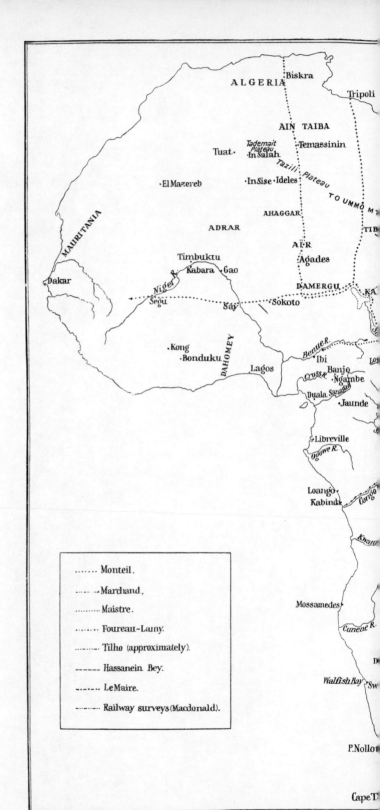

Fig. 38. Africa after 188.

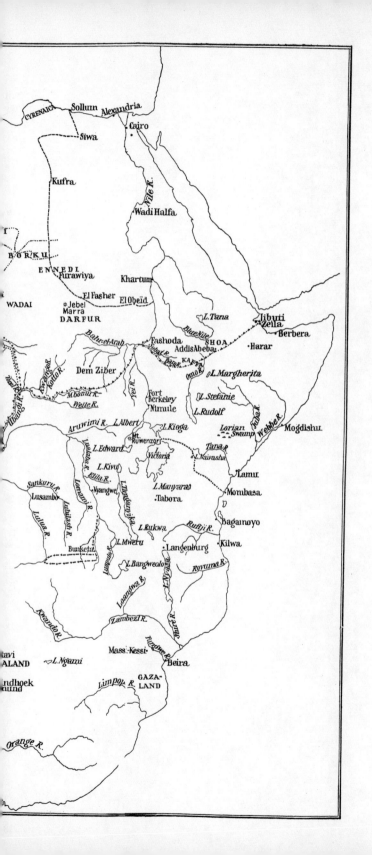

intensive geographical activity in 1884 and succeeding years, in which A. Schenck, H. Schinz, H. Pohle, and F. M. Stapff took a prominent part. Schinz travelled northward from Walfish Bay to the Cunene river in 1884, and almost as far east as Lake Ngami. The two following years were spent in Ovamboland and on the borders of the Kalahari Desert. Schinz made valuable botanical and ethnological investigations of the regions through which he passed. Stapff's geological work in Namaqualand in 1885–86 was supplemented by that of Schenck between Walfish Bay and the Orange River. In 1888–89 Baron von Steinäcker explored large parts of Damaraland, and produced the first accurate maps of that region.[1]

A triangulation in Cape Colony and Natal was carried out by Sir William Morris between 1882 and 1893. Extensive topographical mapping was not undertaken at the same time, and little was done in this direction until after the Boer War.

VIII. South Africa after 1889

There was little pioneer work to be done in South Africa after 1889, and most of the journeys are therefore concerned with the investigation of specific problems or with the task of filling in details. The greater part of the work was carried on in the west of British Africa and in German South-West Africa. Thus Von François added to the knowledge of Damaraland and Namaqualand in 1891. In the following year Pfeil travelled from Port Nolloth to the Orange River, and traversed Central and Eastern Namaqualand and Damaraland to Windhoek, whence he reached Walfish Bay. His journey was of value especially for its economic results. The researches of Dove in German South-West Africa, particularly in Damaraland, in the early part of the last decade of the century were supplemented by the geological investigations of Passarge, in the years 1896–98, in the neighbourhood of Lake Ngami and the country to the north-west. Hartmann's explorations for a railway route from the Otavi copper-mines to the coast, in 1900 and 1901, added to the knowledge of the Lower Cunene river and Ovamboland, while the field-work for the demarcation of the boundary between British and German territory in the south, completed by the year 1903, covered a large area with accurate surveys. In December 1907 Pöch set out from Swakopmund, and crossed the continent to Beira, gaining some valuable ethnological information, more especially relating to the Bushmen.

On the eastern side of the continent the surveys for the Anglo-Portuguese boundary, begun in 1892, covered much country that

[1] For further details on German South-West Africa, see *Geographische Zeitschrift*, vol. iv, pp. 388–397.

was previously unknown. The latitude and longitude of Massi-Kessi was determined, and the survey of a narrow strip of country, running from about 18° S. latitude and 33° E. longitude to the north-eastern corner of the Transvaal, was carried out. In Portuguese territory D. Doyle travelled from the Limpopo river through Central Gazaland to about the latitude of 19° S. in 1891, while the sporting trips of R. L. Reid produced rough surveys of the country north of the Pungwe river and added some detail to the map. Similarly, V. Dickens was able to correct the map of South-eastern Mashonaland, and to discover new rivers in that country, as a result of his travels in 1904–5. Elsewhere the activities of railway engineers, mineral prospectors, and the agents of trading companies filled in many details in the country south of the Zambezi river.

IX. Central Africa after 1889

A considerable amount of exploration was carried out in Central Africa during this period. Much of it was associated with the political moves of European Powers ; the British in Nyasaland, the Germans in Tanganyika Territory, and the French in their equatorial possessions are conspicuous in this respect. The result is that much of the exploration appears to be associated with no important geographical problem. It will be discussed first in relation to the unknown country lying to the west of Lake Tanganyika, then so far as it was more directly concerned with the Congo system, and finally in connexion with West Africa in the region between the Congo, Niger, and Nile rivers. East Africa will then be dealt with by proceeding, as on the opposite coast, from south to north. This arrangement is not entirely satisfactory, and will be departed from occasionally, but in general it serves to give a connected account of many small but important pieces of work.

The establishment of British rule in Nyasaland was largely the result of the work of Sir Harry Johnston and Sir Alfred Sharpe, and both men contributed much also to geographical knowledge. The former explored the country between Lakes Nyasa and Tanganyika in 1889, and discovered the southern end of Lake Rukwa, which was found to extend farther to the south than had been supposed. Sharpe in the same year examined the country west of the Shiré river, and in 1890 journeyed from Lake Nyasa to the Loangwa river. He also crossed from the northern end of Lake Nyasa to Tanganyika Lake, and visited Lake Mweru. At the same time Thomson completed his work of exploration in Central Africa by a journey from the Shiré river to the country south of Lake Bangweolo.

Hitherto the explorers had all approached this region from the valley of the Zambezi. Between 1890 and 1892 four explorers came from the Congo side. P. le Marinel started from Lusambo, on the

Sankuru, in December 1890, followed the Lubi, a tributary of the Sankuru, for about 100 miles, and then struck south-eastward to the town of Bunkeia. M. A. Delcommune, who left the lower course of the Lomami in May 1891, took a route roughly parallel to that of Le Marinel, and proceeded beyond Bunkeia to the copper-mines of Katanga and to the Lualaba river. He returned north-eastward to Lake Tanganyika. W. G. Stairs crossed Tanganyika Territory from Bagamoyo to Lake Tanganyika, and reached Bunkeia in December 1891. Bia, who started from Lusambo, followed a route between that of Le Marinel and that of Delcommune, and arrived at Bunkeia in January 1892. These four travellers crossed the tracks of the earlier explorers Cameron, Capello, Ivens, and Arnot, and made valuable additions to the knowledge of the country through which the Luapula and the Lualaba flowed. Stairs and Bia lost their lives in Central Africa.

Sharpe now resumed his explorations from Nyasaland, travelling from Lake Tanganyika to Lake Mweru in 1892 and beginning the systematic exploration of that lake. He proceeded up the Luapula to the Johnston Falls. In the same year the expedition of Baron Dhanis was approaching the same region from the Sankuru. Officers of this party crossed the country to the Congo at Nyangwe, whence Hinde and Mohun in 1894 explored the river upward to its junction with the Lukuga, and for a short distance up the latter stream. Hinde's route thus joined on to that of Delcommune.[1]

In 1896 P. Weatherley surveyed Lake Bangweolo, and found that the existing maps greatly exaggerated its size, while another 'lake,' Rukwa, was visited by Langheld in the following year, and was found at that date to have dried up and to be only a grassy plain.

During this same period A. St H. Gibbons explored the eastern tributaries of the Zambezi (1895–96), while Brasseur and Cerckel completed the examination of the eastern and western branches of the Upper Congo and the country to the west of the Luapula river. They were able to improve Sharpe's map of Lake Mweru and to lay down many tributary streams. Foa also, in the course of a journey from the Zambezi to the Congo (1894–97), covered some new ground between Lake Tanganyika and the Congo above Nyangwe.

To this unofficial exploration there was added, in 1898, the very important survey of the country between Lakes Tanganyika and Nyasa, by Captains C. F. Close and F. F. R. Boileau, for the purpose of delimiting the Anglo-German boundary. In the south of the protectorate Anderson and others produced a map of the Shiré Highlands in 1899, while Fergusson discovered that the longitude of Lake Tanganyika was wrongly given as a result of the earlier pioneer work of Hore.

Captain C. Lemaire was able to supplement the work of Fergusson,

[1] See *G.J.*, vol. v, p. 426, for Hinde's account of his journeys.

and to confirm his observations, in the course of his Mission Scienti-
fique du Katanga, in 1898–1900. He also explored the Congo-
Zambezi divide between the 22nd and 27th meridians, and proved
that the alleged " character of indecision " in the water-parting did
not exist. His work was in turn supplemented by Major Gibbons,
who returned in 1898 to complete his earlier explorations on the
Zambezi tributaries, and in the course of the next two years not
only accomplished his main task, but performed a journey through
Africa by Lakes Mweru, Tanganyika, Kivu, Edward, and Albert to
Uganda, and so to Egypt. With his work, and that of Lemaire,
exploration in this region may be considered closed. In the country
to the east and north-east of Lake Bangweolo the French ' White
Fathers ' collected some valuable information in the course of their
work between 1895 and 1902, while the boundary between British
and Belgian territory on the Zambezi-Congo divide was surveyed in
1911.

In Angola Baum went inland from Mossamedes in 1899, and
reached the little-known southern parts of the country. Four years
later Cunninghame, also from Mossamedes, travelled north-eastward
to the Kwanza and south-westward to the Cunene. To the work of
both must be added that of the Rohan-Chabot expedition of 1912–14.
It traversed the coastal districts of the south of the country, and
carried out valuable work in the basin of the Cunene and on the
borders of the Zambezi river.

In the Lower Congo valley a considerable number of details were
filled in during the last years of the nineteenth century. Becker in
1890 crossed from the Aruwimi to the Welle, and filled in many
blanks in the country between the two rivers ; A. Delporte fixed a
number of positions on the Lower Congo ; Hodister went up the
Lomami and examined the region between it and the Congo at
Nyangwe ; and Van Gèle reascended the Ubangi, fixed the position
of its great northern bend, and almost reached the point at which
Junker had arrived earlier : the intervening distance was covered
by Roget. The region between the Kasai and the Sankuru was
explored by Stache in 1896. A Belgian expedition, under Lieutenant Glorie, filled in another blank space in the map in 1898,
advancing up the Elila, a tributary which joins the Congo below
Nyangwe, and crossing the country to the east, to within a short
distance of Lake Kivu. By the end of the century the main features
of the Congo system were known. In 1899 Wauters completed his
map of the area on the scale of 1 : 2,000,000, and in 1902 Grenfell's
map of the Congo appeared. While some of the rivers are still
represented by dotted lines, and many small areas remain unexplored, it is unlikely that any more discoveries of the first order will
be made in this region.

To the north of the Congo many attempts have been made to

solve the problems of the hydrography of the Shari, the Benue, and the larger tributaries of the Ubangi, as well as to cross from the Congo to the Nile. At the same time detailed exploration, both in French Equatorial Africa and in the Cameroons, has added considerably to geographical knowledge.

In 1889 Crampel crossed the country between the Ogowe and the Likuala, a tributary of the Congo. In the following year he ascended the Ubangi, but was murdered on his journey from that river toward Lake Chad. Yet his work was not entirely lost, and formed a valuable addition to the cartographical knowledge of the region visited. The circumstances of his murder were investigated in the next year (1891) by Dybowski, who also set out from the Congo and reached the upper course of the Shari. At the same time Cholet explored part of the Sangha river.

In 1892 Fourneau tried, unsuccessfully, to cross from Woso, on the Sangha river, to the Shari, but Maistre, who set out from the Congo, actually reached the Shari, passed through Baghirmi, and arrived on the Benue. He was the first to give a clear definition of the various streams which combine to form the Shari. His work was in turn supplemented three years later by the explorations of Clozel on the Congo-Shari divide. Beyond this Captain Loefler, in 1901–2, surveyed the country traversed by the Logone, the most important tributary of the Shari from the south-west, and covered much new ground in the Shari basin.

In the Ubangi valley Julien surveyed the country to the north of the middle course of the river and to the west of the Mbonui in 1899, while other expeditions in 1901 explored parts of the middle course of the Kotto and the course of the Kwango, both flowing to the Ubangi from the north. Still farther toward the Nile valley, Roulet surveyed over 1000 miles of routes on the divide, while Cureau in 1898 crossed from the Mbonui to Dem Ziber, in the Bahr-el-Ghazal region.

While much of the interior of the continent was thus being explored the regions nearer the coast were often neglected. In 1899 and 1900 the Grendon mission supplemented the earlier work of De Brazza and Mizon in the country between the Ogowe and the Congo, while on the coast, and in the district behind it, the earlier expedition of Dybowski, from Loango to Libreville, in 1894, had covered much ground neglected by other explorers. The Kabinda-French Congo boundary was delimited in 1901, and between 1905 and 1907 surveys for the boundary between the French Congo and the Cameroons were completed.

In Tanganyika Territory the last blanks were filled in rapidly. The detailed studies of O. Baumann in the north-eastern parts of the colony, and in the block of land lying between Lake Victoria, Tabora, and Lake Tanganyika, did much to solve minor problems,

349

among them the real limits of the basin of the Kagera river, the most important stream draining into Lake Victoria. Of a similar nature was the less extensive work of Meyer in the Kilimanjaro region : he was the first to reach the top of the mountain.

In 1891 Von Behr explored some of the country between the Rovuma and the Rufiji rivers, while two years later Baron von Schele, whose objects were to suppress the raids which troubled the country between the Rufiji and the Rovuma, and to discover the best line of communication from Langenburg, at the north end of Lake Nyasa, to the coast, removed the last big blank from the map of Tanganyika Territory. He was successful in both objects, and opened up a new route from the lake to Kilwa. One of his subordinates, Captain Ramsay, remained, to carry out much valuable work in the country.

In the Rift Valley, between Lakes Manyara and Naivasha, A. Kaiser in 1896 added to the knowledge of one of the most striking features of East African topography : it had already been examined northward from Lake Naivasha to Lake Baringo by J. W. Gregory in 1893. Farther westward Capus and Von Wulffen also filled in some details in the district immediately to the south of Lake Victoria.

The work of Von Schele was supplemented by that of two other German explorers in the south of the colony. Lieder completed some detailed exploration in the country immediately to the south of Von Schele's routes, and more particularly added to the knowledge of its physical geography, while Prince in 1895 examined the country to the north-east of Lake Rukwa. Detailed investigations of the geography of Tanganyika Territory continued to be made, but by the end of the century its general features were well known.

In the first years of the period now under consideration German activities extended into what is now Kenya Colony. Here J. R. W. Pigott had explored the Tana river for some considerable distance in 1889. He was followed, in the next year, by the German Peters, who gained notoriety by his political activities, and added slightly to the knowledge of the Tana river. In 1891 the surveys of Dundas, on the same river, supplemented the work of these two earlier explorers. Peters roused the British through his attempts to secure political influence in the interior, and the steps taken to counteract his activities led to the exploration of both Kenya Colony and Uganda. Jackson and Gedge travelled through the Kikuyu country, from Mombasa to Uganda, in 1889–90, and opened up a new route west of Lake Naivasha to Lake Victoria. In 1891 MacDonald began his very valuable surveys for a railway from Mombasa to Uganda, and was able both to give precision to details in the country already known and to traverse new ground. Similarly, the

350

political and military activities of F. (later Lord) Lugard, Williams, and Portal in Uganda had important results for geography.[1] Although the first named denied that his journeys were in any sense scientific exploration, he was able to gather much valuable information about the country to the north of Lake Victoria and between that lake and Lake Albert. The zoological expedition of Neumann in 1893–95 added still further to the knowledge of Southern Uganda, and covered in addition a strip of country extending from Kilimanjaro to the southern end of Lake Rudolf.

After considerable delay the British Government established a protectorate over Uganda in 1894, but it was some years before the country was brought under control. Among the officers engaged in the subjugation of Uganda and the Upper Nile country was Seymour Vandeleur, who carried out valuable surveys in the region east and north of Lake Albert and between Lake Victoria and the Rift Valley. These surveys, made between 1894 and 1896, supplied a reasonably accurate basis for the detailed mapping of Uganda. To this work must be added that of MacDonald's party, in 1896–97, which corrected the position of Lake Kioga and mapped its outline, and surveyed a large area to the north of Lake Victoria, and also that of Hobart, who surveyed parts of South-western Uganda in 1897–98.

Meanwhile the boundary between Kenya and Tanganyika Territory was being surveyed. Work on the first section, from the coast to a point to the south-east of Kilimanjaro, was completed in 1892; the remaining section, from the mountain to Lake Victoria, was surveyed by Colonel G. E. Smith in 1905, while to the west of Lake Victoria the task was carried out between 1902 and 1904. Among other pieces of detailed work undertaken during this period were Dècle's surveys west of Lake Victoria, between the Upper Kagera and the lake, in 1900; the Uganda-Congo State boundary, the work on which was finished in 1908; and the explorations of Archer, in 1909–12, in the north of Kenya and to the south-west of Lake Rudolf.

There remain for notice three general expeditions which are not directly connected with any of the developments outlined above, but which made important additions to the map. The romantic figure of Emin Pasha has already been mentioned. After his arrival at the east coast he joined forces with Stuhlmann, and the two men plunged again into the heart of the continent on an exploit which was not wholly geographical in aim. They crossed Tanganyika Territory, and reached the region west of Lake Albert. Here Stuhlmann turned back, but Emin determined to proceed to the west coast, and lost his life just before reaching the Congo. Stuhlmann, whose powers of observation and description were of a high order,

[1] See Lord Lugard, *The Rise of our East African Empire* (2 vols., 1893).

351

produced a work which threw much light on a little-known part of Africa.[1]

In 1894 Count von Götzen crossed Africa from Tanganyika Territory to the mouth of the Congo. He discovered Lake Kivu, and was able to add considerably to the knowledge of the regions between Lake Edward and Lake Tanganyika.

In 1906 the Duke of the Abruzzi climbed Ruwenzori, and his party mapped much of the range hitherto unvisited. With this expedition the history of discovery in Central Africa may be closed.

X. NORTH-EAST AFRICA AFTER 1889

North-east Africa was in many parts almost entirely unknown in 1889. But in the last thirty years a large number of journeys have been made in the country, and while all the blanks have not been removed from the map its main features have been established.

In 1891 several important Italian expeditions were made to Somaliland. Captain Baudi di Vesme went inland from Berbera, and reached the upper course of the Webbe river, but his surveys were confiscated, and the results of his work were thus lost. Robecchi traversed the northern part of the Somali peninsula. Starting from Mogdishu, he reached the country already visited by James and Aylmer in 1885. In the same year Dundas navigated the Juba river for 400 miles.

Further investigations into the Juba river were made in 1892–93 by Bottego. He had already explored part of Eritrea, and now visited the Somali-Galla country, and was the first to throw light on the hydrography of the region. He returned to the middle course of the Juba in 1895, and then went westward to Lake Rudolf, subsequently making the journey to the coast again at Mombasa. Bottego settled the course of the Omo river, which he showed was identical with the Niam-niam of other explorers, examined the western shore of Lake Rudolf, and defined the general features of the Sobat. He also discovered a new lake, to which he gave the name Regina Margherita.

Bottego's work was supplemented by that of Cavendish, who set out from Berbera in 1897, reached the Juba river, and then turned westward to Lake Rudolf. He was able to collect much useful information about the country between the lake and the White Nile before he too made his way to Mombasa. Both travellers added to the knowledge of Northern Kenya : in addition this latter region was examined in 1892–93 by Chanler and Von Höhnel, the companion of Teleki on his earlier journey to Lake Rudolf.

In 1894–95 Donaldson Smith, also from Berbera, reached Lake Rudolf, and tried to connect the work carried out by Teleki with

[1] *Mit Emin Pascha ins Herz von Afrika* (1894).

that of other explorers farther north. Donaldson Smith returned in 1899, again crossed from Berbera to Lake Rudolf, and went on to the Nile, which he reached at Fort Berkeley in March 1900.

In 1897 a number of explorers started from Berbera toward the interior. Darragon reached the Galla country south of Shoa, already visited by Donaldson Smith, and Count von Wickenburg penetrated into Northern Somaliland : in the north-east of Somaliland Parkinson and Brander-Dunbar in 1896, and Aylmer in 1897, were able to add a few details to the map.

Thus a great many travellers were attacking the unknown region from the east. Their work was now supplemented by others from the north or west. In 1897–98 Bonchamps, who was co-operating with Marchand, whose remarkable trans-African journey startled the political world,[1] reached the head of the Sobat river in the Nuer country, and then returned to Addis Abeba. He accurately determined the greater part of the Upper Sobat between latitude 6° and 10° N. and longitude 33° and 36° E. Shortly afterward British officers extended this work by surveys on the frontier of Abyssinia. In the winters of the years 1899–1901 Gwynn and Austin were engaged in this task ; the latter travelled from the Uganda Railway, by the Rift Valley, to Lake Rudolf, and from the lake north-westward to the Sobat and the Nile ; and both officers contributed valuable surveys of the country between the Blue Nile and the Sobat. Count von Wickenburg also approached from the north in 1901, traversing the country between Addis Abeba and Lake Stefanie, and reaching the Lorian Swamp, which he found to be nearly dry. He then went on to the Tana river, and arrived on the coast at Lamu. Lake Stefanie was also reached by Harrison and others, whose expedition from Zeila was made in 1899–1900.

Lake Stefanie was reached a third time, during the expedition of Butter and Maud in 1902–3. They started from Jibuti, and journeyed through Addis Abeba. Passing to the west of Lake Stefanie, they arrived at Lake Rudolf, travelled along its eastern side, and made their way southward to Lake Baringo, in the Rift Valley. They were able to make a large number of astronomical observations and to carry out valuable surveys.

In 1899–1900 Wellby, who had already distinguished himself as an Asiatic explorer, approached Lake Rudolf by the Omo river, and subsequently investigated part of the course of the Sobat, while in 1898 Major Austin surveyed the west shore of Lake Rudolf.

At the beginning of the present century Baron Erlanger crossed from Zeila to Harar, went south-westward into the Galla country, and finally reached the Sobat. Although his main object was zoological research, he was able, through his route survey, to add to the map of this region.

[1] See below, p. 357.

Between 1901 and 1903 the expedition of Vicomte R. du Bourg de Bozas examined the country between Harar and the northern end of Lake Rudolf and between the lake and the Nile at Nimule; the Somaliland expedition of 1903 resulted in the survey, by Captain Beazeley, of about 15,000 square miles of British Somaliland; while the expedition of B. H. Jessen in 1904 produced a survey, based on a compass traverse only, of part of the valley of the Upper Sobat and the south-west of Abyssinia. The accidental occurrence of these three expeditions in widely scattered regions of the north-east in a single year is characteristic of the exploration of this area during the last thirty years.

Among the remaining expeditions in the north-east mention must be made of four. In 1905 H. Weld Blundell surveyed the Blue Nile, from Addis Abeba to about the longitude of 35° E., thereby continuing a work he had begun in 1899. In 1908 Major Gwynn delimited the southern frontier of Abyssinia. In the south of that country, and in the region west of the Kaffa district, Montandon was able to collect new information in 1910. Two years later the problem of the Lorian Swamp was investigated by Dracopoli. He found that in wet seasons water flows out of the swamp to the Indian Ocean.

XI. The Guinea Lands after 1889

The main features of the lands round the Gulf of Guinea were known before 1889, and here, in contrast with North-east Africa, there was very little pioneer work to be done. This section, however, will cover an area beyond the strict geographical region of the Guinea lands, and will include the exploration of the Nile-Congo divide, so far as it originated from the Gulf of Guinea. It will be convenient to deal with the subject first as far as it relates to Nigeria and the lands to the west, then with the Cameroons, and finally with the Nile-Congo problem.

The establishment of British influence in what is now Nigeria followed, in many respects, a course similar to that already referred to in Uganda. Here was a trading company anxious to secure its trading privileges, and here too the British Government was slow to accept responsibility. The initial work of Thomson did much to secure the region for Great Britain, and the succeeding enterprise of Sir George Goldie made success permanent. The result was that at the beginning of this period, when Mizon sailed up the Niger to secure the hinterland for France, he met with failure. At the same time, in 1890, MacDonald and Mockler-Ferryman began the work of surveying the Niger and many of its tributaries, while Gallwey in the following year performed a similar task on the Benue as far as its source.

354

AFRICA

In 1892 Binger added to his fame as a great explorer by covering a large and little-known region in the hinterland. His main objects were to determine the boundary-line between the Gold Coast and the Ivory Coast, and to explore the Southern Sudan between Bonduku and Kong. In all he travelled over 1200 miles, about a quarter of which was through new country. His work was of a very high order, and, taken with his earlier exploit, must entitle him to rank among Africa's great explorers. He was fortunate, too, in his successor, for P. L. Monteil was able, in 1892, to supplement Binger's work in important respects. He started from Senegal, crossed the bend of the Niger to Say, travelled on through Sokoto and Bornu to Lake Chad, and then went over the Sahara to Tripoli. It was a valuable piece of work, and marks the beginning of intensive activities by many able French officers in that great area which is now part of the colonial empire of France.

In 1893 Fowler carried out surveys between Lagos and the Niger, while in 1896 Hourst made a remarkable voyage down the Niger from Kabara, the port of Timbuktu, to the sea. He was able to supplement the work of another Frenchman, Toutée, who had attempted a similar journey in 1895.

Meanwhile Colonel Trotter in 1896 marked out the Sierra Leone boundary and determined the position of the Niger sources. Thus from three directions accurate geographical work was converging on the river. Within its great bend German explorers had been active in their own colony of Togoland, and by 1896 were able to produce a good general map of the south of the country; it was extended to the north three years later.

In Nigeria great progress was made in the knowledge of the country after its transfer to the Crown in 1899 and the arrival of F. (later Lord) Lugard as High Commissioner of Northern Nigeria in the following year. The Anglo-French Niger and Chad Boundary Commission in 1902–3 fixed the northern boundary, parts of which had been surveyed a year or two earlier. Afterward Captain Tilho carried out very valuable work in the region of Lake Chad, more especially in the country to the east of the lake. In 1904 Lenfant ascended the Benue and the channel connecting it with the Shari river, thus proving that at some times of the year it was possible to reach Lake Chad from the ocean. Subsequent exploration, however, showed that this discovery was of little practical importance.

The same year (1904) was notable for Boyd Alexander's expedition across Africa from the Niger to the Nile. He used boats for the journey, and only had to carry them for fourteen days. His surveys added to the knowledge of Northern Nigeria and the Lake Chad region, and he showed that Lake Chad itself was not one continuous piece of water, but two larger lakes joined by a series of very small lakes. Unfortunately, his party suffered heavy casualties in

European lives, and the surveys of the later part of the journey were not therefore so thorough, but his route beyond Lake Chad by the Shari, Welle, Yei, Bahr-el-Jebel, and Nile did not afford much scope for discovery.

In Southern Nigeria Steel and others carried out much survey work, between 1904 and 1907, to the north of the latitude of 5° 30′, between the Niger and the Cross rivers. To the south of that parallel the country had been examined rather superficially between 1892 and 1895, and more thoroughly after the last date. On the east the Nigeria-Cameroons boundary surveys between Yola and the Cross river were completed by the year 1909 ; between Yola and Lake Chad the boundary had been surveyed in 1903. With the reorganization of the Southern Nigerian surveys in 1910 the exploration of the country may be said to have ended.

Farther toward the west much progress was made during the first ten years of the present century. The Dahomey-Togoland boundary was delimited in the period 1898–1900 ; the surveys for that between Togoland and the Gold Coast were begun in 1902 ; and the Anglo-Liberian boundary was delimited in 1903. The Franco-Liberian boundary surveys were completed by 1909, while by the same year the surveys of Parkinson, Owen, and others in the interior of Liberia had removed many blank spaces from the map. The Gold Coast Survey began its operations in 1901 ; and the French in the Ivory Coast have since that date completed the geographical investigation of their own colony. Thus, with the exception of some parts of Liberia, the whole of the country from Nigeria to the Gambia can now be described as well known.

To the east of Nigeria German explorers have similarly removed the blanks from the map of the Cameroons. In 1889 Zintgraff crossed the country from the coastal station of Duala to the Benue river. The next year Morgen covered the region between the mouth of the Sanaga river and the inland station of Jaunde, and in 1891–92 crossed northward to Banjo, traversed the mountainous regions, and reached the Benue at Ibi. Other explorers, following much the same lines of approach, reached Ngambe in 1893, in which year Passarge began his geological investigations of the country south of Yola. At this time also (1891–93) Mizon, who had failed on the Niger, was crossing the Cameroons from the Benue to the Sangha, a tributary of the Congo.

After a pause between 1894 and 1898 Carnap pushed into the north-east, and reached the Congo by the Sangha river. The opening up of North-west and South-east Cameroons soon followed, some of the geographical exploration being the direct result of the many military expeditions which the Germans were obliged to send into parts of the country. Among the explorers mention must be made of Baron von Stein, who during the period 1895–1907 did much to improve the knowledge of the southern parts of the colony. German explorers were still actively engaged in the more remote parts of the Cameroons in 1914.

The filling in of the blanks in the Benue-Shari-Congo-Nile region was a lengthy process, and directly contributed toward a better knowledge of the eastern parts of the Cameroons. The journey of Mizon already mentioned begins the exploration in this last period : some of its aspects have also been referred to in connexion with the work of explorers in Central Africa. It was from the Congo side that Hanolet, in 1895, penetrated to about latitude 9° N. in his efforts to explore the Shari basin. The next year Gentil went up the Ubangi to its most northerly bend, followed the Tomi to the limit of navigation, and eventually arrived on the Shari. He surveyed the river, traced it to Lake Chad, and sailed on the lake.

In 1898 Marchand made his famous journey from the Congo to the Nile. He went up the Welle and reached Fashoda. Unable to remain there, he continued to move eastward, and, using in part the Sobat river, finally reached the Gulf of Aden. His exploit has received much attention because of its political importance, but it was also instrumental in adding considerably to geographical knowledge.

In 1902 Colonel Destenave completed the first accurate survey of Lake Chad and the Lower Shari ; in the same year Chevalier reached the sources of the Shari and penetrated to an almost unknown region to the south-west of Darfur and Captain Loefler explored the Logone, a tributary of the Shari, from the south-west. Shortly after this Lenfant sailed from the Benue to the Shari, and Boyd Alexander crossed from the Niger to the Nile. Both expeditions added to the knowledge of this region now under consideration. Lenfant returned in 1907 to the southern part of the Shari basin and continued his valuable geographical work. Boyd Alexander began his last journey in 1910, when he attempted to cross the continent from the Cameroons to Khartum, but he succeeded only in reaching a point near the Wadai-Darfur boundary, where he was murdered.

While much exploration was thus taking place from the west and south-west British officers in the Sudan were busily pushing into the unknown region from the east. The successful clearing of a channel through the sudd region by Peake in 1900 conveniently marks the beginning of a new movement. Even before that year the officers of the Anglo-Egyptian Sudan had been crossing the country south of the Bahr-el-Arab with their survey routes, and that process went on unceasingly. One of the latest journeys in this region, that of Major Christy in 1916, was productive of much useful information.[1]

[1] For the activities of British officers in this region see the useful map in *G.J.*, vol. xxx, p. 527.

XII. The Sahara after 1889

The last of the regions of Africa to be fully explored is, as might be expected, the desert region of the Sahara. It had been crossed several times in the nineteenth century, but by regular routes, and the last period of exploration had closed with the failure of the French to conquer its western borders. During the ten years following 1889 the desert was conquered, and since the present century began many of its unknown regions have been explored.

The task of exploration has been carried out almost entirely by the French, who were anxious to repair the disasters which had befallen Flatters, and who were given a free hand when, in 1890, the political agreement with Great Britain placed the whole of the Western Sahara within their sphere of influence. Moreover, they were naturally anxious to consolidate their possessions in North Africa, and this political aim was stimulated by the bequest, in 1897, of a large sum of money " pour favoriser les missions qui, à l'intérieur de l'Afrique, peuvent contribuer à faire un tout homogène de nos possessions actuelles de l'Algérie, du Soudan, et du Congo." This date conveniently divides the conquest of the Sahara into two periods. Before 1897 the work was in the nature of a reconnaissance: after 1897 it was a triumph.

During the first period no spectacular discoveries were made. G. Méry pushed outward from Algeria, and reached Temassinin in 1892, and two years later B. d'Attanoux went beyond that point to the edge of the oasis country. Meanwhile F. Foureau had been trying repeatedly to penetrate the desert. Beginning in 1890 with an advance toward In Salah, he succeeded in reaching the foot of the Tademait plateau. In 1893 he made three journeys, with Temassinin as the central point. The next year he approached In Salah from the north-east, and in 1895 penetrated to the east of Temassinin ; in 1897 he went to the south of that post. All this work was apparently unsuccessful, but it proved of the greatest value in making less difficult the subsequent journey of himself and Lamy in 1898.

To the Foureau-Lamy mission of 1898–1900 is due the conquest of the Sahara. They followed a line almost due south from Biskra, through Ain Taiba, Temassinin, Agades, to Sinder, and thence to Lake Chad, where they joined forces with Meynier from the Niger and Gentil from the Congo. It was a remarkable achievement of human endurance, and at the same time produced most valuable results. Geographical, geological, and biological observations were made by Foureau, and although he considered them to be so disconnected as to render any broad generalizations unsound, yet they furnished the basis of modern studies on the whole region from Algeria to Lake Chad. Foureau continued his journey across Africa to the mouth of the Congo, whence he returned by sea.[1] Subsequent progress in the Sahara in part depended on the military conquest of the region and in part anticipated the work of the soldiers. But in and after the year 1900 it was steady and continuous. It is only necessary here to single out for mention a few of the more distinguished exploits of the many French officers to whose efforts is due the present knowledge of the western portion of the desert.

In 1902 Cottenest marched against the Tuareg, making an important journey from In Salah to Ideles, in Ahaggar, and Guilo-Lohain, in the same year, penetrated into the heart of that region. In the next year Laperrine set out from Tuat and reached In Sise, to the west of Ahaggar, while in 1904 Laperrine from the north and Theveniaut from Timbuktu met in Adrar. In 1905 Gautier crossed the Sahara from Tuat to the Niger and Flye Sainte-Marie began the exploration of the desert to the west of Tuat. The Sahara was again crossed in 1906 by Captain Arnaud, who was accompanied for part of the way by Lieutenant Cortier and who was met by detachments from the Sudan. Cortier remained in Adrar while Arnaud proceeded to Gao, on the Niger, whence he reached the coast of Dahomey. In all he covered over 3000 miles, of which 750 were over new ground.

In 1906 Vischer also crossed the desert from Tripoli to Northern Nigeria, being the first Englishman of modern times to accomplish the journey.

Cortier and Niéger carried out important surveys in the north and central parts of the Sahara in 1909, including the Tazili plateau, Ahaggar, and Aïr. A large amount of new country was explored, and the first reasonably complete map of Aïr was produced in 1910.

From 1913 onward two most important explorations were in progress. Captain Augiéras began a series of journeys to the south-west of Tuat, thereby extending the earlier work of Flye Sainte-Marie. He crowned this work by the highly successful journey of 1920. Setting out from Algeria, he met Major Lauzanne, who had come from Mauritania, at El Mazereb, in the centre of the unknown Western Sahara, and then continued his journey to Dakar. He thus succeeded in crossing the desert from the north-east to the south-west and exploring one of the least known of its regions.

Meanwhile another French officer, Commandant Tilho, whose work round Lake Chad has already been noticed, was removing a great blank farther to the eastward. He was appointed to the command of Kanem in 1912, and carried out successful military operations against the Senussi of Tibesti. Subsequently he explored much of Borku, Ennedi, and the uplands of Tibesti, and in 1917

[1] For a brief account see *G.J.*, vol. xvii, p. 135. The official report was published under the title of *Documents scientifiques de la Mission Saharienne* (three volumes of text and one of maps, 1902–5).

359

returned home through Wadai and Darfur. It was a most successful piece of work, marked throughout by the accurate determination of a large number of positions, and produced very valuable results, which are given in the words of the explorer:

> The great geographical problem of the ancient fluvial communication between the basins of the Chad and the Nile is definitely solved; the mountainous barrier encircles the basin of the Chad from the Toummo Mountains on the north to the Djebel Marra on the south-east, passing through the massif of Tibesti, the plateau of Jef-Jef, the tablelands of Erdi and Ennedi, the hills of Zagawa, and the mountains of Western Dar Four. . . . The lowest altitudes of the Chad basin are found in the plains of the low-lying region situated to the north-east of Lake Chad. . . . A third important result has been to reveal the geographical form of important mountain masses like Tibesti and Ennedi, hitherto shown in a very imperfect fashion on the maps of Africa, and the existence of another important massif called that of Erdi, connecting the two above mentioned. Moreover, the information we received permits us to reveal to geographers the existence in the centre of the Libyan Desert of yet another mountain mass, the Djebel el Aouinat, situated about 150 miles south-east of the oasis of Koufra.

After recounting the corrections in longitude and in altitude that he was able to make, and referring to the geological results, Tilho concludes:

> The establishment of the geographical *liaison* between the Niger, the Chad, and the Nile, by a chain of astronomical positions determined with very satisfactory exactitude, constitutes a result all the more interesting in that it will permit the drawing up of four sheets of the international map of the world, thanks to the 10,000 kilometres of surveys traced by my collaborators and myself during this long expedition.[1]

In concluding the story of the western half of the Sahara mention should be made of the explorations of Mr R. Rodd, in 1922 and in 1927, in Aïr and Damergu. A number of positions were fixed, considerable additions to the detail of the map were made, and important anthropological investigations were carried out during these two expeditions, which represent, both in their intensive study of a small area and in their excellent organization, the kind of geographical exploration which is typical of the age when the great discoveries have all been made.

In the eastern part of the Sahara exploration has been entirely unconnected with that of the west. The officers of the Geological Survey of Egypt, since its establishment in 1896, have made valuable additions to knowledge. W. J. Harding King penetrated the Libyan Desert in 1909 and 1911, in a region to the north-west of Halfa: to the east of the Nile the officers of the Geological Survey carried out

[1] *G.J.*, vol. lvi, pp. 257–259.

a series of explorations, between the latitudes of 22° and 25° N., in 1904 and the following years. Farther northward Dr W. F. Hume and Dr J. Ball have added greatly to the knowledge of the deserts of Egypt, more particularly from the point of view of their physical geography.[1] These official surveys were supplemented by the reconnaissances of British officers engaged during the Great War on the western frontier of Egypt and by the expeditions of Prince Kemal el Din Hussein to the west and south-west of Halfa : these latter journeys, made with motor-cars, have added greatly to the knowledge of the inaccessible parts of the desert, and have extended almost as far as the country reached by Tilho from Lake Chad.

The striking journey of Mrs Rosita Forbes and A. M. Hassanein Bey from the coast of Cyrenaica to the Kufra oasis was more remarkable for its success and its daring than for the scientific results, although the travellers were able to cross some unknown country both on their journey to Kufra and on their return through Jaghbub and Siwa to Alexandria. " We brought back merely the notes for a simple compass traverse of the route," wrote Hassanein Bey.

Hassanein Bey was not satisfied, and determined to make a second journey beyond Kufra to the Sudan, and this he accomplished in 1923.[2] He set out from Sollum on January 2, and travelled by Siwa and Jaghbub to Kufra. Thence he proceeded first south-eastward to the Egyptian boundary (which he crossed roughly on the meridian of 25° E. longitude) and then south-westward to French territory, through which he passed to Darfur, reaching Furawiya, a little beyond the Wadai-Darfur boundary, on July 2. Continuing thence through El Fasher, he struck the railway at El Obeid, and arrived in Cairo on August 1. The journey was one of first-class importance, and produced results of the greatest value. Not only did it cover much unknown country, but it linked up, for the first time, known regions in the north with the Sudan and formed a most valuable supplementary exploration to that of Tilho : it has in turn been supplemented by the work of Prince Kemal el Din Hussein, Major R. A. Bagnold, and Mr W. B. Kennedy Shaw.[3] It is characteristic of the most recent phase of exploration that this remote region should have been reached three times within a period of about ten years, and that each journey should have covered new ground. The result has been to remove one of the largest blanks from the map, and if large areas of the Sahara remain unexplored, it is doubtful if any more discoveries of first magnitude will be made.

[1] See J. Ball, " Problems of the Libyan Desert," in *G.J.*, vol. lxx, p. 21, and W. F. Hume, " The Egyptian Wilderness," in *G.J.*, vol. lviii, p. 249.
[2] See *G.J.*, vol. lxiv, pp. 273, 353, 367, 386, and 388, for an account of the journey and the geographical results.
[3] See Major R. A. Bagnold, "Journeys in the Libyan Desert, 1929 and 1930," in *G.J.*, vol. lxxviii, p. 13, and " A Further Journey through the Libyan Desert," in *G.J.*, vol. lxxxii, p. 103 ; and W. B. Kennedy Shaw, " An Expedition in the Southern Libyan Desert," in *G.J.*, vol. lxxxvii, p. 193.

XIII. MADAGASCAR [1]

Although Madagascar was visited many times during the seventeenth and eighteenth centuries, and was the subject of a number of romantic stories, very little was known about its geography. The first geographical description of any value was that of M. de Flacourt, which was published in 1658. In the eighteenth century

> the most important travels in the interior were those of one Mayeur, interpreter at the French establishments, who between 1774 and 1785 traversed the northern part of the island to the Sakalava country, visited the northern extremity, and made two journeys to the Hova province of Merina. His accounts were not entirely superseded until the end of the nineteenth century.[2]

During the nineteenth century very little progress was made before the year 1865. The coasts were surveyed, and narrow strips of the interior were examined, by Captain W. F. Owen in 1832, while missionaries on the east coast gathered together some fragmentary knowledge of the interior. In 1865, however, A. Grandidier visited Madagascar, and in the course of several journeys made during the next five years gathered a more accurate knowledge of the island than any of his predecessors, and for the first time produced a correct account of its major features. His work was supplemented in detail by Catholic and Protestant missionaries. Among the latter were Mullens, who visited Central Madagascar shortly after Grandidier's journeys; Shaw, who penetrated into the south-east in 1874 and 1875; Sibree, who also reached unknown country in the south-east in 1876; and Sewell, who travelled westward from Antananarivo in 1875. The Catholic missionaries Rollet and Colin carried out important scientific work in Imèrina province in 1873 and subsequent years, and produced a good map of the country, while a number of isolated expeditions added details along the east coast.

Political complications led to the active intervention of the French, and at the conclusion of the war in 1886 France assumed a protectorate over the island. During the struggle and after its close,

[1] On Madagascar see the following works :

A. GRANDIDIER, *Histoire de la géographie de Madagascar* (2nd edition, 1892).

E. DE MARTONNE, " La Cartographie de Madagascar," in *Annales de géographie*, vol. xix (1910), pp. 49–69.

J. MULLENS, " Recent Journeys in Madagascar," in *Proc. R.G.S.*, old series, vol. xxi, pp. 155–175.

J. SIBREE, " History and Present Condition of our Geographical Knowledge of Madagascar," in *Proc. R.G.S.*, new series, vol. i, pp. 646–665, and " Imèrina, the Central Province of Madagascar," in *Proc. R.G.S.*, new series, vol. xiv, pp. 737–753.

[2] E. Heawood, *The History of Geographical Discovery in the Seventeenth and Eighteenth Centuries*, p. 415.

up to the year 1895, considerable progress was made in the know-ledge of the island. In 1889 L. Catat and C. Maistre crossed from Tamatave to the north-west coast at Majunga, and then, returning to Imèrina, travelled to Fort Dauphin in the extreme south-east. To this period also belongs the work of H. Gautier, who produced an account of the physical geography of Madagascar based on his own travels in 1892 and subsequent years and on the earlier work of others already mentioned.

The attempt to bolster up native rule was not a success, and in 1895 the French were compelled to undertake the conquest of the island. In the following year Madagascar became a French colony. This had important results, for not only was General Galliéni sent out to administer the new territory and to initiate a period of great prosperity, but also Commandant Verrier and his brother-officers of the Service Géographique de l'Armée began the systematic exploration of the country. Among the outstanding contributions to knowledge was the journey of G. Grandidier (1898–1902), whose work in the south and west not only supplemented that of his distinguished father, but also served to open up country which was almost unknown.

When the officers of the Service Géographique de l'Armée began their work Madagascar was, for all practical purposes, unexplored. Even in 1899 Galliéni reported that three-quarters of the island was to be classed as unknown. This is no longer true : a large part of the west has been surveyed in detail, and the whole of the island has been explored.

CHAPTER XV

AMERICA

I. CANADA [1]

THE exploration of Western Canada, which had received such impetus from the arrival of the free traders after 1763, went on with undiminished vigour during the first quarter of the nineteenth century. In particular it owes much to four men, Peter Fidler, D. W. Harmon, Simon Fraser, and David Thompson.

Fidler succeeded Turner as official surveyor to the Hudson's Bay Company in 1792, but appears to have actively assisted Turner in the previous year. His journals are now lost, but some idea of his explorations can be gathered from the records of maps. It is known that he explored a route from Fort George, on the North Saskatchewan, to the Little Bow river, near the Rocky Mountains; at least that part of the South Saskatchewan from its junction with the Red Deer River to a point about 120 miles above the Forks, and perhaps the whole river; and the North Saskatchewan, the Athabaska, and the Peace rivers.

> There can be no reasonable doubt that Fidler was the first white man to explore the Churchill from Frog Portage to the Bay. He is equally entitled to the credit of exploring Seal River from its mouth to the height of land leading to South Indian Lake on the Churchill, as well as Etawney Lake and the river which drains its waters into Hudson Bay.[2]

A great area lying between Lake Athabaska and Hudson Bay was covered by the surveys of this able man, who continued working up to the year 1821. Much of the information found its way into the maps of Arrowsmith and Taylor.

Harmon was a very different man. He spent the greater part of nineteen years moving about the country west of Lake Winnipeg, and " his journeys covered nearly every section of what is now Western Canada, from Lake Superior to Northern British Columbia, and from the International Boundary north to Great Slave Lake." [3] As a servant of the North-west Company Harmon spent a number of years in the Upper Assiniboine and Swan river districts, and wandered extensively over the western plains. After 1807, as an independent trader, he visited the Peace river, crossed the Rockies,

---

[1] On this section see L. J. Burpee, *The Search for the Western Sea* (1908).
[2] Burpee, *op. cit.*, pp. 184–185. [3] *Ibid.*, p. 485.

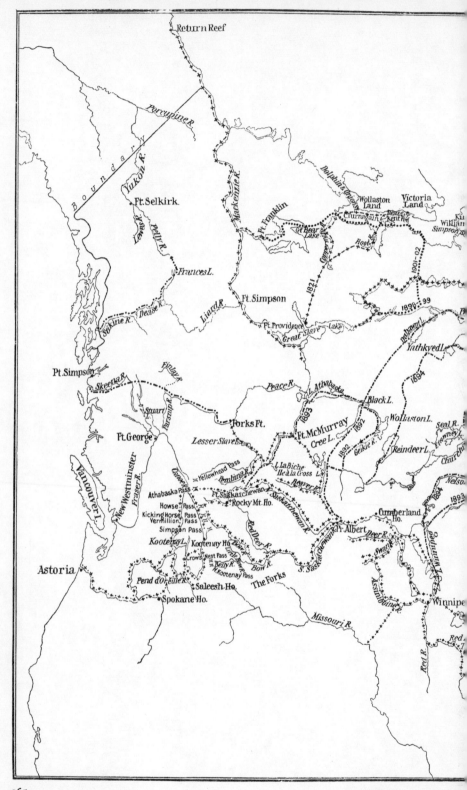

Return Reef

Porcupine R.

Boundary

Yukon R.

Ft. Selkirk

Lewes R.

Pelly R.

Mackenzie R.

Ft. Franklin

Dolphin & Union

Wollaston Land

Victoria Land

Gt. Bear Lake

Coppermine R.

Chantry In. Kent Ra.

1901-02

King William Simpson

Hood R.

Frances L.

1821

Liard R.

Ft. Simpson

1898-99

Ft. Providence

Great Slave Lake

Dubawnt L.

Yathkyed L.

Stikine R.

Dease R.

Finlay R.

1894

Pt. Simpson

Skeena R.

Parsnip R.

Peace R.

L. Athabaska

Black L.

Wollaston L.

Seal R.

Stuart L.

Forks Ft.

1893

Ft. McMurray

Cree L.

1892

Geikie R.

Reindeer L.

Churchill R.

Ft. George

Lesser Slave L.

1892

Nelson R.

Vancouver I.

Fraser R.

New Westminster

Canoe R.

Yellowhead Pass

Pembina R.

L. LaBiche
Ile à la Cross L.

Beaver R.

Athabaska Pass

Ft. Saskatchewan

Saskatchewan R.

Cumberland Ho.

1893

Deer R.

Columbia R.

Howse Pass

Rocky Mt. Ho.

Kicking Horse Pass
Vermillion Pass

Simpson Pass

Red Deer R.

N. Saskatchewan R.

Pr. Albert

Swan R.

Astoria

Kootenay L.

Kootenay Ho.

Columbia R.

Bow R.

S. Saskatchewan R.

Assiniboine R.

Crows Nest Pass

Red Deer R.

Pelly R.

Kootenay Pass

The Forks

Winnipeg

Pend d'Oreille R.

Saleesh Ho.

Spokane Ho.

Missouri R.

Red R.

Red R.

365

Fig. 39. Canada after 1800

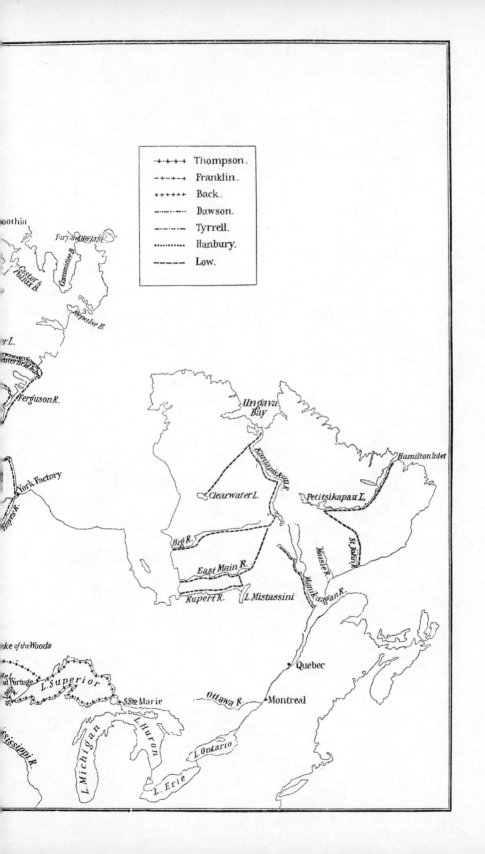

Thompson.
Franklin.
Back.
Dawson.
Tyrrell.
Hanbury.
Low.

and collected much general information both of the country and of its inhabitants. His map, which was based on that of Mackenzie, shows many important additions and corrections, and in spite of some obvious mistakes, was probably at the time it was published (1820) " the most complete and accurate map of the northern half of the continent." [1]

The main work of Simon Fraser has been perpetuated in the name of one of the best-known rivers of North America. Like Harmon, he was a servant of the North-west Company. His most important work as an explorer was begun in 1805, when he established a small post on McLeod Lake, a part of the Parsnip river. In the following year, with the help of John Stuart, he discovered a number of lakes and streams which emptied themselves into the Fraser, inlcuding Fraser Lake, the Nechako river, Stuart river, and the lake of the same name. In 1807 he established Fort George, at the junction of the Nechako and the Fraser, and from this post he set out to trace the course of the main stream, which he and others still believed was the Columbia. In spite of great difficulties he successfully followed the Fraser to a point near to the modern town of New Westminster. He found that his latitude was 49° N., and so was convinced that this was not the mouth of the Columbia. Greatly disappointed because of his supposed failure, and because he had not seen the sea, Fraser returned to the north. His discovery was relatively useless, but was the result of a journey which for the courage and enterprise of its leader must rank very high in the annals of exploration.

The work of David Thompson touched at many points that of Fidler, Harmon, and Fraser, and was undoubtedly of greater importance. Indeed, Thompson's journeys are so extensive, and his surveys of such high order, that parts of his maps have not yet been replaced. He entered the service of the Hudson's Bay Company in 1785, and in the winter of 1789–90 signalized the beginning of his work as a surveyor by determining the exact position of Cumberland House. In 1790 he surveyed the Saskatchewan river to its mouth, and thence proceeded by the regular route to Hayes river and Hudson Bay. The Nelson river and parts of the Churchill were surveyed in 1792 and 1793, and during the remainder of his service with the Hudson's Bay Company he devoted much attention to the country between Cumberland House and York Factory, opening up a number of new routes.

In 1797 Thompson joined the North-west Company, and it was in their employ that he made his most extensive travels. His first journey in their service was remarkable for the extent of ground covered. He left Cumberland House on June 27 for Grand Portage, at the western end of Lake Superior, which was reached

[1] Burpee, *op. cit.*, p. 486.

about a month later. Setting out from Grand Portage again on August 9, he went back to Lake Winnipeg, crossed it and Lake Manitoba to Lake Winnipegosis, and rode up the Swan river valley. He next surveyed the Assiniboine and Red Deer rivers to their sources, and on November 28 set out for the Missouri. On the last day of December he reached "the principal village of the Mandans," and remarks of the journey: "We have taken thirty-three days to perform a journey of ten days in good weather, but this has given me the opportunity of determining the latitude of six different places; and the longitude of three, on the Road to the River. The distance we have gone over is 238 miles."[1] The return journey to the Assiniboine took from January 10 to January 24, after which, says Thompson, "my time for full three weeks was employed in calculating the astronomical observations made to and from the Missouri river; and making a map of my survey, which with my journal, was sealed up and directed to the Agents of the North-west Company."[2] By February 26 he was ready to continue his explorations. He followed the Assiniboine to its mouth, and turned up the Red River to a trading-post which was found to lie in latitude 48° 58' 24" N. "This house," wrote Thompson, "is therefore . . . in the United States. . . . I pointed out the Boundary Line to which they must remove; and which line, several years after, was confirmed by Major Long." A little higher up the valley, actually on the banks of Red Lake river, Thompson found the North-west Company's trading-post, and spent a short time there. The spring thaw made travelling with dogs impracticable, and the melting ice in the rivers caused delay, but at length, after an unpleasant journey of nineteen days, he reached Turtle Lake, which he believed to be the source of the Mississippi. Actually the river rises in Itaska Lake, a little to the south of Turtle Lake. Of the future of the valley he made an interesting prophecy:

> Whatever the Nile has been in ancient times in Arts and Arms, the noble valley of the Mississippi bids fair to be, and excluding its pompous, useless Pyramids and other works; its Anglo-Saxon population will far exceed the Egyptians in all the arts of civilized life, and in a pure religion. Although these are the predictions of a solitary traveller unknown to the world they will surely be verified.[3]

Thompson went down the Mississippi for a short distance, turned eastward to the St Louis river, and reached Lake Superior. He surveyed its southern shore as far as Sault Ste Marie, and then

---

[1] J. B. Tyrrell, *David Thompson's Narrative of his Explorations in Western America* (1916), pp. 223–224. This edition of Thompson's *Narrative* is the main authority for the work of the explorer and has been freely used. There is a short but useful life of Thompson in the "Canadian Men of Action" series, by C. N. Cochrane (1924).

[2] *Ibid.*, pp. 241–242.   [3] *Ibid.*, p. 280.

returned to Grand Portage, where he arrived on June 7, 1798, almost a year after he had left Cumberland House. He set off again on July 14, went up to Ile à la Cross Lake, and from that point surveyed the Beaver river as far as Lake La Biche, where he spent the winter.

The year 1799 was devoted to extensive exploration still farther to the west. Thompson visited Fort Saskatchewan, on the North Saskatchewan river, and then went to the north-west and struck the Pembina river. He followed the waterway to the Lesser Slave Lake, which he surveyed. Returning by the Athabaska river to Fort McMurray, he reached Ile à la Cross Lake, and thence, by the usual route, made his way to Grand Portage. He went back to the Saskatchewan, and passed the winter at Fort George.

The year 1800 was spent mainly in surveying the country round the headwaters of the two branches of the Saskatchewan and the Bow river. Thompson was assisted by Duncan McGillivray, whose explorations of the North Saskatchewan he incorporated in his map. In 1801 and the two following years Thompson's journeys were less extensive. He again spent much time near the headwaters of the Saskatchewan. In 1802 he surveyed a route from the Lesser Slave Lake to the Peace river, and here, at Mackenzie's old Forks Fort, he passed the greater part of the next year.

Thompson's most important work during the years 1804 and 1805 was a general exploration of what he called the " Muskrat Country " lying to the north-east of Cumberland House. Parts of this region have never since been visited, and when J. W. Tyrrell made his explorations in this country in 1896 he was obliged to rely on the map compiled by Thompson.

The greater part of the year 1806 was spent in trading at Rocky Mountain House, far up the North Saskatchewan river, and in preparations for a journey to the west of the Rockies which Thompson had been instructed to make in order to extend the fur-trade of his employers.

On May 10, 1807, Thompson set out from Rocky Mountain House, up the Saskatchewan river, and crossed the mountains by the Howse Pass to the Columbia, which he ascended to a point in latitude 50° 32′ 15″ N., where he built Kootenay House and spent the winter. The next year he traced the Kootenay river to the southern end of Kootenay Lake, and then, turning north-eastward, reached the river again by the Moyie valley. From this point he went up the river to the Columbia, and down that river to the Blaeberry, where he crossed the Rockies ; he then made his way to Cumberland House. By the end of October he was back on the Columbia, and wintered at Kootenay House. In 1809 his main explorations were farther south, and were based on Pend d'Oreille Lake, which he reached in September. He examined the river flowing from the west of the lake, and then journeyed back south-eastward up the valley from its entrance on the south-east. Up this, the Saleesh, he built a post where he spent the winter, and from which he made extensive journeys in the next year. He endeavoured to sail through the Pend d'Oreille Lake and the river of the same name in order to return to the east by the Columbia, but, finding this impossible, he again made use of the Kootenay. On his way back from the east he discovered the Athabaska Pass, on January 10, 1811.

> A day of snow and southerly gale of wind, the afternoon fine, the view before us was an ascent of deep snow, in all appearance to the height of land between the Atlantic and Pacific Oceans, it was to me a most exhilarating sight, but to my uneducated men a dreadful sight, they had no scientific object in view, their feelings were of the place they were. . . . Many reflections came on my mind ; a new world was in a manner before me, and my object was to be at the Pacific Ocean before the month of August. . . . Early next morning we began our descent, here we soon found ourselves not only with a change of climate but more so of forest trees.[1]

In this way he opened up what was to be the main route from the east to the Columbia for many years. Thompson reached the Columbia at the mouth of the Canoe river. After some delay he went up the Columbia and down the Kootenay to Saleesh House. He then went through Pend d'Oreille Lake, down Clark's Fork, and across by Spokane House to the Columbia at Kettle Falls, and reached Astoria, seven miles from its mouth, on July 15. "The next day," says Thompson,

> in my canoe with my men I went to Cape Disappointment which terminates the course of this river, and remained until the tide came in. Thus I have fully completed the survey of this part of America from sea to sea, and by almost innumerable astronomical observations have determined the Mountains, Lakes, Rivers, and other remarkable places on the northern part of this Continent ; the maps of all of which have been drawn, and laid down in geographical position, being now the work of twenty-seven years.[2]

Thompson's return journey was made on horseback to the Kettle Falls, and then up the river to Canoe river. He had thus completed the survey of the whole course of the Columbia.

Thompson's work was by no means ended. At the conclusion of the Anglo-American war he was appointed British representative on the Commission to survey the boundary from the St Lawrence river to the Lake of the Woods, and this work occupied him for ten years, until 1826. He then retired, but poverty compelled him to resume his labours, and among his later surveys were the canoe route from Lake Huron to the Ottawa and the shores of Lake St Peter. He died in poverty in February 1857.

Thompson was one of the greatest explorers of all time, and is

[1] Tyrrell, *op. cit.*, pp. 448–449.   [2] *Ibid.*, p. 502.

probably the greatest of all those who opened up the New World. Whether judged by the distance travelled, or the hardship endured, or the accuracy of his work, he probably has no equal. It is estimated that he travelled 50,000 miles, much of it over country quite unknown before his time. His achievement is all the greater when it is remembered that he did his geographical work incidentally to his main business of a fur-trader. When he retired he proposed to issue a map which should embody the whole of his work, as well as that of others engaged in the same field, but apparently not enough subscribers came forward, and the map never appeared. Nor did he publish his *Narrative* and his *Journals*, so that his great achievements were unknown to his contemporaries, and it is only within recent years that his merits have been recognized.

Before dealing with other areas of Canada it will be convenient to finish the story of discovery in the south-west. In 1828 Simpson set out from York Factory, and reached the source of the Peace river. He then portaged to the Fraser, and sailed down it. In the same year Finlay traced the northern arm of the Peace river, and it has since borne his name. On another transcontinental journey in 1841 Simpson crossed the Rockies by the Simpson Pass, and went down the Columbia valley.

The expedition commanded by Captain Palliser during the years 1857–60 was instructed, *inter alia*, " to ascertain whether one or more practicable passes exist over the Rocky mountains within British Territory, and south of that known to exist between Mount Brown and Mount Hooker." In 1857 it examined the country between Winnipeg and the international boundary as far as 105° W. The next year was spent in the region between the North and South Saskatchewan, and it was at this time that the Kicking Horse, Vermillion, Crow's Nest, and North Kootenay Passes were discovered. The expedition continued its work for two more years, adding considerably to the detailed knowledge of the south-west, in British Columbia and Alberta.

In 1862 Lord Milton and W. B. Cheadle undertook an expedition " with a view of exploring a route across the continent to British Columbia through British territory, by one of the northern passes in the Rocky Mountains." They crossed the mountains by the Yellowhead Pass, and went down the North Thompson. They urged that along this route a road might be constructed without any great difficulty, and claimed that it was " in many respects superior to others hitherto more generally known." [1]

In the far west many details were filled in between the journeys of Thompson and that of Cheadle and Milton. In 1834 McLeod, a servant of the Hudson's Bay Company, ascended the Liard to

[1] *The North-west Passage by Land* (8th edition, 1875), p. 323. The pass was discovered about 1827 : the railway crossed it in 1910.

Simpson Lake, in the Yukon, and the Dease to Dease Lake, from which he reached the upper waters of the Stikine. Still farther to the north Campbell, from Frances Lake, journeyed to the Pelly river, and in 1843 descended it to the confluence of that river and the Lewes. He here built Fort Selkirk, and in 1850 went down the Yukon to the mouth of the Porcupine (discovered by Bell in 1842), up that river and over to the Mackenzie, up which he journeyed to Fort Simpson, at the mouth of the Liard.

While these major features were thus being revealed the Geological Survey which had been established in 1840 was beginning to fill in the details.[1] One of its ablest servants, G. M. Dawson, had served as geologist to the North American Boundary Commission, and had investigated the geology of the 49th parallel from the Lake of the Woods to the Pacific. In 1875 he transferred his activities to British Columbia and the North-west Territories. Up to 1878 he was engaged in the former province, exploring the central region round the upper waters of the Fraser river. In 1877 and 1878 he worked in Vancouver Island, much of the interior of which had already been explored by R. Brown in 1863-65, and in 1878 he went to Manitoba to survey the Red and Assiniboine rivers. Returning to the Peace river country and Northern British Columbia, he explored a route from Port Simpson on the west coast, by way of the Skeena and Peace rivers, to Edmonton. The Bow and Belly rivers were surveyed in 1880–82 and parts of the Western Rockies during the next two years, as well as the Selkirk range. In 1887–88 Dawson made one of his most famous expeditions, this time to the Yukon district, and it is to him and his assistants McConnell and McEvoy that the credit for the real discovery and description of that region must be given.

The exploration of the Rocky Mountains was for a long time delayed owing to their inaccessibility. They had been visited by Thompson and others of the earlier explorers, and they were examined, in part, by the Palliser expedition, which concluded that no practicable way through the mountains existed. But after the entry of British Columbia into the Dominion of Canada it became necessary, as part of the agreement with that province, to build a railway across Canada. The surveys for the construction of the line added very considerably to the knowledge of the Rockies, and the Canadian Pacific Railway, opened in 1886, made it possible to reach the area much more quickly. Hence a new era of exploration in the Rockies begins with G. M. Dawson's expeditions, the results of which were published in 1886. In that same year R. G. McConnell explored the Bow River Pass and its immediate vicinity.

The necessity of surveying other areas in Canada compelled the

[1] For useful summaries of the topographical work of the Canadian Geological Survey see *G.J.*, vol. x, p. 623, and vol. xxviii, p. 277.

officers of the Geological Survey to abandon exploration of the Rockies, but further progress was made as the result of the journeys of A. P. Coleman and J. N. Collie. The former, in 1892 and 1893, explored the range in the region of Mount Brown and Mount Hooker. Collie made four expeditions between 1897 and 1902, and returned in 1910 to complete his work. On the first four journeys he covered much of the higher ground between Laggan and the headwaters of the Athabaska river, while his last expedition was made to the region of the Yellowhead Pass, across which the railway had just been built.

To the north of Mount Robson there remains a considerable area which is imperfectly known in spite of the work of G. B. Milligan, who examined about 20,000 square miles of country in the Peace river district in 1913 and 1914.[1]

In the first half of the nineteenth century the outline of the whole of the north coast was made known. When the century began it had been reached at three points, by Hearne, Mackenzie, and Cook. Its further exploration was due largely to the desire to settle the problem of the North-west Passage.

The first expedition of Franklin in 1819–21 traced a new route from Fort Providence on Great Slave Lake to the mouth of the Coppermine river, where the main work of the party began. They were " to explore the northern coast of America from the mouth of the Coppermine river to the eastward." This instruction was carried out, and the coast was mapped as far as Cape Turnagain, 175 miles to the eastward. So arduous was the task that in exploring this comparatively short stretch the party actually sailed 640 miles. The rapids on the Hood river prevented their return by that route, and they were compelled to make a long and difficult journey overland to Fort Providence. Their provisions were exhausted, some of the party died, and the survivors were saved only by the friendly help of some Indians.

In 1825–26 Franklin again led an expedition to the north. He proposed to go " overland to the mouth of the Mackenzie river, and thence, by sea, to the north-western extremity of America, with the combined object also of surveying the coast between the Mackenzie and Coppermine rivers." John Richardson and George Back, who had been on the earlier journey, again accompanied him, as well as E. N. Kendall. From Fort Franklin, on Great Bear Lake, the party made its way to the Mackenzie, and on reaching the delta took

[1] See *Report of Department of Lands, Survey Branch, British Columbia* (1914). For Collie see H. E. M. Stutfield and J. N. Collie, *Climbs and Explorations in the Canadian Rockies* (1903), and *G.J.*, vol. xxxix, p. 223. In the latter place a brief summary of exploration is given. Some interesting matter relating to the less-known explorers of the Rockies in the neighbourhood of Athabaska Pass will be found in L. J. Burpee, *On the Old Athabaska Trail* (1926).

different directions. Franklin and Back, sailing to the westward, reached Return Reef (longitude 148° 15′ W.), while Richardson and Kendall took the east channel and explored the coast to the Coppermine river, discovering Wollaston Land and giving the names of their boats, the *Dolphin* and the *Union*, to the strait which separates it from the mainland.

In 1826 Elson, of the Beechey expedition, rounded Icy Cape and reached Point Barrow, 160 miles from the limit of Franklin's journey.

George Back returned to the north in 1833, and from Great Slave Lake went down the Great Fish river to the coast. He sighted Simpson Strait and King William Island, but failed to reach Cape Turnagain (1834).

Two servants of the Hudson's Bay Company, P. W. Dease and T. Simpson, next spent the years 1837–39 in surveying previously unknown parts of the north coast. In the first year they connected the discoveries at Point Barrow with those at Return Reef. In 1838 they reached the Arctic Ocean by way of the Coppermine river, and got as far as Dease Strait, sighting Victoria Land. In their third journey from the Coppermine they gained the point reached by Back. Simpson went on beyond this to Castor and Pollux Bay, and also explored the south shore of King William Island. These two men, profiting by the experience of Franklin and his companions, had thus completed a highly successful piece of work.

Simpson's premature death for a time ended exploration, but it was resumed in 1846 by John Rae, who was also in the service of the Hudson's Bay Company. From Repulse Bay he went overland into Committee Bay, but was obliged to abandon his efforts to get farther. In the next year, with sledges, Rae explored the west side of the bay, and later in the year, on the east side, all but reached Fury and Hecla Strait. " This expedition practically completed the exploration of the coast of North America. There remained only the north-west shores of Boothia Felix and the south-eastern part of King William Land." [1] These blanks were filled in during the search for Franklin,[2] and were completely banished from the map by Hall's discovery of the gap between the point reached by Rae in 1845 and that of Parry in 1825 in Fury and Hecla Strait.

A number of scientific expeditions have since visited parts of the north coast and have corrected the details of earlier explorers, while the entire length westward from the Kent Peninsula to the boundary of Alaska has been resurveyed by the Canadian Arctic Expedition during the years 1914–16.[3]

That part of Canada which lies south of the Arctic coast and east and north of those regions already described was until quite recently

[1] A. W. Greely, *Handbook of Polar Discoveries* (4th edition, 1910), p. 125.
[2] See below, p. 458.
[3] See *Report of the Canadian Arctic Expedition*, 1913–1918, vol. xi (1924).

almost entirely unknown. The French missionary E. F. St Petitot contributed something to the knowledge of the districts in the Mackenzie basin and round the Great Bear and Great Slave Lakes during his long residence in the north (1863–78), while Franklin and his associates produced reasonably accurate maps of the areas through which they passed. McConnell in 1887 and 1888 added more precise information about the lands near to the Mackenzie, Slave, and Liard rivers, while R. Bell examined the Great Slave Lake in 1899 and J. M. Bell continued the work from that lake to the Great Bear Lake in the following year. A more recent survey of the Great Slave Lake, by G. H. Blanchet, in 1922–24, has, however, revealed many inaccuracies in these earlier efforts. The Topographical Survey branch of the Department of the Interior has recently (1921) undertaken active work in the Mackenzie valley.

To the east of this valley exploration owes much to the journeys of J. B. and J. W. Tyrrell. In 1892 J. B. Tyrrell went from Prince Albert, on the Saskatchewan, by Ile à la Cross Lake and Black Lake to the eastern end of Lake Athabaska, returning by Wollaston Lake and Geikie river. "During the season," he wrote, "we made 1300 miles of new surveys, 540 miles of which were on routes that had never before been travelled by white men, and 260 miles without guides of any kind except our instruments." [1]

In the next year the two men surveyed the northern shore of Lake Athabaska, and then proceeded to Black Lake, from which they plunged into the unknown country " without any other guide than the little Indian map obtained the year before." Their route lay to the north-east, along almost continuous waterways, to Dubawnt Lake, Baker Lake, and Chesterfield Inlet. From the mouth of that opening they followed the coast of Hudson Bay to Churchill, then crossed overland to York Factory, and made their way, by Hayes and Hill rivers, to the northern end of Lake Winnipeg. Driving over the frozen lake to its southern end, they reached Winnipeg in January 1894. Of the results of their journey J. B. Tyrrell wrote : " During the course of the expedition we travelled, beyond our railway journeys, a total distance of 3200 miles, viz. 2150 miles in canoes, 610 miles on foot on snowshoes, 350 miles in conveyances drawn by dogs, and 100 miles in conveyances drawn by horses." Lengthy surveys were made on the journey : " Seven hundred and seventy miles over lakes . . . two hundred and seventy-two miles of river, and three hundred and sixty miles of the tidal shores of Chesterfield Inlet and Hudson Bay." Geological and botanical investigations were also carried out.[2]

In 1894 J. B. Tyrrell made a third journey into the same country,

---

[1] *G.J.*, vol. iv, p. 438.
[2] See *G.J.*, vol. iv, pp. 437–450. This article is illustrated by a useful map showing the routes of 1892 and 1893.

on this occasion going north-eastward from Reindeer Lake to Yathkyed Lake, and out to Hudson Bay by the Fergusson river. From Churchill he went overland to the Nelson river and the northern end of Lake Winnipeg. During a period of about seven months he covered a distance of nearly 3000 miles.[1]

Further details were added to this region by the extensive journeys of D. T. Hanbury in 1898–99 and 1901–2. He followed routes from the Great Slave Lake to Chesterfield Inlet and from the mouth of the Dubawnt river northward to the sea, along the coast westward, and then inland again to the Great Bear Lake.[2]

A number of subsequent travels have added scraps of knowledge. The extensive journeys of Stefansson and his crusade against the term 'barren' lands are well known.[3]

Another explorer who has solid work to his credit is J. Keale, who examined a large piece of country between the Yukon and Mackenzie basins in 1907. Within the last decade great progress has been made. Aerial surveys and air-reconnaissances have covered vast areas never visited by white men. The economic investigations of Major L. T. Burwash between 1925 and 1928 extended over Northern Canada from the Mackenzie river to Repulse Bay, and were particularly valuable for the light thrown on Eskimo life. Similarly much information has come from the biological investigations of H. B. Hoare (1924–26 and 1928) and A. E. Porsild (1926 and 1929) in the Mackenzie district, and the field-work of the Southern party of the Canadian Arctic Expedition of 1913–18, under the direction of Dr R. M. Anderson. In addition detailed investigations of smaller regions have been made by the officers of the Geological Survey, especially since the construction of the Hudson Bay railway offered some chance for the economic exploitation of the north of Canada. Although much remains to be done, especially in the direction of accurate mapping, the interest now shown in what were formerly described as 'barren' lands leads to the conclusion that the whole of Northern Canada will soon be completely explored.[4]

By contrast with the north-west, Labrador remains largely unexplored. The coastal regions and a few points near to the coasts were visited by isolated expeditions during the early years of the nineteenth century, among them being McLean, who crossed the country from Ungava Bay to Hamilton Inlet in 1838 and saw

---

[1] See *G.J.*, vol. vi, pp. 438–448 (with map).
[2] See *G.J.*, vol. xvi, p. 63, and vol. xxii, p. 178.
[3] *E.g.*, see *G.J.*, vol. lxiii, p. 283.
[4] See F. H. Kitto, *The North-west Territories*, 1930 (Department of the Interior), and G. H. Blanchet, *Preliminary Report on the Aerial Mineral Exploration of Northern Canada* (Department of the Interior, 1930). An account of Major Burwash's expedition of 1925–26 is in *G.J.*, vol. lxxiv, p. 553. For later expeditions see below, p. 462.

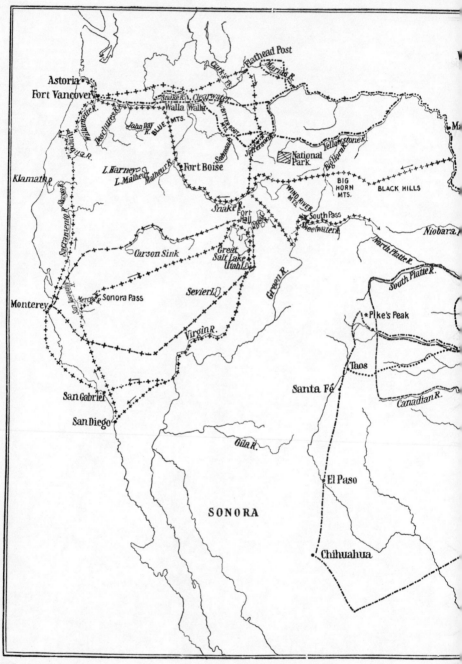

Fig. 40. The United States of America, 1800–37

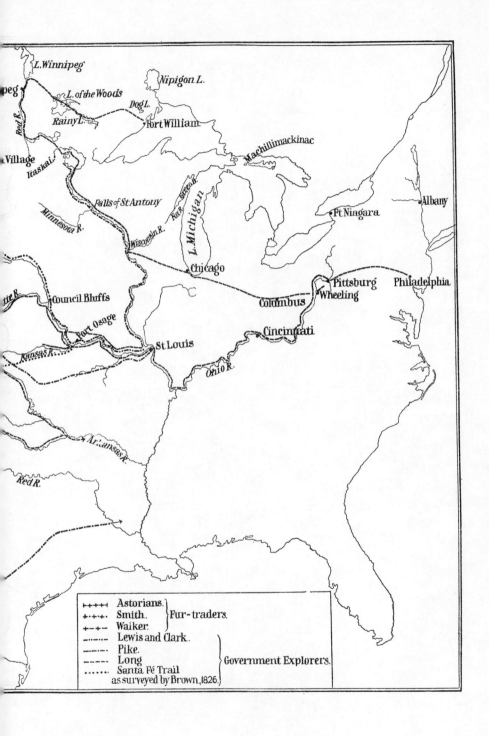

L.Winnipeg

Nipigon L.

peg

L.of the Woods

Dog L.

Red R.

Rainy L.

Fort William

Village

Itaskai

Machillimackinac

Falls of St Antony

Fox & Green R.

Albany

Minnesota R.

Wisconsin R.

L. Michigan

Ft Niagara

Chicago

Pittsburg

Philadelphia

tte R.

Council Bluffs

Columbus

Wheeling

Fort Osage

Cincinnati

Kansas R.

St Louis

Ohio R.

Arkansas R.

Red R.

Astorians.

Smith.   Fur-traders.

Walker.

Lewis and Clark.

Pike.

Long   Government Explorers.

Santa Fé Trail
    as surveyed by Brown, 1826.

the Grand Falls of the Hamilton in the following year. From the south H. Y. Hind penetrated far into the interior by the Moisie river in 1861. But nearly all knowledge of the peninsula, except the coastal regions, comes from the extensive journeys of A. P. Low between 1884 and 1904. He traced the Rupert river from Lake Mistassini to its mouth; he explored the East Main river, the Big river, and the Kaniapiskau river; he went up the Hamilton Inlet to Petitsikapau Lake and thence southward to the St Lawrence, at the mouth of the St John river; he ascended the Manikuagan to its sources; he surveyed a route from Clearwater Lake to Ungava Bay. Others have since added fragments to the maps which are based on Low's work, but, as the recent boundary dispute between Newfoundland and Quebec has abundantly shown, very little real exploration has been done, and the interior of Labrador is for practical purposes an unknown land.[1]

II. THE UNITED STATES OF AMERICA [2]

While pioneers in large numbers were making important additions to the knowledge of the country between the Appalachians and the Mississippi, Jonathan Carver set out from Boston in 1766, and, travelling through Albany, Fort Niagara, and Machillimackinac, reached Lake Michigan. He crossed the lake, went up the Fox river to the Wisconsin, and down that river to the Mississippi. He then went up the Mississippi to the Falls of St Anthony, and spent the winter with the Indians on the Minnesota river. In the spring of 1767 he carried out further explorations west of Lake Superior, but was unable to fulfil his plans owing to lack of supplies. "What chiefly I had in view," he wrote,

> after gaining a knowledge of the manners, customs, languages, soil, and natural productions of the different nations that inhabit the back of the Mississippi, was to ascertain the breadth of that continent . . . in its broadest part between 43 and 46 degrees northern latitude. Had I been able to accomplish this I intended to have proposed to Government to establish a post in some of those parts about the Straits of Anian.

Carver connected a mythical 'river of the west' with a river called Oregan, which itself was doubtless the Columbia. He secured some support for a second expedition, during which he hoped to reach this river, but was never able to carry out his plan. Some doubt has been thrown on his veracity, and it certainly seems as if part of his work is merely a compilation. If he really performed

[1] In 1928 H. G. Watkins contributed materially to the knowledge of Hamilton river and the surrounding country. See *G.J.*, vol. lxxv, p. 97.
[2] In addition to the works mentioned in the footnotes to this section see E. W. Gilbert, *The Exploration of Western America* (1933).

this journey he is the first English-speaking traveller to explore the country west of the Mississippi river.

A little later John Ledyard outlined an ambitious scheme to cross the continent from Nootka Sound, and actually was well on his way, across Asia, to Kamchatka when the Russian Government withdrew its approval and he was obliged to abandon the expedition. Ledyard subsequently carried out some work in Africa,[1] and no one revived his project for a west to east journey in America.

With the beginning of the nineteenth century political events in America drew the attention of the United States to the possibilities, and the dangers, of an undeveloped west. On January 18, 1803, Jefferson, who had already interested himself in Carver's project, sent a special message to Congress urging the appropriation of $2500 " for the purpose of extending the external commerce of the United States," with the understanding that this money was to be used to send out an expedition to explore the country of the north-west. To arrange matters in this way, he argued, " would cover the understanding from notice and prevent the obstructions which interested individuals might otherwise previously prepare in its way."

The men selected for the task were Captains Meriwether Lewis and William Clark.[2] " The object of your mission," their instructions read,

is to explore the Missouri river and such principal streams of it, as, by its course and communication with the waters of the Pacific Ocean, whether the Columbia, Oregan, Colorado, or any other river, may offer the most direct and practicable water-communication across the continent, for the purposes of commerce.[2]

They were ordered to make careful observations of the geography and geology of the country, its economic possibilities, and its inhabitants, and were to find out all they could about the lands not on their immediate route. They were to ascertain if the mouth of the Columbia might be as convenient a centre for the fur-trade as Nootka Sound, and whether that trade might as easily be conducted overland instead of by the sea-route round South America.

The party set out from the Missouri in May 1804, and in November went into winter quarters with the Mandan Indians, 1600 miles from St Louis, in the modern state of Dakota. In the following April the journey was resumed up the Missouri, the Rockies were crossed, and the Columbia river was reached. They arrived at the mouth of the river on November 14, 1805, and established themselves for another winter. Lack of supplies at length compelled

[1] See above, p. 303.
[2] On this expedition see the journals of the members of the party, edited by R. G. Thwaites (1904), and the various reprints of the Biddle edition of 1814 by Coues, Barnes, and McMaster in the " Great American Explorers " series (1905). The last has been used here.
[3] McMaster, op. cit., vol. i, p. xvi.

them to return, and they left their quarters on March 23, 1806. They followed the Snake river and one of its tributaries, the Clearwater, and entered the Bitter Root Mountains. The account of their journey explains an important diversion at this point. The order runs as follows :

> Captain Lewis with nine men are to pursue the most direct route [over the Lolo Pass] to the falls of the Missouri, where three of his party are to be left to prepare carriages for transporting the baggage and canoes across the portage. With the remaining six he will ascend Maria's river, to explore the country and ascertain whether any branch of it reaches as far north as the latitude of fifty degrees, after which he will descend the river to its mouth. The rest of the men will accompany Captain Clark to the head of Jefferson river, which Sergeant Ordway and a party of nine men will descend with the canoes and other articles deposited there. Captain Clark's party, which will then be reduced to ten, will proceed to the Yellowstone at its nearest approach to the three forks of the Missouri. There he will build canoes and go down that river.[1]

This plan was carried out successfully ; the two sections met again on the Missouri, and on September 23, 1806, they arrived back at St Louis. They calculated that their outward route was 4134 miles long, while the shorter route of Lewis on the return journey was 3555 miles from the mouth of the Missouri to the Pacific Ocean.

Careful records were kept of the journey. Of the actual crossing of the divide the account records :

> In passing from the falls of the Missouri, across the Rocky Mountains, to the navigable waters of the Columbia, you have two hundred miles of good road, one hundred and forty miles of high, steep, rugged mountains, sixty miles of which is covered from two to eight feet deep with snow in the last of June.[2]

A useful weather record was kept, and much valuable information about the Indians was collected. Lewis drew up some " observations and reflections on the present and future state of Upper Louisiana in relation to the government of the Indian nations inhabiting that country, and the trade and intercourse with the same." He advocated the establishment of " a few posts, where there shall be a sufficient guard to protect the property of the merchants in their absence " and that " to these common marts all traders and Indians should be compelled to resort for the purposes of traffic."

The direct result of the expedition of Lewis and Clark was to prove the practicability of a route across the mountains, and thus to prepare the way for the great transcontinental journeys of the next fifty years. Indirectly, however, the expedition had even more important consequences, for it directed the attention of fur-traders at St Louis to a wealthy and unexploited region. Actually traders

---

[1] McMaster, *op. cit.*, vol. iii, pp. 161-162.   [2] *Ibid.*, vol. iii, p. 322.

had gone west of the Mississippi as early as 1794, and a certain John Mackay had established posts between the Niobara and the Platte rivers, and Evans, his associate, had reached the Mandan villages. Mackay collected some useful geographical information, and it seems likely that his work was known to Lewis and Clark.[1]

While Lewis and Clark were away in the far west Lieutenant Z. Pike was exploring the Mississippi upward from its junction with the Missouri.[2] In 1806-7 he made another important journey to the Arkansas valley, which he followed to its head in the Rocky Mountains. Climbing the ridge, which he called White Snow Mountains, he got into another valley, and thought it might be the Red River, for which he was looking. He followed the valley southward, but was taken prisoner by Spanish troops and carried off to Santa Fé. The river which he had been following was the Rio Grande del Norte, and led straight into Spanish territory. Pike was obliged to pass through a large part of Mexico before he reached Chihuahua and explained his case to General Salcedo. He was deported, but required to return by way of Texas.

Pike used his eyes and his ears to advantage in Mexico, and brought back a most valuable account of the region, which he supplemented from Humboldt's *Observations on New Spain*. It was to this expedition that the United States authorities owed their first accurate knowledge of New Mexico, Texas, and Northern Mexico. Taken in conjunction with the journey of Lewis and Clark, it enormously enlarged the geographical horizon.

Although much valuable knowledge came from expeditions such as have been described, real progress in the west was primarily due to the activities of the fur-traders. John Colter, who had left Lewis and Clark on their homeward journey to act as guide to a trading-party moving up the Missouri, wandered far to the west, and perhaps reached the neighbourhood of what is now the Yellowstone National Park. As he came down the Platte river and steered his boat into the Missouri he encountered Manuel Lisa, one of the first to take advantage of the information gathered by Lewis and Clark, who was then (1807) leaving for his first expedition up the Missouri.

As the leading spirit of the Missouri Fur Company Lisa continued for many years to engage in this profitable enterprise, but refused to allow strangers from the east to join the Company. The result was that John Jacob Astor founded a new Pacific Fur Company, and staffed it with men drawn from the North-west Company of Canada.

[1] K. Coman, *Economic Beginnings of the Far West* (two volumes in one, 1925), vol. i, p. 235, and F. J. Teggart, *American Historical Association's Annual Report*, 1908, vol. i, p. 183 (" Notes Supplementary to Edition of Lewis and Clark "). Miss Coman's work is very useful for the history of early exploration and settlement in the west, and contains a good bibliography.
[2] See *The Expeditions of Zebulon M. Pike*, edited by E. Coues (3 vols., 1895).

Two expeditions were sent out, one by sea to the mouth of the Columbia and the other by land, and with this new venture another chapter in the history of the far west is reached.

In 1811 the party of Astor's fur-traders, under W. P. Hunt, left St Louis, and, moving westward on horseback, skirted the northern slopes of the Black Hills and Big Horn Mountains and reached the north fork of the Snake river, on which they embarked. They soon found that navigation was impossible, and in their efforts to follow the river suffered great hardship. At length they crossed the Blue Mountains to Walla Walla, and arrived at Astoria in 1812. A return party, under Stuart, came back by the Snake and the North Platte rivers to St Louis in the following year, and perhaps made use of the South Pass. The main expedition opened up at least one more route from the Mississippi valley to the mouth of the Columbia.[1]

The operations of the fur-traders were naturally undertaken primarily in the interests of their trade, but they did much to collect information about the vast unknown area lying between New Mexico and the Columbia river. Only a few of the more extensive journeys can be mentioned here.[2] Thus P. S. Ogden, a servant of the North-west Company, operated in the Snake river country in 1824 and succeeding years. He followed up the rivers John Day and Deschutes, left-bank tributaries of the Columbia, to their sources; he reached the lakes Harney and Malheur; he saw the Humboldt river; he discovered the Klamath and Shasta rivers, which enter the Pacific Ocean; and he collected much valuable information, which was sent home to England for the benefit of cartographers working for the Hudson's Bay Company.

In 1823 a party of traders of the Rocky Mountain Fur Company went up the North Platte river to South Pass and on to the Green River. They opened up this pass to traders, and disclosed a very valuable fur-bearing region. In the following year one of their number, W. H. Ashley, reached the Green River from the South Platte, and ultimately made his way to Sevier Lake and Great Salt Lake, where he found traces of the activity of P. S. Ogden. Later he established a post on Utah Lake, and he and other servants of the Company exploited the region to the full. Thus Utah Lake was rediscovered and the white man sailed his canoes on Great Salt Lake.

[1] On this venture see Washington Irving, *Astoria; or, Enterprise beyond the Rocky Mountains* (3 vols., 1836). On the South Pass see E. W. Gilbert, " South Pass : A Study in the Historical Geography of the United States," in *Scottish Geographical Magazine*, vol. xlv, p. 144.

[2] See H. M. Chittenden, *History of the Early Western Fur Trade* (3 vols., 1902), and, for a good popular account, E. Hough, *The Way to the West* (1903). The last deals in a spirited manner with many little-known incidents in the western expansion of the early settlers.

One of the longest and most remarkable journeys was that of Jedidiah Smith. In 1824 he had reached the Snake river from the Green River and come across the Hudson's Bay Company's post at Fort Boise. Two years later he started from Great Salt Lake for the south-west. Using the Virgin river, he reached the Colorado. Thence he struck westward, and succeeded in gaining the coast at San Diego, where he was arrested by the Spaniards. He was not allowed to visit the coastal towns, but he made his way over the mountains to the valley of the San Joaquin-Sacramento, up it to the Merced river, over the mountains again by the Sonora Pass, and across the desert to Great Salt Lake. He returned to San Gabriel on the west coast in 1827, and took ship to Monterey, where he was once more arrested and only released on condition that he left California. This he did by following the valley up the Sacramento, and then crossing the Cascade Mountains by the Siskiyon Pass, reaching the Umpqua river and so arriving on the west coast. He ultimately made his way down the Willamette to Fort Vancouver, where he was hospitably received by the traders of the North-west Company. With them he visited Spokane House and Flathead Post, on one of the tributaries of the Missouri, in 1829, before returning to the Snake river, where he met other members of the Company. In his five years of wandering Smith had probably covered more new ground than any other American of the time.[1]

Up to the middle of the century the geographical knowledge of the far west came from the activities of the fur-traders, though it received important additions from scientific expeditions which were sent out from time to time, and to which it is now necessary to turn. In 1819 Major S. H. Long and eight assistants started from Pittsburg, went down the Ohio, and up the Mississippi and Missouri to Old Council Bluff. On the way a party was sent up the Kansas to explore the country between that river and the Platte and to return down the latter to the Missouri. In the next year Long reached the Rocky Mountains where the South Platte leaves them, and examined these mountains southward as far as the Arkansas river ; in the course of the march Dr E. James made the first ascent of Pike's Peak. On the return journey one party, under Major Bell, came down the Arkansas, while the other, under Long, reached the Canadian river, and, thinking it was the Red River, followed it down until it joined the Arkansas. Thus Long's mistake, like that of Pike, had led to important though unexpected results.

Major Long led a second expedition in 1823. He started from Philadelphia, and, travelling through Wheeling and Columbus, reached the southern end of Lake Michigan, where he found Chicago

[1] See H. C. Dale, *The Ashley-Smith Explorations and the Discovery of a Central Route to the Pacific* (1918).

" a few miserable huts inhabited by a miserable race of men." He went on to the junction of the Wisconsin and Mississippi rivers, and then proceeded to carry out the " first authentic exploration of the sources of the St Peter's river." Long subsequently ·reached the Red River and followed it down to Lake Winnipeg. He returned to Lake Superior by way of the Lake of the Woods, Rainy Lake, and the Dog river to Fort William.

A number of smaller surveys added considerably to the detailed knowledge of country already known in its broad features. J. C. Brown's survey of the Santa Fé trail from Fort Osage to Taos in 1825–27, the activities of the Boundary Commission entrusted with carrying out the provisions of the Treaty of Ghent, and the work of H. R. Schoolcraft are worthy of mention.[1] The last named made an expedition, with Cass, to the sources of the Mississippi in 1820. " The specific objects of this journey," he wrote,

> were to obtain a more correct knowledge of the names, numbers, customs, history, condition, mode of sustenance, and dispositions of the Indian tribes ; to survey the topography of the country and collect the materials for an accurate map ; to locate the site of a garrison and to purchase the ground ; to investigate the subject of the north-western copper mines, lead mines, and gypsum quarries, and to purchase from the Indian tribes such tracts as might be necessary to secure to the United States the ultimate advantages to be derived from them.[2]

Schoolcraft visited the Wabash and Illinois rivers in 1821, and in 1832 journeyed to Itaska Lake, where one of the sources of the Mississippi is located.[3] On the last occasion he was accompanied by Lieutenant J. Allen, who produced the first accurate map of the sources of the river.[4] Schoolcraft shares with Allen the credit for the exploration of the sources of the Mississippi although the completion of this task hardly solved, as he had suggested it would, the last problem of American geography.

Attention was drawn westward again by the activities of the Patties, whose record was first published in 1831.[5] Sylvester Pattie and his son went to Santa Fé in 1824, and in the course of a trapping expedition to the Gila river visited the Santa Rita copper-mines,

[1] On these expeditions see G. K. Warren, *Memoir to accompany the Map of the Territory of the United States* (" Reports of Explorations and Surveys to ascertain the most Practicable and Economical Route for a Railroad from the Mississippi to the Pacific Ocean . . .," vol. xi, 1855), pp. 26–30.

[2] *Narrative Journal of Travels from Detroit North-west through the Great Chain of American Lakes to the Sources of the Mississippi River in the Year 1820* (1821), p. xiii.

[3] These journeys are recorded in *Travels in the Central Portions of the Mississippi Valley* (1825), and *Narrative of an Expedition through the Upper Mississippi to Itaska Lake* (1834).

[4] Allen's map shows the Mississippi from Lake Pepin to its source.

[5] Reprinted in R. G. Thwaites, *Early Western Travels* (32 vols., 1904–7), vol. xviii.

near the source of that river. The father remained here, but his son, J. O. Pattie, began an extensive journey first to the Colorado river, then by way of South Pass to the Big Horn and Yellowstone rivers, and finally back to Santa Fé. His furs were confiscated, so Pattie turned to trade in Mexico, and visited Sonora, Chihuahua, and El Paso. He went back to Santa Rita a wealthy man, and found his father had settled down as a farmer. Both were ruined, however, by a scoundrel who went off to buy stores and decamped with their money. Turning once more to furs, they went again to the Colorado, crossed the desert to San Diego, and were imprisoned by the Spaniards. Sylvester died here, but his son was released. He paid another visit to Mexico before returning, a ruined man, to Cincinnati, but the story of his adventures roused much interest.

Shortly after this J. Gregg wrote *The Commerce of the Prairies*,[1] a classical description of the Santa Fé trail. Between 1831 and 1839 he made eight expeditions to the west, and lived for a long period in Mexico.

In spite of all this activity, knowledge of the west was very scrappy, and in some respects quite inaccurate. The Great Salt Lake had been discovered in 1824 by a trader named James Bridger, but the main hydrographical features of the Great Basin were imperfectly known, and some believed that a large river, the Buenaventura, ran westward from the Rockies to the Pacific at San Francisco. The general features of the mountains were also imperfectly understood. Some at least of this ignorance was dispelled by the work of Captain B. L. E. Bonneville between 1832 and 1836. His chief aim was the prosecution of the fur-trade, but he also had definite scientific projects. His first year was spent in a journey over South Pass to the Green River, the sources of the Snake river, and to the Salmon river, where he spent the winter. At this time he examined the great lava plain between the Salmon and Snake rivers. The next year he detailed his assistant, Walker, to explore Great Salt Lake and the neighbouring country. Walker was unable to carry out the scheme as Bonneville intended, but he reached the Humboldt river, followed it to the 'sinks,' crossed the Sierra Nevada, and arrived at Monterey. The return journey was made round the southern end of the Sierra Nevada and across to the Bear river by the Santa Fé-Californian trail. Meanwhile Bonneville had been busily engaged farther north. He first explored the country round the sources of the Yellowstone river, visiting the valleys of the Wind, Green, and Sweetwater rivers, but failing in an effort to cross the Wind River Mountains. During the winter of 1833–34 he visited the Snake river, crossed the Blue Mountains, and reached the Columbia at Walla Walla. The Columbia was revisited in the summer of 1834, and he returned home in the following

[1] Reprinted in R. G. Thwaites, *Early Western Travels* (1904–6), vols. **xix, xx.**

year. Although Bonneville's maps were not of high accuracy, they showed correctly the river-systems west of the Rockies. Writing in 1859, Lieutenant G. K. Warren declared :

> Although the geographical positions are not accurate, yet the existence of the great interior basins, without outlets to the ocean, of Great Salt Lake, of Ogden's or Mary's river [now Humboldt], of the Mud Lakes, and of Sevier river and lake was determined by Captain Bonneville's maps, and they proved the non-existence of the Rio Buenaventura and other hypothetical rivers. They reduced the Willamette river to its proper length, and fixed approximately its source, and determined the extent and direction of the Sacramento and San Joaquin rivers. The map of the sources of the Yellowstone is still the best original one of that region.[1]

Warren exaggerated the importance of Bonneville's map. It was not even the first accurate map of the west, for in 1836, a year before it appeared, A. Gallatin compiled a map of Western America for his *Synopsis of Indian Tribes within the United States*. This map is comparatively unknown, while that of Bonneville was well advertised by Washington Irving.[2]

Very important contributions to the geography of the Mississippi valley were made at this time by I. N. Nicollet, who was assisted in the years 1838–40 by J. C. Frémont. Of his earlier work Nicollet wrote :

> I determined, after having explored the Allegany range in its various extension through the southern States, and having ascended the Red river, Arkansas river, and to a long distance the Missouri river, to undertake the full exploration of the Mississippi river from its mouth to its very sources. During the five years that I was engaged in these excursions, I took occasion to make numerous observations calculated to lay the foundation of the astronomical and physical geography of a large extent of country, and more especially of the great and interesting region between the Falls of St Anthony and the sources of the Mississippi.[3]

Nicollet died before he had finished the account of his explorations, and no complete record of his work was preserved. This is unfortunate, because those surveys which survived were of a high order. They covered a large piece of country between the Missouri and Mississippi and between the 44th and 48th parallels of latitude. Of his work Warren says :

> Mr Nicollet was the first explorer who made much use of the barometer for obtaining the elevation of our great interior country above the sea. An abstract of the methods and principles by which

[1] Warren, *Memoir*, p. 33.
[2] I am indebted to Mr E. W. Gilbert for bringing this fact to my notice. For a reproduction of Gallatin's map see H. C. Dale, *op. cit.*, p. 302. Bonneville's work was popularized by Washington Irving in *The Rocky Mountains ; or, Scenes, Incidents, and Adventures in the Far West . . .* (2 vols., 1837).
[3] Warren, *Memoir*, p. 40.

he was governed in his explorations is given in his report, and has served as a guide to many subsequent explorers. His map was one of the greatest contributions ever made to American geography.[1]

This expedition had another importance in that it furnished an admirable training to J. C. Frémont. This man, one of the greatest of American explorers, returned with Nicollet to work up the results of the exploration, but was hurriedly sent off again in 1841 to make a survey of Des Moines river. The alleged reason was that the progress of settlement necessitated a good topographical map: the real explanation was the friendship between Frémont and Jessie, daughter of Senator Benton. Frémont carried out his survey in about six months, and returned to Washington to marry Jessie Benton. Frémont was doubly fortunate, for his marriage brought great personal happiness and the influential backing of his father-in-law.

Benton was much interested in the west, but his heart was in politics, and he wished to see the north-west settled in order to counter the influence of Great Britain. Without systematic exploration this aim could not be achieved. Hence the happy combination of circumstances which led to Frémont's first expedition of 1842. It was not strictly a journey of exploration, for he only penetrated to the South Pass, and climbed a high peak in the Wind River Mountains which still bears his name. Frémont was fortunate in securing the services of Kit Carson as guide, for no man knew better than he did the country west of the Mississippi. In a long life he traversed it from Mexico to Canada. Another member of the party, Charles Preuss, later made his name as a cartographer. The work of survey was accurately done, but most important was Frémont's *Report*, which indicated that, contrary to general opinion, the country west of the Mississippi was well suited for agricultural settlements. Its immediate result was to set a stream of settlers moving westward. The results of the scientific side of the expedition were well stated by Senator Linn when moving that extra copies of the *Report* should be printed:

> The object of the expedition was to examine and report upon the rivers and country between the frontiers of Missouri and the basis of the Rocky Mountains; and especially to examine the character and ascertain the latitude and longitude of South Pass, the great crossing place to these mountains on the way to Oregon. All the objects of the expedition have been accomplished. . . . In executing his instructions Mr Frémont proceeded up the Kansas river far enough to ascertain its character, and then crossed over to the Great Platte, and pursued that river to its source in the mountains, where the Sweet Water, a head branch of the Platte, issues from the neighbourhood of the South Pass. . . . He went through the Pass and saw the headwaters of the Colorado . . . and he climbed the loftiest peak

[1] Warren, *op. cit.*, p. 42.

384

in the Rocky Mountains.[1] . . . He returned by the valley of the Great Platte. Over the whole course of this extended route barometrical observations were made by Mr Frémont, to ascertain elevations both of the plains and of the mountains ; astronomical observations were taken to ascertain latitudes and longitudes ; the face of the country was marked as arable or sterile ; the facility of travelling and the practicability of routes noted ; the grand features of nature described, . . . military positions indicated, and a large contribution to geology and botany was made.[2]

Allowing for the exaggeration of an enthusiast, there is enough left to show that at least Frémont had won his place as a competent explorer.

In 1841 the naval expedition under the command of Charles Wilkes reached Oregon, and carried out a survey of the Columbia as far as Walla Walla. One party went up the Willamette and over to the sources of the Sacramento, down which they travelled to San Francisco. Another party from Puget Sound crossed the Cascade Mountains near Mount Rainier, went over the Columbia and on to the mouth of the Spokane, and then proceeded up the Columbia to Fort Colville. After exploring the country to the south-east they returned to Walla Walla. As a result of these expeditions a considerable improvement was made in the map of the north-west.

In the south some additional general information was supplied by G. W. Kendall, who accompanied a military expedition from Austin, in Texas, to Santa Fé in 1841. His only object was a desire to travel, and no topographical information was obtained, but it is likely that this expedition was the first to visit the sources of the Red River.

Frémont was sent out again in 1843, with a well-equipped expedition. Its object was to connect up his previous work round the South Pass with the regions which had been explored by Wilkes and his subordinates in 1841. He was to examine the whole country lying between the Columbia, the Pacific Ocean, and the Spanish possessions in California, and to do for that region what he and Nicollet had already done for other parts of the country east of the Rockies. Frémont left Kansas City on May 29, and, in the hope of discovering a new route through the Rockies, took a more southerly line than he had done in his first expedition. Early in July he caught sight of Long's Peak, and when close to the Rockies turned southward as far as Pueblo, where he met Carson and endeavoured to replenish his supplies. Unable to secure all he needed, he was obliged to turn northward again. He traversed the Black Mountains, passed round the north end of the Medicine Bow Mountains, and arrived at the North Platte river. An attempt to reach the South Pass by a direct route failed, and the party went on to the

---

[1] This was an oratorical exaggeration.
[2] Quoted in J. Bigelow, *Memoir of the Life and Public Services of John Charles Frémont* (1856), pp. 65–66.

Sweetwater, by which they made their way to the pass. From this point the Oregon trail was followed by one party under Fitzpatrick, while Frémont led a second party to the Great Salt Lake, which he reached early in September. He made a scientific examination of the northern part of the lake, and his report led to the establishment of the Mormon colony four years later. Frémont rejoined his companions at Fort Hall, on the Snake river, and the expedition proceeded down it, reaching Fort Boise at the end of October and arriving on the Columbia in November. Frémont himself went down to Fort Vancouver, but did not actually reach the mouth of the river.

The return journey was made by a route which took Frémont round the Great Basin. He was anxious to locate certain features, including Mary's Lake and the Buenaventura river, in whose existence he believed. He reached the Lower Klamath Lake early in December, crossed the Klamath river, and by Christmas Day was at Warner Lake. By the middle of January, when on Carson river, he had resolved to cross into California on the pretext of want of supplies. The crossing of the snow-covered sierras was attended with grave risk, but Frémont was successful, and on February 20, 1844, stood on the summit: shortly afterward he reached Sutter's Fort, on the site of the modern Sacramento.

From Sacramento, where he obtained a needed supply of animals, Frémont went southward up the San Joaquin valley, round the southern end of the sierras, and along the trail to Santa Fé. At the beginning of May he was at Las Vegas (Nevada), and at the end of the month on Utah Lake, which he mistook for a southern projection of Great Salt Lake. Instead of following well-known routes Frémont plunged into the Wasatch and the Uinta Mountains, explored the ranges at the headwaters of the North and South Platte rivers, and did not reach Pueblo until the end of July.

Frémont's *Report* of this expedition is a valuable document. He traced the essential differences between the east and the west sides of the continent, described the river-systems, and made some speculations about the Great Basin, of which he had seen a part. "The existence of the Basin," he wrote,

is an established fact in my mind; its extent and contents are yet to be better ascertained. It cannot be less than four or five hundred miles each way, and must lie principally in the Alta California; the demarkation latitude of 42° probably cutting a segment from the north part of the rim. Of its interior but little is known. It is called a desert, and, from what I saw of it, sterility may be its prominent characteristic; but where there is so much water there must be some oases. The great river, and the great lake, reported, may not be equal to the report; but where there is so much snow there must be lakes to hold the accumulated waters, or sands to swallow them up.[1]

[1] Bigelow, *op. cit.*, pp. 119–120.

Frémont was careful to point out that this somewhat gloomy picture did not apply to Oregon, where good pasture was to be found and whose commercial value must be great,

> washed as it is by the North Pacific Ocean, fronting Asia, producing many elements of commerce, mild and healthy in its climate, and becoming, as it naturally will, a thoroughfare for the East India and China trade.[1]

At this time the relations between the United States and Mexico were very unsatisfactory, and Frémont was drawn into the political arena. His third expedition had for its objects the exploration of the Rockies west of Pueblo, a more careful examination of the Great Basin, and the discovery of passes through the Sierra Nevada into California. There is no doubt that possibilities of war with Mexico were taken into consideration, and although Frémont went out to make geographical discoveries, he was sent equipped to fight if the necessity arose.

Frémont again used the Arkansas river to reach the Rockies, crossed the Utah Pass, followed the White River down to the Green River, and passed through the lower country south of the Uinta Mountains to Utah Lake. Turning northward to Great Salt Lake, he spent several days in a survey of its southern portion, and then began his traverse of the Great Basin. In order to cover more ground the party was divided, one section under E. M. Kern taking a more southerly route. Both parties met at Walker Lake, at the foot of the sierras. These journeys proved that a practicable route existed across the basin.

Once more the expedition divided, Frémont taking a party over the sierras to Sutter's Fort, while Kern went round the southern end of the mountains. This party subsequently rejoined Frémont near to San José. After some delay Frémont went northward up the Sacramento river into Oregon. He reached Upper Klamath Lake, and turned westward to explore the Cascade range. But he had become involved in Californian politics, and at this point received a message from the east which brought his explorations to an end. As Bancroft put it, he was " absolved from any orders as an explorer and became an officer of the American Army." [2] The subsequent adventures of Frémont belong to political and military history. They led to the conquest of California and the arrest of the explorer. No full report of the expedition was made, but Frémont compiled a *Geographical Memoir* and a map of Oregon and California, which at that time was far superior to any other in existence.

While these great expeditions were in progress minor contributions to the geography of the country continued to be made. Among

[1] Bigelow, *op. cit.*, p. 122.
[2] Quoted in A. Nevins, *Frémont, the West's Greatest Adventurer* (2 vols., 1928), vol. i, p. 279. This work deals fully with the career of Frémont.

these may be mentioned the survey of the boundary between Louisiana and Texas in 1840, the journey of Captain J. Allen to the source of Des Moines river in 1843, and the exploration, in the same year, by Captain N. Boone, of entirely unknown country between the Arkansas and Canadian rivers, as far west as the 100th meridian. West again of this meridian a large area was surveyed by J. W. Abert and W. G. Peck in 1845, extending southward from the Arkansas to the north fork of the Red River.

Political events at this time gave added opportunities for geographical exploration. The annexation of Texas in 1845 was followed, in the next year, by the outbreak of the Mexican War. This led to the dispatch of armies to California and to Mexico. W. H. Emory, who went with the advance-guard of the Army of the West, carried out a reconnaissance from Santa Fé to the west coast at San Diego. His route lay down the Rio Grande for over 200 miles, down the Gila river, and across the Colorado Desert. Two of the party, left behind at Santa Fé, carried out extensive surveys in the neighbourhood of that town. Another route, to the south of that of Emory, and running across the Rio San Pedro and through Tuscon, was taken by Colonel Cooke in 1846–47. Still farther to the south lay the route of A. Wislizenus, who began a scientific journey at his own expense, and subsequently served as an Army doctor. From Santa Fé he went down the Rio Grande to El Paso and Chihuahua, where he was delayed for six months. He was then able to join Colonel Doniphan and proceed with him to Monterey.

In the winter of 1848 Frémont, who had resigned from the Army, made his fourth expedition. The main object of the explorer was to get to California, where he had bought some land and where he proposed to settle. But he was anxious to see a railway built to the west, and hoped to find a suitable route from the headwaters of the Rio Grande, approximately along the 37th parallel. In order to see conditions at their worst he determined, against all advice, to make the expedition in winter. From Pueblo he crossed the Robidoux Pass in the Sangre de Cristo Mountains to the headwaters of the Rio Grande. Beyond this point lay the San Juan Mountains, which proved impassable. Frémont found himself in a situation of grave danger, which he graphically described in a letter to his wife written shortly after the event.

> We pressed up towards the summit, the snow deepening ; and in four or five days reached the naked ridges which lie above the timbered country, and which form the dividing grounds between the waters of the Atlantic and Pacific Oceans. Along these naked ridges, it storms nearly all winter, and the winds sweep across them with remorseless fury. On our first attempt to cross we encountered a *pouderié*,[1] . . . and were driven back, having some ten or twelve

[1] " Dry snow driven thick through the air by violent wind " (Frémont).

men variously frozen, face, hands, or feet. The guide [Bill Williams] became nigh frozen to death here, and dead mules were already lying about the fires. Meantime, it snowed steadily. The next day we made mauls, and beating a road or trench through the snow crossed the crest in defiance of the *pouderié*, and encamped immediately below in the edge of the timber. The trail showed as if a defeated party had passed by; pack saddles and packs, scattered articles of clothing, and dead mules strewed along. A continuance of stormy weather paralyzed all movement. We were encamped somewhere about 12,000 feet above the sea. Westward, the country was buried in deep snow. It was impossible to advance and to turn back was equally impracticable.[1]

Eleven men and a large number of animals lost their lives, and the project had to be abandoned. Frémont went down the Rio Grande to Taos, and reached California by a southern route through Santa Cruz and Tuscon.

Further knowledge of the south-west came as the result of a number of important surveys undertaken at this time. In 1849 J. H. Simpson was engaged to the west of the Rio Grande, while R. B. Marcy explored the country east of that river, on the borders of New Mexico and Texas. In the last-named state a large party under Colonel J. E. Johnston began work in the same year, covering the greater part of the country south of the 34th parallel and west of longitude 96° W. In this year also the United States-Mexican Boundary Survey was begun. It continued until 1856, and greatly increased the geographical and geological knowledge of this region.

The exploration of the Colorado also received attention at this time. In 1851 Captain L. Sitgreaves crossed a portion of the Great Colorado Plateau between the Zuni river and the San Francisco Mountains, and, continuing to the westward, reached the Colorado and followed it down to Yuma. In the same year Lieutenant Derby ascended the Colorado by boat to Yuma.

The exploration of the sources of the Red River, in 1852, by R. B. Marcy, completed the major features of the south-west, with the exception of the Colorado river, where work was not resumed until 1857.

Farther north the expedition of Captain H. Stansbury resulted in the discovery of another route through the Rocky Mountains and much new information about the Great Salt Lake. Leaving Fort Leavenworth, on the Missouri river, on June 1, 1849, Stansbury followed the usual emigrant road through the South Pass to Fort Bridger, on the Blackforks, a tributary of the Green River. "From Fort Bridger," Stansbury reported,

there are now two routes as far as the Humboldt river, where they again unite. The old road strikes Bear river, follows down its valley by the Soda Springs to Fort Hall [on the Snake River], whence it

[1] Quoted in Bigelow, pp. 367–368.

pursues a south-westerly course to the Humboldt. . . . The other route was laid out by the Mormon community in 1847, and conducts the emigrant to their city, in the southern part of Salt Lake valley, causing him to vary from the line of his direction rather more than a degree southwardly : this he has to recover by a direct north course to the crossing of Bear river near the north end of the lake, whence he proceeds in a north-west direction until he intersects the old road from Fort Hall. I was desirous of ascertaining whether a shorter route than either of these could not be obtained by pursuing a direct course to the head of the lake, or to the point where Bear river enters its basin through the Wahsatch range from Cache valley.[1]

Stansbury was successful, though he was of opinion that the road should pass slightly farther northward than his own route.

Leaving the main party at Salt Lake City, he next proceeded to explore a road to Fort Hall. This again was successful, demonstrating " the entire practicability of obtaining an excellent wagon-road " between the two points. On the return journey the exploration of the deserts to the west of the Great Salt Lake was begun. Stansbury returned to Salt Lake City in November, and found that his assistant, Gunnison, who had now moved to Utah Lake, had during his absence surveyed a large area between the two lakes.

As soon as the weather allowed work was resumed in 1850. Stansbury conducted an examination of the Great Salt Lake, while Gunnison surveyed its eastern side. By August 28 they were ready to return. Fort Bridger was left on September 10, and a new route was followed through the mountains, in a general easterly direction, skirting the northern end of the Medicine Bow Mountains and the southern end of the Laramie Mountains, to the North Platte river. " The distance from Fort Bridger to Fort Laramie by the present route," Stansbury reported,

is four hundred and eight miles ; while by the new route from Fort Bridger to the eastern base of the Black Hills (a point equidistant with Laramie from the forks of the Platte) it is but three hundred and forty-seven miles. . . . It must be kept in mind too that the distance thus ascertained was measured by an odometer, following all the undulations of the natural surface, in the course of a very rapid reconnaissance, without any minute knowledge of the localities, or any endeavour whatever to make even an approximate location for a road. . . . It had been my intention to continue the reconnaissance from the head of the Lodgepole to its junction with the Platte, and thence either on the dividing ground between that river and the Republican, or by the valley of the latter stream ; either of which lines would have led us over ground as yet unexplored. Circumstances, unfortunately, prevented this design from being carried into execution.[2]

Stansbury had met with a bad accident, which made him quite

[1] H. Stansbury, *Exploration and Survey of the Valley of the Great Salt Lake of Utah* (1852), pp. 75-76.
[2] Stansbury, *op. cit.*, pp. 261-263.

unfit for work. He had, however, carried out a useful and accurate exploration of an important piece of country, and in addition to the surveys had made collections which illustrated the geology and natural history of the region. Not the least interesting part of his report was that dealing with the Mormon settlements. Stansbury found these people industrious, well-behaved, and hospitable, and attributed a great measure of his success to the help which he received from them.

The main features of exploration in the United States during the first half of the nineteenth century were the extensive but not scientifically accurate information gathered by traders in the west and the intensive operations of military officers, belonging for the most part to the corps of Topographical Engineers. But the growing number of settlers moving westward, which had been increased by Frémont's famous *Report* and by the discovery of gold in California, accentuated the problem of communication between the east and the west. This led to the great railway surveys which began in the year 1853. Five routes were to be surveyed across the continent. In the north the party under Governor Stevens, operating from St Paul, was to join hands with that of Captain G. B. McClellan, who began at Fort Vancouver, on the Columbia. A second route was to be surveyed by Lieutenant E. J. Beckwith near to the 41st parallel. Farther south Captain J. W. Gunnison was to cross between the 38th and 39th parallels. The route along the 35th parallel was to be examined by Captain A. W. Whipple, while a fifth survey was to be made from California by way of Yuma, Tuscon, and El Paso to Texas. These surveys were modified somewhat as the result of practical experience. Gunnison was unable to complete that entrusted to him, and was eventually murdered near Sevier Lake. They were also supplemented by a number of subsidiary surveys, as, for example, that of Lieutenant R. S. Williamson from the Sacramento to the Columbia river. The whole of the results were published in the valuable series of Pacific Railroad Reports.

Frémont had anticipated that his unrivalled knowledge would have been used to help in these surveys, but he was given no appointment. He therefore determined to undertake an expedition on his own responsibility, and intended to complete the work which he had found impossible in 1848. He left Kansas City in the autumn of 1853, crossed the Cochetopa Pass, and passed through the mountainous country by the Gunnison and Grand rivers. His route lay over the Wasatch Mountains to Parawan, and then in a southwesterly direction to one of the southern passes in the Sierra Nevada. A good account of the country thus examined was given in a letter to the *National Intelligencer*.[1] This marks the end of Frémont's

[1] See Bigelow, *op. cit.*, Appendix C, for this report.

career as an explorer. His reputation had won for him recognition from foreign geographical societies, and he had a well-deserved place among the great pioneers in the Western United States. Much of his work was of a high order of accuracy; he had a good eye for country, and was quick to see the salient features of its geography. If a somewhat unfortunate rashness led him into difficulties and unnecessary dangers it was often only by such methods that he could accomplish his objects.

> He was not a Pathfinder; he was a Pathmaker. He travelled over trails which had for the most part been found long before by trappers, hunters, and traders, and through regions that were at least partially known to frontiersmen. His distinction lay in the scientific equipment he brought to the task of surveying, observing, and describing these trails and regions. For his period he was an excellent topographer, surveyor, and mathematician, and a good amateur geologist and botanist.[1]

Frémont died in July 1890, at the age of seventy-seven years.

The railway surveys and the last expedition of Frémont mark the end of the great pioneer journeys in the United States. Even before their inception much had been done to fill in the blank spaces in the map: after their completion this work went on as fast as circumstances permitted. The year 1857 was notable for Lieutenant G. K. Warren's explorations in Nebraska and Dakota and for the journey of Lieutenant J. C. Ives up the Colorado in order to see if that river was navigable. The latter went as far as the Black Cañon by boat, and managed to reach the Grand Cañon overland. The work of the whole expedition, which included geologists and botanists, was carried out with success for nearly 600 miles, but even then the exploration of the river was incomplete.

As a result of the work of Captain J. H. Simpson in 1859 two practicable routes across the Great Basin were discovered, both of which were better than that previously made known by Frémont. The longitude of Salt Lake City was also accurately determined. In the same year Lieutenant J. Dixon opened up a wagon-road from Dalles, on the Columbia, to Salt Lake City.

In 1858 the Commissioners began the demarcation of the boundary along the 49th parallel which had been fixed in 1846. In 1859 and 1860 the expedition of Captain W. F. Raynolds "first pointed out a route for a wagon-road, which was subsequently opened from the Platte to the three forks of the Missouri, skirting the eastern base of the Big Horn Mountains, and first located correctly the Yellowstone river from where it leaves the mountains to the mouth of Powder river." Raynolds heard of "burning plains, immense lakes, and boiling springs" near the sources of the Yellowstone, but was unable to visit them. Their existence was proved by

[1] A. Nevins, *Frémont*, vol. ii, p. 703.

Lieutenant G. C. Doane in 1870, while the whole country round was surveyed by two expeditions, the first in 1871, under Captain Barlow, and the second, two years later, under the command of Captain W. A. Jones. These detailed investigations, and the surveys for the construction of wagon-roads in the west, filled in many blanks in the map, but the outbreak of the Civil War for a time caused operations to be suspended.

The year 1867 is notable for the beginning of C. King's geological exploration of the 40th parallel. The objects of the expedition were wider than its title indicates. The main purpose was

> to examine and describe the geological structure, geographical condition, and natural resources of a belt of country extending from the one hundred and twentieth meridian eastward to the one hundred and fifth meridian of longitude, along the fortieth parallel of latitude, with sufficient expanses north and south to include the lines of the Central and Union Pacific Railroads, and as much more as may be consistent with accuracy and a proper progress.

Botany and zoology were to receive attention, and material was to be collected for the compilation of special as well as of topographical maps of the country. Five seasons were spent in the field, and the material collected was not finally dealt with until 1879. In all somewhat over 86,000 square miles of territory were examined. When this expedition ended, in 1879, the United States Geological Survey was organized as a bureau of the Department of the Interior, and to it was allocated the duty of preparing topographical maps. In spite of considerable activity, less than half of the United States had been mapped in 1913.[1]

Another outstanding piece of exploratory work was begun by J. W. Powell in the Colorado valley in 1869. This valley had already attracted attention, but systematic survey had not been carried out since the time of Ives' visit in 1857. Powell used four row-boats, and made the descent of the river from what is now Green River Station to the mouth of the Virgin river, a distance of more than 1000 miles. In 1870 and the early part of 1871 the time was spent in exploring ways down into the Grand Cañon from the north, and in the summer of 1871, again using row-boats, Powell passed through the greater part of the Grand Cañon. This task was by no means easy, for the actual course of the river was unknown, and it was commonly believed that navigation was impossible owing

---

[1] In 1927 the area mapped was 42·3 per cent. of the total area. For a map showing this area see Mrs I. J. Thomas, "Some Contrasts in Standard Topographic Maps of Great Britain and the United States of America," in *Geography*, vol. xv, p. 274. Full details are given in the *Annual Report* of the United States Geological Survey. G. P. Merrill, *The First Hundred Years of American Geology* (1924), although primarily concerned with geological progress, contains much material dealing with the geographical activities of the geologists, and a number of useful maps.

to cataracts and to the disappearance of the river underground in places. The expedition was carried out with complete success.

The Colorado exploration was only one of many activities on the part of Powell and his companions who were working in the west, mainly in Wyoming, Utah, and Arizona, between 1867 and 1878. Classical works like Powell's *Exploration of the Colorado River of the West* and Gilbert's *Geology of the Henry Mountains* owe their origin to these explorations.

Powell's work on the Colorado was supplemented by the surveys of Lieutenant G. M. Wheeler, who was in command of a large party engaged on geographical surveys west of the 100th meridian. The expedition originated in

a permanent and legitimate want of the War Department for current topographic information of the vast area west of the Mississippi, within which constant military movements were and are required. It was in a measure a continuation of such disconnected topographic works as the War Department had begun to prosecute for special objects prior to the war of the rebellion, and which were resumed at the headquarters of the military divisions and departments at the close thereof. It added to all existing data a complete survey commencing with initial astronomic and geodetic points, with added topographic and hypsometric details upon which the orographic chart was based, thus forming a connected detail map of the region, suitable for all purposes for not less than fifty years.[1]

The results of this very important expedition are set out at length by Wheeler in his *Report*.[2] They included the discovery and naming of the Colorado Plateau ; the exploration of the Colorado river ; the determination of passes of the western, north-western, and south-western rim of the Great Basin and of the continental divide, to the south of the 40th parallel ; the demonstration that ' Preuss Lake,' thought to lie in Eastern Nevada, did not exist ; and much detailed work on the physical geography of the region. The percentage of the areas of the western states covered by this survey will give some idea of its magnitude ; it was as follows : New Mexico, 66 per cent. ; California, 41 per cent. ; Nevada, 60 per cent. ; Arizona, 54 per cent. ; Utah, 46 per cent. ; Colorado, 32 per cent. ; Oregon, 9 per cent. ; with small areas in Wyoming and Texas. In all, considerably over 300,000 square miles of country were examined.

While this vast land-surface was being surveyed the water-surface had not escaped attention. The Lake Survey began a survey of the Mississippi river in 1876, and this work was continued by the Mississippi River Commission from 1879. Similarly, surveys on the Missouri, begun in 1878, were continued by the Missouri River Commission after 1884.

---

[1] G. M. Wheeler, *Report upon the United States Geographical Surveys West of the 100th Meridian*, vol. i (" Geographical Report," 1889), pp. 761–762.
[2] *Ibid.*, pp. 21–146.

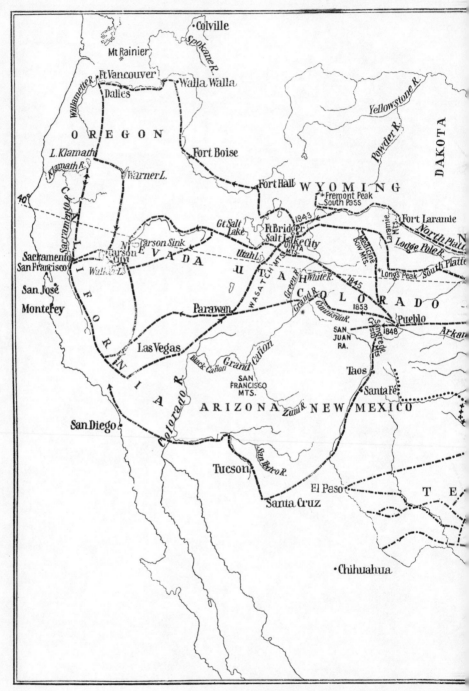

Fig. 41. THE UNITED STATES OF AMERICA AFTER 1838

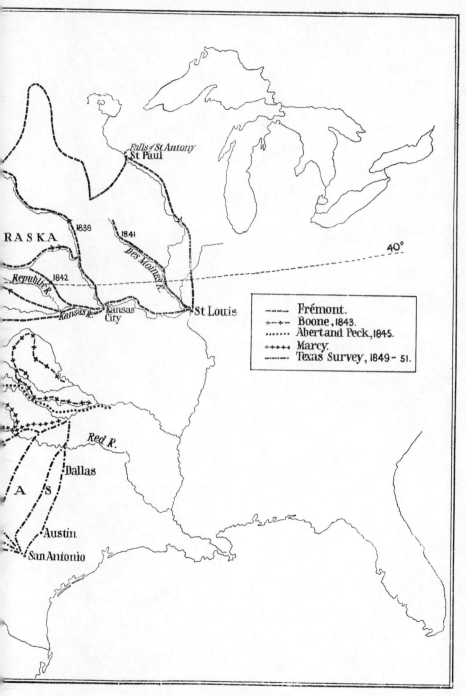

AMERICA

The Coast and Geodetic Survey originated in 1807, when Congress passed an "Act for surveying the coasts of the United States." The survey did not begin until 1816, and then had a somewhat chequered career until its reorganization in 1843. Since that time it has completed a first survey of the Atlantic, Gulf, and Pacific coasts of the United States, and carried an important line of triangulation across the continent in the neighbourhood of the 39th parallel.

III. Mexico and Central America

During the nineteenth century little geographical exploration was carried out in Mexico and Central America, although great additions to the knowledge of those regions came through the investigations of specialists in many fields, and particularly in archæology and in geology.

At the beginning of the century Mexico was imperfectly known, for much information lay hidden in Government offices, and a policy of seclusion kept out scientific investigators, so that it is hardly surprising that Humboldt's visit in 1803 should be regarded as the rediscovery of the country. Humboldt and his companion, Bonpland, landed at Acapulco, on the west coast, in January, and in time reached the city of Mexico, where they made their headquarters. A number of excursions took them to Guanajuato in the north, Jorullo in the west, and to the eastern edge of the plateau at Jalapa. They finally left the country, early in 1804, from the port of Vera Cruz. But although their traverse of the country was short, their investigations went far beyond the actual line of their route, and they were able to collect much valuable information about the whole of Mexico. In his *Essai politique sur la royaume de la Nouvelle Espagne* Humboldt gave to the world a new and enlightened account of one of the oldest of the Spanish colonies.[1]

The work of Humboldt was supplemented, in the south of Mexico, by that of Burkart between 1825 and 1834, and by the activities of the Instituto Nacional de Geografia y Estadistica, founded in 1829.

Political complications, so frequently favourable to the prosecution of geographical work, resulted in a much greater knowledge of Mexico, and especially of its northern parts, through the surveys of the United States officers and the activities of the Boundary Commission. At the same time a number of German investigators increased the information available about Central and Southern Mexico. Among the many who thus indirectly supplied geographical material were J. W. von Müller, who visited Central Mexico in 1856, and C. B. Heller, who spent three years, from 1845 to 1848, in the south of the country.

[1] On Humboldt's work generally see below, Section v, "South America."

The intervention of the French in Mexican politics in 1861 enabled a number of officers to cover a large area of the country, and although they were not equipped to make scientific surveys their observations were of considerable value. Similarly, the French ethnologists C. E. Brasseur de Bourbourg, who visited Mexico in 1864, and D. Charnay, who travelled in many parts of the world, and was twice in Mexico (1857–61 and 1880–83), were able to add to geographical knowledge, as were the German investigators, including Ratzel in 1871 and 1875 and Von Raths in 1883.

Among the many foreign visitors who have thus added details to the general map of Mexico was Carl Lumholtz, who made four expeditions to North-western Mexico between 1890 and 1898, and renewed his investigations in those regions in the first decade of the present century. Although mainly concerned with anthropological matters, he travelled through a region which had not been visited by other Europeans during the century, and had not been described by eyewitnesses since the days of the Coronado expedition.[1] Here, as in the south and south-west, there are still considerable areas unsurveyed: in the east the country is covered by a map of reasonable reliability. It may be said, however, that Mexico is well known, and the detailed investigation of those parts unsurveyed is unlikely to add anything of great importance.

Central America,[2] like Mexico, was not fully explored at the beginning of the nineteenth century, and remained neglected until nearly half that century had passed, except for a few small expeditions which touched parts of the coastline. A change came with the journeys of John Stephens, whose *Incidents of Travel in Central America, Chiapas, and Yucatan* called attention to the wealth of archæological remains awaiting the investigator.[3] The gold-rush to California also helped exploration by turning the country into a temporary resting-place for those who were travelling to the west coast, and the question of a through route, which had moved Bolivar to action in 1825, and had taken Biddle to Panamá ten years later, became now a matter of urgency. The Panamá railway was opened in 1855, and provided the first transcontinental line in the New World.

Specialist expeditions at this time brought in much valuable detail. In particular mention must be made of the archæological and geological work of Squier in Nicaragua between 1848 and 1851, the biological investigations of Wagner and Scherzer in Costa Rica

[1] Carl Lumholtz, *Unknown Mexico* (1903), and *G.J.*, vol. xxxi, p. 126, and vol. xl, p. 503.
[2] On Central America generally see K. Sapper, " Die geographische Forschung in Mittel-America im 19 Jahrhundert," printed in *Verhandlungen des dreizehnten Deutschen Geographentages zu Breslau* (1901), p. 285.
[3] This work was published in four volumes in 1841–43.

in 1854, and the surveys of Codazzi, in 1854, in the Isthmus of Chiriqui. In 1853 other surveys were made which formed the groundwork of Squier's map of Honduras and Salvador. One line ran from Puerto Cortez southward to the Gulf of Fonseca, a second from Leon, in Nicaragua, to Tegucigalpa and Comayagua, and a third from Comayagua westward to Santa Rosa, southward to San Salvador, and finally eastward to La Union, on the Gulf of Fonseca.

In Costa Rica the botanists Frantzius (1861 and 1869) and Polakowsky (1877), the geologist Gabb (1873), and the zoologist Bovallius (1877) added much to geographical knowledge, while the lengthy service of Pittier, a Government official, was of the greatest value. He explored some quite unknown regions, such as the Rio Grande de Terraba, and perhaps did more than any other man to reveal the main features of the country. In the last years of the century a strip of Costa Rica was described in detail in the *Report* of the Nicaragua Canal Commission, published 1899.[1]

In British Honduras Henry Fowler, the Colonial Secretary, journeyed through the unknown interior in 1878, and a number of other explorations were made from time to time. During the present century this region has been the scene of much archæological activity, and a great wealth of Maya remains has been disclosed by Captain Joyce and his subordinates. The comparatively unknown interior, where paths through the forest are quickly overgrown, stands in strange yet significant contrast with the coastline, which has long been notorious through the activities of the logwood-cutters and the buccaneers.

In Nicaragua the journeys of Mierisch in 1892 and 1893, in the eastern gold-bearing regions, and those of K. Sapper, together with the investigations of the Canal Commission, were the outstanding pieces of work during the second half of the century. In Honduras, apart from the information derived from C. Charles and K. Sapper, there is little progress to record. But in Salvador and Guatemala not only did the French geologists Dollfus and Montserrat collect valuable information in the course of their journeys in 1866 and 1867, but the happy accident which caused A. P. Maudslay to desire to pass the winter of 1880 in a warm climate led to his fruitful archæological discoveries in Central America and to some valuable geographical work. The outstanding figure of the period, however, is Karl Sapper, who spent the greater part of the last twelve years of the century in travelling through these regions. Though he was mainly interested in geology, he in no way neglected geographical investigations. He visited all the states from Panamá to Yucatan, and through his work became the recognized authority on Central America.

[1] On Costa Rica in 1897 see the paper by Colonel Church in *G.J.*, vol. x, p. 56 (with map).

The successful completion of the Panamá Canal in 1914 marks the final stage of a long history which has in the course of four centuries been much concerned with projects for the discovery of a waterway from the Atlantic to the Pacific. That search was particularly fruitful, and it is but fitting that the new artificial route should be constructed in that region where the Spaniards first sought for a natural waterway to the Spice Islands and Cathay.

IV. ALASKA [1]

Although the coasts of Alaska were probably sighted before the year 1741, their real discovery dates from that year, when Bering and Chirikov made their expedition across the North Pacific. They were followed by Russian traders, who gradually gained some knowledge of the coastlands, but made no effort to penetrate into the interior. At the end of the century explorers of other nations added considerably to the geographical knowledge of the coast in the course of expeditions which were not primarily directed to Alaska. Of such were the surveys of Quadra and Cook, of Malaspina and Vancouver. Both Cook and Vancouver greatly improved the existing charts, and the former inaugurated a new era in the exploration of the Alaskan seaboard.

In the nineteenth century Russian naval officers were very active, and from 1826 until about 1850 explored many parts of the coast. Beginning with Bristol Bay and Norton Sound, these surveys were extended to the northern coast in 1827, and to the southern coast a few years later. Captain M. D. Tebenkov deserves special mention, not only for his own work in Alaska, but for his atlas of charts of the north-west coast of America, from Lower California to Bering Strait, which has been described as " the most important contribution to the geography of Alaska made during the entire Russian occupation." [2]

Arctic explorations during the first half of the century also con-tributed incidentally to the knowledge of the coasts. The expedi-tions of Beechey, Franklin, and Simpson have already been men-

---

[1] The following are the main sources for the exploration of Alaska :

A. H. BROOKS, *The Geography and Geology of Alaska*, United States Geological Survey *Professional Paper*, No. 45, which contains a valuable bibliography.
Narratives of Explorations in Alaska, a compilation (1900).
M. BAKER, *Geographic Dictionary of Alaska*, United States Geological Survey *Bulletin*, No. 299 (2nd edition, 1906).
R. H. SARGENT, " Progress of Alaskan Topographical Surveys by the United States Geological Survey," in the *Bulletin of the American Geographical Society*, vol. xliv, p. 481.

On the Alaska boundary demarcation see *G.J.*, vol. lxix, p. 49 (with map).
[2] Brooks, *op. cit.*, p. 115.

tioned in this connexion : the Franklin search expeditions of Moore, Kellett, McClure, Collinson, and others are referred to elsewhere,[1] though their work in Alaska was not great. The major features of the coast had all been discovered by the year 1837.

In 1867 the United States Coast and Geodetic Survey began its work in Alaskan waters, and two years later published the first of its series of charts. The work of remapping the 20,000 miles of coastline is still in progress.

Inland exploration in Alaska presents some striking contrasts with that of the seaboard. For a long time there was no incentive to exploration, and when the growth of the fur-trade led to more investigation the country was considered to be almost worthless for any purpose other than that trade.

Four phases of inland exploration may be recognized. Up to the year 1799 the Russian occupation had been practically confined to a few coastal stations. These were mainly to be found on the south coast, at Yukatal, in Prince William Sound and Cook Inlet, and on Kodiak Island.

In the year 1799 the company prosecuting the fur-trade obtained a new charter, and was henceforward known as the Russian-American Company. With better organization and greater financial resources, it sent its agents into the interior, and they began the collection of geographical data. One of them, by name Glasanov, crossed from Norton Bay to the Yukon, and thence to the Kuskokwim river. Malakov explored the Yukon as far as Nulato and also the Sushitna river, and with Glasanov opened up the Yukon valley to the fur-traders. Even more important were the explorations of Zagoskin, who went up the Yukon to the mouth of the Tanana and examined the lower course of the Koyukuk. From the Lower Yukon he reached the Kuskokwim by way of the Innoko river (1842–43). Shortly after this, in 1850, English traders from Canada went down the Yukon to the mouth of the Tanana, thus finishing the exploration of one of the great rivers of America.

The last official Russian survey was made in 1863, when the lower valley of the Stikine was examined with a view to determining if it was in Russian territory.

In the same year the Western Union Telegraph Company began surveys in Alaska. Their main purpose was to link the line in British Columbia with that in Siberia, and, although this project was ultimately abandoned, their servants did much good exploratory work. The scientific party was led by R. Kennicott, who had previously reached Fort Yukon from Canada. "The geographical results of this survey in Alaska are a map of the Yukon river, definitely establishing the identity of the Yukon of the Hudson's Bay Company with the Kwikpak of the Russians, and important

[1] See Chapter XVII.

additions to the knowledge of the Yukon Delta, Seward Peninsula, and the Norton Bay region." [1]

The third phase of inland exploration opens with the sale of Alaska to the Government of the United States in 1867. In that year, apart from the regions surveyed by the Telegraph Company and the lower courses of the main rivers, which had been explored by the Russians, the country was virtually unknown. Yet very little interest was taken in it by the Government and people of the United States. Captain C. W. Raymond was sent up the Yukon in 1869 to assert the rights of the new rulers and to curb the encroachments of the Hudson's Bay Company traders. After that little was done until Petrov published his remarkable account of the country in the *Report of the Tenth Census*. Brooks remarks that " he seems to have been the first man to have a clear conception of the distribution of the mountain ranges in Alaska." [2] In 1883 Lieutenant F. Schwatka crossed the Chilkoot Pass, and reached the Lewes river, where he built a raft in which to make a journey down that river and the Yukon to the sea. Homan, who accompanied him, was the first to survey these two rivers. Two years later another officer, Lieutenant H. T. Allen, crossed the country from south to north, following the Copper river for 300 miles and the Tanana to its junction with the Yukon. He descended the Yukon, turned north to the Koyukuk, and explored that river back again to the Yukon, from which he made his way overland to Norton Sound. Allen's work was of a high order, and his journey was " one of the most remarkable in the annals of Alaskan exploration." [3]

Between 1883 and 1886 much exploration was carried out in the country round Kotzebue Sound. W. L. Howard crossed Northern Alaska from the Sound to Point Barrow, and was the first white man to visit these regions.

The fourth and final phase of Alaskan exploration dates from 1895, when the Geological Survey began operations. In the following year the discovery of gold in the Klondike led to a great rush of fortune-seekers, and two years later similar discoveries near Nome increased still more the fame of this hitherto despised country. The Geological Survey could not work fast enough, and demands for geographical knowledge could not be met. The members of the Survey, assisted in the early years of their work by military officers, began the systematic exploration of the country, and that work is not yet complete. About half the country has been mapped, but the task is of necessity slow and costly, and an effort is being made to supplement the groundwork by aerial surveys.[4] These have been started in North-eastern Alaska, which has hitherto been unexplored. The south-eastern part of the country is well known, and it is

[1] Brooks, *op. cit.*, p. 118.   [2] *Ibid.*, p. 121.   [3] *Ibid.*, p. 122.
[4] See below, Chapter XVII, p. 462, for such surveys by Sir Hubert Wilkins.

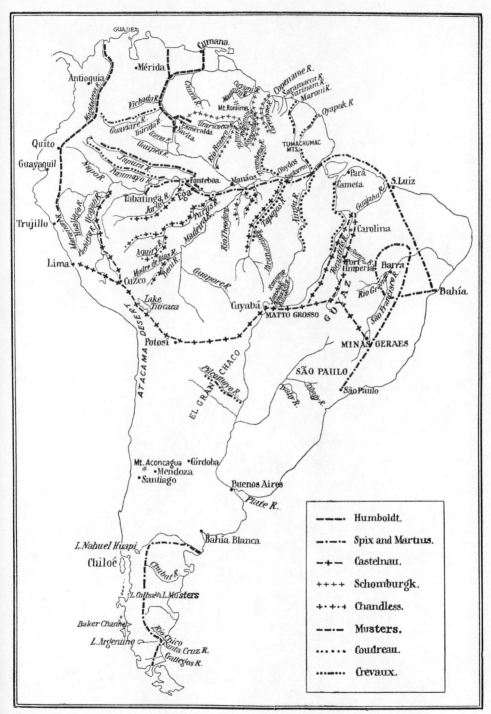

GUAJIRA

Cumana
Mérida
Antioquia
Coyuni R.
Copename R.
Saramacca R.
Surinam R.
Maroni R.
Vichada R.
Caura R.
Mt. Roraima
Oyapok R.
Guaviare R.
Inirida R.
Iceina R.
Uraricoeva
Esmeralda
Yarita
Quito
Guayaquil
Japura R.
Uaupes R.
TUMACHUMAC
MTS.
Rio Branco
Negro R.
Maumayo R.
Fonteboa
Manáos
Obydos
Santarem
Pará
Cameta
S. Luiz
Trujillo
Marañon R.
Hualiaga R.
Pachitea R.
Ucayali R.
Tabatinga R.
Jurtia R.
Ega
Purus R.
Madeira R.
Rio Theodoro
Tapajos R.
Xingu R.
Guajahu R.
Carolina
Lima
Aquiry R.
Madre de Dios R.
Beni R.
Guapore R.
Branduilinha
Jamaha Mukokus R.
Remaor
Joyazinha R.
Fort Imperial
Barra
Rio Grande
Bahía
CUZCO
Lake Titicaca
Cuyabá
MATTO GROSSO
GOYAZ
São Frascisco R.
MINAS GERAES
Potosi
SÃO PAULO
São Paulo
ATACAMA DESERT
EL GRAN CHACO
Pilcomayo R.
Verde R.
Tiete R.
Mt. Aconcagua
Córdoba
Mendoza
Santiago
Buenos Aires
Plate R.
Bahía Blanca
L. Nahuel Huapi
Chiloé
Chubut R.
L. Colhue
L. Musters
Baker Channel
Rio Chico
L. Argentino
Santa Cruz R.
Gallegos R.

– – – – ·	Humboldt.
– · – · – ·	Spix and Martius.
– + – + –	Castelnau.
+ + + +	Schomburgk.
+ · + · +	Chandless.
– – · – –	Musters.
· · · · · ·	Coudreau.
· · · – · ·	Crevaux.

Fig. 42. SOUTH AMERICA AFTER 1800

unlikely that any important features remain hidden in the few unexplored regions of the west.[1]

V. SOUTH AMERICA

In South America geographical exploration from the time of the Spanish conquerors until the end of the eighteenth century had, as already indicated, been carried on from a number of different localities, and had not followed any regular lines. Thus the continent had been crossed from the Atlantic to the Pacific in each of the centuries during which Europeans had been in the country. Similarly, the activities of Azara and of the French expedition under La Condamine had been carried on in regions whose major features were already known. Hence in South America one cannot trace any continuous advance from known to unknown regions such as marked the steady progress of explorers in the northern continent.

In the following pages the arrangement suggested by Sievers[2] will be followed, although, as he points out, it is not entirely satisfactory. He divides the century into two periods. The first was characterized by the epoch-making journeys of Humboldt and by a number of important explorations in certain parts of the continent such as Brazil and Guiana. During the second half of the century, with a few notable exceptions, the work was of a more detailed and systematic character.

To Alexander von Humboldt geography owes a great debt, for not only was he an able explorer, but he brought to his work a knowledge rarely surpassed in the history of discovery, and used the results of his travels to lay the foundations of the sciences of physical geography and meteorology as they are now taught. As another great scientist of the century, Louis Agassiz, has said : " Every child in our schools has his mind fed from the labours of Humboldt's brain wherever geography is no longer taught in the old routine."

Humboldt studied under Werner and with Von Buch. He travelled in England and on the Rhine with Forster. He read meteorology at Paris, where he made the acquaintance of Bonpland, who accompanied him on his travels. Leaving Corunna on June 5, 1799, he landed at Cumana on July 16. " I had long prepared myself," he wrote,

> for the observations which were the principal object of my journey
> to the torrid zone. I was provided with instruments of easy and

---

[1] On more recent exploration see P. S. Smith and J. B. Mertic, *Geology and Mineral Resources of North-western Alaska* (United States Geological Survey, Bulletin 815 (1930)). This contains a valuable map showing routes.

[2] W. Sievers, " Die geographische Erforschung Südamerikas im 19 Jahrhundert," in *P.M.*, vol. xlvi, p. 121. This is a very useful summary of exploration in the century.

convenient use, constructed by the ablest makers, and I enjoyed the special protection of a government which, far from presenting obstacles to my journey, constantly honoured me with every mark of regard and confidence. I was aided by a courageous and enlightened friend, and it was singularly propitious to the success of our participated labour, that the zeal and equanimity of that friend never failed, amidst the fatigues and dangers to which we were sometimes exposed.[1]

Humboldt was more than a mere explorer. While he wished to make known " regions which for ages have remained unknown to most of the nations of Europe " he also aimed at collecting " such facts which are fitted to elucidate a science of which we as yet possess scarcely the outline, and which has been vaguely denominated Natural History of the World, Theory of the Earth, or Physical Geography." With this latter object this book is not concerned, for it belongs rather to the history of scientific geography. It will therefore suffice to quote Humboldt's views of physical geography :

> The ultimate aim of physical geography is . . . to recognize unity in the vast diversity of phenomena, and by the exercise of thought and the combination of observations, to discern the constancy of phenomena in the midst of apparent changes. In the exposition of the terrestrial portion of Cosmos, it will occasionally be necessary to descend to very special facts ; but this will only be in order to recall the connection existing between the actual distribution of organic beings over the globe, and the laws of the ideal classification by natural families, analogy of internal organization, and progressive evolution.[2]

Humboldt's explorations were carried out in three regions, of which one, Mexico, has already been considered. In South America he first spent four months on the Orinoco or in the neighbourhood of that river, travelling about 1700 miles. He proved the connexion of the Orinoco and the Amazon and determined the position of the bifurcation. He ventured a prophecy as to the future of this region :

> The Cassiquiare, as broad as the Rhine, and the course of which is one hundred and eighty miles in length, will no longer form uselessly a navigable canal between two basins of rivers which have a surface of one hundred and ninety thousand square leagues. The grain of New Granada will be carried to the banks of the Rio Negro, boats will descend from the sources of the Napo and the Ucuyabe, from the Andes of Quito and of Upper Peru, to the mouths of the Orinoco, a distance which equals that from Timbuctoo to Marseilles. A country nine or ten times larger than Spain and enriched with the most varied productions, is navigable in every direction by the medium of the natural canal of the Cassiquiare and the bifurcation of the rivers.[3]

[1] *Personal Narrative of Travels to the Equinoctial Regions of America*, translated and edited by T. Ross (3 vols., 1851), vol. i, p. ix.
[2] A. von Humboldt, *Cosmos* (5 vols., 1849–58, Bohn's edition), vol. i, p. 43.
[3] *Travels*, vol. ii, p. 431.

AMERICA

Having added greatly to the general knowledge of Venezuela, Humboldt went to Cuba, returning shortly afterward to South America, when he ascended the Magdalena river and crossed the mountains to Quito. The Andes were examined as far as Northern Perú, and the headstreams of the Amazon were visited. From Trujillo Humboldt sailed to Lima, where he spent four months. He left South America in January 1803, and landed in Bordeaux on August 3, 1804.

The second part of Humboldt's journey furnished him with material with which to construct an elaborate, though incorrect, theory of the Cordilleras of the Andes. " This," he wrote,

> is the most continuous, the longest, the most uniform in its direction from south to north and north-north-west of any chain of the globe. It approaches the north and south poles at unequal distances of 22° to 33°. . . . We may consider as the two extremities of the Andes, the rock or granitic island of Diego Ramirez, south of Cape Horn, and the mountains lying at the mouth of the Mackenzie River, more than twelve degrees west of the Greenstone mountains, known by the name of Copper Mountains, visited by Captain Franklin.[1]

He then indicated how his particular researches had improved the knowledge of parts of the South American Andes.

> The structure of the Cordillera . . . that is, its division into several chains nearly parallel, which are again joined by knots of mountains, is very remarkable. On our maps this structure is indicated but imperfectly ; and what La Condamine and Bouguer merely guessed, during their long visit to the tableland of Quito, has been generalised and ill-interpreted by those who have described the whole chain according to the type of the equatorial Andes. . . . The Cordillera of the Andes, considered in its whole extent . . . to the isthmus of Panama, is sometimes ramified into chains more or less parallel, and sometimes articulated by immense knots of mountains. We distinguish nine of these knots, and consequently an equal number of branching-points and ramifications.[2]

It was Humboldt's ability to analyse his discoveries and correlate his data with the results of others that gave his work such value. He further stimulated exploration in South America by calling attention to its wealth of geographical material and its many unknown regions.

During the fifty years which followed Humboldt's travels the motive which inspired travellers was almost entirely a desire to improve scientific knowledge. This is seen first in the expeditions made to Brazil between 1810 and 1822. W. L. von Eschwege (1811–14), Prince Maximilian of Wied-Neuwied (1815–17), Auguste de Saint-Hilaire (1816–22), J. B. von Spix and C. F. P. von Martius (1817–20), and J. E. Pohl and Natterer (1817–21) were the chief explorers, and they covered an area lying east of longitude 50° W. Natterer went farther, crossing Matto Grosso, between the head-

---

[1] *Travels*, vol. iii, p. 294.   [2] *Ibid.*, vol. iii, pp. 296, 315.

waters of the Araguaya and the Guapore, and travelling down the latter and the Madeira to the Amazon. Pohl descended the Tocantins to below Carolina. Both these journeys were additional to travels through inner Minas Geraes and Goyaz. The two first-named explorers confined their work mainly to short distances from the coast, but Spix and Von Martius travelled extensively, and produced more important results than any of the others. They first made a land journey from São Paulo to Bahía, and then across North-eastern Brazil to the Amazon. Most of the country visited was already known, but their expedition was none the less a considerable achievement. The second part of their exploration was on the Amazon, which they both ascended to Ega. Spix followed the main stream to Tabatinga, while Martius followed the Japura to "the foot of the mountain Arascoara in the middle of the southern continent, separated from Quito only by the Cordilleras." This was the first scientific work carried out on the Amazon since the expedition of La Condamine.

In the central and northern regions of the Cordillera there was considerable activity between 1822 and 1842. J. B. Boussingault travelled very extensively between 1822 and 1835, including not only Colombia, Ecuador, and Perú, but also Venezuela and the Orinoco in his journeys. The geographical results were not proportionate to the amount of ground covered. The first survey of Venezuela was undertaken by A. Codazzi during this period (1830–40), and he began a similar work in Colombia, but died in 1859 before the task was finished. In the Bolivian Andes J. B. Pentland carried out useful observations, and during a long period spent in this and neighbouring regions, extending from 1825 to 1837, examined Lake Titicaca and measured the heights of a number of peaks. Farther north, in Perú, J. J. von Tschudi, between 1838 and 1842, made considerable additions to geographical knowledge, although his main interests were in biology and in archæology.

While the details of these lands in the Cordillera were thus being filled in a number of important and larger travels were made in the country. Between 1826 and 1833 the French zoologist and ethnologist A. D. d'Orbigny was engaged in highly important researches, and his expeditions covered a very wide field in Southern Brazil, Uruguay, Argentina, Patagonia, and on the west of the Cordillera. His was the first scientific examination of the lands round the La Plata during the new age of exploration, while to the south of that river he traversed a region that was very little known. At the same time E. Pöppig (1827–32) was opening up new country on the west. He visited Chile, and from Santiago went to Lima, where his more important work began. Crossing the Cordillera, he reached the Huallaga, one of the headstreams of the Amazon, and travelled down it to the delta.

Two other transcontinental journeys were performed at this time. In 1827 H. L. Maw started from Lima for Trujillo, whence he crossed the Peruvian Andes, partly on foot, to the Cachiyaco, and after many adventures reached Santarem. Seven years later Lieutenant W. Smyth and F. Lowe set out from Lima. The journey was undertaken " with the hope of ascertaining that from the port of Mayro, on the Pachitea, the river might be found navigable to its junction with the Ucayali, and that by means of the latter and the Amazon a good communication might be found to exist between Perú and the Atlantic Ocean." The object of this journey was not attained, because the party could not reach Mayro. " The course of our navigation," wrote Smyth,

> was down the Huallaga from Casapi, which is about forty miles from Huanco, to the mouth of the Chipurana ; up that stream and the Yanayacu as high as canoes could go ; then across the intervening part of the Pampa to Santa Catalina ; and down the stream which bears that name to the Ucayali . . . and down the Ucayali into the Marañon and by the latter to Pará.[1]

The river was surveyed as far as the mouth of the Negro, and Smyth claimed that " in the positions we have laid down we have been tolerably accurate."

Meanwhile another British expedition had been carrying out very valuable work in the south. Between 1826 and 1830 King and Fitzroy surveyed the coasts from the Plate river to Chiloé. Fitzroy returned in 1831, and his ship, the *Beagle*, carried Charles Darwin, whose explorations in the south may be compared with those of Humboldt in the north. The surveys were completed as far as Guayaquil on the west coast, and part of unknown Patagonia was visited. The Santa Cruz river was followed for about 250 miles and to within sight of the Andes, when shortage of food made a return necessary. Darwin's extensive researches during his long stay in the country are recorded in his *Geological Observations on South America* and in his *Journal of Researches into the Natural History and Geology of the Countries visited during the Voyage of H.M.S. "Beagle" round the World*, and proved of great value to him in the composition of his later and more famous *Origin of Species*.

The last of the journeys during this period was that of Count François de Castelnau, who commanded a French expedition in the years 1843–47. He spent some time in the interior of Brazil, examining the country already visited by Natterer, descending the Araguaya, and ascending the Tocantins. He travelled into the interior, to Cuyabá, determined the sources of the Paraguay, and greatly improved the knowledge of the basin of that river. He then visited El Gran Chaco, crossed to Bolivia, and explored the country between Potosí and Lima, after which he returned to Cuzco, whence

[1] *J.R.G.S.*, vol. vi, p. 11 (with map).

he set out again for the east in 1846. Travelling by the Urubamba, the Ucayali, and the Amazon, he reached Pará. This expedition covered much ground, and added greatly to geographical knowledge, although all the astronomical and meteorological records of the journey were lost owing to the murder of Viscount d'Osery, in whose charge they had been placed.

Between 1835 and 1844 R. H. Schomburgk carried out very important explorations in British Guiana and neighbouring regions. The country was by no means unknown, and had attracted much attention in the days when El Dorado had proved so powerful a magnet. It had been visited during the seventeenth and eighteenth centuries by a number of explorers, including La Condamine. Yet Humboldt was able to point out that to the south and east of Esmeralda, on the Upper Orinoco,[1] there was a region three times as large as Spain " without a single position determined astronomically." It was to this region that Schomburgk devoted his attention. Between 1835 and 1838 he explored the Essequibo and Rupununi rivers, discovering the sources of the former. He also crossed to the Rio Branco, and explored the Caruma range, which lies to the east.

In the autumn of 1839 an expedition was made to the westward to explore Roraima Mountain. Schomburgk reached Esmeralda, all but discovered the sources of the Orinoco, and returned by the Cassiquiare, Negro, and Branco rivers. In this journey of over 3000 miles he definitely linked the Guiana territory with the lands already explored by Humboldt.

In 1841 Schomburgk explored the delta of the Orinoco, and surveyed a number of the smaller rivers lying between it and the Essequibo, and in the following year reached the sources of the Takutu, on the south-western borders of what is now British Guiana. In his last journey, in 1843–44, he crossed from the upper valley of the Rupununi to the Corentyne (which now forms the eastern boundary of British Guiana), and followed that river to the sea. Schomburgk's "botanical and zoological collections over all the region form a valuable acquisition to the British Museum, while his observations of the various aspects of British Guiana may be said to form the bases of all subsequent explorations."[2]

By the middle of the century the main features of South America were known, although three large blanks still appeared on the maps. These were to be found in the Amazon basin, most of the rivers of which were imperfectly mapped, in El Gran Chaco, and in Patagonia. The work of succeeding explorers has been to fill in these gaps and to study with increasing intensity and care those parts of the continent already known.

[1] In the Amazonas Territory of Venezuela.
[2] *Royal Geographical Society: Supplementary Papers*, vol. iii, p. 184.

AMERICA

This systematic exploration of known areas was very conspicuous in the period from 1850 to 1860. It is marked by the work of Codazzi in Colombia, Pissis in Chile and the Atacama Desert, Philippi in Chile, Burmeister in Brazil and the Argentine, and Raimondi in Perú. Codazzi's activities as a surveyor have already been mentioned : his work belongs strictly to an earlier period, for his mapping in Colombia was ended by his death in 1859. Aimé Pissis, of French origin, mapped large areas in Chile, and produced a very important work on the republic, which was illustrated by an atlas. R. A. Philippi visited the Atacama Desert in 1853–54, travelled extensively in Chile between 1850 and 1883, and occupied the Chair of Natural History at Santiago. The German H. K. Burmeister, who became Director of the National Museum of Buenos Aires, examined the country between the Paraná system and the Cordillera, and crossed the continent to Copiapo. In Perú A. D. Raimondi did excellent work, more especially in his surveys made between 1851 and 1869. While the maps of Pissis and Cadozzi have for the most part been replaced by more modern surveys those of Raimondi are still of great value for their " general accuracy and quality of compilation and reproduction." [1]

A large amount of specialized work was done by foreign visitors to South America during this period : H. Reck's mapping of the Bolivian plateau between 1850 and 1866, the accounts of the journeys of R. Avé-Lallemant (1858–59) and of Von Tschudi (1857–60) in Brazil, the south of which was explored by the latter in a pioneer expedition, the botanical investigations of H. Karsten in Venezuela and Ecuador (1849–56), and the researches of M. Wagner in Ecuador and Colombia (1857–60) are among the more conspicuous efforts. Halfeld's exploration of the São Francisco river in 1852–54 and Page's work in the Paraná-Paraguay valley also deserve mention. It was during this period also that the English geographer C. R. Markham made his journey through part of the forest region of the Eastern Peruvian Andes.

The blank spaces in the Amazon valley were to some extent reduced, and the courses of the rivers more accurately determined, in the period between 1862 and 1880. Special mention must be made of the great work of A. R. Wallace and H. W. Bates. The two men set out for Pará in 1848, and both lived in that city for a year and a half. They made an expedition up the Tocantins in the later months of 1848, and again in 1849 went to Cameta. They then journeyed up the Amazon to Santarem and Obydos, and thence to the junction of the Rio Negro, where they parted. Wallace went to the Orinoco, and stayed for a month in Yavita. He returned to England in 1852. Bates followed the main stream for 370 miles, to Ega, where he lived for over a year before returning to Pará.

[1] *Geographical Review*, vol. xx, p. 139.

In October 1857 Bates again left Pará, and for the next three and a half years made his headquarters at Santarem, from which place he undertook frequent journeys, including one up the Tapajos. He returned to Ega for another four years, and then proceeded by steamer up the river to Fonteboa, in (approximately) longitude 66° W. He proposed to go to the foot of the Andes, but illness compelled him to return to Ega, and he finally left for England in February 1859. He collected over fourteen thousand specimens, of which about eight thousand were new to science.

Bates became Assistant Secretary to the Royal Geographical Society in 1864, and devoted the rest of his life to giving the public the benefit of his most valuable experience of life in the tropical lands of South America. He died in 1892. The work of Wallace and Bates, though not geographical in a narrow sense, had a great effect on the thought of the period, and both men contributed powerfully to that reorientation of geographical outlook which was a marked feature of the second half of the nineteenth century.

The tracing of the courses of the many tributaries of the Amazon was a lengthy task, and occupied explorers of all nationalities for more than twenty years. On the main river it began with the explorations of Acevedo and Pinto, between 1862 and 1864. At the same time Chandless was engaged in his excellent work higher up the valley. He surveyed the Tapajos from its sources ; he ascended the Purus for 1866 miles, and mapped a great area of its basin ; he explored the Aquiry for 465 miles, and from it made a long journey into the forest in an effort to reach the Madre de Dios ; in 1867 he went up the Jurua for 1200 miles from its mouth ; in the following year he traced the Canuma, Abacaxio, and Masé-assu rivers ;[1] and in 1869 he explored the Beni. Few men did more extensive and more accurate work in the Amazon basin.

The Peruvian feeders of the Amazon, and in particular the Napo, were investigated by Orton, while Tucker, between 1868 and 1874, explored the Ucayali, the Pachitea, and the Pichis, and Werthemann surveyed the Tambo, Samarez, and Putumayo. Church on the Madeira and Purus, C. B. Brown on the southern tributaries of the Amazon, and Selfridge on the Madeira all added to geographical knowledge between 1875 and 1878, while the Putumayo was again visited by Reyes in the first of those years.

These more specialized journeys were followed by the very important travels of the French explorer Jules Crevaux. His activities on the Amazon basin date from 1879, when he followed the Putumayo to its sources and returned by the Japura. In 1880–81 he went to the Magdalena, and then from the mountains of Colombia descended the Guaviare, and thus reached the Orinoco. The next year he began an exploration of the Pilcomayo, but in an attempt to

[1] These rivers enter the Amazon between the Madeira and the Tapajos.

throw some light on the unknown El Gran Chaco was murdered. His work was of a very high order, and he must rank, with Chandless, as one of the greatest of the explorers of this period. In honour of his achievement the Geographical Society of Paris issued an atlas of the rivers of South America, based in part on his work.

Among the other explorers who contributed to knowledge in the Amazon basin must be mentioned those engaged on the Venezuela-Brazilian Boundary Commission of 1880–82 and P. Labre. Labre explored the country round the source of the Madre de Dios, where earlier in the century Maldonado had lost his life in proving that the river ran into the Madeira and not into the Purus.

H. Coudreau, on the Tapajos in 1895, on the Xingú in the next year, on the Araguaya in 1896–97, and especially by his discovery of many of the rivers between the Tocantins and the Xingú in 1898, added very considerably to the knowledge of the hydrography of the Amazon basin and completed the work of scientific discovery in the century. Others after him worked on rivers already known, and added to knowledge of those rivers, but the era of great expeditions was at an end.[1]

The two remaining areas of unknown land in 1850 lay within the republic of Argentina. In this state and in Southern Chile almost all of the blanks in the map were filled in after 1870,[2] and the greater part of the work was accomplished by 1890. In the Argentine the researches of many able Germans attached to the University of Córdoba, and the Indian wars of 1879–80 and 1884–85, brought much valuable geographical information. The journeys of J. Fontana, between 1875 and 1880, for the first time opened up the southern part of El Gran Chaco. Crevaux endeavoured to add still more to the knowledge of this region, but was murdered by Indians : his work was, however, completed by A. Thouar, who approached the Pilcomayo river from Bolivia, and crossed the Chaco by that route in 1883. Thus the Pilcomayo route to Bolivia and the Bermejo route to the Cordilleras were both known. The surveys of J. Page on the Bermejo, the explorations of Baldrich on the Pilcomayo and to the south of that river, and the numerous attempts to open up routes across the continent filled in many of the details of the southern part of the Chaco, but the northern regions remained practically unknown at the end of the century.

In Southern Argentina D'Orbigny's journey from Buenos Aires to Bahía Blanca at the end of the third decade, and the expedition of the *Beagle*, together with some investigations of the coastline and a

[1] Other explorations were : 1897, Labre on the Madre de Dios ; 1892, Pando on the Madre de Dios ; 1893, Pando on the Purus-Aquiry ; 1894, Pando on the Jurua and Javary.

[2] The great work of Burmeister, already mentioned, and the journeys of De Moussy in the country south of the Bermejo in the period 1854–63 are notable exceptions to this statement.

second ascent of the Rio Negro in 1833, had all increased the meagre knowledge which existed in 1800, but the region as a whole was unexplored. Its discovery owed much to the pioneer journey of an Englishman, G. C. Musters, who traversed the country from Punta Arenas, on Magellan's Strait, to the mouth of the Rio Negro in 1869–70. From Santa Cruz he followed the Rio Chico nearly to its source, and then skirted the foothills of the Andes. He lived with the Indians, and was unable to make precise observations, but he had an opportunity of collecting many important facts of physical and human geography, and he must be given the credit for the pioneer exploration of Patagonia.[1]

Although Musters had done much good work, he had failed to discover many of the important features of the country. This task was undertaken without delay. Between 1881 and 1897 no less than nine expeditions visited Tierra del Fuego ; the exploration of the interior was completed by Bove, Lista, Popper, and Scheltze. Farther north the discovery of Lake Argentino by Feilberg in 1873 marks the beginning of intensive exploration in Southern Patagonia. Two years later Francisco Moreno began a long series of expeditions, which continued throughout the remainder of the century. Moreno told the story of his exploits to the Royal Geographical Society in 1899. " It was in 1873," he said,

> when I made my first excursion to Patagonia, that I visited the Rio
> Negro. The year following, I returned to the same places, and went
> as far as Santa Cruz. In 1875 I crossed from Buenos Aires to Lake
> Nahuel-Huapi and the Andean Cordillera, between the parallels of
> 39° 32' and 42°. In 1876 I visited Chubut, and ascended the river
> Santa Cruz, recognizing that the lake found by Feilberg was not the
> one Viedma discovered [in 1782], and that these lakes, with many
> others, formed a vast system situated in a longitudinal depression
> parallel with the Cordillera. . . . In 1877 some Chilian officers visited
> the sources of the river Santa Cruz in the lake. Steinmann shortly
> afterwards reached the same point, as well as the Argentine travellers,
> Castillo, Moyano, and Lista. Moyano crossed from Santa Cruz to
> the Chubut, partly following the route taken by Musters and that
> of Durnford, who had visited lakes Musters and Colhue in 1877. In
> 1879 I again returned to the Rio Negro, crossed Patagonia as far as
> the Cordillera, on parallel 44, and followed the slopes towards the
> north, again examining Lake Nahuel-Huapi and reaching nearly up
> to parallel 39°. It was at this period that the 1881 treaty was made
> [between Argentina and Chile ; both sides began to explore the
> Cordillera along which the boundary between the two states ran].
> I myself set to work to carry out similar investigations. From 1882
> to 1895 I examined the Andean regions of the Republic, between
> parallels 23° and 34° ; and, in 1896, I returned to Patagonia by the
> slopes of the Cordillera and the interior thereof, until I reached Lake
> Buenos Aires. . . . In 1897 I visited the Patagonian region situated
> between the straits of Magellan and 51°. . . . In 1898 I ascended, for

[1] See *J.R.G.S.*, vol. xxxiv, p. 205, and Musters' own book, *At Home with the Patagonians* (1871).

the second time, the Santa Cruz river ; and along the eastern slopes I traversed the territory as far as Lake Nahuel-Huapi and Puerto Montt.[1]

Moreno was recognized as the foremost authority on the geography of the Argentine. He served on the Commission to demarcate the boundary between Chile and the Argentine in 1902, and five years later was awarded the Founders' Medal of the Royal Geographical Society.

In order to give a connected account of Moreno's explorations it has been necessary to anticipate many of the pioneer journeys in Patagonia and Southern Chile. Among them were Moyano's exploration of the Rio Chico in 1878 and Durnford's work in Central Patagonia, referred to above. In the same region Moyano crossed from the Chubut to the Deseado river in 1880, and Fontana explored the Chubut river in 1886. A number of subsequent journeys filled in the blanks in the neighbourhood of this river. Farther southward Moyano's discovery of the sources of the Coilé and Gallegos rivers marked the beginning of intensive investigation in this region, where between 1886 and 1898 much useful work was accomplished. From the side of Chile came the surveyors attached to the Chilean Hydrographic Office, and the British and German officers with the *Alert* and the *Albatross* began the systematic mapping of the coastal fringe, while inland among the more prominent explorers were Krüger and Steffen. The latter, like Moreno, served ultimately on the Argentine-Chile Boundary Commission, and brought to this work an extensive knowledge of the Western Cordillera, gained as the result of his explorations, begun in 1891. During the remainder of the century he gave his attention to the mountains, rivers, and lakes of this complicated and little-known area, covering more particularly the region lying between Lake Nahuel-Huapi and Baker Channel. The Boundary Commission, under the charge of Sir Thomas Holdich, did much supplementary work in those districts which Steffen and Moreno had made peculiarly their own.[2]

In the Cordillera farther to the northward of the regions just considered the attempts to find suitable routes from Mendoza to the Argentine led to much valuable and detailed investigation by Stelzner (1872–73) and Avé-Lallemant, while the efforts to climb Mount Aconcagua, and particularly the success of Fitzgerald, attracted attention to a little-known region. Host's investigations of the country lying between the parallels of 39° and 36°, and those of

[1] *G.J.*, vol. xiv, pp. 242–244.
[2] On the Boundary Commission's work see Sir Thomas Holdich, *The Countries of the King's Award* (1904), and *G.J.*, vol. xxiii, p. 153. Steffen gave some account of his work in a paper on " The Patagonian Cordillera and its Main Rivers between 41° and 48° South Latitude," in *G.J.*, vol. xvi, p. 14.

Brackebusch, who made five expeditions between 1881 and 1888, added materially to geographical knowledge. The latter devoted his attention more especially to the region lying north of Mendoza. He carried out very extensive researches, collected much material, and used it for the compilation of many maps of Argentina. In Chile the scientific work of the Philippis was of a high order. That of R. A. Philippi has already been mentioned. His son, F. Philippi, carried on his work in the Atacama region in 1885. Further knowledge of the desert came through the expeditions of A. Bertrand, who also explored the mountains to the eastward, and produced a good map of the Cordillera between the parallels of 21° and 27° S. In 1890 the Atacama was again studied by the German engineer Darapsky.

In the Peruvian-Bolivian Cordillera a very large number of investigators contributed to the growth of geographical knowledge. Among the travellers were André (1875), Wiener (1875–76), Baron von Thielmann (1877), and Hettner (1888–89). Useful maps of parts of the region were constructed by Minchin, Musters, and Werthemann. Heath explored the upper course of the Beni. Pando mapped the country between the Beni and Cuzco, while still farther north Senèze and Nötzli, Reimbach, James, and Ordinaire examined the Peruvian Cordillera in their search for suitable routes to the east.

Two scientists, W. Reiss and A. Stubel, whose names are connected with many important investigations in the north-eastern part of the continent, form a connecting-link between those whose work lay mainly in Perú and others in Ecuador, Colombia, and Venezuela. The chief interests of both men lay in geology and ethnology, but they made valuable contributions to the physical geography of the regions they visited. Beginning in 1868 in the extreme north of Colombia, they followed the Magdalena route to Quito, and began a systematic examination of the mountain ranges both in Colombia and Ecuador, a work which occupied them until 1874, after which they visited Perú. They produced a valuable map of Ecuador. T. Wolf, a geologist, also mapped Ecuador, being commissioned by the Government to travel over the country.

In Colombia R. B. White (1862–78) examined Antioquia, where at the end of the century F. Regel (1896) also did useful work. Hettner's explorations in the Eastern Cordillera, and especially those of W. Sievers on the borderlands of Colombia and Venezuela, were further valuable contributions to the geography of a country in which so many distinguished men have worked. Farther eastward, in Venezuela, the inaccessible Guajira was visited by the Englishman Simons in 1878, while two years before Sachs had crossed the Llanos to the Orinoco. Here also Sievers collected many geographical facts in his travels, first in 1884–85 in the Cordillera of Mérida, and later (1892–93) through Central Venezuela.

In the Guianas and neighbouring regions exploration was renewed in 1872, and carried on throughout the remainder of the century. Even before this date the long residence of Appun in Eastern Venezuela, where he was engaged in botanical and zoological researches from 1849 to 1868, added somewhat to general geographical knowledge, while C. B. Brown's survey work in the years following 1868 was of the greatest importance and solved the problems of many of the rivers of British Guiana. The investigations of Montolieu (1872), Chaffanjon (1884–91), and Stradelli (1888) in the Orinoco basin threw some light on the sources of that river. Montolieu explored the Inirida and Stradelli the Vichada, both of them in Colombia, while Chaffanjon made expeditions to the upper courses of the Caura and the Orinoco. In this little-known region a large number of geographical facts were determined by the Brazil-Venezuela Boundary Commission of 1880–82, the Venezuela-British Guiana Boundary Commission, whose results were published in 1897, and the travels of Hübner in the Upper Orinoco and Branco regions in 1895.

The earlier work of Schomburgk and Brown in British Guiana was supplemented by that of many other travellers. The attempts to climb Roraima Mountain took Boddham-Whetham (1878), Whitely (1883), and Im Thurn (1884) to the country, and the work of the last named, more especially in natural history and ethnology, was of great value. He contributed much to the accurate knowledge of the western parts of the colony, and by his explorations of the rivers, among them the Cuyuni and the Mazaruni, was able to extend the topographical work of the pioneers.

In Dutch Guiana Zimmerman in 1877 and Loth in 1879 traced the greater part of the Surinam and Saramacca rivers, while the geologist Martin and the ethnologist Kate contributed indirectly to the geography of the country. In 1901 an important expedition, commanded by Major L. Bakhuis, explored a part of the interior of the country, and in particular did valuable work on the Copename river.

In French Guiana Crevaux, whose work in other parts of South America has already been noticed, traced the Oyapok and Maroni rivers in 1877, and crossed the Tumachumac Mountains to the Jary river, which he explored. This was an important journey in that it connected the surveys in Guiana with the lands round the delta of the Amazon, which were already known. His explorations were continued, and very largely supplemented, by H. A. Coudreau in the region of the Tumachumac Mountains, on the rivers of the country, and in the lands lying immediately north of the Amazon delta. Coudreau began his work in French Guiana in 1881, and in the course of nearly twenty years explored many parts of South

America, both within the French colony and elsewhere.[1] He died of fever in 1899, during the exploration of the Trombetas, a large river flowing into the Lower Amazon from the north.

Of the many important contributions made to the knowledge of Brazil during this later period only a few of outstanding significance can be mentioned. The Englishmen J. W. Wells and P. Bigg-Wither each explored unknown regions. The latter in 1872, in the course of railway surveys, examined much new country in Southern Brazil, in the valleys of the Ivahy and Tibagy. Wells, who lived for a very long period in the country, made his more important contributions to geography in the north, in the valleys of the São Francisco and Tocantins. He followed the first to the Rio Grande, and then by way of the Rio Somno reached the Tocantins, which he explored to Carolina. Thence by the Guajahu he travelled to the coast at S. Luiz. "Wells made a special study of the physical geography and orography of Brazil, the results of which as embodied in his maps and memoirs were of high value." [2]

It was, however, mainly due to the work of a number of able German explorers that most progress was made during this period. With the exception of the valuable geological researches of the American O. A. Derby in Minas Geraes, Goyaz, and São Paulo (1886) and the expeditions of Coudreau (to which reference has been made) in the north, nearly all the discoveries are to be placed to their credit. Conspicuous among them was C. von den Steinen, who led a party in 1884 down the whole course of the Xingú from the Batovy to its junction with the Amazon. Three years later he explored the Kulisehu, another of the headstreams of the Xingú, and acquired some further information about the inhabitants of the region. Some of the other headstreams of the Xingú remain to the present day unexplored.[3] It was in this same region that H. Meyer carried out his most valuable work. In 1895–96 he partly explored the Jatoba and Ronuro. He returned in 1899, and again devoted his attention to the Ronuro and its tributaries, while his party added greatly to botanical and ethnological knowledge through their researches.

The last expedition which requires notice is that of the Brazilian Commission for the exploration of Central Brazil. The Commission was sent to select a site for the new capital of Brazil, and in the course of its work explored a large piece of country in Eastern Goyaz. Specialists collected valuable information on the geology and botany, while many corrections were made to the poor maps then available and the positions of a number of places were definitely

---

[1] See above, p. 408, for Crevaux, and p. 409, for Coudreau.
[2] *Royal Geographical Society: Supplementary Papers*, vol. iii, p. 186.
[3] On this expedition see *Zeitschrift der Gesellschaft für Erdkunde zu Berlin*, vol. xxviii, p. 243.

established. The expedition carried out its task between the summer of 1892 and the beginning of the following year, under the command of L. Crulo, Director of the Observatory of Rio de Janeiro.

The exploration of South America during the nineteenth century presents some striking contrasts with that of North America. In the latter, although the Spaniards had established themselves on the west coast and in Texas, they made little effort to extend their knowledge eastward. The political conditions in New Spain, and the relations between it and the home country, as well as the desert conditions to be found north of Mexico proper, doubtless explain these circumstances. In addition the vast work of geographical reconnaissance performed by fur-traders finds no counterpart in South America. In that country the progress of geographical exploration during the nineteenth century followed much the same general lines as that of the two earlier centuries, with greater intensity and confusion arising from the number of explorers, the wealth of material, and the vastness of the problems. Even here, however, progress was delayed by geographical conditions, and at the beginning of the present century there remained a great area within the Amazon basin which was entirely unknown. Difficulties of movement away from the rivers and difficulties of supply have preserved this region for the explorers of the future.

Many scientific expeditions continue to devote their attention to systematic work on the geography of the known portions of South America or to the exploration of its unknown regions. Among the latter it is natural that the great basin of the Amazon should attract much attention. Three expeditions only can be referred to here. The most important geographical work in this region within the present century has been carried out by Dr Hamilton Rice. He began in 1907, when he made his way into the north-west of the basin and surveyed the Uaupes river to its junction with the Rio Negro. This work was continued in 1912–13 by a survey of the Içana and part of the Inirida, while in 1917 the survey of the Rio Negro was completed down to Manáos. In 1919–20 Dr Rice surveyed the Negro up to the Cassiquiare river and the Orinoco, while on a fifth expedition, in 1924–25, he did similar work on the Rio Branco and the Uraricoera. The accounts of his journeys not only bring out his own great contribution to the accurate knowledge of a vast area of South America, but form a valuable commentary on the work of many others who have travelled in these regions. By his excellent work Dr Rice has earned a place among the greatest of South American explorers.[1]

On the southern side of the basin is another region very imperfectly known. As long ago as 1890 a British syndicate was formed to

[1] On Dr Rice's expeditions see *G.J.*, vol. xxxv, p. 683, vol. xliv, p. 137, vol. lii, p. 205, vol. lviii, p. 321, vol. lxxi, pp. 113–143, 209–223, 345–356.

survey the western part of Matto Grosso, but it was not able to complete its work. In this region Colonel Rondon, first alone, and then with Theodore Roosevelt, carried out important explorations, and, although the results were not all that were anticipated, they were yet of great value, and one of the rivers which was explored now bears the name of the leader of the later expedition.[1]

Farther to the eastward, in that region where Von den Steinen and Meyer had worked at the end of the nineteenth century, Colonel Fawcett was in all probability murdered by natives some time after the end of May 1925. Fawcett had many explorations in South America to his credit. He had acted as Chief Commissioner on the Bolivia-Brazil Boundary Commission in 1906, and again in 1909,[2] and his explorations in Eastern Bolivia were of much value. He forms a link with the earliest explorers in this region. As he himself said in 1910:

> The story of Hernandez Pizarro and his trying march from Quito to the Amazon has to be repeated if any considerable force be taken. It may reasonably have the same quest, for ever since that notable pursuit of an elusive Indian civilisation there have been rumours in the interior of South America of the existence of a strange tribe.[3]

> [Fawcett] made exhaustive studies of these legends and saw in them the answer to the riddle of Lost Atlantis. With the object of proving his theories he set out in 1925, accompanied by his son Jack and a young friend Raleigh Rimell, confident that he was on the eve of making momentous discoveries that would startle the whole world.[4]

> [He had] proposed to leave civilization at Cuyabá and strike north with mules to the Paranatinga, descending that river by canoe to about latitude 10° south, and then striking eastward on foot, cross to the Xingu, and thence to the Araguaya, make for Port Imperial on the Tocantins, and come out at Barra do Rio Grande on the São Francisco.[5]

He has never returned, and there is good reason to believe that he has been murdered. In a remarkable search expedition Commander G. M. Dyott crossed the country from Cuyabá to the Kulisehu river, reached the Xingú, and followed it to the Amazon.[6]

It is a strange fact that the beginning and the end of exploration in the Amazon valley should have almost the same object. The quest is dangerous and attended by many hardships, due in large measure to geographical conditions, and the region still holds many problems for solution by scientific investigators.

[1] Roosevelt's expedition is described in his book *Through the Brazilian Wilderness* (1914).

[2] On Colonel Fawcett's Bolivian exploration see *G.J.*, vol. xxxv, p. 513, and on his last expedition *G.J.*, vol. lxxi, p. 176, and vol. lxxiv, p. 513.

[3] *Ibid.*, vol. xxxv, p. 522.   [4] *Ibid.*, vol. lxxiv, p. 513.

[5] *Ibid.*, vol. lxxi, p. 176.

[6] His account is in *G.J.*, vol. lxxiv, p. 513. The problem is no nearer solution, in spite of reports that Fawcett has been seen or that some of his belongings have been found. See *G.J.*, vol. lxxxviii, p. 66.

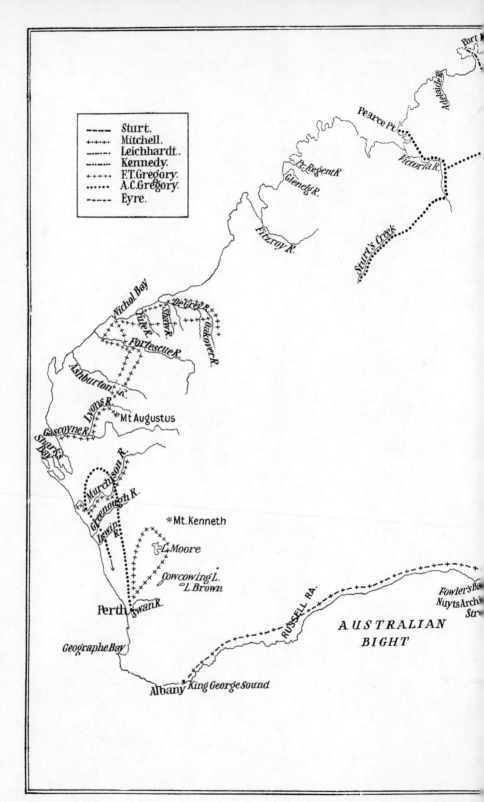

Fig. 43. AUSTRALIA TO 185

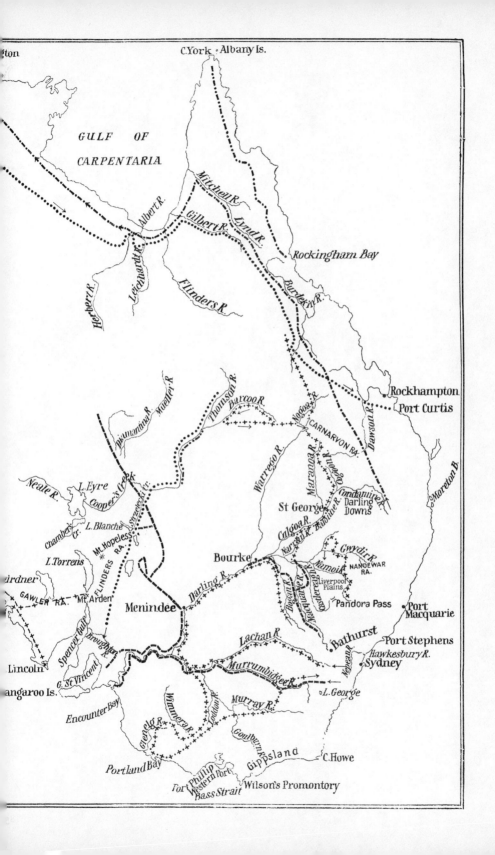

CHAPTER XVI

AUSTRALASIA AND THE EAST INDIES[1]

WHEREAS in the other continents Europeans had acquired a considerable amount of knowledge before the period of modern discovery begins, in Australia, New Guinea, and New Zealand inland exploration is confined to the last hundred and fifty years. Even in some of the larger islands of the Pacific and Indian Oceans little had been done, although some, like Borneo and Sumatra, had been known and visited for three hundred years.

In the East Indies exploration begins, for all practical purposes, with the travels of A. R. Wallace (1854–60) ; in New Zealand, although a little had been done to open up the interior during the first half of the century, a great impetus to settlement was given by the discovery of gold in Otago in 1861. The exact form of New Guinea was not determined until Captain Moresby visited the south-eastern extremity in 1873, and while inland exploration begins with Wallace's residence on the north coast in 1858, little real progress was made for another fifteen years.

In Australia, to which the major part of this chapter is devoted, exploration falls broadly into three periods. During the first period, beginning in 1788 with the settlement on Port Jackson, exploration was concerned with the coastal regions and the rivers which originated behind the eastern mountains. It may be called the exploration of the Murray-Darling system, and was complete by the year 1842. During this first period, also, the outlines of the coast were finally determined, and a small amount of progress was made in the west ; the two areas of discovery were joined by the transcontinental journey of Eyre in 1841.

[1] For Australia see the following :

> E. FAVENC, *History of Australian Exploration* (1888), the best general work.
> E. SCOTT, *Terre Napoléon* (1910).
> —— *Australian Discovery*, vol. i, " By Sea," vol. ii, " By Land " (1929). This contains valuable introductory chapters and extracts from the original accounts of explorers. It has been used extensively, and is cited as *Discovery*.
> *The Australasian School Atlas* (edited by J. G. Bartholomew and K. R. Cramp, 1915) contains valuable maps illustrating the exploration of the continent, and has also an introductory sketch of the history of exploration.
> IDA LEE, *Early Explorers in Australia* (1925), deals at great length with Cunningham's work.

GEOGRAPHICAL DISCOVERY AND EXPLORATION

The next period covers the years 1843 to 1875, during which all the major features of Australia were discovered : after that year the task of the explorers, in the third period, was to fill in the details, more particularly in the western regions of the continent.

I. AUSTRALIA, 1788–1842

Although the major features of the coastline of Australia had been revealed by the Dutch explorers and James Cook, there were still some details to be filled in by the English, who had settled at Port Jackson in 1788. It was from this settlement that Captain Matthew Flinders and George Bass began the examination of Botany Bay and Georges river in 1795. They extended their surveys down the coast to the south of the bay, and in 1798 Bass, again in an open boat, made a voyage of eleven weeks round the coast and into the strait between Tasmania and Australia. He was convinced from the stormy nature of its waters that it was a strait and not a bay, although he was unable to prove the truth of his theory. At the end of 1798, however, the problem was solved, for Bass and Flinders, in the sloop *Norfolk*, sailed through the strait and round Tasmania, fixing by observation the more prominent landmarks.

The next piece of work to be undertaken was the survey of the south coast, which was imperfectly known, especially in its eastern half. Flinders was commissioned to examine the coast, more particularly between King George Sound in the south-west and Cape Howe in the south-east. He made a successful voyage in 1801–2, and discovered the large openings of Spencer Gulf and St Vincent Gulf, as well as Kangaroo Island. Shortly after leaving Encounter Bay he met the French scientific expedition under Baudin, in *Le Géographe*. This explorer had made some discoveries on the south coast, but not so many as were afterward claimed. " At the above situation of 35° 40' south and 138° 58' east," wrote Flinders,

the *discoveries* made by Captain Baudin upon the south coast have their termination to the west ; as mine in the *Investigator* have to the eastward. Yet Mon[sieur] Peron, naturalist in the French expedition, has laid a claim for his nation to the discovery of all the parts between *Western Port* in Bass Strait, and *Nuyts' Archipelago*; and this part of New South Wales is called *Terre Napoléon*.[1]

Flinders performed a valuable service to geography in that his surveys of the south coast disproved the theories of some geographers that a strait divided the continent into two large islands.

In a subsequent voyage in 1803 Flinders circumnavigated Australia and made a particularly careful examination of the east coast and the Gulf of Carpentaria. Next to Cook he must rank as

[1] Scott, *Discovery*, vol. i, p. 392.

the greatest of Australian explorers by sea ; his surveys, often made under great difficulties, have not entirely been replaced.

Between 1817 and 1822 Captain P. P. King commanded a number of survey expeditions to the western and northern coasts of Australia, and made many valuable additions to the existing charts. His work, like that of Flinders, was of a high order, and it marked the conclusion of the main task of coastal exploration.

In its earliest stages the inland exploration of Australia consisted of a series of short journeys into the country behind Sydney. In the course of ten years the country between the Hawkesbury and Nepean rivers and the coastline was well known as a result of the work of Governor Phillip, Captain Tench, and Lieutenant Dawes, but the settlement was faced with serious difficulties. Space was limited and population was increasing, but the nature of the Blue Mountains made the task of penetrating beyond these mountains very arduous. With the partial exception of Barrallier's expedition to a point 137 miles beyond the Nepean river, the explorers failed to pass the mountains.

For a time the settlers abandoned inland exploration, but the severe drought of 1813 made further expansion imperative. Accordingly Lieutenant Lawson, G. Blaxland, and W. Wentworth set out from Blaxland's farm at South Creek, " for the purpose of endeavouring to effect a passage over the Blue Mountains, between the Western river and the river Grose." [1] They pushed inland into the mountains to Mount Blaxland, beyond which they reported good country, with a plentiful supply of water. Their discoveries were followed up by a Government surveyor, G. W. Evans, who reached the Bathurst Plains and the valley of the Macquarie river. Flocks and herds were now driven over the mountains, a road was built, and in 1815 the town of Bathurst was founded. In the same year Evans discovered the Lachlan river.

The first main geographical problem, the crossing of the mountains, had by its solution raised a second, and John Oxley now proceeded to discover whither flowed the rivers whose upper courses had been seen. In 1817 he reached the Lachlan, but found its course obstructed by great marshes. He therefore turned eastward to the Macquarie below Bathurst, but was unable to discover its exit. Oxley tried again in 1818, and made a journey of 130 miles on the Macquarie, but when in about latitude 31° S. he was baffled by marshes. He turned eastward, discovered the Castlereagh river, crossed the Arbuthnot range into the splendid country of the Liverpool Plains, and in September reached the ' Peel ' river (*i.e.*, the Namoi). He recrossed the mountains to Port Macquarie, and followed the coast southward to Port Stephens.

[1] Scott, *Discovery*, vol. ii, p. 1.

Oxley failed to solve the problem of the rivers, but his opinion of their termination was important. " To assert positively," he wrote,

> that we were on the margin of the lake or sea into which this great body of water [*i.e.*, the Macquarie] is discharged, might reasonably be deemed a conclusion which has nothing but conjecture for its basis ; but if an opinion may be permitted to be hazarded from actual appearances, mine is decidedly in favour of our being in the immediate vicinity of an inland sea, or lake, most probably a shoal one, and gradually filling up by immense depositions from the higher lands, left by the waters which flow into it. It is most singular, that the highlands on this continent seem to be confined to the sea coast, or not to extend to any great distance from it.[1]

Oxley's work was continued by the botanist A. Cunningham, whose discovery of the Pandora Pass in 1823 opened up a shorter route to the Liverpool Plains. In 1827 he crossed the Nandewar range and reached the Condamine river and the Darling Downs, while in 1828 he discovered a route inland from Moreton Bay to the mountains, from which he looked down into the country he had explored in the previous year.

Cunningham's opinion on the interior of the continent in 1828 was half-way between Oxley's erroneous but natural speculation and the truth.

> Viewing between the parallels of 34° and 37° a vast area of depressed interior, subjected in seasons of prolonged rains to partial inundation by a dispersion of the several waters that flow upon it from the eastern mountains whence they originate, and bearing in mind at the same time that the declension of the country within the above parallels is uniformly to the N.N.W. and N.W., it would appear very conclusive that either a portion of our distant interior is occupied by a lake of considerable magnitude or that the confluence of those large streams—the Macquarie, Castlereagh, Gwydir, and the Dumaresq, with many minor interfluent waters, which doubtless takes place upon those low levels,—forms one or more noble rivers which may flow across the continent . . . to the north or north-east coasts, on certain parts of which recent surveys [*i.e.*, of King] have discovered to us extensive openings by which the largest accumulations of waters might escape to the sea.[2]

Meanwhile H. Hume and W. H. Hovell had made an important journey to the south-west in 1824. From Lake George, where Hume lived, they went overland across the Murrumbidgee river, within sight of the snow-covered Australian Alps, and over the Murray river (which they named Hume), to the Goulburn river. " In all our travels," wrote Hovell," I have seen no country better adapted for feeding sheep, the hills adjoining the Goulburn river being nearly clear of timber, grass to the top, and in the hollows below an abundance of herbage of a very excellent quality." [3]

[1] Scott, *Discovery*, vol. ii, p. 52.
[2] Captain Charles Sturt, *Two Expeditions into the Interior of Southern Australia* (1834), vol. i, pp. 154–155.   [3] Scott, *Discovery*, vol. ii, p. 96.

Hume and Hovell continued their journey across the modern Victoria to Port Phillip, but failed to solve the problem of the rivers. Indeed, Hovell added another theory to the growing list. " My opinion," he wrote, " is that they empty themselves, first into one immense lake, and the waters from the lake are carried off into the ocean in the N.E. or S.W. coast, as part of the coast, in these directions, is low." [1]

The problem was thus extended by the discovery of more rivers flowing inland and complicated by a wealth of speculation. Its solution was the work of two men, Charles Sturt and Thomas Mitchell. The drought of 1826–28 was so severe that, as Sturt explained, " the face of the earth became so parched up that minor vegetation ceased upon it. Settlers drove their flocks and herds to distant tracts for pasture and water, for neither of them were forthcoming in the located districts." Thus the necessity of finding pasture must be added to the desire to settle the courses of the rivers as the cause of Sturt's first journey.

Sturt, accompanied by Hume, left Sydney in September 1828, and in due course reached the point on the Macquarie where Oxley had turned back. Beyond this the two men conducted independent expeditions to the northward, in the hope of finding a way round the marshes, and finally, after joining forces again, discovered the Bogan river on January 1, 1829. This creek was followed to " the banks of a noble river," the Darling, whose waters were unfit to drink owing to the presence of brine springs. They therefore returned to their starting-point, and after a short rest set out for the Castlereagh, which was reached on March 10. This was found to be dry, but the channel was explored, and proved to drain into the Darling river. Sturt decided to abandon further exploration, " not from want of means but a conviction of the futility of further efforts " ; his journey had, however, at least put a portion of the Darling river on the map and found an outlet for two of the streams discovered by Oxley.

Unsuccessful in the north-west, Sturt now tried the south-west, and, leaving Sydney in November 1829, followed Hume's earlier track, and launched a boat on the Murrumbidgee on January 7, 1830. This " bold and desperate measure," as Sturt describes it, was rewarded with success. After a week's voyage the junction of the Murray was reached. " To myself personally," wrote Sturt,

the discovery of this river was a circumstance of a particularly gratifying nature, since it not only confirmed the justness of my opinion as to the ultimate fate of the Murrumbidgee, and bore me out in the apparently rash and hasty step I had taken, . . . but assured me of ultimate success in the duty I had to perform.[2]

[1] Scott, *Discovery*, vol. ii, p. 90.   [2] Sturt, *op. cit.*, vol. ii, p. 86.

On January 23 the entrance of another river was reached, and Sturt rightly thought that it was the Darling. The explorer continued to follow the current of the stream, and reached its mouth on February 9. " Immediately below me," wrote Sturt,

> was a beautiful lake, which appeared to be a fitting reservoir for the noble stream that had led us to it. . . . The ranges were more distinctly visible, stretching from south to north, and were certainly distant forty miles. They had a regular unbroken outline ; declining gradually to the south, but terminating abruptly at a lofty mountain northerly. I had no doubt on my mind of this being Mount Lofty of Captain Flinders ; or that the range was that immediately to the eastward of St Vincent's Gulf.[1]

Soon afterward they reached the sea, but not before they had discovered, to their disappointment, that the " beautiful lake " was so shallow as to be practically useless for navigation.

Sturt now decided to return up the river. In spite of incredible hardship and fatigue he succeeded in his purpose, and reached Sydney on May 26, 1830. His two journeys had been of immense importance. The first had showed clearly that Oxley's theory of inland marshes was without foundation : the second had disclosed the real nature of the interior rivers of South-east Australia.

The final problems of the river-system were solved by the three journeys of Major Thomas Mitchell. In 1831 he crossed the Liverpool Plains to the Namoi river, and early in February reached the Gwydir. After following it for a short distance he turned northward, made a loop to the Darling, and traced that river to the mouth of the Gwydir. As his stores had been stolen and two of his men killed by natives, Mitchell decided to return. He had, as he said, " proved that any large river flowing to the north-west must be far to the northward of latitude 29°. All the rivers south of that parallel . . . have been ascertained wholly to belong to the basin of the Darling." [2]

Mitchell had found the Darling to be a very different river from that seen by Sturt on his first journey, and had described it as being " as broad as the Thames at Putney." His early impressions were hardly borne out by his second journey of 1835. This time he traced the Bogan to its junction with the Darling, and built Fort Bourke at the confluence. The fresh water of the Darling again contradicted Sturt, and Mitchell set out hopefully to trace it to its termination. After a journey of over 300 miles, having reached a country where trees were few and grass very scanty, he turned back. " The identity of this river," he recorded, " with that which had been seen [by Sturt] to enter the Murray now admitted of little

[1] Sturt, op. cit., vol. ii, pp. 157–158.
[2] Quoted in A. F. Calvert, The Exploration of Australia (2 vols., 1901), vol. i, p. 85.

doubt; and the continuation of the survey to that point was scarcely an object worth the peril likely to attend it." [1]

Mitchell began his third and most successful journey in March 1836. He seems to have been very confused as to the real nature of the Murray-Darling basin and to have imagined that well-defined mountain ranges existed within it. Moreover, he apparently had forgotten his earlier conclusions about the Darling, and began to wonder if it joined the Murray: he even thought that Sturt might have mistaken the Lachlan for the Darling. However, he began by tracing the Lachlan to its junction with the Murrumbidgee, and then continued his journey to the point where the Darling entered the Murray. Turning up the Darling, he traced it until it became a chain of pools and he could walk on its bed. "While I stood on the adverse side, or right bank of this hopeless river," he wrote, "I began to think I had pursued its course long enough. The identity was no longer in question."

Returning to the Murray, Mitchell went up that river, and on July 8 discovered the Loddon, which he named "from its resemblance in some respects to the little stream in England." A number of other streams in the larger valley were found, and the whole country impressed Mitchell by its excellent prospects. He wrote:

> We had at length discovered a country ready for the immediate reception of civilised man ; and destined perhaps to become eventually a portion of a great empire. Unencumbered by too much wood, it yet possessed enough for all purposes ; its soil was exuberant, and its climate temperate ; it was bounded on three sides by the ocean ; and it was traversed by mighty rivers and watered by streams innumerable. Of this Eden I was the first European to explore its mountains and streams, to behold its scenery, to investigate its geological character, and, by my survey, to develop those natural advantages, certain to become, at no distant date, of vast importance to a new people. [2]

Mitchell's discoveries were, it must be admitted, of great value, but he apparently forgot the earlier work of Hume and Hovell.

On July 15 Mitchell added the Grampian Hills to the map, three days later he discovered the Wimmera river, and on the last day of the month he found the Glenelg, named "after the Right Hon. the Secretary of State for the Colonies, according to the usual custom." Turning southward, but without actually following this valley, Mitchell reached the sea on August 20. He determined the latitude, surveyed the mouth of the river and the adjacent country, and, he adds, "on re-entering the river from the sea, I presented the men with a bottle of whisky, with which it was formally named Glenelg."

Continuing eastward, Mitchell reached Portland Bay, where he

[1] Quoted in Favenc, *op. cit.*, p. 111.
[2] Scott, *Discovery*, vol. ii, p. 198.

found the Hentys had been established for two years, engaged in "importing sheep and cattle as fast as vessels could be found to bring them over." From this settlement he crossed the country to the Murrumbidgee, which was reached toward the end of October. As a result of this important journey the main features of the Murray-Darling basin east and south of the Darling were reasonably well known.

A few smaller expeditions completed the outlines. A. McMillan and Count Strzelecki first opened up the country of Gippsland, lying between Wilson's Promontory and Cape Howe. The ranges and impenetrable thickets effectively shut off this region from Melbourne, while it was approached from the sea only with difficulty, so that until the visit of these men, in 1840, it was practically unknown. In the same year a settlement was established on the Condamine river, and in 1842 Stuart Russell traced the course of that river to its junction with the Darling. Thus by 1842 South-eastern Australia had been superficially examined as a whole, and some parts were well known. Settlers gradually made their way into it, and in the course of settlement many details were added to the map.[1]

Meanwhile a little progress had been made on the west coast. Rumours of French colonizing activities led to the occupation of King George Sound in 1826. In the following year Captain Stirling examined the Swan river, and reported favourably on it, while in 1831 the two localities of King George Sound and Swan river were connected by the journey of Captain Bannister.

From Perth Lieutenant Roe undertook a journey eastward in 1836, but made few discoveries of importance, except some salt lakes, including Lake Brown. But in the next year Lieutenant Grey began his work, and progress was more rapid. Grey was ordered to go by sea to Prince Regent river, and thence to proceed to a great opening behind Dampier's Land. "You will use the utmost exertions to penetrate from thence to Swan river," his instructions proceeded, "as by adopting this course you will proceed in a direction parallel to the unknown coast, and must necessarily cross every large river that flows from the interior towards that side of the continent." Grey started his inland journey from Prince Regent river on December 17, 1837, but after a four months' struggle had accomplished little beyond the exploration of the Glenelg[2] and Prince Regent rivers, and toward the end of April he sailed for Mauritius. He returned to Swan river in September, and then made two short expeditions into the unknown hinterland.

In 1839 he carried out his last expedition, sailing from Fremantle to Sharks Bay, whence he intended to explore the country to the

[1] For this aspect of the development of the country see S. H. Roberts, *History of Australian Land Settlement* (1924), with many useful maps.
[2] Not the same as that discovered by Mitchell, but in North-west Australia.

north-eastward. Through remarkable ill-luck he landed on a waterless island, and while searching for water lost most of his stores in a hurricane. But he discovered the Gascoyne river, to the north of the bay, and spent some time in its valley. Then lack of food compelled him to begin the return to Perth. The party started in open boats, but were obliged to put into Cantheaume Bay for water, and during the operation both their boats were wrecked. Nothing remained but to walk to Perth, 300 miles away. Grey, who pushed on ahead to bring relief, reached Perth on April 21, and the remainder of his party arrived on May 9. The journey had resulted in the discovery of some ten rivers, including the Gascoyne, Murchison, Greenough, and Irwin, as well as parts of the Darling and Victoria 'Ranges.'

Other details of the coast were explored at this time by Wickham and Stokes, including the mouths of the Fitzroy, Victoria, Adelaide, Albert, and Flinders rivers and some of their valleys.

Thus on both east and west considerable progress had been made. By Eyre's journey in 1841 the two areas of exploration were connected. E. J. Eyre had a sheep-run about 150 miles to the north of Adelaide, and in 1839 he explored part of the Flinders Range to the north-west of Broughton river, which he discovered. From a hill afterward named Mount Eyre he saw Lake Torrens. Returning to Adelaide with the news of his discoveries, he was sent to examine the coast west of Port Lincoln, and this he did until he reached Streaky Bay. Here he decided to go eastward across the head of the Lincoln Peninsula, and he succeeded in reaching Spencer Gulf.

In 1840 Eyre set out northward, following the Flinders Range beyond his earlier discoveries, until, deceived by the numerous patches of salt water, he concluded that Lake Torrens stretched in a great horseshoe expanse to prevent further advance. Accordingly, at Mount Hopeless he turned back. His curious mistake about Lake Torrens found its way into the maps of the period, and was not corrected until the year 1858.[1]

Eyre went back to his depot at Mount Arden, and proceeded thence to Streaky Bay, from which place he made numerous excursions to the westward. He obtained more stores from Adelaide, and on February 25, 1841, set out from Fowler's Bay, accompanied by John Baxter and three natives. To attempt the crossing of the continent with such inadequate resources was foolish, and the party suffered much from lack of food and water. Eyre, however, determined to push on. The natives became discontented, and it is little surprising, for on April 9 they were still 600 miles from their destination, with only enough food for three weeks. Ten days later Baxter was murdered, and two of the natives deserted. Still Eyre went on, until by June his supplies were at an end. Then a

---

[1] See, for example, the *National Atlas* of Keith Johnston (1850).

marvellous piece of good luck saved him, for he was able to attract the attention of a ship and secure rest and refreshment. With renewed strength he continued the journey to King George Sound, reached on June 14, and finally to Albany.

Eyre made few discoveries. He was able to prove—what most people already believed—that no great river entered the Australian Bight. His journey also demonstrated the difficulties of the country which separated South and Western Australia. But his fame rests rather on the success of a risky adventure than on any great contribution to geographical knowledge.

II. AUSTRALIA, 1843–75

The first big advance in knowledge which followed the exploit of Eyre was due to the distinguished scholar Dr Ludwig Leichhardt. In 1844 he set out to find a route from Moreton Bay to Port Victoria, a town founded near to the earlier but abandoned settlement of Port Essington, on the north coast. On October 7 he reached the Condamine river, and, following a route to the north-west, crossed the divide to the Dawson river, down which he travelled. Crossing Expedition Range, still following a north-westerly direction, he reached the southern tributaries of the Burdekin river in February 1845. Using this river valley to get through the mountains to the northward, Leichhardt arrived at the Lynd river, and, partly by that river and partly by the Mitchell, approached the Gulf of Carpentaria. After rounding the southern end of the gulf and crossing a number of rivers, he reached Port Victoria in the middle of September. Leichhardt returned to Sydney by sea.

This expedition had made valuable discoveries. It had covered a distance of 3000 miles, had revealed many mountains and rivers, as well as much good country, and had accomplished its main purpose of finding a route from the east to the north coast.

Leichhardt set out again, two years later, to cross Australia from east to west, but he disappeared, and in spite of efforts of many search expeditions no traces of his party have ever been discovered.

Leichhardt's work was linked up with that of his predecessors by Mitchell in 1846. He still believed in a dividing range beyond the Darling river, and beyond that again a great river, and he set out, with a large survey party, to test this theory. Crossing the Narran river to the Culgoa and moving up to the Balonne, he established a depot on the site of the modern town of St George. From that point the party travelled to the Cogoon river, followed it to the divide, and discovered the dry bed of the Maranoa.

Mitchell proceeded westward to the Warrego, and then marched northward, and crossed the Carnarvon Range to the Nogoa river. Finding that stream led to the east, he abandoned it, and turned to the north-west, until he reached a point in, approximately, latitude 21° 30′ S., longitude 147° 10′ E. ; as this route, if continued, would lead to the country opened up by Leichhardt, he determined to return, and in the course of his journey discovered the upper part of the Barcoo river, and followed it while his provisions lasted. Mitchell had conducted a most successful expedition, and although he did not know it, had discovered the upper part of a river already discovered, in its lower reaches, by Sturt.

In 1844 Sturt had set out from Adelaide, and, passing up the Murray and Darling rivers, completed the exploration of the latter which had been left undone by himself in 1830 and by Mitchell in 1835–36. He then went toward the north-west, passed Lake Frome, and discovered what he called the Great Stony Desert and two creeks, named Strzelecki and Cooper's, both of which were part of the Barcoo river. Sturt arrived home again in January 1846, after a very successful expedition in which he all but reached the centre of Australia. Taken in conjunction with his earlier efforts, it rightly entitles him to rank as one of the greatest of Australian explorers. He had been led to embark on this journey by the belief, derived from the study of bird-migration, that there was good pasture-ground in the centre of Australia, but although he did not reach that region, he found instead a poorly watered country : beyond, perhaps, lay the promised land, but of that he was not sure. It would be a good thing, he thought, " to raise the veil which still shrouds its features, even though, like those of the veiled prophet, they should wither the beholder." [1]

The work of Sturt and Mitchell was completed by E. B. Kennedy who was sent from Sydney, in 1847, to find out whether the Barcoo flowed to the Gulf of Carpentaria, as Mitchell thought, or to the south-west, as seemed more probable. He followed Mitchell's route, penetrated farther than that explorer, and, although driven back by starvation, was able to get far enough to disprove Mitchell's theory and to connect the Barcoo with the creeks discovered by Sturt. On his return he made some additions to the knowledge of the Warrego and Culgoa rivers.

Kennedy was sent out again in 1848 to explore Queensland. He started from the coast of York Peninsula, at Rockingham Bay, and intended to cross to the northern point. In this he was all but successful, but was murdered when within sight of his goal. His fate was related by a native who had accompanied him : the other members of the party, who had been left behind, were rescued subsequently.

Two other expeditions completed the main outlines of North Queensland. In 1864 F. L. and A. W. Jardine followed a route along the western side of the peninsula, and reached the northern

---

[1] Quoted in Scott, *Discovery*, vol. ii, p. xxi.

coastline opposite to Albany Island early in March of the following year. They lost most of their cattle, and suffered at the hands of the natives, and, like the party led by Kennedy, brought back no encouraging results. But in 1872 W. Hann led a scientific party to investigate the country as far north as the latitude of 14°, and in particular to look for minerals, especially gold. They discovered gold on Palmer's Creek, brought back much useful information, and stimulated detailed exploration on the Leichhardt, Lynd, Gilbert, and other rivers.

In Western Australia the limits of the known area were gradually pushed eastward. In the south-west J. S. Roe made a journey from Perth to Albany, and thence as far as the Russell Range, when lack of water and of food compelled a retreat. He accordingly followed the coast westward to Albany, and thence crossed to Geographe Bay, and so made his way back to Perth. The expedition added to the knowledge of the geography, the geology, and the botany of the region.

To the north of Perth F. T. Gregory discovered Lake Moore in 1846, while his brother, A. C. Gregory, started out to reach the Gascoyne river and to examine the country behind Sharks Bay. He proceeded toward the north-west, and reached latitude 27° S., covering about 1500 miles, but he failed in the main object of his expedition.

These discoveries were supplemented as a result of the journey of R. Austin in 1854 and a second journey of F. T. Gregory in 1857. The former discovered Lake Cowcowing, proceeded north-east to Mount Kenneth, and then turned toward the north-west. Soon after crossing the Murchison river he was compelled by lack of water to return. Gregory followed up the Murchison to the Impey river in 1857, and in the next year, from the Gascoyne basin, explored Lyons river, and reached Mount Augustus, named after his brother. In 1861 he made a third journey, starting from the coast at Nichol Bay, and, first going in a southerly direction, discovered the Fortescue river, and followed its course as far as practicable. Beyond this he discovered the Ashburton river, and arrived within sight of Mount Augustus. After returning to Nichol Bay to refit Gregory went eastward as far as the nature of the country allowed, discovering the Yule, Shaw, De Grey, and Oakover rivers, but failing to penetrate the desert country to the east of the last river. He returned down the Oakover to the coast, and so made his way back to his starting-point.

Gregory's expeditions were of considerable importance. He described the physical features of the country visited with detailed accuracy, and he discovered a number of fertile regions. As a result of his journeys a settlement was founded near De Grey river in 1863.

In South Australia also considerable progress was being made.

In 1856 Babbage crossed the country by which it was thought Lake Torrens was encircled and found Lake Blanche. Goyder was sent there in the next year to survey the neighbourhood, and returned with stories of many freshwater lakes. But his reports were not confirmed by the Surveyor-General Freeling, who declared

> the extensive bays described in Mr Goyder's report, the bluff head-lands, the several islands between the north and south shores, have all been the result of mirage, and do not in point of fact exist as represented. The conclusion drawn in that report that the lake is only subject to the most trifling variations of level is also proved to be an erroneous deduction.[1]

Two expeditions, under S. Hack and P. E. Warburton, explored the country round Gawler Range in 1857, but their reports were contradictory. In the next year Babbage discovered a lake named Gregory, subsequently called Lake Eyre, but no one believed him, and he was recalled, to be succeeded by Warburton. It was Warburton who established the fact that Lake Torrens was not of horseshoe shape, and his report was confirmed by J. M. Stuart, who also examined the country to the west of Lake Eyre, and discovered Chambers Creek and Neale river.

While details were thus being filled in on all sides Australian explorers began a series of transcontinental journeys. It will be recalled that Leichhardt had already performed one such journey, and had perished on a second attempt. In 1855 A. C. Gregory set out to examine Victoria river, in Northern Australia, and to look for traces of Leichhardt's expedition. He landed near Pearce Point, successfully explored the Victoria, and discovered Sturt's Creek, and then followed a route similar to that of Leichhardt in 1845, but a little farther inland. He reached the east coast, at Port Curtis, in December 1856, after a successful expedition, although he failed to find Leichhardt. Two years later, in a second expedition, Gregory completed the exploration of the Barcoo river, followed it to Strzelecki Creek, and then travelled by Lake Blanche to Adelaide. Thus he completed two transcontinental journeys of much importance, discovered a large area of new country, and in many respects supplemented the work of earlier explorers who had been working inward from the south or the east.

The first men to cross Australia from south to north were R. O'H. Burke and W. J. Wills. Their instructions were to explore Central Australia, and to reach the Gulf of Carpentaria near the Albert river, discovered by Stokes in 1841. They left Menindee, on the Darling river, in October 1860, arrived on the Barcoo in November, and by the following February were on the estuary of the Flinders river. They did not, however, reach the coast. On the return both leaders died in an attempt to cross to Adelaide from Cooper's

---

[1] Quoted in Calvert, *op. cit.*, vol. ii, p. 100.

Creek. The scientific results of this journey were small in comparison with the resources expended, and Burke and Wills hardly stand in the front rank as explorers. They owe their fame more to their tragic deaths than to their geographical achievements.

A number of relief parties sent out to search for this expedition did, however, make valuable contributions to the geography of Central Australia. Howitt reached Cooper's Creek and rescued King, the survivor of the party. M'Kinlay went to the west of Lake Blanche, followed Cooper's Creek and the Mueller river, and arrived at the mouth of the Albert river, on the Gulf of Carpentaria. He returned to Queensland by the Burdekin river, and in his reports showed that in good seasons much of the land thought to be desert carried good pasture. Landsborough, who started from the Albert river, discovered the Herbert river, returned to the Albany, and then, crossing to the Flinders and Thomson rivers, reached the Barcoo. Thence he travelled by the Warrego to the Darling. Walker journeyed from Rockhampton by the coast to the Burdekin and the Albert rivers, and returned by the Thomson and the Barcoo. Thus as a result of these explorations nearly all the main features of Australia east of a line drawn from the Albert river to Spencer Gulf were known.

To the west of that line, J. M. Stuart explored the country to the north of Lake Gairdner in 1858, and in 1860 began a series of journeys with the object of crossing the continent from south to north. He started from Adelaide, passed to the west of Lake Eyre, and discovered many rivers, including the Alberga and the Finke, and a range of mountains named after MacDonnell, the Governor of South Australia. On April 22 he reached what he called the centre of Australia, and near there named " a high mount " " Central Mount Sturt." The name was subsequently changed to Stuart.[1] Soon afterward the threatening attitude of the natives made it inadvisable to go farther.

In January 1861 Stuart renewed his attempt, and was able to get a little nearer to the north coast. He followed his previous route, and skirted the Ashburton Range, near which he found the creek named Newcastle Water, but was unable to penetrate the thick scrub which lay beyond. Shortage of provisions and of water compelled him to retreat.

The third and final journey was made in 1862. On this occasion Stuart was able to find a way through the scrub and to discover a creek named Daly Waters. On June 30 he crossed the Roper river, and followed up one of its northern tributaries, the Chambers. Crossing the divide, Stuart used the valley of the Adelaide, although marshy country made *détours* necessary, and reached the coast on July 24. " Thus have I," he records,

[1] See Scott, *Discovery*, vol. ii, p. 411.

through the instrumentality of Divine Providence been led to accomplish the great object of the expedition, and take the whole party safely as witnesses to the fact, and through one of the finest countries man could wish to behold—good to the coast and with a stream of running water within half a mile of the sea. From Newcastle Water to the sea-beach, the main body of the horses have been only one night without water, and then got it within the next day. If this country is settled, it will be one of the finest Colonies under the Crown, suitable for the growth of any and every thing—what a splendid country for producing cotton! [1]

Stuart's journeys were of great importance. He had himself already served in the Central Australian expedition of Sturt, and he was able to make good use of his long experience of the semi-arid regions of Australia. His journeys proved that with careful preparation and reasonable precaution these regions need not be feared: they also showed—what had been demonstrated by the Burke search expeditions—that there was plenty of good country in areas about which Sturt and others had written rather gloomy accounts.

Between the route taken by Stuart and a relatively narrow belt of country along the west coast was a vast unknown area. Between 1862 and 1875 most of this region was explored. In 1869 J. Forrest journeyed for some distance west of Lake Barlee, and in the next year followed Eyre's route in the reverse direction along the south coast. In 1871 Alexander Forrest reached East Coolgardie from Perth, and then crossed the unknown country to the southward, as far as Esperance Bay. In 1872 Giles examined the higher reaches of the Finke river, and in the following year penetrated Gibson's Desert. Meanwhile Gosse, from South Australia, had explored westward of the Alberga river in 1873. There was still, however, a large gap in the centre of the continent between the points reached by Giles and Gosse and the known lands of the west.

This gap was first crossed by J. Forrest in 1874. He set out from the west coast in March of that year, with the object of travelling from Perth to the Overland Telegraph Line, which had been carried from Port Darwin to Adelaide in 1872. Forrest began by following the Murchison river, and then made use of a line of springs. Eventually even this source of water gave out, and by August he found himself in the same kind of country which had defeated Giles and Gosse a year before. He persisted, however, and reached the telegraph line on September 27. He had accomplished a very valuable piece of work, although the results were not encouraging, for he considered that the only part of the country he had traversed that was fit for settlement was in the valley of the Murchison river.

Meanwhile P. E. Warburton had crossed from east to west in a more northerly latitude. He left Adelaide in 1872, and set out from the Telegraph Line at Alice Springs in April 1873. His route

[1] Scott, *Discovery*, vol. ii, p. 420.

lay first to the head of Sturt's Creek, already discovered by A. C. Gregory, and then westward to the Oakover river and the coast at Roebourne. Warburton also showed that only small fragments of the arid interior were suitable for settlement.

A third traverse of the western desert was made by E. Giles in 1875. He left Port Augusta in May of that year, and crossed the unknown region between the coast and the route taken by Forrest in 1874. He passed by Lake Moore, and reached the west coast, at Perth, in November. He then went northward to the headwaters of the Ashburton river, where he struck eastward across the desert. Thus after crossing Gibson's Desert he reached the country already explored by himself in 1874. His reports added considerably to the geographical knowledge of the region, but, like those of Forrest and Warburton, they proved that very little of the arid interior was fit for settlement.

These three men removed many blanks from the map of Australia, and with their work the period of pioneer exploration ends. There were many journeys made after 1875 which added materially to knowledge, but the main features of Australia were by now all known, and subsequent discoveries merely confirmed existing knowledge or added precision to it.

III. AUSTRALIA AFTER 1875

In the country to the south and south-west of the Gulf of Carpentaria Hodgkinson followed up the Flinders river in 1875, crossed the Selwyn Range, and went down the Diamantina river almost as far as the South Australian boundary. He then turned northward, proceeded up the Georgina river, and crossed over the Barkley Tableland to the Gregory river, and so back to the Gulf of Carpentaria. Three years later the same region was crossed by the Queenslander expedition under Favenc. Starting from Barcaldine and following a north-westerly direction, the party passed to the south of the Selwyn Range, and reached the Telegraph Line at Daly Waters, afterward continuing to Port Darwin. Favenc returned, in 1883, to trace the McArthur river to the Gulf of Carpentaria. Meanwhile Buchanan had crossed Favenc's earlier track in his journey from the Barkley Tableland to the Telegraph Line at Tennant's Creek.

West of the Queensland border Barclay examined the Hay river and its tributaries in 1878, and many years later, in 1904, explored the upper reaches of the Finke river. Similarly, Lindsay traversed the country between the Georgina and the Finke rivers, and between the Finke and the lower part of the Hay river, in 1885–86. In 1891 he made a longer journey from the Alberga river to the western desert, where he turned south to Lake Cowan, in Western

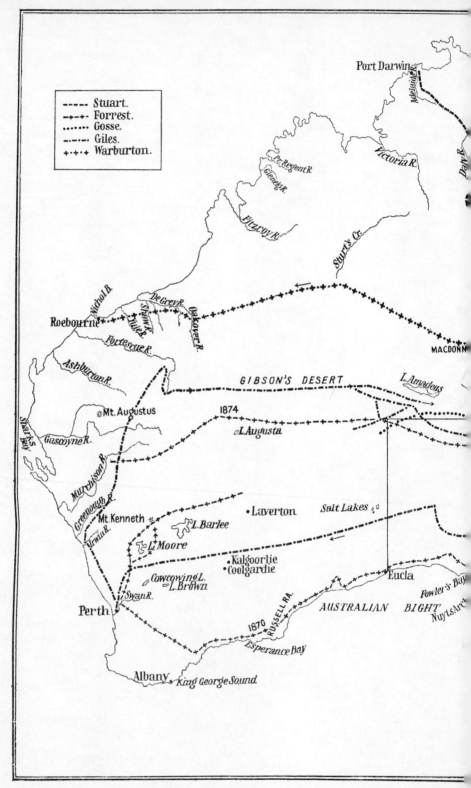

Fig. 44. AUSTRALIA, 1858-75

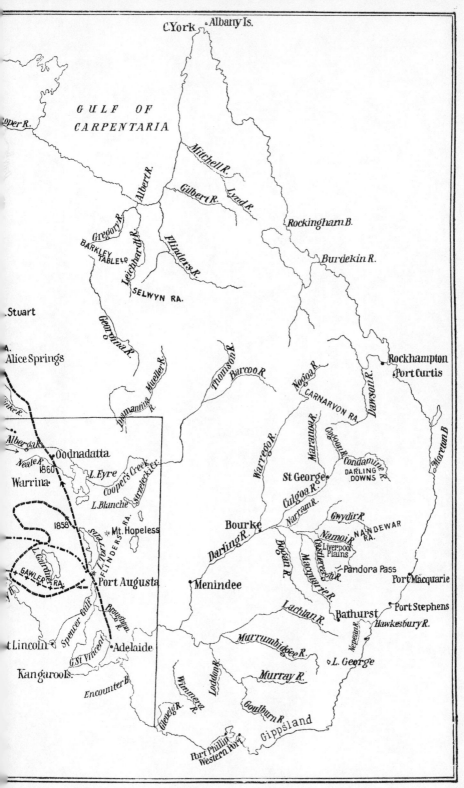

C. York • Albany Is.

GULF OF
CARPENTARIA

Cooper R.

Mitchell R.

Gilbert R.

Lynd R.

Rockingham B.

Albert R.

Gregory R.

Leichhardt R.

BARKLEY
TABLE LD

Flinders R.

Burdekin R.

SELWYN RA.

Georgina R.

.Stuart

A.
Alice Springs

Burke R.

Diamantina R.

Mueller R.

Thomson R.

Barcoo R.

Nogoa R.

Rockhampton
Port Curtis

CARNARVON RA.

Dawson R.

Alberga R.

Oodnadatta

Neale R.

1860

Warrina•

L. Eyre

Cooper's Creek

Strzelecki Cr.

Warrego R.

Maranoa R.

Cogoon R.

St George

Condamine R.

DARLING
DOWNS

Moreton B.

L. Blanche

1858

FLINDERS RA.

*Mt. Hopeless

Willochra R.

Culgoa R.

Narran R.

Gwydir R.

NANDEWAR
RA.

Gardner RA.

GAWLER RA.

Port Augusta

Bourke

Darling R.

Bogan R.

Namoi R.

Liverpool
Plains

Castlereagh R.

Macquarie R.

Pandora Pass

Port Macquarie

t Lincoln•

Spencer Gulf

Broughton R.

Menindee

Lachlan R.

Bathurst

Port Stephens

Hawkesbury R.

G. St Vincent

Adelaide

Murrumbidgee R.

Wepean R.

•L. George

Kangaroo Is.

Encounter B.

Loddon R.

Murray R.

Glenelg R.

Wimmera R.

Goulburn R.

Gippsland

Port Phillip
Western Port

Australia. He then continued his journey north-westward by Lake Barlee to the Murchison river. To the north of this route Tietkins had explored the country between Alice Springs, Lake Amadeus, and Lake Macdonald in 1889. Still farther northward, the elaborate Horn expedition of 1894 set out to examine the country between Oodnadatta and the MacDonnell Range. Their objects were geological and anthropological rather than strictly geographical, but they were able to make valuable additions to knowledge of the little-known regions of Central Australia.

Interest now shifts to the country west of the ranges of Central Australia. Already in 1891 Lindsay had pushed across to Western Australia, and in the next year L. A. Wells advanced from the west and reached the lake which now bears his name. In 1896, as the leader of the Calvert expedition, he made further additions to knowledge. He began from the north of Lake Barlee, and, travelling in a general northerly direction, skirted Lake Augusta, and passed by Separation Well and Joanna Spring to the Fitzroy river. Two of the party lost their lives while crossing the country to the north of Separation Well.

In 1896 D. W. Carnegie followed a route roughly parallel to that of Wells, crossing from Doyle's Well, in the East Murchison Gold-field, to Sturt's Creek, and returning by a more easterly track by Lake Macdonald. In the previous year W. Carr-Boyd left the Kalgoorlie Goldfield, traversed the Mount Margaret Goldfield, and passed to the north of Lindsay's route of 1891, eventually reaching Warrina, in South Australia. He passed through a considerable stretch of new country. Hübbe in 1896 led an expedition in the reverse direction, starting at Oodnadatta and keeping to the south of the Musgrave Range. He crossed the desert to the Mount Margaret Goldfield.

Mason, also in 1896, explored the country behind the Australian Bight and between Eucla and the Salt Lakes of Victoria Desert. In the following year H. Russell crossed between Mount Margaret and Mount Squires by a route to the south of that taken by Hübbe. This region was again examined by F. Hann in 1903 ; he travelled from Laverton to Oodnadatta, along a somewhat more southerly track than that of Russell. Beyond his track J. Muir, in 1901, explored the country between Kalgoorlie and Eucla, thus supplementing the earlier work of Mason in the south coastal belt.

In the last quarter of the nineteenth century a vast amount of pioneer work opened up many parts of Australia. Much of it was of a valuable nature, and was concerned with the search for minerals or for pastoral country. The large number of expeditions which have here been mentioned were made chiefly in the western region, where pasture is very limited, and they served to emphasize those limitations and at the same time to discover many springs and wells which were of use in the crossing of the arid regions. In the last decade of the century the opening up of the West Australian gold-fields attracted men from all parts of the world, and led to much unofficial exploration and to the settlement of some regions : nothing less than the magnetic attraction of gold would otherwise have enabled them to retain their inhabitants.

During the present century discoveries have not been numerous, although the age of scientific exploration in Australia is by no means over. Thus in 1908–9 S. Weston explored much unknown country between Sturt's Creek and the mountains of Central Australia, and reported that although there was a complete absence of surface water, yet the country was covered with timber and bushes, many of which afforded " excellent sustenance for the camel," and there was plenty of good grass.[1] Similarly, the Mackay expedition to Central Australia, in 1926, set out

> to fill in a blank that remained in the south-western corner of the map of the Northern Territory ; to visit and verify the positions of ranges and hills which early explorers had seen in the distance and placed by estimation on the map ; and to examine [the] country and form an opinion of the possibilities, if any, which it possessed from a pastoralist's standpoint.[2]

The country examined lay between Oodnadatta and Petermann Range. It was considered to hold no future for the pastoralist, " chiefly owing to the uncertain rainfall," but also because of the rabbits, which are " eating out much of the natural feed " and " will eventually deplete Central Australia of all pasturage." The geologist of the party, Dr H. Basedow, concludes that it is " an area of exceptionally great possibilities as a goldfield."

Another expedition, led by M. Terry, in 1928 examined the country between Sturt's Creek and Lander Creek, with the object of supplementing the earlier work of A. A. Davidson and of finding the limits of the large dry marsh then discovered. Terry concluded that the marsh was connected with Lander Creek, and that perhaps in the past the latter had sent its waters into this region.

In the northern part of Australia a number of important journeys have been made since 1875. In 1879 A. Forrest traversed the coast region from the De Grey river to the Fitzroy, and from the upper waters of the latter crossed to the Telegraph Line at Daly Waters. D. Lindsay in 1883, and again in 1895, explored a large part of Arnhem Land, while F. Hann, in 1896–98 crossed from the Gulf of Carpentaria through the Kimberley Division to Roebourne. Hann again explored part of the Kimberley Division to the north of the Fitzroy river in 1900, and in the following year Brockman examined a large area between King Leopold Range and the north coast.

The Terry Australian Expedition of 1925 crossed from the

[1] *G.J.*, vol. xxxvi, p. 693.   [2] *Ibid.*, vol. lxxiii, p. 258.

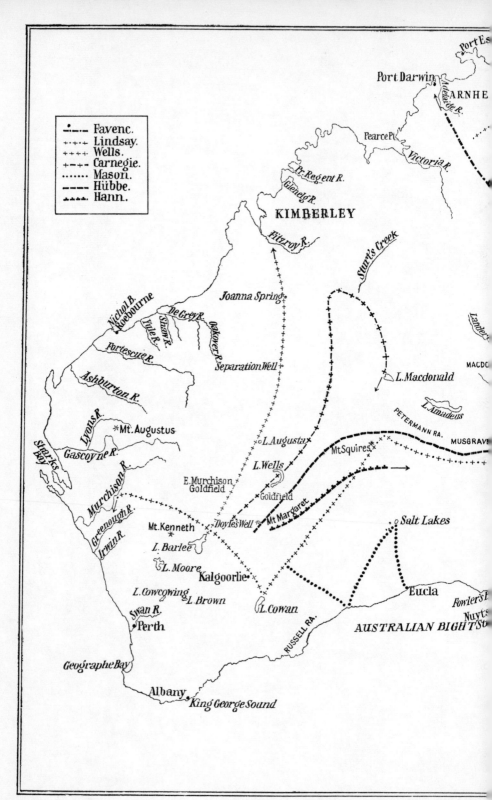

Fig. 45. AUSTRALIA AFTER 1875

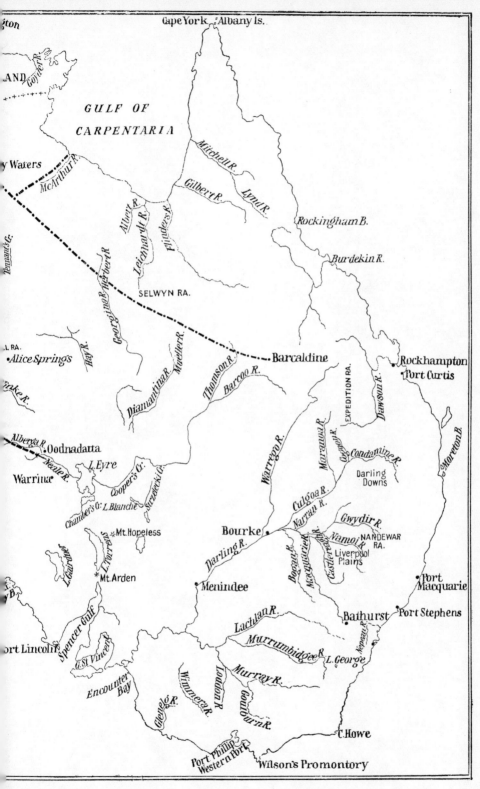

Darwin railway terminus to the Fitzroy river and Broome. It was able to determine a large number of positions and to report on many different types of country between the forested north and the desert round Sturt's Creek. One result is of great interest, from both the human and the agricultural point of view. Terry reported [1] " a curious weakness in the quality of the sunlight," so that " no member of the party became half so sunburnt as might have been expected after four months in the bush." This fact may, as Terry says, " affect the growth of crops or the quality of wool," and it may also have some bearing on the suitability of this tropical land for white settlement.

To the east of the Darwin railway D. Mackay carried out a valuable piece of exploration in 1928, selecting " one of the last portions of Australia that had not been examined." There is plenty of water in this region, except to the east of the Goyder River, and timber is abundant, although the trees are " only of medium size " ; yet " from a pastoralist's point of view the country is disappointing. Most of it might be called second-class cattle country." [2] Dr Basedow, who collected much geological information, concludes that " there is little or no chance of finding any mineral of economic value in the quartzites and sandstones composing the great plateau of Arnhem Land."

It is very significant that one of the last areas to be explored was very near to the coasts reached by the Dutch in the seventeenth century. Hostile natives and lack of water have kept this northern land free from white penetration. Indeed, throughout the history of Australian exploration the factor of water has been of great importance. With the use of the camel, and more recently the motor-car and the aeroplane, this difficulty has been to some extent removed, and one may assume that within a short time there will be no large regions in the country entirely unknown. For all practical purposes, however, Australian discovery has ended, and future expeditions are unlikely to find new features, although they can still profitably study many problems of Australian geography.

IV. New Zealand [3]

The history of exploration in New Zealand falls broadly into three periods. From the time of Cook's rediscovery of the islands to the

[1] See *G.J.*, vol. lxviii, p. 302, for the report of this expedition.
[2] *Ibid.*, vol. lxxiv, p. 568, for this expedition.
[3] On this section see the following :

> T. M. HOCKEN, " Some Accounts of the Earliest Explorations in New Zealand " (*Report of the Third Meeting of the Australian Association for the Advancement of Science*, 1891).
> J. R. ELDER, *The Pioneer Explorers of New Zealand* (1929).
> *Surveys and Maps: An Exposition of the Work, Methods, and Organization of the New Zealand Survey* (1925).

year 1839, when the work of colonization began, very little progress was made. Cook's charts were supplemented in one or two areas, but remained substantially unaltered until after 1834. The second period extends from 1839 to 1865, when Hector was appointed Director of the Geological Survey of New Zealand ; with that appointment the last phase of exploration begins.

The early visits of whalers, sealers, and traders who came to cut *kauri* trees, then in demand for masts, added a few details to the knowledge of the coasts and some new islands. Thus Captain Bristow discovered the Auckland Islands in 1806 ; Stewart Island was found by a sealer in 1809 ; and in 1810 the Campbell Islands were discovered. Such visits as these, however, were unlikely to result in great advances in knowledge. But Herd's journey to the east coast, in 1825, to establish the New Zealand Flax Society, resulted in the determination of about fifty positions. In Hauraki Gulf, and else-where to a less extent, Dumont d'Urville's expedition of 1827 made further additions, while in 1831 La Place surveyed a large part of the Bay of Islands. British Admirality surveys began in 1834, and were completed within twenty years.

Important as were these expeditions, they were mainly confined to the coastline. In the interior progress was due almost entirely to the missionaries, of whom Samuel Marsden was the pioneer. Marsden was not primarily interested in geographical discovery, but he paid seven visits to the North Island between 1814 and 1837, and in his travels through the country lying to the north, west, and south of Hauraki Gulf added greatly to a little-known part of New Zealand. His work was supplemented by other missionaries. W. Colenso pushed into the centre of North Island in 1841–42, and traced the course of the Waikato river, and in 1843 penetrated as far south as the Ruahine Mountains. In 1844 G. A. Selwyn crossed North Island from Auckland to Wellington. But in spite of this activity, when the first period ends knowledge was confined to a small part of the North Island.

The arrival of the *Tory* in Queen Charlotte Sound in August 1839 marks a turning-point in the history of discovery. The first party of settlers, led by Gibbon Wakefield's brother, soon abandoned South Island, and selected a site on Port Nicholson for their home. Here, subsequently, the city of Wellington developed. Soon after their arrival Bidwill, who was the first European to visit the hot springs and Lake Taupo, joined the colony. Another early explorer from Wellington reached Taranaki ; and the geologist E. Dieffen-bach succeeded, at the second attempt, in climbing Mount Egmont in 1839, and in the following year crossed North Island from North Cape to Lake Taupo. Subsequent exploration in North Island is the detailed record of the activities of surveyors. The Royal Instructions of 1840 provided for the appointment of a Surveyor-

General, and the first holder of the office, F. Mathew, began work in May 1841. A year earlier the surveyors of Wakefield's company had started their explorations northward from Wellington.

In 1858 the Austrian expedition in the *Novara* landed Dr F. von Hochstetter on the North Island. He and his assistant (Sir Julius) von Haast began a geological survey of parts of Auckland. The two men made many additions to the knowledge of North Island, and, later in 1858, transferred their activities to the Nelson District of South Island.

The expansion of settlements in North Island, together with the work of the surveyors and of special explorers like Hochstetter, was thus responsible for the accumulation of much knowledge, and this was supplemented as the result of the Maori wars. But in South Island progress had not been so rapid. In 1841 Captain Daniell and Mr Duppa made a preliminary examination of the east coast, and in the next year Captain W. M. Smith surveyed the coast from Otago to Foveaux Strait. The last named made many corrections to the existing map, but, most unfortunately, lost all his records in a shipwreck.

In the north of the island T. Brunner, C. Heaphy, and W. Fox penetrated from Nelson to the Buller valley in 1845-46, and began the exploration of the west coast. Brunner and Heaphy resumed their work in the summer of 1846, and reached the Taramakau river, a short distance beyond Grey River. Brunner continued the work of exploration in this region until 1848, tracing out the courses of the Grey and Buller rivers, and for his discoveries was given a special award of twenty-five guineas by the Royal Geographical Society in 1851.

Farther south F. Tuckett examined the country between Banks Peninsula and Stewart Island in 1844. In the upland regions of Otago the first surveys were made by J. T. Thomson in 1856 ; in the following year he worked inland from Invercargill. Thomson " explored, surveyed, and mapped the whole territory from the eastern seaboard to the lake district." [1] His work was completed by J. McKerrow, who surveyed the larger lakes in 1862, and by Hector in the west coast region.

The expansion of settlements also contributed to exploration. The first colony at Nelson (1841) was not conspicuously successful. Dunedin followed seven years later, Canterbury in 1850, and Invercargill in 1857. The gold-rush to Otago in 1861 also brought many new settlers and ended the isolation of the province.

In the year 1861 James Hector, who had served with distinction on the Palliser expedition in Canada,[2] transferred his services to New Zealand, and began his work in Otago Province, while in the same year Von Haast was appointed Provincial Geologist of Canterbury.

[1] Elder, *op. cit.*, p. 76.   [2] See above, p. 369.

Both men devoted themselves to the systematic study of the regions in which they worked, and by no means confined themselves to a geological survey. In particular they explored much of the mountainous country of South Island. To Haast belongs the honour of having made the first recorded exploration of a New Zealand glacier, for he visited the Forbes Glacier in 1861 and the Hooker and Tasman Glaciers in the following year. During this period Hector was engaged in exploring the mountainous regions of Otago, where he discovered the low pass between Martin's Bay and Lake Wakatipu.

Hector's appointment as Director of the Geological Survey of New Zealand in 1865 marks the beginning of the third and last phase of exploration in the Dominion. It is characterized by the unostentatious progress of surveyors who rapidly removed the blanks from the map. Von Haast and Hector continued their work in the Alpine regions, where also E. P. Sealy explored the glaciers near Mount Cook in 1867 and 1870. R. von Lendenfeld's work between 1881 and 1886 included the first complete exploration of the Tasman Glacier in 1883, while the Rev. W. S. Green all but reached the summit of Mount Cook in 1882. Among other achievements at this time illustrating the detailed nature of New Zealand exploration were L. Cussen's triangulation of a large part of King County, in North Island, the exploration of much of the same county by J. H. Kerry-Nicholls, and the pioneer work of Mueller on the west coast of South Island, between Jackson's Bay and Martin's Bay. Among the later explorers who succeeded in completing the work in the Central Alpine regions are A. P. Harper, whose surveys were made in 1890 and succeeding years, and E. A. Fitzgerald, who made the first crossing of the High Central Alps in 1894–95. Although there are parts of the extreme south-west which are little known, and there are very few good topographical maps of the Dominion, New Zealand may be regarded as fully explored.

V. NEW GUINEA [1]

Although New Guinea was known in the early years of the sixteenth century, it remained unexplored until quite recent times, and even its coastal features were undetermined. A large number of explorers had added scraps to the charts, and in the nineteenth century a Dutch expedition, in 1826, greatly improved the knowledge of the south-west coast. Similarly, the surveys of Blackwood in the *Fly* in 1843, of Owen Stanley in the *Rattlesnake* in 1849, and

[1] See M. Krieger, *Neu-Guinea* (1899), Chapter II, for a brief account of exploration up to 1899, and C. Trotter, " New Guinea : A Summary of our Present Knowledge with regard to the Island," in *Proc. R.G.S.*, new series, vol. vi (1884), p. 196.

of Moresby in 1873 are commemorated by well-known features on the map. Moresby's survey was particularly important. He discovered the harbour which now bears his name, examined the east coast from Astrolabe Bay to the eastern end of the island, and definitely settled the shape of New Guinea.

Inland exploration begins with the visit of A. R. Wallace, who lived at Dorei, in the north-west, for a period of three and a half months in 1858. His work was not followed up, however, until 1872, when D'Albertis visited the Arfak Range and the coast near Dorei and Miklukho-Maclay travelled along a considerable portion of the north coast. In the next year A. B. Meyer crossed from McClure Inlet to Geelvink Bay. At this point inland exploration entered upon its first stage.

Soon after the visit of Moresby missionary activity on the south coast added many new features to the map. In 1875 S. Mac-Farlane and O. C. Stone went up the Baxter river, discovered two years earlier, and then MacFarlane and D'Albertis ascended the Fly river for over 100 miles. D'Albertis returned to the Fly river in 1876 and traced it for a distance of about 500 miles, and visited it for a third time in 1877, when he made a journey a little less extensive than that of the previous year.

From 1878 onward the missionaries Lawes and Chalmers were very active on the south coast, particularly round the Gulf of Papua, and Chalmers continued throughout the remaining years of the century to move about in a region which he had made his own. He was murdered on one of the islands that fringe the coast in 1901.[1]

In the course of her political expansion overseas Germany became ruler of a part of New Guinea in 1884, and with that thoroughness which characterized her work in Africa began the exploration of Kaiser Wilhelm Land. In 1884 Finsch covered about 1000 miles of coastline from the east cape to longitude 141° E., and discovered the Kaiserin Augusta river. This important discovery was confirmed by Dallmann, who went up the river for forty miles in 1886. His work was in turn extended by Admiral von Schleinitz and Dr Schrader, who reached a point 326 miles from the mouth. At the same time other explorers were examining the coast between Astrolabe Bay, the Kaiserin Augusta river, and Huon Gulf, where nine rivers were discovered. Schrader and Schleinitz continued their exploratory work behind the coastline in 1887, when the former ascended the Kaiserin Augusta river for 380 miles, almost to the boundary of Dutch territory, and completed a survey of its course. At the same time Count Pfeil examined the country behind Finsch Harbour.

Detailed work of this nature continued to occupy the Germans

[1] See R. Lovett, *James Chalmers : His Autobiography and Letters* (1902).

for a number of years, after which there was a pause until 1896, when Lauterbach went inland from Astrolabe Bay to the Bismarck Mountains. Two years later Tappenbeck proved that the Ramu river, which Lauterbach had discovered, was identical with the Ottilien, whose mouth near the Kaiserin Augusta river was already known. The examination of this river revealed a second important waterway into the heart of German New Guinea.

After another pause in exploration Dammköhler and Fröhlich examined the Markham river region, in the south-east of the colony, in 1907, and in the following year Full ascended the Kaiserin Augusta river for 200 miles. By 1909 the Commission for the demarcation of the Anglo-German boundary had finished its work. At the same time, in 1908 and 1909, Neuhauss was exploring the Markham river, which he ascended to a point higher than any previously attained. In 1910 the German-Dutch Boundary Commission went up the Kaiserin Augusta river and its tributary the Sepik, and reached the 141st meridian, about sixty miles from the British frontier. This was followed up by the Germans, who sent an expedition to the Kaiserin Augusta river in 1911–12 to examine the country lying to the south of the lower course of the river.

In the years immediately preceding the World War the Germans had shown much activity. In 1914 Thurnwald explored the country between the Sepik river and the north coast, while in 1913 the missionary Pilhofer travelled from the Waria river, near the Anglo-German boundary, to the Markham river. One German wandered about New Guinea during the war years, visiting the Waria river, Mount Chapman, and the Bismarck Mountains, until ill-health compelled him to seek shelter with friendly natives.

While the Germans had thus been outlining the main features of their colony the British had not been idle. In 1886 Chalmers discovered the "Wickham" (Alele) river. At the same time T. F. Bevan was engaged in his excellent work of mapping the Aird and neighbouring rivers. In 1887 two explorers, Hartmann and Hunter, reached the summit of the Owen Stanley Range. Strode Hall examined the Mai Kassa or Baxter river in 1888, and found it was not part of the Fly system, as was supposed.

Sir William MacGregor began his important work in British New Guinea in 1889, when he explored the country behind Milne Bay. He then went up the Vanapa river to Mount Victoria, in the Owen Stanley Range. In the winter of 1889–90 he navigated the Fly river for 605 miles, to the German boundary. MacGregor crossed New Guinea from the Mambare river to the Vanapa river in 1896, and in the reverse direction in 1897, when he also explored the north coast of the British territory.

A further piece of exploration carried out in 1897 was Giulianetti's ascent of the Vanapa river to its source.

440

Meanwhile activity along the coastline continued. As early as 1887 French missionaries had discovered and explored the St Joseph river, and they continued their work on the south coast for many years. In 1888 Everill surveyed and named the Strickland river, in 1890 Belford ascended Mount Yule, and in 1893 the Anglo-Dutch boundary was delimited. During the present century many new features have been discovered in New Guinea. In 1907 Monckton travelled from the Waria river to the Gulf of Papua, and a year later Mackay and Little explored the Upper Purari river. In 1910 and 1911 Staniforth Smith for the first time traversed a large area north-west of the Gulf of Papua and east of the Fly river basin.

Fig. 46. New Guinea, to illustrate Recent Exploration

This expedition, originating in the suggestions of Mackay and Little that coal existed in the interior, opened up the largest area previously unexplored in British territory.[1]

The task of filling in the details in British territory is proceeding apace, and is being accomplished by administrative officers in the course of their official duties. Space will not allow more than a mention of the names of some of the explorers and their sphere of activity. Thus in 1913 Ryan travelled from Kikori to the Ramu river; in 1915 Macdonnell crossed from Tufi, near Cape Nelson, to Port Moresby; in 1917 Humphries travelled south-eastward from Nepa, near the German boundary, and ultimately reached the coast at Morobe, while Chinnery explored the Kunimaipa valley and proved its identity with the Lakekamu; in 1922 Flint and Saunders were working in the Samberigi valley and Austen in the Alice river district; in 1924 Austen and Thompson completed the

---

[1] See *G.J.*, vol. xxxix, p. 313, and for the Mackay-Little expedition *G.J.*, vol. xxxviii, p. 483.

examination of the north-west corner of Papua,[1] between the Palmer and the Alice rivers, and the former reached the Fly river 605 miles above its mouth ; and in 1927–28 Karius and Champion succeeded in crossing the island by the Fly and Sepik rivers, thus linking up the regions where British and German exploration began.[2] Since that date remarkable journeys in the central mountains of New Guinea, made partly in search of gold, have added greatly to the knowledge of this inaccessible region, and have been productive of results of great importance both to anthropologists and to geographers.[3]

In Dutch New Guinea practically no exploration of the interior was carried out before 1893, except in very restricted localities. Mention has already been made of the early visits to Dorei and the Arfak Range and to McClure Inlet. In this latter district there was some further exploration by Ellis and Host in 1888. Contrary to an opinion strongly held in some quarters, they came to the conclusion that there was no waterway between McClure Inlet and Geelvink Bay. Their view was upheld by the later expedition of P. E. Moolenburgh, in 1901. But in spite of efforts such as these the interior of Dutch New Guinea was, not unfairly, described as "a complete blank" in 1893.[4]

The region explored by D'Albertis was extended by the journey of E. St Vraz in 1896–97, and still further by an expedition inland, to the west of Geelvink Bay, in 1903. Thus some considerable progress was being made in the north-west peninsula of the island.

In the south of Dutch territory R. P. Meyjes set out in 1904 to reach the mountains of the interior, but was obliged to change his plans and devote his time to an exploration of the Digul river. In 1908 and 1909 surveys were made of the rivers entering the south coast, and some further efforts were directed toward the interior. In the latter year Lorentz was successful in reaching the ' Snowy range,' meeting permanent snow at a height of 13,200 feet. He continued the examination of the Digul river, and fixed the highest point of the range, Wilhelmina Peak, at about 15,580 feet. This important work of Lorentz was extended by Schaeffer in 1911. His plan to cross the island from East Bay failed, for reasons of health,

[1] Papua is the name of the original British territory : the former German territory is now known as the Mandated Territory of New Guinea.
[2] Recent exploration in territories under British administration is dealt with fully in Sir Hubert Murray's *Papua of To-day : An Australian Colony in the Making* (1925). For the journey of Karius and Champion see *G.J.*, vol. lxxiv, p. 305.
[3] See E. W. P. Chinnery, " The Central Ranges of the Mandated Territory of New Guinea," in *G.J.*, vol. lxxxiv, p. 398 ; K. L. Spinks, " Mapping the Purari Plateau," *ibid.*, p. 412 ; K. L. Spinks, " The Wahgi River Valley of Central New Guinea," in *G.J.*, vol. lxxxvii, p. 222 ; and M. Leahy, " The Central Highlands of New Guinea," *ibid.*, p. 229. Mr Leahy's ten journeys cover a period from April 1930 to October 1934.   [4] *G.J.*, vol. ii, p. 493.

but he explored a considerable area of the mountains east of the district reached by Lorentz.

Meanwhile in 1909–10 a beginning was made with the exploration of the Mamberamo river, and in 1910 J. J. de Wal traced the eastern branch of this river almost to the foot of the central range. Thus the Dutch were closing in on the centre from both coasts. Their work was supplemented by the expedition of Goodfellow, who was succeeded in the command by Captain C. G. Rawling. This party reached the Nassau Mountains from the south coast, and thus added considerably to the known area in Dutch New Guinea. As a supplement to this expedition came the ascent of Mount Carstensz by A. R. F. Wollaston in 1913.

The broad outlines of the central range were now rapidly taking shape. In 1913 Herderschee reached the highest point of Mount Wilhelmina, and Weyermann explored the upper branches of the Digul river and determined the height of Mount Juliana (15,488 feet). On the western side of the territory Captain Ten Klooster explored the unknown country to the south and south-east of Geelvink Bay in 1913, and in 1914 Captain Oppermann continued the examination of the Mamberamo river, and discovered some new tributaries. In the same year Lieutenant Stroeve explored the Rouffaer river, a western tributary of the Mamberamo, and then crossed to Geelvink Bay, where he died. Some of the results of this important journey were unfortunately lost through Stroeve's death. The War interrupted work in New Guinea, but it was resumed soon after 1918, and is still proceeding.

VI. The East Indies [1]

It is remarkable that although the islands of the East Indies had been known to Western Europe from very early times, there had been very little exploration of the land behind the coastline, with the exception that Java was better known than any of the other islands. Nor was this changed until after the second half of the nineteenth century, when A. R. Wallace [2] called attention to the many interesting problems of this unknown part of the world. But although he spent six years in the archipelago (1854–60), and collected much information, he alone could do little to remove the

---

[1] For the East Indies see the following :
   C. M. Kan, *Histoire des découvertes dans l'archipel-indien* (1883).
   —— "Geographical Progress in the Dutch East Indies, 1883–1903 (in *Report of the Eighth International Congress*, 1905).
   C. Rabot, " L'Œuvre géographique des Néerlandais in Malaisie " (in *La Géographie*, vol. xxxii, pp. 10–19).
   H. Zondervan, " Die Entwickelung der Kartographie von Niederländisch-Indien " (in *P.M.*, vol. xlii, pp. 187–192, and 239–241).
[2] See A. R. Wallace, *Malay Archipelago* (2 vols., 1869).

blank spaces on the map, and in 1858 Sir Roderick Murchison could truthfully say that "the larger portion of it is still to be discovered." [1]

The island of Java has always been the most important of the Dutch possessions in the East Indies. Its pre-eminence is probably due not to any peculiarly favourable soil conditions, but to the fact that approach from the sea and penetration of the interior is easy, whereas in other islands forests, marshes, or very broken country immediately adjoin the coastline. Hence the Dutch were well informed about Java before the nineteenth century.

In the early years of the nineteenth century Java fell into the hands first of the French and then of the English. The energetic Governor Daendels (1808–11) was responsible for the first topographical map of Java, while his successor, Stamford Raffles (1811–1814), travelled extensively, and accumulated much information.

The island was restored to Holland in 1814, but in 1825 a great rebellion broke out, and involved the Dutch in a serious war, lasting until 1830. This incident, however, still further increased geographical knowledge. Soon after its end F. W. Junghuhn began his long work in Java (1835–49) ,the results of which were published in 1857, and shortly after this the Dutch undertook systematic surveys. By 1882 the triangulation of Java was completed, and subsequent geographical work has been concerned with special investigations, such as Verbeek's ; his geological surveys are well known.[2]

In Sumatra Junghuhn explored part of the Batak country in 1843, and in 1843–47 Beyerinck was engaged in surveys of the western districts. Steck worked in Bencoolen (in the south-west), Lampong (in the south), and Palembang (in the south-east) in 1856, and others discovered the Ombilin valley coalfield in 1869. Cluysenaer made a number of surveys in the western districts (1873–75).

Hitherto exploration in Sumatra, as in other Dutch colonies, had been spasmodic and unco-ordinated. With the foundation of the Dutch Geographical Society in 1873 a change occurred, and in 1877 P. J. Veth took out an expedition organized by the society. In that year there were many blanks in the map outside the coastal districts, and Veth spent his time in examining the Batang-Hari valley, in Central Sumatra, and the Padang highlands. On his return in 1879 the blank area in Central Sumatra had been largely reduced. The island was first crossed from east to west by Lieutenant Schouw Santvoort at this time (1877). It was also in Central Sumatra that B. Hagen carried out his explorations in 1883 and, much later (1907), that A. Maass did valuable work.

In 1883 the triangulation of Sumatra began, and with it much detailed exploration of small areas.

---

[1] *Proc. R.G.S.*, old series, vol. ii, p. 308.
[2] *E.g.*, R. D. M. Verbeek and R. Fennema, *Description géologique de Java et Madoura* (1896), and a number of other works.

444

Borneo shared to a less extent in the political changes which had affected Java and Sumatra, and was consequently less known. Wallace had visited the extreme south of Sarawak in the course of his travels. Spencer St John was working in North Borneo in 1847 and succeeding years, as was C. A. C. de Crespigny about ten years later. In the south Schwanaer crossed from Banjermassin to Pontianak, and explored much of the intervening country, between 1843 and 1847. In spite of this only the north-west coast was reasonably well known in 1859 ; with the exception of a few of the rivers the east, south, and west coasts were unknown.

The gradual establishment of the rule of Rajah Brooke in Sarawak led to greater knowledge of that part of the island, and it was here that C. Hose did his important work. Between 1884 and 1892 he was engaged in exploration of the Baram river valley, where Crespigny was Resident, and where he succeeded to that office in 1890.[1] His journeys entirely changed the map of a large area in Northern Sarawak.

Similar results were obtained by the servants of the British North Borneo Company. As early as 1878 T. S. Dobree went to North Borneo " for the purpose of ascertaining if the land was suitable for coffee." He was followed by Witti, who made three journeys between 1880 and 1882, and " settled once for all the vexed question of the existence of the large mythical Kinabalu lake," which he showed did not exist. Witti was murdered in Sabah in 1882, and it was to the central and western parts of this district that L. B. von Donop was sent in 1882 and 1883. In the latter year D. D. Daly began operations in the country behind Sarawak, and continued working there until 1887. Thus in all parts of the territory over which the British exercised an influence active work was in progress. In 1897 H. M. Hiller ascended the Rejang river for 300 miles, and thus opened up the largest river in the north and west of the island.

The Dutch also began active operations in Borneo about this time. Their surveys date from the year 1886. In 1893 they dispatched an important scientific expedition to Central Borneo, with G. A. F. Molengraaff as geologist and A. W. Nieuwenhuis as doctor and ethnologist. The latter returned in 1897 to complete the work begun in 1893, and crossed Borneo by the Kapuas river, which enters the sea on the west coast, and the Mahakam river, on the eastern side of the island. A traverse in the reverse direction, from Banjermassin to Pontianak, was made by Lieutenant Messemaekers van der Graaf in 1905. Seven years later the Dutch Commission for the delimitation of the frontier began operations, while among other smaller, but no less important, pieces of work was the examination of a large part of the Barito valley in the south-east in 1915 and 1917.

[1] See " In the Heart of Borneo," in *G.J.*, vol. xvi, p. 39.

Celebes was even less known than Borneo in the early part of the nineteenth century, and, indeed, remained virtually unexplored until the last decade of the century, although parts of its coasts were visited by A. R. Wallace and others who, like him, were engaged in general scientific work in the East Indies. In 1893, however, the brothers F. and P. Sarasin began their explorations, making two journeys in the north-east peninsula and a third across the centre of the island from north to south. Their travels revealed for the first time the major features of the relief of the island. The eastern peninsula was examined by A. C. Kruijt in 1899, and to him is really due the discovery of Lake Poso. At the same time the Dutch warship *Siboga*, whose voyage in the East Indian waters was made in 1899–1900, carried out valuable work on the sea to the south and east of Celebes.

The Sarasin brothers returned to the island in 1902–3, and this time examined the western central districts. In Central Celebes E. C. Abendanon explored the country between the Gulfs of Boni and Tomini in 1909–10, and in 1919 Dr Kaudern undertook valuable work in the north-east peninsula. Thus all parts of the island have received some measure of attention. The Dutch authorities are now giving much time and money to a more systematic examination of their extensive empire, and there is little doubt that within a short space of time it will all be reckoned among the regions of the world which are well known.

CHAPTER XVII
OCEAN AND POLAR EXPLORATION

I. Ocean Exploration

DURING the closing years of the eighteenth century much attention had been given to the Pacific Ocean, and especially to that part of it lying south of the equator, with the result that most of the island groups had been discovered. This interest did not cease during the nineteenth century, which is marked by the dispatch of many well-known ships for the prosecution of scientific research. In most cases some additions to geographical knowledge resulted from these expeditions.

The first voyage, in chronological order, is that of the Russians Captain A. J. de Krusenstern, commanding the *Nadezhda*, and J. Lisianski, commanding the *Neva*. Their main object was to conduct a Russian envoy to Japan, but the cruise has a wider interest, for it marks the entry of the Russians into the waters of the Southern Hemisphere and it accomplished valuable geographical work. The ships left Kronstadt in July 1803, and after some delay at Falmouth sailed across the Atlantic Ocean, and rounded Cape Horn. The Pacific Ocean was entered in February 1804, and the first surveys and observations were made in the Marquesas Islands. Krusenstern proceeded to Kamchatka and thence to Japan, but, although he waited for five months, he found that the Japanese were unwilling to receive the Russian Ambassador. Turning northward, therefore, he examined the strait between Sakhalin and the mainland, but did not add materially to the knowledge already gained by La Pérouse and Broughton. Krusenstern then returned to Kamchatka, but later revisited the northern part of Sakhalin, and explored the strait between it and the mainland from the northern end. He wrongly concluded that Sakhalin was a peninsula of Asia, and this error remained until corrected by Nevelskoi fifty years later.

Meanwhile Lisianski had discovered the island named after him in the North Pacific, and had made some observations on the west coast of North America, where a cargo of furs was collected. The two ships then sailed to Canton, and discharged their goods, returning thence to Kronstadt, which was reached in August 1806. The voyage was important for measurements of temperature in deep water, for astronomical observations and observations of the currents and tides, and for ethnological researches, as well as

447

for the more direct contributions to the geography of the Pacific Ocean.[1]

The work of Krusenstern was continued by one of his subordinates, Lieutenant O. E. Kotzebue, who was sent out in 1815 to discover a passage through Bering Strait and round North America to Europe. His ship, the *Rurik*, rounded Cape Horn in January 1816, visited Easter Island, and proceeded to the Paumotu Archipelago, where a number of islands were discovered. After a voyage to Bering Sea, where the Diomede Islands were mapped, Kotzebue returned to the Marshall Islands and made further discoveries. He arrived back in the Baltic in July 1818.

Although Kotzebue had failed in the main object of his voyage, he had added considerably to the knowledge of the Pacific Ocean, and had improved the maps of a large part of the west coast of Alaska, where Kotzebue Sound now stands as a memorial of his work. In addition the reports of the naturalists who accompanied the expedition were of great value.

A third Russian voyage was that of Captain F. G. Bellingshausen in the *Vostok* and Lieutenant M. Lazarev in the *Mirni*. Bellingshausen had served with Krusenstern, and Lazarev had already made a Pacific voyage in 1814. Their joint enterprise, begun in 1819, is the only instance of a Russian Antarctic expedition. In the Pacific Ocean their main researches were carried out in the Paumotu group, in July and August 1820, and resulted in the discovery of seventeen small islands. This, however, must be regarded rather as an interlude in the Polar exploration of Bellingshausen, to which reference is made below.

Before considering the French and English voyages it will be convenient to complete the story of Russian enterprise, although only the more important expeditions are mentioned. In 1823–26 Kotzebue made a second voyage round the world, taking with him the physicist O. Lenz, who carried out valuable oceanographical researches. His most important discoveries were the group of Bellingshausen Islands (latitude 150° 48′ S., longitude 154° 30′ W.) and a few islands in the Marshall Archipelago.

Kotzebue reached Russia in July 1826, and in the following September Captain T. Lütke set sail in the *Seniavin*. He visited the North Pacific, where he supplemented the work of Kotzebue, and discovered, in the Caroline group, the islands which now bear the name of his ship. His exploration of the coast of North-eastern Asia was particularly important, while the observations of the specialists who accompanied him were of great value, especially for the sciences of botany, zoology, and geology.

During the first half of the nineteenth century the French main-

[1] For an account of Russian work in the Pacific Ocean see *The Pacific-Russian Scientific Investigations* (Academy of Sciences of the U.S.S.R., 1926).

tained their interest in the South Sea, and sent out a number of important expeditions. That of Baudin to the south coast of Australia was largely a failure, but one of its officers, Louis de Freycinet, cartographer to that expedition, was sent out again in 1817 in the *Uranie*, to carry out magnetic researches in the Pacific. He visited the west coast of Australia, but, like the earlier Dutch navigators, was not impressed by its geographical conditions, and, by contrast, thought Timor a Paradise on earth. From this island he made a wide sweep of the Pacific, passing through the Caroline group, the Ladrones, and the Sandwich Islands, to the Samoa group, where Rose Island, named after his wife, who accompanied him, survives as one of his few real discoveries. He returned to Europe round Cape Horn, and was wrecked on the Falkland Islands.

Freycinet had been able to make a number of useful observations in accordance with the main purpose of the voyage, and these were supplemented by the work of Duperrey, who served as a lieutenant under Freycinet, and was sent out in 1822 in command of the *Coquille*. He spent a month in the Falkland Islands, adding considerably to the geographical knowledge of the group, and then crossed the Pacific to New Ireland. After cruising in the neighbourhood of New Guinea he visited New South Wales and New Zealand, where a few minor discoveries were made. Duperrey returned through the Carolines to New Guinea, and then sailed through the East Indies. In addition to the discovery of a few small islands he succeeded in obtaining much information relative to magnetic variation.

Duperrey's work was in turn supplemented by that of J. S. C. Dumont d'Urville, one of the most distinguished of French maritime explorers during the century. He had already served with Duperrey in the voyage just described, and he returned in the *Coquille*, renamed the *Astrolabe*, in 1825. During this voyage he obtained definite evidence of the wreck of La Pérouse on the island of Vanikoro, one of the Santa Cruz group. The same fact was also established by Captain Dillon, with the help of the Indian Government, in 1826, but his work was not known to the French at the time of D'Urville's voyage. D'Urville made many important additions to the knowledge of the Pacific islands. His visits to the north coast of New Guinea and to New Zealand resulted in improved charts of those regions, while he also carried out valuable work in the Fiji Islands, the Carolines, and the Moluccas. He returned to France in 1829.

D'Urville was sent out again in 1837, with instructions to endeavour to make some discoveries in the South Polar regions, where sealers had been reporting new land. Thus the Pacific portion of D'Urville's voyage forms an interlude between his first southward journey of 1838, approximately on the longitude of 45° W., and his second attempt of 1839, when he sailed southward from Hobart and discovered Adélie Land. During the two years

449

that he spent in the Pacific he made many valuable additions to the geography of its western parts.

Two other voyages must suffice as examples of the increasing attention which was given to maritime exploration at this time. In 1831 Fitzroy, in command of the *Beagle*, continued the survey work which had already been carried out by that ship on the east and west coasts of South America. He visited the Paumotu Archipelago, the Society Islands, New Zealand, Australia, and the Keeling Islands in the course of a voyage round the world. Apart from useful work with chronometers, carried on throughout the voyage, this expedition gave invaluable experience to Charles Darwin, and furnished the material not only for his well-known *Journal*, but also for his *Geological Observations on South America* and *Structure and Distribution of Coral Reefs* and other works.

Shortly after the return of the *Beagle* Charles Wilkes, of the United States Navy, went out with a large though not too happy expedition. Like D'Urville, he was ordered to the Antarctic regions, where he added Wilkes Land to the map, near to, and west of, the Adélie Land of the French explorers. In the Pacific he began the survey of the Paumotu group—a work completed in 1840–41 by his brother officer Ringgold—and visited Tahiti, the Samoa group, Australia, New Zealand, the Tonga Islands, Fiji, and the Sandwich Islands before proceeding to the west coast of North America, where some important discoveries were made in the region of the Columbia river.[1] Wilkes returned across the Pacific to Manila, and made his homeward voyage round the Cape of Good Hope. He was accompanied by J. D. Dana, a distinguished American geologist, who used this voyage to gather information for his work on *Corals and Coral Islands* and his many contributions to the literature of oceanography. With this American expedition the first period of maritime exploration comes to an end.[2]

During the second half of the nineteenth century maritime exploration is characterized by the number and importance of expeditions sent out to investigate problems of the oceans rather than to explore land-surfaces. The Austrian ship *Novara* in 1857 begins this new period with scientific exploration among the Pacific islands. Hochstetter's classical work on New Zealand is one of the direct results.[3] But the outstanding voyage of the period is that of H.M.S. *Challenger*. This scientific expedition arose out of the work of the *Lightning* and *Porcupine* in the waters immediately to the west of the British Isles, and was carried out through the co-operation

---

[1] See above, Chapter XV, p. 385.
[2] Among the voyages not described here were those of Beechey (1826: Bonin Islands and Paumotu Archipelago), La Place (1837–40: Tahiti, Marquesas, Hawaii), and Belcher (1840: New Hebrides, Bismarck Archipelago).
[3] See above, Chapter XVI, p. 437.

of the British Admiralty and the Royal Society. On the naval side the command was given to Captain (afterward Sir) G. S. Nares, while the scientific *personnel* were led by Sir Charles Wyville Thomson, and included (Sir) John Murray. The route was so arranged that the Atlantic and Pacific Oceans should be crossed, or partly crossed, both in a north-south and in an east-west direction, and no efforts were spared to make the scientific results of the expedition as complete and as accurate as possible.

The *Challenger* sailed from Sheerness on December 7, 1872, and returned on May 26, 1876. Up to October 1873 the ship cruised in the Atlantic Ocean, making two traverses in the northern half and one in the south. After leaving Cape Town the *Challenger* proceeded, in high latitudes, to Melbourne. In the Pacific the ship visited New Zealand, the East Indies, Japan, the Sandwich Islands, Tahiti, and the southern coast of Chile. The return to Sheerness was made through the Strait of Magellan and by Montevideo, Ascension Island, and the Azores. At its end the author of the general account of the voyage wrote:

> The cruise has been successfully accomplished, and the intentions of the expedition happily achieved. That it will exalt our national reputation to a very considerable extent, in one of the most popular branches of the service, cannot for a moment be doubted. The completion of surveys; the success of soundings; configuration of the depths of the great ocean, with its nature and temperatures, and the composition of its bottom, have all been investigated and carried out by the hydrographic staff; and Professor Thomson and his talented assistants may well be complimented on their labours, which have contributed such an abundance of material to the various departments of natural history and the other scientific branches under their direction.[1]

The results of this expedition, when published, occupied fifty large volumes, and were of the greatest scientific value. Among them may be placed the following:[2]

(1) Proof that the variation of the compass can be determined as accurately in a ship as on shore if the ship is magnetically suitable.

(2) The determination, for the first time, of the depths and main contour lines of the great ocean basins.

(3) The determination of oceanic temperatures and their independence of seasonal variation below the depth of 100 fathoms.

[1] W. J. J. Spry, *The Cruise of H.M.S. " Challenger "* (12th edition, 1895), p. 314.
[2] W. Herdman, *Founders of Oceanography and their Work* (1923), pp. 58–59. For details of the expedition see the *Report on the Scientific Results of the Voyage of H.M.S. " Challenger "* (50 vols., 1880–95). Vol. i, Parts 1 and 2 (1885), is narrative.

(4) Proof of constant bottom temperatures over large areas in the ocean.

(5) The determination of the exact position of many islands and rocks the longitude of which had been previously uncertain.

(6) The charting and surveying of various little-known parts of the world and their biological investigation.

(7) The determination of the ocean currents, both on the surface and at various depths.

(8) Increase in knowledge of the details of the structure and probable mode of formation of coral reefs.

Later work has supplemented these results, but the main facts ascertained by the *Challenger* expedition have not been materially changed. Among the other contributors were the German ship *Gazelle* (1875–76), which added numerous soundings in the North Atlantic, and the United States ship *Tuscarora* (1874–76), whose work in the North Pacific was particularly valuable. More recently Alexander Agassiz has made many additions to the knowledge of the oceans. His work in the *Blake*, between 1877 and 1880, was devoted to the Caribbean Sea, while in the last years of the century, and again in 1904–5, he was engaged with the *Albatross* in the Pacific. Agassiz covered over 100,000 miles in the course of his voyages, and his work entitles him to rank as one of the most distinguished maritime explorers.

Other work of great value has been carried out by well-known ships. In 1895 the *Penguin* discovered the deep of that name in the South Pacific; in 1899 the United States vessel *Nero* found the deepest known waters (5160 fathoms) also in the Pacific; while this record was in turn passed by the German ship *Planet*, which located the Swire Deep (5348 fathoms), off Mindanao, in 1912. The Dutch expedition in the *Siboga* (1899–1900) to the East Indian waters and that of Sir John Murray and Dr J. Hjort in the *Michael Sars* to the Atlantic Ocean in 1910 are also of prime importance. The ambitious programme of the German Atlantic expedition in the *Meteor* was not wholly carried out owing to a series of accidents, but something was done toward making a complete survey of the Atlantic Ocean (1925–27), and important additions were made to knowledge of bathymetry in southern latitudes. The numerous Antarctic expeditions of the present day are also equipped to investigate the unsolved problems of the oceans, but while many new facts will doubtless be obtained it is probable that the main features of the ocean floor and of the oceanic waters are now reasonably well known. As on the land, so here in the oceans modern exploration must be of the intensive rather than of the extensive variety if it is to justify itself.

452

Taimir
Peninsula

Nor
L

New Siberian Is.

Bennett Is.

Henrietta Is.
Jeannette Is.

C. Chelagski

Wrangel Is.

1927

Herald Is.

Bering St.

Beaufort

Point Barrow

Sea

M

Sve

Ma

Fairy

MC

B. of Mercy   Melville

Banks   Melville Is.   Cornwallis

Island   Bathurst

Mackenzie R.   MC   Mc Clintock Sd.   Cornwallis

M   Franklin
Bay   Prince of Wales Is.

Victoria Land   AU   P

Coppermine R.   Wollaston   F
Land   A   William

Coronation   Dease St.   Is.
Gulf   Simpson   Adelaide
Pen.

North-west ---→

RI   ROSS I (Lancaster Sound).
PI   PARRY I (Barrow Strait).
P2   PARRY II (Fury and Hecla Strait).
P3   PARRY III (Prince Regent Inlet).
R2   ROSS II (Prince Regent Inlet).
F   FRANKLIN.
AU   AUSTIN.
C   COLLINSON.
MC   McCLURE.
M   McCLINTOCK.
A   AMUNDSEN.
 –..– CANADIAN ARCTIC EXPEDITION. Northern Party Routes.
 .... WILKINS.

Fig. 47. THE NORTH POLAR REGIONS—I : THE NORTH-EAST AND NORTH-WEST PASSAGES AND GREENL

60°

30°

K. Kreuz

Kara
Sea

Novaya Zemlya
C.Nassau   Matochkin Shar

Barents
Sea

Wilczek Is.
Hall Is.
am Bell Is.   Northbrook Is.
Franz
C.Fligely   Josef
Land

30°

North-
east Land   SPITSBERGEN
Phipps Is.

Danes Is.

Tromsö

85°   80°   70°   GREENLAND   0°
Independence Fiord   SEA
Denmark Fiord

Repulse Harbour   C.Bismarck
Koldewey Is.
Sabine Is.

Dronning   Kaiser
Louise   Wilhelm   Scoresby Sd.
Land   Land   ICELAND
Petermann
Peak

Grinnell
Humboldt
Land   Glacier

K

Ellesmere   Smith Strait   Q
Land   30°

Thule   R(1)

ones Sd.   BAFFIN   NO
ancaster Sd.   BAY   Provet
Disko Is.   NA

BAFFIN   DAVIS   C.Farewell
Melville   STRAIT   Godthaab
Pen.   P(2) & Hecla Str.   ISLAND

60°
Hudson Strait

DSON
AY

North-east
++++ A.E.Nordenskiöld.
-+- Drift of "Jeannette"
Greenland +·+·+
NO A.E.Nordenskiöld.
NA Nansen.
K   Koch.
R   Rasmussen.
P   Peary.
Q   de Quervain.

453

OCEAN AND POLAR EXPLORATION

II. The Polar Regions: Introduction [1]

The failure of earlier efforts and the declining enthusiasm for exploration led to the practical cessation of Arctic voyages until the beginning of the nineteenth century, except in so far as those journeys were related to discoveries in Asia or in America. There are, however, a few exceptions to this general statement. A Dutchman, Willem de Vlamingh, sailed to the north of Novaya Zemlya in 1664, while a fellow-countryman, Cornelius Roule, may have discovered land hitherto unknown, to the north of Novaya Zemlya, in 1700. An Englishman, Captain John Wood, also sailed in the waters round Novaya Zemlya in 1676, but failed to discover the passage which he sought and by which he hoped to reach Japan. He concluded that Novaya Zemlya was joined to Greenland. A fourth voyage, by the Dutch whaler Cornelis Giles, resulted in the supposed discovery of Giles Land to the north-west of Franz Josef Land: a Russian expedition of 1928 " reported that the island was a myth." [2]

The results of the voyage of Giles came to the knowledge of the Hon. Daines Barrington, who interested the Royal Society and the British Government in a project to reach the Pole. Captain C. Phipps was given command of the expedition, which was sent out in 1773, but although he cruised along the ice barrier from the neighbourhood of Spitsbergen to Novaya Zemlya, he could find no channel through it. A few other expeditions were sent out from Denmark or from England at the close of the eighteenth century, but the distractions of the European war and the many failures told against any systematic exploration of these regions.

In the nineteenth century most of the large problems of Polar

---

[1] The literature of Polar voyages is extensive. Among the older works [Sir] John Barrow, *A Chronological History of Voyages in the Arctic Regions* (1818) is still of value.

For the Polar regions in general the following are very useful:

A. W. Greely, *Handbook of Polar Discoveries* (4th edition, 1910).

—— *The Polar Regions in the Twentieth Century* (1929). This is the English edition, and is much superior to the earlier (1928) American edition. The mistakes in the American edition were corrected by Dr R. N. Rudmose Brown.

R. N. Rudmose Brown, *The Polar Regions* (1927). A regional geography, with summaries of exploration.

For the South Pole H. R. Mill, *The Siege of the South Pole* (1905), is invaluable. *Bibliografi Antarktisk Litteratur* in B. Aagaard, *Fangst og forskning i Sydishavet* (Oslo 1930), is also most useful as the only fairly complete bibliography. So much has been done in the Polar regions in recent years that it is impossible to deal fully with this exploration in the space available. Full details will be found in *The Polar Record*, published twice a year by the Scott Polar Research Institute, Cambridge.

[2] *Polar Record*, No. 11, p. 11. Giles Land is, however, probably identical with White Island, and was originally misplaced by Petermann. White Island was the site of Andrée's camp.

geography were solved. For convenience of description they may be stated as follows. First came the attempts to find the North-west Passage: once this was completed, attention was devoted to work in the direction of the Pole itself. Further exploration was taken up with the discovery of the North-east Passage and of lands within the North Polar regions, notably Greenland and Spitsbergen. As a separate piece of work there is the exploration of the Antarctic continent and the discovery of the South Pole.

III. THE NORTH-WEST PASSAGE AND THE CANADIAN ARCHIPELAGO [1]

When the end of the Napoleonic wars set free many experienced sailors it became almost a matter of honour to settle the problem of the North-west Passage, But it was now recognized that the commercial possibilities of such a passage, even if one existed, were negligible. The exploration which followed the first voyage of Captain John Ross in 1818 was therefore solely scientific, and, further, was the beginning of systematic work in the North Polar regions.

Moreover, ice conditions in the northern seas seemed favourable, and in 1817 the coast of Greenland was actually followed by a Hamburg ship from latitude 60° to latitude 70°. Hence, largely due to the inspiration of Sir John Barrow, two expeditions were sent out in 1818. One, consisting of the *Dorothea* and the *Trent*, respectively commanded by Captain Buchan and Lieutenant Franklin, sailed north into the sea round Spitsbergen, but accomplished little; the other, consisting of the *Isabella*, under Captain John Ross, and the *Alexander*, under Lieutenant Parry, sailed to Baffin Bay.

The reason for these expeditions may be found in the words of Sir John Barrow:

> Of the three directions in which a passage has been sought for, from the Atlantic to the Pacific, that by the north-east holds out the least encouraging hope. . . . But the question of a north-west passage which would be much shorter, and of a polar one, which would be shortest of all, rests on very different grounds. That the North Pole may be approached by sea, has been an opinion entertained both by experienced navigators and by men eminent for their learning and science; that several ships have at different times been carried three or four degrees beyond Spitsbergen and the usual limits of the whale fishery, is not merely a matter of opinion; and if the Polar Sea be navigable to a height of 84° there seems to be no other physical obstruction, than the intervention of land, to the practical navigation of that sea to the North Pole itself; as there is no reason to suppose that the temperature of that point is lower in the winter, while it is probably much higher in the summer, than on the parallel of 80°; as it is well-known that the latitude of 80° is generally not colder on the same meridian, and in many places much

[1] See N. M. Crouse, *The Search for the North-west Passage* (1934), for a general account.

less severe, than that of 70° is in others. . . . The case is different with regard to the north-west passage. From the very frequent attempts which have been made for its discovery, it is now known pretty nearly whereabouts such a passage, if it exists at all, must be looked for. It has . . . been ascertained that there is no passage on the coast of America below the Arctic Circle ; but . . . it has not been ascertained whether this coast [joins Greenland or trends away to join the north coast of America]. Many reasons have been assigned for the latter supposition [*e.g.*, arguments based on currents, floating wood, icebergs, Eskimo maps]. Indeed, the best geographers are now of opinion that Greenland is either an island or an archipelago of islands. . . . This supposed insularity of Greenland will most probably be determined by one or other of the expeditions. If in the affirmative, the next question that presents itself is, whether an uninterrupted communication exists between the Pacific and the Atlantic. . . . It must be admitted, at the same time, that although a communication may, and in all probability does, exist between the two oceans, it by no means follows that there must also be found a navigable passage for large vessels ; though it is not unfair to infer that, where large mountains of ice can float and find their way, a ship may do the same. This, however, is the point to be ascertained by the expedition under Captain Ross.[1]

Such were the opinions of the ablest theorist in 1818, and they contrast very favourably with the optimistic conjectures put forward more than two centuries before by Sir Humphrey Gilbert. They represent the advance in knowledge which resulted from the exploration so far considered, and mark the point from which the new explorers started.

The hopes of the Admiralty that Buchan might " remain for a few days in the vicinity of ·the Pole for the purpose of making observations which his interesting and unexampled situation might furnish him " were not fulfilled, and the expedition only reached the edge of the pack to the north-west of Spitsbergen and found it impenetrable. Meanwhile Ross confirmed the existing knowledge of Baffin Bay, explored a portion of the east coast of Baffin Island, and entered Lancaster Sound. Seeing what he took to be land stretching across the opening, he abandoned the expedition against the wishes of his brother officers, and returned home. Thus through ignorance of northern conditions and through incompetence in the north-west very little of value was accomplished.

In the next year Parry, with the ships *Hecla* and *Griper*, set out to examine the sound which Ross had failed to explore. Reaching Lancaster Sound on August 4, 1819, the ships passed with ease westward, through a strait which was named Barrow Strait, discovering a channel which led westward for 630 miles and sailing over the ' land ' which Ross had called the Croker Mountains. Parts of the coasts of Bathurst and Melville Islands were discovered, and the winter was spent on the latter island. In June 1820 Parry

---

[1] Sir John Barrow, *op. cit.*, pp. 370–378.

set out on foot to explore the island, and reached its northern shores, and in August the expedition tried in vain to get farther west. The ships returned to the Thames in November, having accomplished a very great piece of work and having showed the improbability of finding a passage through Barrow Strait.

In 1821 Parry was sent out again, to find a passage in a lower latitude than Melville Sound. The ships *Hecla* and *Fury* explored the lands in the north-west of Hudson Bay, and discovered the Fury and Hecla Strait, separating Baffin Island from Melville Peninsula.

Meanwhile Franklin had undertaken an important land expedition, and had in addition sailed eastward from the mouth of the Coppermine to Cape Turnagain.[1]

In 1824 Parry made a third voyage, this time again to Lancaster Sound. The object was to find a passage through Prince Regent Inlet, but the voyage failed, owing partly to the bad ice conditions and partly to the wreck of the *Fury*.

Expeditions now followed one another almost annually. In 1825 Beechey, in the *Blossom*, sailed through Bering Strait, and, continuing the work of Cook, got as far eastward as Point Barrow. In the following year Franklin explored the coast from the Mackenzie river westward to within 160 miles of Point Barrow, and Richardson followed it eastward to the mouth of the Coppermine. Thus there was only a small blank in the whole shoreline between Cape Prince of Wales, named by Cook, and Cape Turnagain, named by Franklin. This short gap was filled in by Dease and Simpson in 1837.

In 1829 Ross and his nephew, James Clarke Ross, penetrated Prince Regent Inlet, and on August 13 reached the spot where Parry had abandoned the *Fury* in 1825. The land called Boothia in honour of the promoter of the voyage, Sir Felix Booth, was discovered, and by means of land journeys James Ross located the Magnetic Pole. He also traversed the sea-ice to a land to the west which he called King William Land,[2] exploring its northern side as far as Point Victory and reporting exceptionally heavy ice on the shore. Four winters were spent by the party in these regions, until at length they were picked up by a whaler in Lancaster Sound and brought back to England. A search expedition which had been sent out in 1833 under George Back traced the Great Fish river to the Arctic Sea, and thus placed another known point on the map of the North American Coast. The last blanks were filled in by Dease and Simpson during the years 1838 and 1839, by Rae in 1846, and by Hall in 1864.[3]

[1] See above, Chapter XV, p. 371.
[2] Now called King William Island.
[3] These land expeditions are dealt with in more detail in Chapter XV, section I.

OCEAN AND POLAR EXPLORATION

The final act in the search for the North-west Passage is now reached. It will be convenient therefore to take stock of the position prior to the sailing of Sir John Franklin's expedition in 1845. Attempts to find the passage by way of Melville Sound, Prince Regent Inlet, Fury and Hecla Strait, and Bering Strait had all failed. To the north of Barrow Strait the general outline of coast and inlets was known as far as Melville Island, to the south as far as Cape Walker, at the west side of Peel Sound. The whole coast of North America was known, together with parts of Wollaston Land and Victoria Land, and King William Island, which was thought to join on to Boothia Felix.

Franklin [1] left England on May 19, 1845, with orders to make for Cape Walker, whence he was to "push on in as direct a line as possible toward Bering's Strait." The commander was given the liberty to follow either Wellington Channel or the passage to the west of North Somerset Island, as he thought best. His own opinion, which proved to be correct, was that the latter was the right way to proceed. But he first tried Wellington Channel, sailing up it until stopped by ice, and returning southward by a new route between Bathurst and Cornwallis Islands. This was the first piece of discovery accomplished by the expedition. The winter of 1845–46 was spent on Beechey Island. As soon as they were able the *Erebus* and *Terror* moved southward down Peel Sound, and spent their second winter in the pack in latitude 70° 5′ N., longitude 98° 23′ W. Owing to ignorance of the geographical facts no attempt was made to pass eastward of King William Island, and all through the summer of 1847 the ships lay fast in the ice. The only knowledge of what was happening is derived from the scanty evidence collected by the search-parties. The whole story is to be read on a single sheet of paper found on King William Island by Lieutenant Hobson in 1859. First is an entry by Gore to the effect that the wintering of 1845–46 (he says wrongly 1846–47) had been made at Beechey Island, "Sir John Franklin commanding the expedition. All well." He added: "Party consisting of 2 officers and 6 men left the ships on Monday, 24 May, 1847." That was a party sent out to explore King William Island under Lieutenant Gore, and it reached Point Victory. The second note, apparently written by Fitzjames, round the margin of the paper records:

April 25, 1848. H.M. Ships *Terror* and *Erebus* were deserted on the 22nd of April, 5 leagues N.N.W. of this, having been beset since 12th September, 1846. The officers and crews, consisting of 105 souls, under the command of Captain F. R. M. Crozier, landed here

[1] Sir Albert Markham's *Life of Sir John Franklin and the North-west Passage* (1891) contains an account of many Polar expeditions besides those of Franklin himself. Sir Clements Markham's *Life of Admiral Sir Leopold McClintock* (1909) is also very useful.

in latitude 69° 37′ 42″ N., longitude 98° 41′ W. This paper was found by Lieutenant Irving under the cairn supposed to have been built by Sir James Ross in 1831, where it had been deposited by the late Commander Gore in June [*sic.*—read May] 1847. Sir James Ross's pillar has not, however, been found, and the paper has been transferred to this position, which is that in which Sir James Ross's pillar was erected. Sir John Franklin died on the 11th June 1847, and the total loss by deaths in the expedition has been to this date 9 officers and 15 men.

The paper is signed " James Fitzjames, Captain H.M.S. *Erebus* " and countersigned " F. R. M. Crozier, Captain and Senior Officer, and start on to-morrow 26th for Back's Fish River." [1] All that is known of the journey is from reports collected from Eskimos to the effect that about forty men were seen moving southward in search of food. It has been conjectured that the party perished somewhere between Adelaide Peninsula and the Great Fish river. There seems little doubt that they found the real ' passage,' although unable to sail along it. Their failure was due to a number of causes : to incorrect charts, which failed to mark the passage south of King William Island and so compelled the leaders to go southward to the west of that land, and thus to become involved in impenetrable ice ; to the bad provisions supplied by a man named Goldner ; and, as much as anything, to a reluctance of the explorers of those days to live on seal meat. The final march of the survivors must have been a journey of despair, for they expected to find little or no game when they began their march in April.

Franklin's expedition had results more important than the relatively small discoveries which it made. It set a tradition for danger in Polar work which still lingers ; and above all it gave rise to a large number of search-expeditions which practically completed the discovery of the North-west Passage. In the space available it is only possible to indicate briefly the more important of these search-expeditions.

First in 1848 was the expedition of Sir James Ross, approaching from Baffin Bay. About 150 miles of the west coast of North Somerset Island was explored by sledge, but no traces of Franklin's party were discovered. But although the expedition was not thus successful, it was of great importance in that here Leopold McClintock, then a lieutenant, learned his first lesson in sledge-travelling in the Arctic regions.

While this expedition was in progress Richardson and Rae carried out a search by land from Canada, and Kellett from the Pacific side, though equally unsuccessful in the main search, discovered Herald Island.

The year 1850 was notable for a number of expeditions, of which

[1] This document is reproduced in facsimile in Sir Leopold McClintock's *The Voyage of the " Fox " in the Arctic Seas* (1859).

the most important was that commanded by Captain H. T. Austin, under whom McClintock served. With this expedition may be coupled that of the whaler W. Penny. "Of all the arctic expeditions [this] . . . was the happiest, the healthiest, the best administered, and the most successful. . . . Its sledge-travellers in their searches had covered 7025 miles on foot and discovered 1225 miles of new land." [1] These discoveries included the east coast of Melville Island, the east coast of Cornwallis Island, the north-west, north, and east coasts of Prince of Wales Island, Russell Island, the south and west coast of Bathurst Island, and the south coast of Melville Island, the last being the particular contribution of McClintock.

While Austin's parties were exploring from the side of Baffin Bay Collinson and McClure had been sent to search eastward from Bering Strait. Collinson spent the year 1850 in the Beaufort Sea, advanced up Prince of Wales Strait in the following year, and in 1852 went through Coronation Gulf to Cambridge Bay, and examined by sledge Victoria Strait, between Victoria Land and King William Island. Collinson's voyage is " one of the most remarkable and successful on record." [2]

Meanwhile McClure reached Prince of Wales Strait by Franklin Bay, and land parties discovered the insularity of Banks Island and explored the north and south of Wollaston Land. In the summer of 1851 he sailed round the south of Banks Island and reached the Bay of Mercy on the north shore, where he spent the winter of 1851–52 ; there he remained, sending parties to the neighbouring lands, until rescued by a sledge-party from Sir Edward Belcher's squadron. Thus McClure and his crew walked over the frozen North-west Passage, and returned to England by Baffin Bay.

In 1850 an American expedition, under E. J. de Haven, explored Wellington Channel and found a new land, named Grinnell, lying farther north : the latter was part of Devon Island. De Haven's ships were fast bound in the ice, and in that plight they drifted over 1000 miles.

In the year 1851 Captain W. Kennedy wintered in Prince Regent Inlet, and in the spring of 1852 discovered the strait separating North Somerset Island from the mainland of North America. The passage, now known as Bellot Strait, was so named from the French officer, J. R. Bellot, who accompanied the expedition. A second expedition, under Rae, went down the Coppermine river in 1851, crossed to Wollaston Land, and examined a considerable part of the east coast of Victoria Land. To him was due the first definite news of Franklin's fate, which he learned from Eskimo.

Hitherto little evidence of the fate of Franklin had been gained, and the British Government determined to send out a new search-

---

[1] Sir Clements Markham, *Life of McClintock*, p. 133.
[2] A. W. Greely, *Handbook of Arctic Discoveries* (4th edition), p. 150.

party. A large squadron under the command of Sir Edward Belcher was accordingly dispatched to carry out the " two great objects " which his instructions laid down—that is, " first the endeavouring to pass up Wellington Channel with one sailing vessel and one steamer, and second, the advance of a similar force towards Melville Island." [1] On arrival at the southern end of the channel Belcher divided his forces, went north himself with G. H. Richards and Sherard Osborn, and sent Captain H. Kellett and F. L. McClintock to the west. The northern party accomplished some valuable work, discovering North Cornwall Island, a few other islands to the north of Grinnell Peninsula, and part of Bathurst Island. But the western party deserve even greater credit for their explorations. McClintock and others made short journeys in 1852, during one of which Lieutenant Mecham found a message left by McClure. In the following year great advances were made. McClintock covered 1408 miles, of which 768 were on new ground, and discovered, and partly explored, Prince Patrick Island. " This journey," declared Markham in 1909, " is by far the greatest Arctic effort that has ever been made." [2] Mecham explored the south and west coast of Prince Patrick Island, and all but reached the point at which McClintock turned back, He covered 1173 miles, of which 785 were over unknown tracks, and with McClintock completed a most important discovery. Vesey Hamilton, in a journey of 663 miles, covered some new ground on the north of Melville Island. In addition McClure's crew had been rescued by Lieutenant Pim. Although differences of opinion between Belcher and his subordinates hampered the expedition, it accomplished work of great importance.

In the course of a journey to survey the west coast of Boothia Peninsula, in 1854, Rae obtained definite information of the retreat, and death, of a large party of men, and was able to recover some articles which belonged to the party, leaving no doubt that it was the remnants of Franklin's expedition. This satisfied the British Government, and they ceased their efforts to trace the *Erebus* and *Terror*. But Lady Franklin refused to give up the search, and secured the help of McClintock, who made his famous expediton in the *Fox* in 1857. The east side of King William Island was explored, the discovery of Prince of Wales Island was completed, and some investigation of McClintock Channel was made. In all about 800 miles of new discoveries are to be placed to the credit of the expedition. But it had a further success, in that Lieutenant W. R. Hobson found the document quoted above, the only direct evidence of the fate of Franklin's crews.[3]

[1] Sir Edward Belcher, *The Last of the Arctic Voyages* (2 vols., 1855), vol. i, p. 2.   [2] *Life of McClintock*, p. 166.
[3] A few relics were found in September 1930 by Major Burwash in a flight along the coast of King William Land.

OCEAN AND POLAR EXPLORATION

The search for Franklin had revolutionized the map of the Arctic lands to the north of Canada, but it had not resulted in the navigation of the North-west Passage, nor had it gathered very substantial relics of the lost party. Further light on the tragedy was thrown by the expeditions of C. F. Hall along the north coast of Canada in 1864 and the following years. He " gathered from natives much silver that had belonged to the lost ships, and he also filled in a short gap in the known shore line of Melville Peninsula." [1] He found one skeleton, and talked with Eskimos who had seen Franklin.

The navigation of the North-west Passage was successfully accomplished by R. Amundsen, in the *Gjöa*, in 1903–5. He determined the exact position of the North Magnetic Pole (70° 30′ N., 95° 30′ W.), and then, following Franklin's route and Dease Strait, reached the Pacific Ocean.[2]

Among the islands of the Canadian archipelago, which were placed on the map as the result of the search for the North-west Passage, Sverdrup's explorations of 1898–1902 were of great importance ; with him was associated G. Isachsen. They covered nearly the whole of the west coast of Ellesmere Island, both shores of Jones Sound, and the islands to the west of Ellesmere Island. Sverdrup all but connected the work of the earlier explorers in the archipelago with that of Aldrich [3] in the Far North. In turn his discoveries were extended by MacMillan (1913–17), who worked from Etah, on the west coast of Greenland. He explored the greater part of Ellesmere Island, and extended his investigations to the new lands discovered by Sverdrup. In addition to many positive results, he demonstrated that the Crocker Land thought to exist by Peary had in fact no reality. These two expeditions virtually completed the outlines of the islands to the north of Canada.

Much additional exploration has been carried out by the Canadian Arctic Expedition (1913–18), under V. Stefansson.

> Geographically his surveys are estimated to have withdrawn nearly 100,000 square miles from the areas of unknown seas and lands. Approximately these surveys cover 65,000 square miles of Beaufort Sea ; 10,000 of the Arctic Ocean west of Prince Patrick Island ; and nearly 20,000 to the east and north-east of Prince Patrick. In addition to verifying previous discoveries, and filling in unknown coastlines, original discoveries were made by him between latitudes 73° and 86·2° N., and longitudes 98° and 115° W. ; these include three large and several small islands.[4]

[1] Roberts, *op. cit.*, p. 69.
[2] Young, in 1875, attempted the passage unsuccessfully.
[3] See below, p. 473.
[4] A. W. Greely, *Polar Regions in the Twentieth Century*, pp. 67–68. On this expedition see *G.J.*, vol. lii, p. 248 (results), and vol. lviii, p. 283 (general account) ; also, for a full account, the official *Report of the Canadian Arctic Expedition* (16 vols., 1913–18) and Stefansson's *The Friendly Arctic* (1921).

The newly discovered land lies to the north of Melville Island.

The expedition was attended by great disaster, for the ship *Karluk* carrying part of the expedition was crushed in the ice and sank : its crew made their way to Wrangel Island, and some of them were rescued by a relief ship secured by Captain Bartlett, commander of the *Karluk*, who bravely walked to Siberia to bring help. One at least of the fourteen survivors owed his life to the intelligence of a dog named Mollie, whose name deserves recognition among the heroes of the Arctic Seas.[1]

In spite of this disaster much work was accomplished, and the reports of the expedition have been described as " the most valuable scientific contributions relative to Polar Canada ever published." [2]

From Canada, too, many expeditions have been sent to the Far North, while Rasmussen, during his expedition of 1921–24, surveyed a large area in Melville Peninsula and Cockburn Land, the northern part of Baffin Island.[3] In the south of that island Canadian Government officials have made many journeys during the last fifty years, although until recently much that they had accomplished was unknown outside Government offices.[4]

Much detailed knowledge of the Canadian Arctic has come from the annual patrols of the Royal Canadian Mounted Police. In addition, mention should be made of the expedition of H. K. E. Kreuger and R. A. Bjare in 1930. They left Bache Peninsula (Ellesmere Island), then the most northerly post of the Police, and certainly reached the north-east point of Axel Heiberg Island. It is assumed that Kreuger thén " hunted down the west coast of the island for dog food, and probably crossed to Meighen Island. There, it is thought, he and his party in all probability perished during the winter of 1930-31." [5] Diligent search under difficult conditions by officers of the Police failed to gather more definite information. In Ellesmere Island the Oxford University expedition of 1934-35 also has materially added to knowledge by sighting a new range south of Nares' Challenger Mountains, in Grant Land, and adding topographical details in Grinnell Land and along the coast of Ellesmere Island itself.

Farther south the Forbes-Grenfell Labrador expedition in 1931, 1932, and 1935 completed an aerial survey of the extreme north of Labrador,[6] while in 1935 Dr C. Camsell made an important flight

---

[1] See " The Voyage of the *Karluk* and its Tragic Ending," in *G.J.*, vol. li, p. 307.   [2] Greely, *Polar Regions*, p. 68.
[3] See *G.J.*, vol. lxvii, p. 123, for this expedition.
[4] See *Southern Baffin Island : An Account of Exploration, Investigation, and Settlement during the past Fifty Years*, edited by A. E. Milward (1930), and J. D. Craig, *Canada's Arctic Islands* (1923).
[5] *Polar Record*, No. 8, p. 129.
[6] A. Forbes, " A Flight to Cape Chidley, 1935," in *Geographical Review*, vol. xxvi, p. 48.

OCEAN AND POLAR EXPLORATION

over unknown country in northern British Columbia and south-eastern Yukon.[1]

Not the least important were Stefansson's explorations in the Beaufort Sea, where Mikkelsen had made an important sledge journey in 1907. This region has remained almost unexplored until quite recent times, although the expeditions of MacMillan from the eastern border and Stefansson from the south have considerably reduced the blank spaces. It was in this region that (Sir) Hubert Wilkins accomplished most valuable work in the course of his aerial flights of 1926–28. In the first year little more than preliminary flights were made, although these were of great value, in that they covered much unknown country in Alaska. In 1927 Wilkins reached a point in latitude 77° 45′ N., longitude 175° W., and owing to accidents was obliged to complete part of the return journey on foot.· " The chief accomplishment of the flight was the determination of the ocean depth at the farthest point reached," [2] which on calculation is estimated at 5440 metres. A second flight of 200 miles in the direction of Grant Land was cut short by fog.

In his third flight of 1928 Wilkins crossed from Point Barrow to Spitsbergen, and was able to add still further to the knowledge of the Beaufort Sea, although bad weather conditions were experienced. The flight was, however, a splendid achievement, and deserves to rank with the greatest of the pioneer voyages made in the northern waters of the Canadian archipelago.

IV. The Eurasian Archipelago and the North-east Passage

The New Siberian Islands were first visited in 1770 by a Russian trader, named Liakhov, who also discovered the island of that name. They were revisited by Hedenström in 1809–12 and partially surveyed, but operations were much hindered by the difficulties of travelling. Accordingly, another expedition, under Lieutenant Anjou, was dispatched in 1821 ; the survey was completed, but again the thin ice and open water prevented an advance very far to the north, and no confirmation was obtained of the report of a new land to the north of the islands.

While Anjou was thus engaged Wrangel was making sledge-journeys from the mouth of the Kolyma. First in 1820 he surveyed the coast from the Kolyma river to Cape Chelagski. In the following year he advanced for 140 miles northward without making any discoveries, and in 1823, although covering about 900 miles, he was unable to confirm the native report of high land to the north. An even longer journey in 1824 led to no greater success. The land was

[1] Much important work in Alaska is recorded in *The Polar Record*.
[2] *Geographical Review*, vol. xviii, p. 491. See also Sir Hubert Wilkins, " The Flight from Alaska to Spitzbergen (1928), and the Preliminary Flights of 1926 and 1927," *ibid.*, pp. 527–555.

seen, however, by Kellett in 1849, when he discovered Herald Island, lying near it, and it was first explored by Lieutenant Berry, of the United States Navy, in 1881. It is now known as Wrangel Island.

Considerable errors crept into geographical works as the result of this elusive land, and some thought there must be a great continental mass to the north of Siberia. This myth was exploded by the journey of G. W. de Long in the *Jeannette* in 1879. He approached the Arctic Ocean through Bering Strait, and intended to winter on the supposed land-mass, but failed to discover it. He found instead two small islands, Jeannette and Henrietta. His ship was crushed in the ice, and he started to walk to the New Siberian Islands. On the journey he made a third discovery, Bennett Island. The party eventually reached the north coast of Asia, but De Long and some of his men died of starvation before help could reach them.

The exploration of the New Siberian Islands was resumed by the Russians in 1885, when an expedition under Baron von Toll crossed from Siberia. This able investigator resumed his work on the north coast of Asia and the islands in 1893, and made geological discoveries of great value. He renewed his explorations in 1900–2, visited Bennett Island, but unfortunately perished on the return journey.

The islands of Novaya Zemlya[1] had been known to Europeans since the days of the search for the North-east Passage, but some confusion crept into the map, and in the eighteenth century it was unknown whether or not they were part of the mainland. In 1760, however, a Russian expedition was sent to the islands, and succeeded in sailing through the Kara Sea and round the northern point of Novaya Zemlya. This circumnavigation, which involved spending two winters on the east coast, solved one problem connected with the islands.

Further and more detailed investigations were undertaken in the nineteenth century. In 1819 the Russians prepared to survey the coasts, but by ill-fortune the ship was unable to reach the land. Two years later Lütke began a series of voyages, extending until 1824, in which he examined the west coast as far as Cape Nassau, but was not able to penetrate the ice which he found in that locality. A private expedition, under Pakhtussov, succeeded in sailing round the southern island in 1832–33, and in the next three years in extending knowledge of the east coast northward of Matochkin Shar. Another official expedition, in 1838, wintered on the northern part of the west coast, but was so decimated by sickness that it failed to accomplish anything of importance.

Palliser reached a point thirty miles north of Cape Nassau in 1869, and in the next year Johannsen completed the second circumnavigation of Novaya Zemlya.

A number of scientific and trading expeditions have, subsequent

[1] See Sir Albert Markham, " The Arctic Campaign of 1879 in the Barents Sea," for an account of early exploration (*Proc. R.G.S.*, new series, vol. ii, p. 1).

to this journey, visited the lands round the Kara Sea and materially added to the detailed knowledge thus acquired. Among the most important are those connected with the search for the North-east Passage. In this enterprise C. Weyprecht and J. Payer began an investigation of the Novaya Zemlya Sea in 1871. Payer, however, was beset in the ice, and drifted away to the northward: his subsequent discoveries are mentioned later.

More successful was A. E. Nordenskiöld, who made a preliminary voyage to Novaya Zemlya in 1875, reached the mouth of the Yenisei river in a second venture in 1876, and started on his famous expedition in the *Vega* in July 1878. Almost exactly a year after leaving Tromsö Nordenskiöld was able to record:

> By 11 A.M. [July 19, 1879] we were in the middle of the sound which unites the Northern Arctic Ocean with the Pacific. . . . Thus finally was reached the goal towards which so many nations had struggled. . . . Now for the first time, after the lapse of 336 years, and when most men experienced in navigation had declared the undertaking impossible, was the North-east Passage at last achieved. . . . The course along which we sailed is indeed no longer required as a commercial route between Europe and China. But it has been granted to this and the preceding Swedish expeditions to open a sea to navigation, and to confer on half a continent the possibility of communicating by water with the great oceans of the world.[1]

Further detailed knowledge of the north coast of Siberia came from the voyages of the *Maud* in 1918–20 and 1922–25 and from the surveys of the Russians between 1910 and 1915.[2] In 1913 the latter discovered a new land lying to the north of Cape Chelyuskin. They revisited it in 1914, but were unable to trace its whole extent, although its southern and eastern limits were determined. This land, named Nicolas II Land, is now known as Severnaya Zemlya, or Northern Land. The surveys of the Russians during this period covered the whole Arctic coast of Eurasia, from Bering Strait to Barents Sea.[3]

In the far north the Soviet Union has accomplished a vast amount of important scientific work within recent years, in which icebreakers and aeroplanes have played important parts. An expedition in 1930 discovered a new island (Wiese Land) to the east of Franz Josef Land, a small island between Novaya Zemlya and Severnaya Zemlya, and an island group (Serge Kamenev Islands) off the last-named. A party left behind to survey Severnaya Zemlya completed its work in 1932. This and a number of other expeditions were collecting information with a view to opening up the sea-route round the north of Asia. In 1932 an expedition in

---

[1] A. E. Nordenskiöld, *The Voyage of the " Vega " round Asia and Europe* (2 vols., 1881), vol. ii, pp. 68–69.

[2] Also from Nansen's *Fram* expedition, mentioned below.

[3] On these expeditions see *Geographical Review*, vol. xv, pp. 366–398 (with map).

the ice-breaker *Sibiriakov* sailed round Severnaya Zemlya and made the North-east Passage in two months. In the following year the ice-breaker *Chelyuskin* attempted the double passage, but only succeeded in getting eastward to Bering Strait. Here she was caught in the ice, drifted northward, and was ultimately lost : her crew landed on the ice and were rescued by aeroplanes. Investigations continued with increasing success, and in 1934 the *Lütke* made the passage from Vladivostok to Murmansk in a few days less than three months, while in 1935 the passage was made by merchant ships.

This achievement has come about partly at least through the establishment of scientific stations along the north coast, from most of which weather reports and details of ice movements are broadcast, and from some of which important work has been initiated. Thus a large expedition in the Anadir-Chukotsk region of Siberia between 1931 and 1934, a geological expedition south of Cape Severny in 1933–34, and the surveys of S. V. Obruchev in the Chukchis Peninsula in 1934–35 have all been productive of important results, including the improvement of the maps of those parts. Air flights over Kamchatka and the extreme north-east of Asia have supplemented the ground-work.

In the air itself great progress has been made. The whole Soviet section of the Arctic was covered in a single flight in 1936 ; Russian airmen have flown from Los Angeles to Moscow by way of Alaska and Bering Strait ; while others in 1937 " made the first trans-Arctic flight without landing, and covered a distance of 9344 km., of which 5140 km. was above the Barent, Kara, Laptev, and Okhotsk Seas." In 1937 Russian pilots took a party of scientists to a spot near the North Pole, and left them there on the drifting pack-ice to carry out scientific work.

This brief summary does scant justice to the vast undertakings of Russia in the Arctic, which reflect great credit on a number of able scientists, among whom should be mentioned Professor O. Schmidt (Director, General Administration of the Northern Sea Route), who has already made the North-east Passage three times, and Professor W. Wiese (Vice-Director of the Arctic Institute, Leningrad).

The search for the North-east Passage, resulted in the accidental discovery of Franz Josef Land,[1] for, as already stated, Payer found himself beset in the ice in 1872, and was obliged so to pass the winter. In August of the following year he saw land, and ultimately was able to walk across the ice and examine the discovery. Another winter passed, and in 1874 Payer again visited the new land, and carried

---

[1] In 1930 the Soviet Government, which took over this archipelago in 1929, changed its name to Fridtjof Nansen Land.

out more serious exploration. To his earlier discoveries of Wilczek Island and Hochstetter Island he now added Hall Island, Hohenloe Island, and Cape Fligely, the most northerly point of land in the Old World. Beyond he fancied he saw ' Rudolf Land,' and, still farther away, the blue mountain ranges of ' King Oscar Land ' and ' Petermann Land.' Payer was able subsequently to escape from the pack, although obliged to abandon his ship : he was rescued by Russians off the coast of Novaya Zemlya.

Payer's work was continued by Leigh Smith, who surveyed a great part of the archipelago in 1880 ; in the next year he was ship-wrecked off Northbrook Island and compelled to winter there. Smith was thus able to add materially to the knowledge of Franz Josef Land. In turn his work was extended by F. G. Jackson, whose journeys " covered nearly fifteen degrees of longitude, from 42° E. to 56° E., and eighty miles of latitude, from Northbrook Island, south of the eightieth parallel, to 81° 20' N." [1] Jackson rescued Nansen after his perilous dash toward the North Pole, and the latter on his return was also able to add fragments to the map of Franz Josef Land.

In 1898 W. Wellman explored the islands at the eastern extremity of the archipelago, and Baldwin discovered some islands, includ-ing Graham Bell Island. Other land was reported east of Rudolf Island.

The mystery of these reported discoveries was solved by the Duke of the Abruzzi's expedition in 1899–1901. He proved definitely that the large lands reported by Payer and the smaller islands of Baldwin did not exist, and at the same time showed that the whole mass of the archipelago was almost completely covered with ice. It was from Franz Josef Land that Cagni, a member of the Duke's expedition, made his remarkable attempt to reach the Pole in 1901. During the past seven years the Soviet Government has maintained a meteorological station on Hooker Island, and scientific expeditions have done much important work in the archipelago, which was circumnavigated for the first time in 1932. In the following year many new islands were discovered and the maps of existing islands improved. Since then the work has gone on, and in 1936 the archipelago was reached for the first time by an aeroplane. A meteorological station is now maintained on Rudolf Island.

Whereas Franz Josef Land was a discovery of the nineteenth century, the neighbouring archipelago of Spitsbergen [2] was dis-covered in the sixteenth century, though it was possibly known to

[1] Greely, *Polar Regions*, p. 128.
[2] Now known as Svalbard. The earlier name has been retained here, and is correct for the main island. Svalbard is the whole archipelago. For a full account of the archipelago see Dr R. N. Rudmose Brown, *Spitsbergen* (1920).

the Vikings in the twelfth century. It was visited in the seventeenth century, and again by Phipps in 1773. Buchan and Franklin touched at it in 1818, and made some observations on Danes Island, to be followed by Clavering and Sabine in 1824 and Parry in 1829. These were, however, incidental visits, made in voyages the object of which was not solely the exploration of Spitsbergen.

In 1838–39 the French vessel *La Récherche*, under Captain Fabvre, conveyed a body of scientists to Spitsbergen, where much valuable research work was done. But the real pioneer exploration of the country is due to Swedish investigators, of whom O. Torell was the first, in 1858. He took with him A. E. Nordenskiöld, destined to achieve great fame in the Polar world. Torell revisited Spitsbergen in 1861, and gave special attention to the north and north-west of the archipelago ; one of the party visited North-east Land, and reached Phipps Island. In 1864 Nordenskiöld examined more particularly the southern and south-eastern islands and sounds of the group, and on his map " delineated Spitsbergen with an accuracy hitherto unattained in any Arctic land." [1] He returned in 1868, and again in 1872, for his Polar expeditions, for which these islands were the base, and paid a sixth visit in 1890. Subsequent work by other Swedish explorers has filled in the detail of the area, which is now well known.

Great as has been the contribution of Swedish scientists, the exploration of Spitsbergen has received much help from British investigators. Leigh Smith, in 1871 and 1872, explored parts of the north coast and North-east Land ; Sir Martin Conway's " first crossing of Spitsbergen," in 1896, resulted in a survey of about 600 square miles in Central Spitsbergen, as well as important researches in other branches of science : Conway almost accomplished the circumnavigation of the group ; W. S. Bruce explored Prince Charles Foreland ; and the Oxford University expeditions between 1921 and 1924, and those of the Oxford University Exploration Club in 1933, and in 1935–36 under A. R. Glen, were able to contribute materially to a better knowledge of the North-east Land.[2] For the last twenty-five years Norwegian State-aided expeditions have been assiduously mapping and investigating the whole group of islands.[3]

V. GREENLAND [4]

Modern exploration of Greenland begins on May 12, 1721, when Hans Egede, with his wife and family, sailed from Denmark for the

---

[1] Greely, *Polar Regions*, p. 109.
[2] On these expeditions see *Spitsbergen Papers* (1925) (1921 expedition); *G.J.*, vol. lxvi, p. 9, vol. lxviii, p. 200, and vol. lxxxiv, p. 104 ; and *Polar Record*, No. 13, p. 13.   [3] See A. Hoel, *Norwegian Svalbard Expeditions* (1929).
[4] See *Greenland*, edited by M. Vahl and others (3 vols., 1928–29), vol. i, pp. 1–179.

west coast near to Godthaab, and spent the winter in the country. He lived there until 1736, and collected much information about the island, particularly of the south-western districts round his home. He also initiated the modern colonization of Greenland, and by the end of the century ten settlements had been founded on the west coast.

In the nineteenth century scientific exploration of Greenland was carried on with great vigour. The Polar explorers frequently touched at points on the coast, and added their discoveries to the map. Thus Ross in 1818 revived the knowledge of parts of Baffin Bay ; Inglefield in 1852 mapped about 600 miles of coastline near Smith Sound ; Kane in 1853 extended the survey to the Humboldt Glacier ; Hall reached the latitude of 82° 07′ N. in 1871 ; Nares's expedition of 1876 resulted in the exploration of the coast beyond Repulse Harbour ; and in 1882 the Greely-Lockwood expedition added another large strip to the known coastline.

On the east coast Scoresby mapped an area between the latitudes of 64° N. and 75° N. in 1822, and in the following year Clavering and Sabine supplemented these discoveries in the neighbourhood of latitude 74° N. Graah in 1829 carried his surveys from Cape Farewell to beyond latitude 65° N., and renewed his exploration in the winter of 1830–31.

During the first half of the nineteenth century exploratory work had been undertaken mainly along the coasts. A change came with the extensive travels of Dr H. Rink in South Greenland, beginning in 1853 and extending over a period of fifteen years. In 1869 Koldewey and Payer reached Sabine Island, on the east coast, and, continuing northward, named Kaiser Wilhelm Land and partly explored Franz Josef Fiord. These explorations, together with the work of Inglefield and his successors on the west, very considerably enlarged the knowledge of the coastal fringe of Greenland, and form a suitable introduction to the hazardous journeys by which the interior of the country was made known.

In 1870 A. E. Nordenskiöld attempted to cross Greenland from Disko Island, but was unsuccessful. On a second expedition, in 1883, he was able to reach a point in the interior about seventy-five miles from Aulatsivik Fiord. Five years later, in 1888, Nansen crossed the island from a point on the east coast in latitude 64° 30′ N. to Godthaab. This remarkable journey, carried out under great difficulties, revealed for the first time the true nature of the interior of Greenland.

Nansen's crossing was soon followed by further important work in the interior, although mainly in the far north. In 1886 Peary had penetrated for about 120 miles inland from the west coast in latitude 69° 30′ N. Six years later he began an important journey by investigating Inglefield Gulf, and then crossed north-eastward to Independence Fiord. He resumed his work in the north in 1893, and again reached Independence Fiord in 1895. In 1900 he attained the most northerly point of Greenland, in latitude 83° 37′ N.

Within a comparatively short period of fourteen years the map of Greenland had been radically changed. There were, however, a number of important points still awaiting solution, and it was to them that the explorers of the present century devoted their attention. First in order came the expedition of the Duke of Orleans, in 1905. He reached the east coast in latitude 78° 16′ N., and was able to supplement the work done earlier by Koldewey and Payer. In the next year the *Danmark* expedition of Mylius-Erichsen set out to explore the coast from Cape Bismarck (latitude 77° N.) to the limit reached by Peary in 1900. One of the party, J. P. Koch, reached a point about forty miles from Cape Wyckoff, but the leader and two of his men died while exploring Independence Fiord. In 1909 two expeditions were in the field. De Quervain, from Quarajak Fiord went inland for a distance of nearly eighty miles. In the north the *Alabama* expedition (1909–12), which went out partly to investigate the circumstances of the loss of Mylius-Erichsen, succeeded in finding the results left by that explorer before his death, and also examined Danmark Fiord.

In the year that the *Alabama* expedition finished its work K. Rasmussen made the first of his *Thule* expeditions, when he crossed the north of Greenland to Danmark Fiord and returned to the west coast. In 1912 a second crossing was made by A. de Quervain, who started from Jacobshavn, and reached the east coast at Sermilik Fiord. His journey was of great importance, for it traversed Greenland over a distance of somewhat more than 430 miles. A third crossing was made by J. P. Koch, in 1912–13. His object was to winter in Dronning Louise Land, in order to study its geology and geography. This part of his plan failed, but he successfully crossed to the west coast, and ultimately reached Proven.

Further knowledge of the north came as the result of the second *Thule* expedition of Rasmussen and L. Koch in 1916 and the Bicentenary Expedition round North Greenland, under L. Koch, in 1920–23. In both cases a large amount of new material was obtained, and as a result of these explorations the mapping of the coast of Greenland was completed.

While this spectacular work of well-known explorers had been in progress scientific exploration of a more detailed character had made a steady advance. It dates from the year 1876, and was continued after 1878 by the Commission for the Direction of Geological and Geographical Investigation in Greenland. As a result of its labours " the knowledge of Greenland is now greater than that of any other arctic country, or even of regions in considerably lower latitudes." [1] Even so there are areas still unknown, and to one of

[1] *Greenland*, vol. i, p. 136.

these, in East Greenland, the Cambridge expeditions of 1926 and 1929 devoted their attention ; under Mr J. M. Wordie Petermann Peak was successfully climbed, and also much valuable information about the country to the north of Scoresby Sound was collected.[1]

This expedition is typical of a great many which have visited different parts of Greenland during the last ten years. Lack of space prevents detailed references to those expeditions from Norway, Denmark, France, the United States of America, and particularly those of the University of Michigan, of which Professor W. H. Hobbs has been the directing leader, and the Universities of Oxford and Cambridge. Yet some call for particular mention for reasons which will later appear.

Reference has already been made to the explorations of Dr L. Koch. He has continued to lead or to direct Danish research work in north-east Greenland with marked success. Expeditions went out in 1926–27, 1929, 1930, 1931–34, and 1936–37. The longest of these spent four summers and three winters in eastern Greenland between latitude 71° N. and latitude 76° N., and had a total staff of 375 men. Most important geological results were obtained, large areas of unknown country were surveyed from the air or on the ground, and other scientific investigations were undertaken by this expedition.

Farther south two Norwegians, M. Mehren and A. Høygaard, crossed the ice-cap from Kamarujuk Glacier (latitude 71° 10′ N.), on the west coast, which they left on July 6, 1931, to the Strindberg Peninsula, on the east coast, reached on August 18.

This glacier was one of the centres chosen by the German expedition under A. Wegener for meteorological and other observations. Professor Wegener planned to maintain three stations—one on the west coast, a second in the interior (latitude 71° 8′ N., longitude 40° W.), and a third on the east coast in Scoresby Sound. The ice-cap station was manned throughout the winter of 1930-31, and Wegener took a relief party to it in the following summer, but died on the return journey. The expedition was thus deprived of a leader of great ability who had visited Greenland on three previous occasions and had gained a world-wide reputation for his general geological work. His companions remained to make valuable observations, particularly on the thickness of the ice-cap, which was found to extend to a depth of 2700 metres.

Still farther south the British Arctic Air Route expedition, led by H. G. Watkins, was at work. The base of Watkins's party was on the mainland, west of Angmagssalik, and an ice-cap station was maintained in latitude 67° 3′ N., longitude 41° 48′ W. Here A.

---

[1] See *G.J.*, vol. lxx, p. 225, and vol. lxxv, p. 481, for these expeditions. *Cf.* also *G.J.*, vol. lxxi, p. 1, for an account of two journeys by L. Koch on the east coast north of Scoresby Sound.

Courtauld lived alone for five months during the winter of 1930–31. The main expedition undertook some inland exploration and a survey of the east coast northward from the base to Kangerdlugsuak Fjord.

After Courtauld had been relieved one party (consisting of J. M. Scott, A. Stephenson, and Lieutenant M. Lindsay) crossed the ice-cap from the base to Ivigtut, in the south-west ; a second party (J. R. Rymill and W. E. Hampton) went north-westward across the ice-cap to Holstenborg, on the west coast ; while Watkins, with A. Courtauld and Captain P. Lemon, went down the east coast in a small boat to Nanortalik. A large amount of surveying work was accomplished by this expedition, which, like that of Wegener, also produced data of great value in connexion with projected air-routes between Europe and America.

Watkins returned to the east coast of Greenland in 1932, and made his base at Lake Fjord, a hundred miles north of Angmagssalik. He had learned to handle a *kayak* with the skill of an Eskimo, but while hunting seal on August 20 an unknown disaster overtook him, and he was drowned. The leadership of the expedition devolved upon J. R. Rymill, and the work was carried out despite this loss. Further valuable information relative to the air-route was obtained.

Lieutenant M. Lindsay, a member of the earlier expedition, returned to Greenland in 1934 to complete a survey of the mountain mass between Mount Forel and Scoresby Sound. This region was most easily approached from the west, and the expedition successfully crossed the ice-cap from Jacobshavn, and reached the old base of the British Arctic Air Route expedition.

VI. Polar Expeditions East of Greenland

The early efforts to reach the Pole were all made to the east of Greenland, and have already been mentioned. It will be recalled that their prime object was not Polar exploration, but the solution of the long-standing problem of a northern ' passage' to the Pacific. Hence they belong properly to the section devoted to the North-west Passage : it is enough here to recall the voyages of Phipps and Buchan.

In 1827 Captain Parry proposed " to attempt to reach the North Pole by means of travelling with sledge boats over the ice, or through any spaces of open water that might occur," and decided to use Spitsbergen as his base. He was able to reach the latitude of 82° 45′ N., thus passing the limit attained by Phipps (80° 48′ N.) and establishing a record which was not broken until 1876.

Interest now shifts to the west of Greenland, where the search for the North-west Passage was being pressed with vigour, and not until some time after the close of that search was Polar exploration resumed to the east of Greenland. In 1868 Nordenskiöld, from Spitsbergen, established a record for ship navigation in the north, attaining the latitude of 81° 42'. In a second expedition from Spitsbergen, in 1872, Nordenskiöld was unfortunate, and only succeeded in reaching Phipps Island, over the ice.

Meanwhile the *Germania*, under Captain Koldewey, had in 1868 attempted to follow the east coast of Greenland. This proved impossible, so Koldewey sailed to Spitsbergen, and reached latitude 81° 05', to the north of that archipelago. A second expedition, in 1869, made no further contribution to Polar exploration, although useful work was accomplished in Greenland.

When these earlier attempts to penetrate the Arctic Ocean to the east of Greenland are remembered some standard by which the next exploit can be judged is obtained. With great daring, and yet as the result of sound deductions based on accumulated facts, F. Nansen decided to get his ship imprisoned in the pack, and so be drifted to the Pole or its vicinity. He sailed with the *Fram* in 1893, coasted Eurasia, and was frozen in to the north of the New Siberian Islands. The drift carried his ship to latitude 85° 57' N., but before this was attained Nansen left the *Fram* and attempted to reach the Pole on foot. Ice conditions were against him, and he only succeeded in reaching the latitude of 86° 12' N. It was, however, a remarkable achievement, both in the brilliance of its conception and in the success of its completion. But Nansen was favoured by fortune : a chance seal supplied food at a critical moment ; his companion, Johansen, survived an attack by a bear ; and both men happened to fall in with Jackson, who was exploring Franz Josef Land in 1896. Allowing for this, the due reward of unsurpassed bravery, the expedition must remain one of the most remarkable and valuable in the whole history of Polar discovery. The *Fram* remained in the ice for thirty-five months, and finally emerged, north of Spitsbergen, on August 13, 1896. Her commander, Captain O. Sverdrup, shares with Nansen the credit of having made known the real nature of a great area of the Arctic Ocean.

Franz Josef Land, at which Nansen had arrived on foot, was the starting-point of a number of Polar ventures. Those of Payer (1874), Wellman (1894), and Jackson (1894) were more directly concerned with discoveries in and round that archipelago, and all failed to attain to a very high latitude, the limit being Payer's discovery of Cape Fligely in 81° 51' N. But the Duke of the Abruzzi's expedition of 1901 was more successful. The actual advance toward the Pole was made by Captain U. Cagni, who left Franz Josef Land on March 11, and reached his highest latitude of 86° 34' N. on April 25. This was a little nearer the Pole than

Nansen's limit, and was highly creditable in view of the physical disabilities under which Cagni suffered. Cagni's record remained undefeated until 1906, but as this later achievement was accomplished by Peary in the Western Hemisphere the results are not strictly comparable.

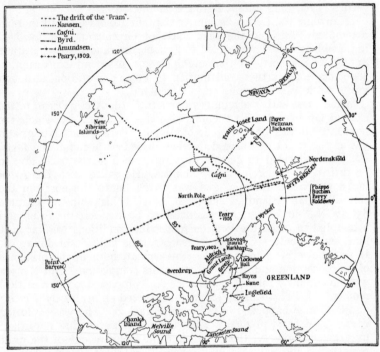

Fig. 48. THE NORTH POLAR REGIONS—II: THE ADVANCE TO THE POLE

Two other classes of exploration remain. The voyage of the *Maud*, which began in 1918, serves to link up the methods adopted by Nansen with those of a new age. The *Maud*, under R. Amundsen, made the North-east Passage in 1918–20, and after some misfortunes started in 1921, under the command of Captain Wisting, to repeat Nansen's drift across the Arctic, while Amundsen attempted to fly by aeroplane to the Pole. Neither project was successful. The *Maud* followed much the same route as the *Fram*, and, although valuable research was carried out, geographical discoveries were few. Amundsen's aeroplane was damaged, and he suffered other misfortunes, but finally he started for the Pole with two flying-boats. He reached latitude 87° 43′ N.

On his return Amundsen, who had the financial backing of Mr L. Ellsworth, started in the airship *Norge*, and flew from Spitsbergen

474

OCEAN AND POLAR EXPLORATION

to Point Barrow, crossing the Pole. Amundsen subsequently lost his life in going to the rescue of General Nobile, who was attempting to repeat this feat in 1928. His death was a great loss to exploration. He had visited both Poles, discovered the South Pole, and sailed along both the North-west and the North-east Passages. Thus his life is an epitome of Polar exploration. Versatility and resource, as well as high courage, characterized his efforts; his tragic disappearance in the performance of an act of great and generous daring is in keeping with the high standard of service associated with those who have explored the Polar regions.

Amundsen was not the pioneer of Arctic aviation. In 1897 Andrée and two companions started to fly from Spitsbergen to the Pole in a balloon. They attained the latitude of 82° 56′ N., and returned on foot to Gilles (White) Island, to the east of Spitsbergen, where they died. Their diaries, which were found by the Norwegian Svalbard and Arctic Ocean expedition of 1930, are now published.[1]

The pioneer work of Binney in 1924 in Spitsbergen showed the possibility of aeroplane work in Polar regions, and in May 1926 R. E. Byrd and F. Bennett, in a Fokker machine, flew from Spitsbergen to the Pole and back again in fifteen hours. In 1937, as already recorded,[2] a Russian expedition landed a party of scientists near the Pole, and returned in safety. The party proposed to remain there for a year.

The history of Polar exploration from the east of Greenland during recent times begins with the record voyage of Phipps beyond Spitsbergen: it is fitting to close it with the record voyages of Arctic aviators, beginning where the work of Phipps ended, and accomplishing feats which now make it more than possible to fulfil the wish of Sir John Barrow to " remain for a few days in the vicinity of the Pole for the purpose of making observations."

VII. POLAR EXPEDITIONS WEST OF GREENLAND

Polar exploration west of Greenland followed much the same general course as that to the east during the first half of the nineteenth century. Baffin's discovery of the entrance to Smith Sound remained as the most northerly limit of progress, and attention was diverted to the search for the North-west Passage. But out of that search there came the relief expeditions following the disappearance of Franklin, and one of these, under Inglefield in 1852, determined the main outlines of Smith Sound, added considerably to the known coastline, and also explored Jones Sound.

Inglefield was followed, in 1853, by Kane, who took his ship, the

[1] See *The Andrée Diaries*, translated by E. Adams-Ray (1931).
[2] See above, p. 466.

Advance, to 78° 37′ N., and by sledge-parties reached Cape Fraser, in Ellesmere Island, and Cape Constitution, in Greenland.

The next advance was made by Hayes in 1860–61, but the contribution to discovery was accidental. Hayes explored Ellesmere Island between latitudes 77° N. and 78° N., and 'discovered' what he called the "open Polar Sea." Actually this was Kennedy Channel, but the news of the 'discovery' raised fresh hopes of a speedy conquest of the Arctic. These were exploited by Hall (1870–73), who reached 82° 26′ N. in the *Polaris*. Hall died after exploring a part of Greenland, but his expedition completed the discovery of the route to the Polar Sea.

Hall was followed, in 1875, by (Sir) G. S. Nares, in command of a British expedition. The *Alert* wintered in 82° 25′ N., and two members of its crew added greatly to geographical knowledge. A. H. Markham attained the high latitude of 83° 20′ N., and Aldrich, travelling westward along the edge of Grant Land, added 200 miles to the known coastline. Further discoveries in Grant Land came from the Greely-Lockwood expedition of 1881–83, when the west coast was reached at Greely Fiord: this expedition also made important discoveries in North Greenland, including the island named after Lockwood.

The final attainment of the Pole was due to the remarkable journeys of R. E. Peary,[1] covering a period of eleven years (1898–1909). In his first attempt Peary reached Fort Conger, on Ellesmere Island, the former base for Greely's expedition, and thence continued the work of exploration in Grant Land, connecting up the discoveries of Sverdrup with those of Greely and Aldrich. He turned next to North Greenland, and reached Cape Wyckoff, in 83° 37′ N. After a failure in the winter of 1900–1 Peary made a dash northward in 1902, and reached the latitude of 84° 17′ N. This was in turn surpassed by him in 1905, when he established a new record, of 87° 06′ N., on an expedition from Grant Land, and again in 1909, when his long and persistent efforts, and his magnificent organization, were rewarded: starting from Cape Columbia, he reached the North Pole.

VIII. The South Pole

The great achievements of James Cook, his positive assertions about the southern continent, and the distractions of other fields of exploration account for the strange fact that there was little scientific discovery in the waters of the Antarctic for fifty years after the second voyage of that great sailor. The one notable exception is the expedition of Bellingshausen in 1819–21. It is unique as the one contribution of Russia to Antarctic exploration.

[1] See W. H. Hobbs, *Peary* (1936).

Bellingshausen reached South Georgia at the end of December 1819, and, continuing southward, discovered three islands to the north of the South Sandwich group. Sailing toward the east, he first crossed the Antarctic Circle, on the meridian of 3° W. A second crossing was made in longitude 18° E. and a third in longitude 36° E. Bellingshausen continued to sail beyond the parallel of 60° S. for a considerable distance before changing his course for

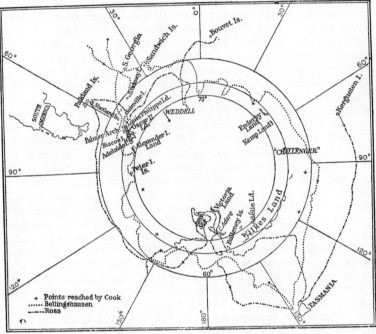

Fig. 49. THE SOUTH POLAR REGIONS—I: NINETEENTH CENTURY

Sydney. Then followed the Pacific voyage already mentioned.[1] The ships were back in Sydney in September, and sailed in November. Once again their course lay in high latitudes, until the Antarctic Circle was crossed in longitude 164° 34′ W. A fifth crossing was made in longitude 120° W. and a sixth in 103° W. Soon after the most southerly point of the voyage was reached in latitude 69° 52′ S., longitude 92° 10′ W. Following this triumph came the discovery first of Peter I Island and then of Alexander I Land, where Bellingshausen had been anticipated by the whalers. He continued his voyage to South Georgia, and thus brought to an end a remarkable Polar expedition.

[1] See above, p. 448.

477

While the track [of his ships] shows that Cook's highest latitude was not equalled by a degree and a quarter, it shows also that the *Vostok* and *Mirni* sailed over 242 degrees of longitude south of 60° S., of which 41 degrees of longitude were within the Antarctic Circle ; while the *Resolution* and *Adventure* made only 125 degrees south of 60° S., and 24° south of the circle. Not only so, but Bellingshausen's care in crossing all the great gaps left by his predecessor demonstrated beyond any doubt the existence of a continuous open sea south of the parallel of 60°.[1]

At the end of his voyage in Antarctic waters Bellingshausen met with a trader named Palmer, and was surprised to find that the region round the South Shetland Islands was apparently well known. This circumstance was due to the many sealing and whaling voyages of enterprising traders, who were, for the most part, Americans. How much in the way of discovery they actually accomplished it is difficult to say, for they were reluctant to make public all their knowledge, but it is at least probable that the South Shetland Islands were reached before their certain discovery by W. Smith in 1819. Smith was followed by Bransfield,[2] sent out to explore the islands at the instance of Captain W. H. Shirreff, then commanding the Pacific Station, and from this date (1820) there is more certainty about the discoveries of the traders. Palmer discovered part of Graham Land in 1821, and Powell found the South Orkneys in the course of his voyage in 1821–22. Even more important was Weddell's voyage southward through the sea which he named after King George IV.[3] He reached a point in latitude 74° 15' S. and longitude 34° 16' 45" W., when "the wind blowing fresh at south prevented progress in that direction."

Further knowledge came through the enterprise of Messrs Enderby, who instructed their captains to make discoveries, when possible, in the course of their sealing and whaling voyages. In this way Biscoe not only supplemented the observations made in high latitudes by Bellingshausen, but also discovered Enderby Land in 1831 and Adelaide and Biscoe Islands in the following year. His voyage, including a course of " 160° of longitude south of 60° S., and almost fifty degrees within the Antarctic Circle,"[4] was a very fine achievement.

Another of Enderby's captains, named Kemp, discovered Kemp Land in 1834, and a third, Balleny, found the islands named after him in 1839, thus proving " for the first time the existence of land within the Antarctic circle south of New Zealand."[5]

---

[1] H. R. Mill, *The Siege of the South Pole*, p. 130.
[2] For arguments in favour of the sighting of Antarctica by Bransfield see Commander Gould, in *G.J.*, vol. lxv, p. 220, and W. S. Bruce, *Scottish Geographical Magazine*, vol. xxxiii, p. 241.
[3] Now known as Weddell Sea.   [4] Mill, *op. cit.*, p. 164.
[5] *Ibid.*, p. 173.

The voyages of these trading captains had been of great importance, not only because of their discoveries, but also because they
roused great interest in Europe and America, and led to three
Antarctic voyages of a new kind. First in point of time came the
French expedition of Dumont d'Urville, who visited the Antarctic
south of America in 1838, and saw Louis Philippe Land and Joinville Island. He made no landing, and, indeed, seemed reluctant to
remain in high latitudes. D'Urville returned to the Antarctic at
the conclusion of his voyage in the Pacific, and discovered Adélie
Land, to the south of Australia, in 1840.

The United States expedition under Lieutenant C. Wilkes (1840)
also discovered land near D'Urville's Adélie Land. Wilkes had to
face many difficulties, for his ships were not suited to prolonged stress
of weather, and his crews were not entirely happy. Yet he persisted, and followed a course in a high latitude, giving names to a
number of points along what he considered to be the Antarctic
continent. The recent expedition of Sir Douglas Mawson has
shown that some at least of these 'discoveries' do not exist.
" Notwithstanding these discrepancies," Sir Douglas said,

> Wilkes's work is of much value. He outlined the edge of the pack
> as it was in 1840, and supplied several shallow soundings more
> convincing as to the proximity of land than his otherwise vague and
> oftentimes ill-founded statements. Whilst criticizing the work of
> Wilkes, however, the magnificent seamanship and heroic determina-
> tion of the leader should never be forgotten. The hazardous voyage
> of the *Vincennes* through 2000 miles of ice-strewn sea in high southern
> latitudes, a zone where gales are frequent even in summer, will ever
> remain a great achievement.[1]

In older maps the name of Wilkes Land stretched over forty
degrees of longitude (100–140° E.), but Sir Douglas Mawson restricts
it to a much smaller area immediately to the west of Adélie Land.

The third and most important of the expeditions was that under
Sir James Clark Ross, in the *Erebus*, with F. R. M. Crozier, in the
Terror (1840–43). The main object of the voyage was to improve
the science of magnetism " by an extensive series of observations
made in high southern latitudes," [2] but it accomplished far more than
a " series of observations." Profiting by the discovery of Balleny,
and deliberately avoiding those regions where D'Urville and Wilkes
had sighted land, Ross " selected a much more easterly meridian
(170° E.) on which to endeavour to penetrate to the southward,
and, if possible, reach the magnetic pole." [3] In January 1841 Ross
began the passage through the pack-ice, and on the 9th had cleared

[1] Sir Douglas Mawson, "Australian Antarctic Expedition, 1911–14," in *G.J.*,
vol. xliv, p. 258. On the question of Wilkes Land see W. H. Hobbs, " Wilkes
Land Rediscovered," in *Geographical Review*, vol. xxii, p. 632, and F. Deben-
ham, " Names on the Antarctic Continent," in *G.J.*, vol. lxxxi, p. 145.

[2] The instructions are printed in Mill, *op. cit.*, pp. 255–260.

[3] *Ibid.*, p. 268.

it ; and two days later he was close to the land where the Admiralty Range was to be seen. The coast was followed southward from Cape Adare, and on January 28 the great mountains named Erebus and Terror were discovered. The highest latitude, 78° 4' S., was reached on February 2, but further efforts to penetrate the ice-barrier at the head of Ross Sea were unsuccessful ; as no suitable place could be found in which to winter Ross returned to the north, reaching Tasmania in April 1841.

In November Ross again sailed for the south, " to endeavour to find a way to the ice-barrier beyond the farthest point reached on the previous trip." [1] The pack was reached on December 18, and on New Year's Day the Antarctic Circle was crossed 1400 miles farther eastward than on the previous trip. But efforts to penetrate the pack were not successful, and on January 28 he had only reached latitude 67° 39' S., longitude 156° W. Struggling on against adverse weather conditions, Ross attained his southern limit in latitude 78° 9' 30" S., longitude 161° 27' W. He then sailed to the Falkland Islands, which were reached on April 5, 1842.

The third Antarctic voyage of Ross began on December 17, 1842. " The intention was to go south on the meridian of 55° W. in the expectation of meeting with a continuation of Louis Philippe Land, by following which it was hoped to combine a survey of the coast with the attainment of a high latitude." [2] He sighted Joinville Island on December 28, but failed to get much farther south. Sailing eastward, and across the track of Weddell, Ross reached the meridian of 12° W., when he made another thrust to the southward, and ultimately reached his southern limit in latitude 71° 30' S., longitude 14° 51' W. This, the third attempt to reach the Pole, had failed. On his return voyage he was also unsuccessful in trying to locate Bouvet Island. The ships reached England at the end of September 1843, almost exactly four years after they had sailed for the Antarctic.

Ross had accomplished more than any other Antarctic explorer. In addition to the many scientific observations made, he had added Victoria Land to the map of the South Polar regions, and had approached nearer to the Pole than any of his predecessors.

The work of Ross was followed up by Lieutenant Moore, but beyond a possible discovery of land in latitude 64° S., longitude 49° E., and a number of additional magnetic observations he made no further contribution to the discovery of the Antarctic. With this voyage of 1844 exploration in these regions ceases until the close of the century. One ship made a southern voyage in 1850, and the *Challenger* entered Antarctic waters in 1874, but the task of continuing the work of D'Urville, Wilkes, and Ross was not undertaken. On the return of Ross his ships were sent to find the North-west

[1] Mill, *op. cit.*, p. 292.   [2] *Ibid.*, p. 317.

Passage, and the whole interest of the maritime world was for a time centred in the Arctic.

One expedition deserves a passing mention. A German, Captain E. Dallman, reached Graham Land in January 1874, in the course of a whaling voyage. Nothing was done to follow up this venture, and it was not until 1892 that four Dundee ships went south to engage in the whale-fishery. With one of them, the *Balæna*, went W. S. Bruce, one of the ablest of explorers both in the north and in the south. Opportunities for scientific work were few, but at least the ships gained touch with Joinville Island, and met there the Norwegian C. A. Larsen, who discovered Oscar II Land in 1893. Another whaler, Evensen, reached the high latitude of 69° 10' S., in longitude 76° 12' W., and sighted Alexander I Land. Another ship, in 1894, carried C. E. Borchgrevink, who made a landing on Cape Adare, the first on the Antarctic continent.

The whaling voyages of these steamers mark a new phase in Antarctic discovery, and were followed by serious work of exploration. The first expedition, under Lieutenant A. de Gerlache, in the *Belgica*, left Antwerp in August 1897, and in January in the following year reached the South Shetlands. The strait separating Palmer Archipelago from the mainland was discovered, Graham Land was followed to Alexander I Land, and, continuing south-westward, the latitude of 71° 30' S. was reached. Here the ship was frozen in, and during the winter drifted considerably in the pack : she did not escape until January 14, 1899. Although no new land had been discovered, much valuable work had been carried out, and the expedition " was of unprecedented importance from the duration and regularity of the routine scientific observations in the far south." [1]

A second expedition, under C. E. Borchgrevink, in the *Southern Cross*, sailed from the Thames at the end of August 1898, and on February 17, 1899, landed at Cape Adare. The ship returned to New Zealand for the winter, and the land-party, living in a wooden hut, carried out some observations in the neighbourhood of Cape Adare. In the following summer exploration was extended to Ross Sea, where the extreme limit of latitude 78° 21' S. was reached by ship, and 78° 50' S. by sledge. A considerable amount of mapping was accomplished, but on the whole the scientific results hardly came up to expectation.

A third expedition, in the *Valdivia*, under Captain Krech, rediscovered Bouvet Island on November 25, 1898, and made a large number of soundings in high latitudes.

The interest of the scientific world was now fully roused, and, stimulated by the efforts of Sir Clements Markham and Sir John Murray in England and Dr G. von Neumayer in Germany, pushed forward the work of exploration with great vigour. Commander

[1] Mill, *op. cit.*, p. 394.

481

R. F. Scott, in the *Discovery*, sailed from England in August 1901, and landed at Cape Adare on January 9, 1902. Much valuable work was then carried out in Ross Sea, where King Edward VII Land was discovered. Transferring his activities to the eastern side of the sea, Scott next proved the insularity of Mount Erebus and Mount Terror, and showed that McMurdo ' Bay ' was a strait. Armitage made the first journey on the high plateau. In the summer of 1902 Scott, Shackleton, and Wilson made a sledge-journey inland to 82° 17′ S., and in the next year Scott went due west to a point in latitude 77° 59′ S., longitude 146° 33′ E., far into the high continental plateau. The *Discovery* returned to England in September 1904, after a most successful and most important expedition. Not only had some additional information been obtained about Ross Sea, but the land-journeys had for the first time revealed the nature of the interior of Antarctica.[1]

A second expedition, under Professor E. von Drygalski, in the *Gauss*, sailed from Kiel on August 11, 1901, called at Kerguelen and Heard Islands, and then headed for the Antarctic continent between the supposed limit of Wilkes Land (Knox's High Land) and Kemp Land. Here Kaiser Wilhelm II Land was discovered, and on it the cone of Gaussberg. Valuable scientific results were obtained during the winter and spring, and in November 1903 the *Gauss* was back in the Elbe.

A third expedition, under Dr O. Nordenskjöld, in the *Antarctic*, sailed from Sweden in October 1901, and sighted the South Shetlands early in January 1902. Exploration of the sea east of Louis Philippe Land was carried out during that and the following summer, the insularity of Ross Island established, and much useful scientific work accomplished. Nordenskiöld was marooned in the Antarctic owing to the loss of his ship, but by a remarkable coincidence the survivors of the ship and rescuers met his own party almost at the same time, and all were carried home by the Argentine warship *Uruguay*.

A fourth voyage, under W. S. Bruce, in the *Scotia*, began from the Clyde in November 1902, and was directed to an examination of Weddell Sea. The objects of the expedition were purely scientific, and the great mass of valuable material accumulated fully justified the enterprise. The extreme point reached was in latitude 74° 1′ S., longitude 22° W., and a new land, named Coats after the two men who had largely financed the expedition, was seen, although not visited. The soundings of Ross in this part of the ocean were corrected.

A fifth expedition, under Dr J. Charcot, in the *Français*, had for its original object the rescue of Nordenskiöld, but when this was effected by the Argentine ship Charcot turned to exploration. In the course of two summer cruises he added much detail to the

[1] See *G.J.*, vol. xxv, p. 353, and R. F. Scott, *The Voyage of the " Discovery "* (2 vols., 1905).

charts of the west coast of Graham Land, and extended his voyage as far as Alexander I Land.

These five expeditions, following closely upon each other in the first five years of the present century, revolutionized the knowledge of the Antarctic continent, and directly contributed to the solution of many of its problems. There were, however, gigantic tasks still awaiting the energies of explorers. The Magnetic Pole, the object of Ross's expedition, was not located; the South Pole was not reached; and there was as yet little information about the interior of the land-mass, which Murray of the *Challenger* expedition believed to be a single continent, but which others thought was made up of two large islands.

The first problem was solved by Shackleton's expedition of 1908, directed, like those of Ross and Scott, to Ross Sea. It included among its members Professor (Sir) T. W. E. David and (Sir) Douglas Mawson, who reached the South Magnetic Pole in latitude 72° 25′ S., longitude 155° 16′ E. Shackleton himself made a splendid effort to reach the Pole, and attained the very high latitude of 88° 23′ S., when scanty provisions and bad weather put an end to the attempt. He showed, however, that the attainment of the Pole was practicable with good organization.

The Pole was reached by two expeditions in 1911 and 1912. First came R. Amundsen, whose great work in the North Polar regions has been recorded. He spent the winter in the Bay of Whales, at the edge of the Ross Barrier, and, then marching due south, reached the Pole on December 14, 1911. His journey had covered new ground, added much to the knowledge of the interior of the continent, and showed clearly that the Pole was situated on a land-mass.

Captain R. F. Scott, in the *Terra Nova*, based his work on McMurdo Sound, and with four companions reached the Pole on January 17, 1912. All perished on the return journey, which will ever live in the history of exploration through the heroism of Oates and the graphic last message of Scott. Apart, however, from its spectacular side, the *Terra Nova* expedition of 1910–13 accomplished much valuable scientific work in the lands adjoining Ross Sea and added Oates Land to the map.

While these two expeditions were in progress a Japanese party organized by Choku Shirase made two voyages to the Antarctic. In 1911 they reached the Ross Sea, but were obliged to abandon further efforts owing to bad weather. They returned the next year, and a party which landed on the Barrier reached the latitude of 80° 5′ S. Another party visited King Edward VII Land. The expedition accomplished little, but in view of its slender equipment it was a very gallant venture and marked " a totally new departure in Japanese exploration." [1]

[1] See I. Hamre, "The Japanese South Polar Expedition of 1911–12," in *G.J.*, vol. lxxxii, p. 411.

Once the problem of the Pole was solved, explorers turned to more detailed examination of smaller regions. Already in 1908–10 Charcot, in the *Pourquoi Pas ?*, had returned to the Antarctic, added Charcot Land to the map, west of Alexander I Land, and explored the sea to longitude 124° W. In 1912 a German expedition under Filchner visited Weddell Sea and discovered Luitpold Land, to the south of Coats Land. Finally the very important Australasian Antarctic expedition under Sir Douglas Mawson, in the *Aurora*, examined the area between Victoria Land and Kaiser Wilhelm II Land, added King George V and Queen Mary Lands to the map, corrected some errors of Wilkes, and accomplished valuable oceanographical work.

The problem of crossing the continent remained unsolved. The project was first contemplated by Bruce, and it was one of the objects of Shackleton's expedition in the *Endurance*, but was not attained. In that journey Shackleton planned to start from Weddell Sea, cross the continent, and meet another party operating from Ross Sea. The latter party successfully accomplished their task of laying out provisions as far as Mount Hope, in 83° 30′ S. which they reached in January 1916. But in the meantime Shackleton had been unable to land on the shores of Weddell Sea, and the *Endurance* drifted northward, was crushed, and sank. Shackleton's party was thus marooned on the ice, and ultimately landed on Elephant Island. Shackleton and a few others sailed in an open boat to South Georgia, crossed the mountainous island to Stromness, and returned to rescue the survivors. The main object thus failed, but the expedition was not without value from the scientific standpoint. In particular the drift of the *Endurance* contributed substantially to the knowledge of the Weddell Sea, and was thus able to supplement the earlier discoveries of Bruce and Filchner.[1] The voyage of Shackleton from Elephant Island to South Georgia is one of the most remarkable episodes in the history of Antarctic discovery.

Shackleton started south again in the *Quest* in 1921, but died at South Georgia in January 1922. He intended to examine the coastline to the west of Enderby Land and to work in the little-known waters lying between the South Shetlands and Gough Island in the South Atlantic. After his death the voyage was continued under the command of F. Wild. " The limits and conditions of the pack ice for 2500 miles, from 18° E. to 52° W. between latitudes of 63°–70° S., were determined," [2] but unfavourable conditions made the examination of any land impossible.

The exploration of the Antarctic continues, and, as in the Arctic, the aeroplane has been put to good use. Four expeditions working

[1] See J. M. Wordie, " The Drift of the *Endurance*," in *G.J.*, vol. li, p. 216, and for a general account Sir Ernest Shackleton, *South : The Story of Shackleton's Last Expedition*, 1914–17 (1919).
[2] F. Wild, " The Voyage of the *Quest*," in *G.J.*, vol. lxi, p. 73.

in the Far South in 1928 and 1929 all used machines of one type or another, and several most important discoveries were made along the edges of the continent.[1] Admiral R. E. Byrd, in 1928–30, established a base at Little America, near the Bay of Whales, examined Marie Byrd Land, to the east of King Edward VII Land,

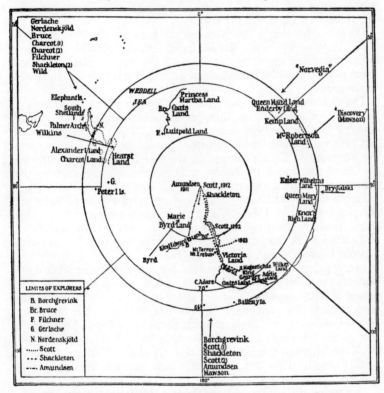

Fig. 50. THE SOUTH POLAR REGIONS—II : TWENTIETH CENTURY

and made one long sledge journey southward to the Queen Maud Range, where corrections were made to the work of Amundsen. On November 28 and 29, 1929, a successful flight to the Pole and back was made.

Sir Hubert Wilkins at the end of 1928 made a flight southward to the east of Graham Land. He discovered a new part of the continent, to which he gave the name Hearst Land, and claimed to have shown that Graham Land was an archipelago : this claim must now be rejected.

[1] See a summary in *G.J.*, vol. lxxv, pp. 252–261, and *The Work of the Byrd Antarctic Expedition* (1930).

Sir Douglas Mawson, in the *Discovery*, made an important addition to the map in 1929 when he found MacRobertson Land. He subsequently examined the edge of the continent westward from King George V Land, and proved that some of the ' land ' reported by Wilkes and D'Urville did not exist.[1] At the end of 1930 the new lands of Sabrina and Princess Elizabeth were discovered, and MacRobertson Land was revisited.

H. Riiser-Larsen in the *Norvegia*, in 1929-30, discovered Queen Maud Land and Princess Martha Land, and in the following season circumnavigated the continent, visiting the unknown area between these newly found lands and there adding Princess Ragnhild Land to the map.

The discoveries of the *Norvegia* have been made in the course of her work of investigation into problems of oceanography and of whaling in the southern oceans. Similar, if less extensive, work has been carried out by the research ship *Discovery II*. In 1929-30 the accuracy of Cook's surveys in the South Sandwich group was confirmed and much further work accomplished, and in 1932 the continent was circumnavigated. In the course of this last voyage valuable data were obtained for a more precise determination of the position of the Antarctic and sub-tropical convergences. This ship has since continued to carry out important oceanographical and survey work, and has rendered valuable help to Admiral Byrd, Lincoln Ellsworth, and J. R. Rymill.

In 1934 Norwegians again made important discoveries when Lars Christensen sighted a new land west of Kaiser Wilhelm Land. He named it Princess Astrid Land. His voyage ended with a circumnavigation of the continent. In the following year the oil-tanker *Thorshavn* discovered new land to which the name Ingrid Christensen was given. A party landed in latitude 68° 39' S., longitude 78° 36' E. and hoisted the Norwegian flag. The ship followed the edge of this new land for 275 miles, of which 65 were free from snow and ice.

As a result of the discoveries of the last thirty years a considerable part of the coastline of the Antarctic continent westward from Marie Byrd Land to the Weddell Sea is now known, at least in outline, but the large blank between Marie Byrd Land and Graham Land remains. There was, therefore, still room for controversy as to the structure and form of the continent—if, indeed, it was a continent, and not two large islands. But the latest of the South Polar expeditions have gone far to end the dispute. The Byrd Antarctic Expedition of 1933-35 made its base in Little America, and while Admiral Byrd went south for 120 miles to make scientific observations the main party undertook further exploration in the land previously discovered by Byrd to the east of Little America,

and made a journey to the Queen Maud Range. On his return to
the base Admiral Byrd made several flights to the south ; he at
first thought he had found a strait through the continent, but
finally " gave as his opinion that no passage could exist east of the
150th meridian from the 75th parallel to the Pole, a stretch of 1000
miles." [1]

The absence of this strait seems to be confirmed by the work of
Mr Lincoln Ellsworth. He had planned to fly from the Bay of
Whales across the continent in 1933, but his aeroplane was badly
damaged on landing and the flight had to be abandoned. He tried
again in 1935, this time landing on Dundee Island, off the north-
east of Graham Land. From that point he flew to within a short
distance of the Bay of Whales. The journey took nineteen days,
some of which were spent in improvised camps on the continent
where positions were fixed. It was a very remarkable feat, and
showed that with suitable conditions and skilful handling an aeroplane could be used for exploration in a way hitherto unknown.
It is almost certain that there is no strait through the continent
anywhere along the route followed in this flight.

Further light on the nature of the continent has been shed by
the British Graham Land Expedition of 1934–37, under the leadership of Mr J. R. Rymill. The schooner *Penola* returned to England
in the summer of 1937, and as yet the full results of the expedition's
work are unknown. But it has clearly done enough to rank as one
of the more important of the Antarctic expeditions of the present
century. A survey has been made of about 1000 miles of coastline
and much of the interior of Graham Land. Flights southward
have shown that many of the details recorded by Sir Hubert
Wilkins are incorrect, and Graham Land must be regarded not as
an archipelago, but as part of the continent. Alexander I Land
has been found to be of much greater size than previously supposed,
and it is separated from Graham Land by a long, narrow strait
averaging fifteen miles in width and " bordered on either hand
by steeply rising mountains of wholly dissimilar appearance and
structure." [2] In view of the modest equipment, small *personnel*,
and some unfortunate accidents, the results must be regarded as
highly satisfactory.

Thus the story of Antarctic exploration closes with many important additions to knowledge. Gradually the coastline of the continent is taking shape, and the features of the surface are appearing
on the map. Corrections of older theories are necessary. Ross
placed Mounts Erebus and Terror on the mainland : Scott removed
them to an island. Wilkes discovered lands which Mawson found

[1] *Polar Record*, No. 9, p. 66.
[2] *The Times*, August 9, 10, 11, 12, 1937.

non-existent. This process must go on, and as new data accumulate they must be regarded not as proofs of the inferiority or the carelessness of the pioneers, but as evidence of improved methods and greater resources. Such changes are inevitable in the history of geographical exploration.

CHAPTER XVIII

CONCLUSION

THE history of geographical discovery and exploration shows no continuous progress, but a series of advances followed by periods of inactivity or of actual retrogression. The geographers of the classical age extended the boundaries of knowledge from a small area round the Eastern Mediterranean Sea to the Atlantic Ocean on the west and to China on the east. In the south the Sahara Desert formed an almost insuperable obstacle, as in the north did the forests of Northern Europe. This progress, which shows no continuity when studied in detail, came to an end in the second century, after which time, until the thirteenth century, there is little to record beyond the long struggle to regain knowledge once possessed. The brilliant if evanescent exploits of the Northmen and the achievements of the Arabs are exceptions to this general statement.

With the reopening of direct intercourse with Asia, the tentative voyages on the Atlantic, and the improvement of ships and appliances in Europe a new period of progress begins. The movement, initiated by Henry the Navigator, is marked by the great exploits of men like Columbus, Da Gama, and Magellan on the oceans ; of Cartier and of Cortes ; of the Spanish generals in South America ; and of a host of adventurers in many parts of the world. Discoveries followed one another with such rapidity that it was almost impossible to realize either the speed of the movement or its magnitude. Inevitably some areas were neglected. Little was done to explore Africa, and the early efforts to find the southern continent and the northern ' passages ' ended with neither problem solved. Yet within one hundred and fifty years from the death of Henry the Navigator a great part of the coasts of Africa, Asia, and the New World, and a fragment of Australia had been put on the map with some accuracy ; Central and South America were reasonably well known ; some small progress had been made with the exploration of the interior of Asia and North America ; and the North Polar regions had been examined with some care from Hudson Bay to Novaya Zemlya.

Once again the rate of exploration slowed down, and attention was concentrated on exploiting the countries already known, in traversing Siberia, in learning more of the populous countries of South-eastern Asia, in opening up North America, and in re-examining the areas already visited in South America. There were

489

few startling discoveries in the seventeenth and in the first half of the eighteenth century, yet there were enough to keep the geographers busy revising their books and maps and inventing theories to keep pace with the growing body of facts.

The last period opens with that outburst of exploring activity which revealed the secrets of the Pacific Ocean, and with which the name of James Cook is prominently associated. Its first fifty years are marked by events of great importance in all parts of the world. In South America Humboldt carried out his epoch-making travels ; in North America Mackenzie crossed from the St Lawrence river to the shores of the Pacific ; in Africa Bruce revisited the sources of the Blue Nile and Mungo Park reached the Niger river ; in Asia Niebuhr began the modern exploration of Arabia and Rennell laid the foundations of the Indian surveys ; in Australia the first settlements and the first inland exploration were made. Thus on all sides the blank spaces were being filled in. The remaining portions of the coastline of Australia were added to the map, the west coast of America was fully explored, and a considerable part of the north coasts of Eurasia and America was examined.

Yet even in this last period there are well-marked divisions. The most distinct turning-point is found near the middle of the nineteenth century. In the later years exploration was especially vigorous in Central Asia, Central Africa, and Central Australia ; in the East Indies and in New Guinea ; and in the North Polar regions. This was no mere accident, but followed naturally from the preliminary work which had been done in the first half of the century, of which the survey of peninsular India, the Russian advances in Siberia and in the south-west of Asia, the solution of the Niger problem, the discovery of the Murray-Darling system, and the search for the North-west Passage are conspicuous examples. In North America the fur-traders completed the main outlines of the continent during the first half of the century, while scientific explorers gave precision to their discoveries during the later period. Only in the South Polar regions was there no counterpart after 1850 to the magnificent work of Bellingshausen, Ross, and traders like Biscoe and Balleny.

There was little in the way of discovery left for the twentieth century to accomplish. This latest period is marked by the final triumphs in the Sahara Desert, in Central Asia, in the North Polar basin, and, most conspicuously, on and around the Antarctic continent. Yet these achievements, considered alone, are remarkable enough. Within a short space of twenty years both Poles have been reached, both on land and by flights through the air ; a great part of the Sahara Desert has been thoroughly explored for the first time ; vast areas of the North Polar basin and the Antarctic continent have been surveyed, and new features have been added to the map. The heroic exploits of men like Shackleton, Amundsen, Tilho, Wilkins, Mawson, Hassanein Bey, to mention but a few, will stand comparison with those of any explorers in any age. Nor has the work of this latest period been wholly romantic and spectacular. Many smaller expeditions have studied parts of the world in great detail ; boundary surveys and the operations of more normal survey establishments have given precision to the maps ; and some inaccessible regions have been surveyed, for the first time, from the air. In these, as in other respects, explorers of the twentieth century are living up to the high standards of their predecessors. Their task is not yet ended. Even in Europe, where all lands may be classed as well known, detailed geographical studies are relatively few : elsewhere there is no single continent where this form of geographical exploration in its widest sense has reached more than its preliminary stages.

Such in outline is the progress of discovery and exploration. The motives which have inspired it have varied but little through the centuries, although, as is natural, some are more conspicuous in one age and some in another. In classical times most exploration was due to curiosity or, perhaps more strongly, to commercial motives. The desire to increase trade, to secure precious metals, to obtain commodities which will only grow in different climates from their own has led explorers in all ages into the remote corners of the earth. The silk of China, the spices of the East Indies, the gold and silver of Central and South America, the ivory of Africa, the furs of North America, the gold of California or the Klondike or Australia, the whales and seals of the Polar waters, have in turn drawn men from distant regions : these examples are no less striking because they are familiar.

Less conspicuous, perhaps, because less ostentatious, is the motive of religion. Missionary enterprise has contributed greatly to the spread of geographical knowledge. The achievements of the Catholic missions in the New World, in Abyssinia, and in Asia, the work of Livingstone and Grenfell in Central Africa, the accomplishments of Chalmers in New Guinea and Marsden in New Zealand, are a few examples of this important aspect of geographical discovery.

Geographical myths and the theories of geographers have also been responsible for much exploration. Prester John, El Dorado, the mythical islands of the Atlantic, the seven cities of Cibola, the lake-sources of the Nile, the mystery cities of Timbuktu and Lhasa, the existence of Terra Australis Incognita, the reported lakes in the centre of Australia, the kingdom of Monomotapa, and many other examples have been recorded in the foregoing pages.

Political motives, sometimes separated with difficulty from any of those already mentioned, must also be added to explain some phases of exploration. The desire for national 'routes' led to some of the most important discoveries of the sixteenth and seventeenth centuries. It was in the main fear of the political consequences of inaction that roused the Spaniards in America in the later years of the eighteenth century, and during that same period was partly responsible for the exploits of French and English sailors in the Pacific Ocean. In the nineteenth century much of the exploration of North America, of Africa, of Asia, and of New Guinea is to be attributed to this cause, and at the present time the nations are staking their claims in the apparently worthless Polar regions.

It is usual to describe modern exploration as 'scientific.' Yet while it is true that ever since the age of Cook exploration has had for one of its objects the improvement of knowledge it is doubtful if very much of that work has been purely scientific in aim. Precise surveys, like those along frontiers in Africa or elsewhere, have their origin in political disputes, and find some of their justification in a desire to avoid a repetition of political 'incidents.' Some exploits stand out conspicuously as 'scientific.' in the accepted sense of the term, and they have been carried out for the most part in countries whose political allegiance is not in doubt or on the oceans. To such a category belongs the greater part of the exploration of South America and Australia, and parts of Asia, in the nineteenth century. The so-called 'scientific' exploration of Northern Canada within recent years would, on the contrary, probably never have been undertaken without the expectation of mineral wealth in those regions, while in Asia, to quote one other example, the rivalry of Russia and England was responsible for much strictly 'scientific' work. Now that the Russian menace of the past century is over the way is clear for the detailed investigations of men like Sir Aurel Stein.

Indeed, except in rare cases it is impossible to separate the motives which have led to exploration, and to select one is to misinterpret human nature and to misunderstand the history of discovery. It is impossible to say how much has been due to a pure love of adventure, perhaps the strongest of all incentives to exploration. Without this spirit it is doubtful if men would have faced so much discouragement and danger and have still been prepared to go back. Modern Polar exploration, strictly 'scientific' in aim as much of it has been, and productive of valuable scientific results, furnishes at the same time an admirable example of this fact, and to the testimony of men like Scott, Shackleton, Amundsen, and Nansen could be added that of many others in this and previous centuries, and in all fields of exploration.

Just as it is difficult to assess the strength of the human motive in exploration, so it is hard to say to what degree man's activities have been influenced by the geographical conditions. No one

492

realized more clearly than Livingstone the part played by the structure, the relief, and the climate of Africa in the history of the exploration of that continent : his account of the natural obstacles has already been given. Yet he was himself a living proof that the conditions could not narrowly control his actions. Geographical factors played their part in delaying the exploration of the East Indies and of Australia ; the forests of the Amazon formed as serious an obstacle as the deserts of North Africa ; the high plateaux and mountains of Central Asia rendered penetration of the interior difficult ; the belt of trade winds, both in the Atlantic and in the Pacific Oceans, cannot be neglected as a factor in the progress of discovery. Yet the geographical influences are not always permanent, and are frequently little more than checks. The seas on which Mediterranean sailors rarely ventured were crossed with success by the Northmen ; the desert which checked the Romans was a small barrier to the Arabs. It may be doubted if the exploration of the interiors of Africa and Australia would have been delayed so long had their economic resources been greater, or better known, or had the field of opportunity elsewhere been less extensive and less productive.

The history of geographical discovery thus illustrates the great complexity of the relations between man and his environment. It is more than a mere chronicle of the growth of the knowledge of the earth's surface ; more than a series of tales of adventure ; more than the history of crusading zeal or commercial penetration. It records the actual contacts between man and nature, and thus furnishes most valuable material alike to the historian and to the geographer. No one has emphasized this point more strongly nor illustrated it better than Vivien de Saint-Martin in the Introduction to his monumental work, *Histoire de la géographie et des découvertes géographiques* : " La géographie dans tous les temps et chez tous les peuples a suivi la marche même de la civilisation et y mesure en quelque sorte ses progrès. . . . Les explorations du globe ne sont pas seulement une branche particulière de l'histoire des sciences ; elles sont une face entière de l'histoire de l'humanité."

APPENDIX

CHINESE EXPLORERS

THE Chinese probably knew of the Roman Empire, or at least of its more eastern parts, before the time of the Emperor Wu Ti (140–87 B.C.), but during his reign an officer was sent on a political mission to the west, reached the Ferghana about 138 B.C., and remained in semi-captivity until his return to China in 126. " He was able to report, from personal knowledge, of the countries on the Jaxartes and Oxus, and, from information he had collected, on other countries of the west." As a result of his journey a land-route was opened up to the west. The sea-route to the west seems to have been known from the early years of the second century A.D. There was much contact, both by land and by sea, with India, whither went many Buddhist pilgrims. The earliest of them of whom records exist, Fa Hian, left Shansi in A.D. 399 and travelled through Khotan and the Pamir region. He returned in 415. His most famous successor, Hiuen Tsang, who travelled between 628 and 645, visited many parts of India, and has left a most valuable account of his journey. Buddhist pilgrims continued to visit India, at intervals, for another four hundred years. Their records are accurate, as modern travellers have testified, but the knowledge which they obtained did not spread to Europe, and they cannot, therefore, be said to have played a very important part in the general history of exploration.

The standard work, from which an extract is quoted above, is Sir Henry Yule, *Cathay and the Way Thither*, new edition by H. Cordier (Hakluyt Society, second series, vol. xxxviii). See also Lord Curzon, " The Pamirs and the Source of the Oxus," in *G.J.*, vol. viii, pp. 240–246, and the authorities there cited ; Sir Aurel Stein, " The Desert Crossing of Hsüan-Tsang, A.D. 630," in *G.J.*, vol. liv, p. 265, and " A Chinese Expedition across the Pamirs and Hindukush, A.D. 747," in *G.J.*, vol. lix, p. 112 (this was a military expedition) ; and O. Lattimore, " Caravan Routes of Inner Asia," in *G.J.*, vol. lxxii, p. 497. An account of a journey to the Hindu Kush in the thirteenth century is in *The Travels of an Alchemist*, translated and edited by A. Waley (" Broadway Travellers," 1931).

THE PRE-COLUMBAN DISCOVERY OF AMERICA

The term ' pre-Columban ' is usually applied to supposed discoveries of America in the fifteenth century : were the Northmen included there could be little controversy, since there is overwhelming

495

evidence in favour of their ' pre-Columban ' discovery. But was the continent seen again between their time and that of Columbus ? There are, broadly, three possibilities. (1) Danish discoveries in the north, with which the Portuguese may have been associated. The evidence is somewhat doubtful, and no definite conclusions can be reached. (2) Portuguese discoveries of Newfoundland or the neighbouring mainland. This claim rests upon the rather strained interpretation of some documents and on the evidence of some maps in the early years of the sixteenth century. It has not received general support. (3) The discovery of some part of the coast of South America by the Portuguese. This claim rests largely on the interpretation of some early maps (fifteenth century), and in view of the activities of the Portuguese south of the Cape Verde Islands and the geographical relationship of South America and West Africa it is at least more probably genuine than (2). Here again the matter has not been definitely settled and perhaps never will be.

Attempts are sometimes made to use the Treaty of Tordesillas as evidence. In 1479 the Portuguese had agreed to the retention of the Canary Islands by Spain, while they themselves held north-west Africa, Guinea, and the islands in the south. Suspecting that Columbus was encroaching on this region, the King of Portugal asked, in 1492, for a stringent observance of the treaty. In return Spain secured four Bulls from the Pope, each more menacing than its predecessor to the Portuguese, the second establishing a line of demarcation 100 leagues west and south of the Azores and Cape Verde Islands, and the fourth recognizing Spain's right to the Indies if she could get there before the Portuguese. The Treaty of Tordesillas (1494) fixed the line of demarcation at 370 leagues west of the Cape Verde Islands. This is to be regarded as a compromise. The Portuguese wanted an east-west line so as to preserve their route to the Far East round Africa. They accepted a north-south line, but one fixed so far west that it gave them complete control of the South Atlantic. The treaty is, therefore, essentially related to the early Portuguese efforts to get round Africa, and can hardly be used to support arguments for discoveries in the west.

Claims have also been put forward that other Europeans, including Basques, Welsh, and Irish, discovered the New World before 1492. Most of these can be dismissed as fanciful.

Among the very numerous works relating to these matters the following may be mentioned : C. R. Beazley, *The Dawn of Modern Geography* (3 vols, 1897–1906) ; H. Harrisse, *The Discovery of North America* (1892) ; W. H. Babcock, *Legendary Islands of the Atlantic* (1922) ; S. Larsen, *The Discovery of America Twenty Years before Columbus* (1925) ; H. Yule Oldham, "A Pre-Columban Discovery of America," in *G.J.*, vol. v, p. 221 ; J. Batalha-Reis, " The Supposed Discovery of South America before 1448, and the Critical Methods of the Historians of Geographical Discovery," in *G.J.*, vol. ix, p. 185 ; E. G. R. Taylor, note on "A Pre-Columban Discovery of America," in *G.J.*, vol. lxvii, p. 282 ; J. Cortesao, "The Pre-Columbian Discovery

APPENDIX

of America," in *G.J.*, vol. lxxxix, p. 29; and G. R. Crone, "The Alleged Pre-Columbian Discovery of America," in *G.J.*, vol. lxxxix, p. 455. On the supposed Basque discovery śee L. D. Sciso, "Pre-Columbian Discovery by Basques," in *Proc. and Trans. of the Royal Soc. of Canada*, third series, vol. xviii, Section II, p. 51.

THE VOYAGE OF DE FONTE

In an extract from Cook's *Voyages* reference is made to this voyage (page 170). It is probable that the voyage was never made, but some geographers accepted it as genuine. According to the story, B. de Fonte led an expedition to the west coast of North America in 1640, and one of the party actually reached Davis Strait from the west, making use of various lakes and rivers. De Fonte claimed that his voyage proved that the North-west Passage did not exist.

THE STRAIT OF ANIAN

This strait, referred to on pages 129 and 375, was commonly thought to mark the end of the North-west Passage leading to the Pacific Ocean, and was accepted by geographers as the strait in the north corresponding to that discovered by Magellan to the south of South America. It was falsely claimed that Gasper Corte Real had discovered it in 1500.

So far as is known the strait first appears on a map in 1566. The question has been discussed at length by Mr G. E. Nunn in *Origin of the Strait of Anian Concept* (privately printed, Philadephlia, 1929).

INDEX

ABACAXIO river, 408
Abbadie, A. T. d', in Abyssinia, 310–311
Abbott, J., journey of, to Khiva, 258
Abdul Subhan, in Central Asia, 286
Abendanon, E. C., in Celebes, 446
Abert, J. W., in the United States, 388
Abibe Mountains, 100
Abich, G. H., in Caucasia, 241, 243; in Persia, 258
Abor, 263
Abruzzi, Duke of the, in the Himalaya, 264; in Central Africa, 352; in the Arctic, 467, 473
Abu Dhabi, 251
Abyssinia, Greeks in, 28; Cosmas in, 35; Bracciolini on, 54; Pinto in, 180; Mauro's map of, 197; Paez in, 198; missionaries in, 201, 491; Portuguese in, 202; knowledge of, in 1788, 302; modern exploration of, 303, 310, 311, 323–324, 353, 354; Rohlfs in, 317; Schweinfurth in, 320
Acapulco, 93, 395
Acevedo, —, in South America, 408
Acla, 93
Aconcagua, Mount, 411
Acosta, B. de, on the population of the Amazon valley, 229
Acre, 43, 46
Acuña, Cristoval de, on the Amazon river, 229
Adam of Bremen, 37
Adamawa, 314, 318
Adams, W., in Japan, 114; map of Japan by, 184
Adare, Cape, 480, 481, 482
Addis Abeba, 324, 353, 354
Adelaide, 425, 427, 429, 430, 431
Adelaide Island, 478
Adelaide Peninsula, 458
Adelaide river, 425, 430
Adelard, in the Near East, 40
Adélie Land, 449, 450, 479
Aden, 20, 53, 54, 179, 250, 251; Jourdain on, 184; Gulf of, 357
Admiralty Islands, 159
Admiralty Range, 480
Adrar, 200, 316, 359
Adrianov, —, in Western Siberia, 237

Adriatic Sea, 18, 31
Adua, 324
Advance, the, 476
Adventure, the, 166, 478
Ægean Sea, 18, 27
Afghanistan, 55, 287, 292; route from, to Samarkand, 56; Ibn Battuta in, 62; in the nineteenth century, 233, 256–261, 293; boundary of, surveyed, 240; Rawlinson in, 246
Africa, voyages to India from, 19, 20, 70, 71; joined to China by Ptolemy, 21; Carthaginian settlements in, 21–22; circumnavigation of, 23; exploration of, in classical times, 27–29, 34; exploration of, in medieval times, 39, 200; route round, 50; Jordanus on, 51; Arabs in, 59, 60; Portuguese on the coasts of, 64, 65, 66; Teixeira in, 181; exploration of, from 1500 to 1788, 197–204, 489, 490; exploration of, in modern times, 302–363, 376, 490, 491, 493; Portuguese in, 496
Africa, South, 197, 202, 203, 204
African Association, 197, 302, 308
Agades, 314, 358
Agassiz, A., voyages of, 452
Agassiz, L., on Humboldt, 401
Aghil Ranges, 265
Agisymba, 29
Agra, 183, 184, 187, 189, 190, 191
Aguilar, M. de, on the west coast of North America, 158
Aguirre, L. de, expedition of, to the Amazon river, 98
Agulhas Current, 69, 71
Ahaggar, 316, 359
Ahlquist, A. E., in Siberia, 235
Ahmadabad, 182, 184
Ain Taiba, 358
Ainsworth, W. F., in Asia Minor, 242–243; in Mesopotamia, 246
Aïr, 317, 359, 360
Aird river, 440
Ajmer, 183, 185
Ak-su, 288, 290, 297
Akaba, 254; Gulf of, 254
Akbar, Emperor, 181
Akhdar, 251
Ala Kul, 42, 44

INDEX

INDEX

INDEX

Burckhardt, J. L., in Palestine, 244 ; in Arabia, 248 ; and the Niger problem, 306 ; in Egypt, 309
Burdekin river, 426, 430
Burhanpur, 184
Burkart, H. J., in Mexico, 395
Burke, R. O'H., in Australia, 429, 430
Burma, 46, 54, 73, 185, 270 ; exploration of, from 1600 to 1800, 187 ; exploration of, in modern times, 265–269
Burmeister, H. K., in Brazil, 407
Burnes, Sir A., in Afghanistan, 257 ; in Sind, 262 ; journey of, to Bokhara, 264
Burpee, L. J., on Kellsey, 222 ; on Turner, 225, 226 ; on Fidler, 364 ; on Harmon, 365
Burrough, S., voyage of, in search of the North-east Passage, 120–121, 122
Burton, Sir R. F., in Arabia, 250 ; in West Africa, 318 ; in Abyssinia, 324 ; in East Africa, 325–326, 333, 339
Burton Gulf, 336
Burwash, Major L. T., in Canada, 374 ; in the Arctic, 460 n.
Bury, G. W., in Arabia, 254
Bushire, 257, 258, 259, 260, 261
Bushmanland, 311
Bushmen, 203, 345
Bussa Rapids, 306, 307, 308
Butakov, A., in South-west Asia, 240
Butler, S. S., in Arabia, 254
Butter, A., in North-east Africa, 353
Büttner, Dr, in Central Africa, 342
Button, Sir T., voyage of, to discover the North-west Passage, 137–138, 141, 142
Bylot, R., voyages of, to discover the North-west Passage, 137–138, 140, 141
Byrd, R. E., in the Arctic, 475 ; in the Antarctic, 485, 486, 487
Byrd, W., in North America, 214
Byron, J., in the Pacific Ocean, 155, 159
Byzantium—see Constantinople

CABIT, 111
Cabot, J., voyages of, 82–83
Cabot, S., expedition in the North Atlantic, 84 ; expedition to the Plate river, 102 ; and the North-east Passage, 119
Cabot Strait, 116, 118
Cabral, J., in the Eastern Himalaya, 190
Cabral, P. A., voyage of, to India, 68–69, 74

Cabrillo, J. R., expedition of, to Lower California, 93
Cacella, S., in the Eastern Himalaya, 190
Cache valley, 390
Cachiyaco river, 405
Cadiz, 81, 248
Cæsar, Julius, 22, 30, 31
Cagni, U., in the Arctic, 467, 473–474
Caillaud, F., in North Africa, 309
Caillié, R., in North Africa, 307, 316
Cairo, 178, 198, 248, 250, 303, 305, 309, 322, 361
Cajamarca, 94
Calabar, 306, 308
Calabar river, 308
Calcutta, 192
Cali, 100
Calicut, 54, 61, 64, 70, 72
California, 88, 111, 113, 205, 218, 219, 220, 380, 385, 386, 387, 388, 391, 394, 396, 491
California, Alta, 386
California, Lower, 89, 93, 113, 218, 219, 398
California, Gulf of, 89, 91, 93
Call, J., in Southern India, 192
Callao, 146
Callender, J., on the Pacific Ocean, 162
Calvert, A. F., organizes Australian exploring party, 433
Cam, D., explores the west coast of Africa, 65, 201
Cambaluc, 47
Cambay, 54, 183
Cambodia, 51, 272, 273
Cambridge Bay, 459
Cambridge expeditions to Greenland, 471
Cameron, J., journey of, from China to Burma, 268
Cameron, V. L., in Central Africa, 335, 336, 337, 339, 341, 347
Cameroons, 318, 319, 349, 354, 356, 357
Cameta, 407
Campbell, J., in South Africa, 311
Campbell, R., in Canada, 370
Campbell, Captain, in North Africa, 306
Campbell Islands, 436
Campeachy, Bay of, 81
Camsell, C., in North America, 462–463
Canada, Cartier in, 117 ; explorer from New England in, 212 ; exploration of, 1600 to 1800, 205–211, 220–228 ; modern exploration of, 364–375, 384, 399, 461, 462, 492
Canadian Pacific Railway, 370

507

INDEX

INDEX

INDEX

INDEX

INDEX

INDEX

Medicine Bow Mountains, 385, 390
Medina (Africa), 303
Medina (Arabia), 178, 248, 250, 254, 255
Megasthenes, embassy of, to India, 26
Mehren, M., in Greenland, 471
Meighen Island, 462
Mekong river, 74, 188, 266, 267, 269, 270, 271, 272, 273
Mela, Pomponius, 45
Melbourne, 424, 451
Melville Island (Arctic Ocean), 455, 457, 459, 460, 462
Melville Island (Australia), 153, 155
Melville Peninsula, 456, 461, 462
Melville Sound, 456, 457
Memphis, 91
Menam river, 73, 269, 270
Mendaña, A. de, expedition of, to the Solomon Islands, 111, 112 ; second expedition of, 113, 114
Mendez, —, commands expedition to Florida, 92
Mendocino, Cape, 93
Mendoza, 104, 411, 412
Mendoza, G. H. de, in Chile, 96, 97
Mendoza, P. de, in South America, 102
Menindee, 429
Mercator, G., map of Asia by, 122 ; supports the theory of Terra Australis, 145
Merced river, 380
Mercy, Bay of, 459
Mergui, 188
Mérida, 413
Merina, 362
Meroë, 28
Merv, 27, 60, 241, 258, 292, 297
Méry, G., in North Africa, 358
Merzbacher, G., in the Tian Shan Mountains, 293
Meshed, 241, 257, 259, 260, 261
Meshed Ali, 250
Mesopotamia, 18, 24, 25, 34, 60, 61, 191 ; modern exploration of, 245–247
Messerschmidt, —, in Siberia, 195
Meta Incognita, 129, 130
Meta river, 100, 101
Meteor, the, 452
Methye Portage, 224, 225
Mexico, 81, 91, 112, 182, 206, 387, 402 ; Spanish exploration in, 86–90, 93 ; Spanish exploration from, 1550 to 1800, 217–220, 415; modern exploration of, 378, 382, 384, 388, 395–396
Mexico City, 86, 88, 90, 395
Mexico, Gulf of, 85, 88, 90, 130, 205, 209, 211, 216, 217

Meyer, A. B., in New Guinea, 439
Meyer, H., in South America, 414, 416
Meyer, H., in Tanganyika Territory, 350
Meyjes, R. P., in New Guinea, 442
Meynier, —, in North Africa, 358
Miani, G., in North Africa, 319, 323, 327
Michael, the, 128
Michaux, A., in North America, 215–216
Michaux, F. A., in North America, 215–216
Michie, A., in China, 274
Michigan, Lake, 207, 208, 209, 375, 380
Michigan University expeditions to Greenland, 471
Midacritus, Greek trader, 21
Middendorf, A. T., in Siberia, 234–235, 237
Middleton, C., attempts to find the North-west Passage, 221
Midian, 249, 250
Mierisch, B., in Nicaragua, 397
Mignan, R., 246
Mikkelsen, E., in the Arctic, 463
Miklukho-Maclay, N., in New Guinea, 439
Mildenhall, J., in India, 183
Miles, S. B., in Arabia, 251 ; in Abyssinia, 324
Milligan, G. B., in Canada, 371
Millingen, C., in Arabia, 250
Milne Bay, 440
Milton, Lord, in Canada, 369
Min river, 188
Minas Geraes, 228, 404, 414
Minchin, J. B., in South America, 412
Mindanao Island, 108, 452
Minneapolis, 209
Minnesota river, 375
Minoans, 17
Miranda, A. de, expedition of, to Siam, 73
Mirni, the, 448, 478
Mirza Shuja, in Central Asia, 281
Mississippi river, 91, 205, 207, 208, 209, 210, 214, 215, 216, 366, 375, 376, 378, 379, 380, 381, 383, 384, 394
Mississippi River Commission, 394
Missouri Fur Company, 378
Missouri river, 208, 210, 211, 215, 216, 217, 366, 376, 377, 378, 380, 383, 384, 389, 392, 394
Missouri River Commission, 394
Mistassini, Lake, 210, 375
Mitchell, Sir T., in Australia, 421–424, 426, 427
Mitchell river, 426

531

INDEX

Paraguay river, 102, 103, 104, 231, 232, 405, 407
Paraná river, 102, 103, 232, 407
Paranatinga river, 416
Parawan, 391
Paria, 81
Paris (U.S.A.), 215–216
Park, M., in North Africa, 304–306, 307, 315, 320, 490
Parkes, Sir H., map of Siam by, 233, 269
Parkinson, F. B., in North-east Africa, 353
Parkinson, J., in Liberia, 356
Parry, W. E., in the Arctic, 372, 454, 455, 456, 468, 472
Parsees, 51
Parsnip river, 226
Parwan Pass, 189
Passarge, S., in South Africa, 345 ; in the Cameroons, 356
Pastene, J. B. de, on the coast of Chile, 96
Patagonia, 232, 404, 405, 406, 410, 411
Patagonians, 106
Patani, 74, 188, 273
Patani river, 273
Pate Island, 198
Paterson, W., in South Africa, 203
Patna, 185
Patrocles, explores the Caspian Sea, 26
Pattie, J. O., in the United States, 381–382
Pattie, S., in the United States, 381, 382
Paulinus, crosses the Atlas Mountains, 29
Paumotu Archipelago, 107, 448, 450
Pavie, A., in Indo-China, 272, 273
Pavon, —, in South America, 232
Payer, J., in the Arctic, 465, 466–467, 473 ; in Greenland, 469, 470
Payta, 100
Peace river, 226, 364, 367, 369, 370, 371
Peake, Major, in North Africa, 357
Pearce, Colonel, surveys of, in India, 192
Pearce Point, 429
Peary, R. E., in Greenland, 469–470 ; in the Arctic, 474, 476
Pechora river, 120, 121
Peck, W. G., in the United States, 388
Peddie, Major, in North Africa, 306
Pedrarias Davila, in Central America, 93
Pedro, Prince of Portugal, 64
Peel river, 419
Peel Sound, 457
Pegolotti, treatise by, 53, 54
Pegu, 70, 180, 181, 182, 267

Pei river, 188
Peking, 46, 47, 50, 52, 73, 188, 189, 190, 194, 234, 274, 276, 277, 283, 294, 297, 298
Pelliot, P., in Central Asia, 301
Pelly, L., in Arabia, 251, 252
Pelly river, 370
Pelsaert, F., in India, 185
Pemberton, R. B., in Bhutan, 262 ; in Burma, 265, 266
Pembina river, 367
Pend d'Oreille, Lake, 367, 368
Peney, A., in North Africa, 319
Penguin, the, 452
Pennsylvania, 207, 214
Penny, W., in the Arctic, 459
Penobscot river, 83 n., 211
Penola, the, 487
Pentland, J. B., in South America, 404
Pepin, A., journey of, across the Pamirs, 292
Pepin, Lake, 210
Pepys Island, 159
Perak, 273
Perak river, 273
Peranzures, —, expedition of, to the east of the Andes, 104
Pereira, J., in India, 181
Pereira, M. C., in Central Africa, 313
Perene river, 230
Perez, J., in the North Pacific Ocean, 158
Perm, 234
Pernambuco, 229
Peron, F., in Australia, 418
Perry, M. C., expedition of, to Japan, 279
Persepolis, 24
Persia, 34, 239 ; Greeks in, 24, 25 ; Venetians in, 54 ; Ibn Battuta in, 61 ; route from Tartary to, 61 ; Varthema in, 178, 179 ; travellers in, during the seventeenth century, 180, 182, 183, 185, 186, 187, 191 ; modern exploration of, 233, 240, 241, 245, 246, 256–261
Persian Gulf, 18, 19, 24, 248, 251, 252, 258, 260
Perth (Australia), 153, 424, 425, 428, 431, 432
Perú, 90, 113, 229 ; Spaniards in, 94, 95, 96, 97, 100, 102, 104 ; Feuillée on the coast of, 154, 232 ; Jesuits in, 230 ; La Condamine in, 231 ; modern exploration of, 402, 403, 404, 405, 407, 412
Perugia, Andrew of, in China, 50–51
Peschurov, M. A., in Siberia, 236
Peshawar, 189, 256, 257, 281, 286
Pet, A., voyage of, to discover the North-east Passage, 121–122

537

INDEX

INDEX

INDEX

Trotter, H., in Central Asia, 286, 287, 288
Trotter, J. K., in West Africa, 355
Trujillo (Central America), 88
Trujillo (South America), 403, 405
Truter, P. J., in South Africa, 311
Tsaidam Swamp, 284, 289, 290, 291, 294, 297, 298
Tsangpo river—*see* Brahmaputra river
Tsaparang, 190, 191
Tschudi, J. J. von, in Perú, 404 ; in Brazil, 407
Tsetang, 286, 289
Tsientang river, 188, 275
Tsin-ling Mountains, 277
Tsitsihar, 292, 294
Tuareg, 317, 359
Tuat, 200 *n.*, 316, 317, 359
Tucker, J. R., in South America, 408
Tuckett, F., in New Zealand, 437
Tuckey, J. H., exploration of the Congo river by, 306
Tucuman, 232
Tufi, 441
Tula river, 189
Tumachumac Mountains, 413
Tumaco, 94
Tumba, Lake, 341
Tumbez, 94
Tung-kiang river, 274
Tunguska river, 193, 237
Tunis, 29, 308, 314
Turan (Indo-China), 74
Turfan, 189, 288, 293, 301
Turkestan, 25, 61, 62, 291, 296, 297, 298, 300
Turkestan, Eastern, 290, 291
Turkestan, Russian, 241, 256
Turkestan (town), 240
Turks, 40, 56, 57, 63
Turn Again, Cape (New Zealand), 162
Turnagain, Cape (North America), 371, 372, 456
Turner, P., in North America, 225–226, 364
Turtle Lake, 366
Turukhansk, 234, 236
Tuscarora, the, 452
Tuscon, 388, 389, 391
Tym river, 237
Tyre, 34
Tyrrell, J. B., in Canada, 373, 374
Tyrrell, J. W., in Canada, 367, 373

Uaupes river, 415
Ubangi river, 323, 342, 343, 348, 349, 357
Ubsa Nor, 288
Ubun, 271
Ubwari, 336
Ucayali river, 230, 405, 406, 408

Ucuyabe river, 402
Udsk, 235
Uganda, 322, 337, 338, 339, 340, 348, 350, 351, 354
Ugarte, J., examines the coast of Lower California, 218–219
Uinta Mountains, 386, 387
Ujiji, 325, 333, 336, 339, 341
Uliassutai, 284, 287, 288
Ulloa, F. de, in the Gulf of California, 93
Umpqua river, 380
Ungava Bay, 374, 375
Union, the, 372
United States of America, 81, 88, 89, 91, 205, 220, 366, 375–395
United States Coast and Geodetic Survey, 395, 399
United States Geological Survey, 393
Ural Mountains, 24, 60, 192, 196, 234, 235, 237
Ural river, 42, 43
Uranie, the, 449
Uraricœra river, 415
Urdaneta, A. de, discovers the sailing-route across the Pacific Ocean, 110-111
Urga, 283, 284, 290, 294, 296
Urmchi, 298
Ursua, P. de, expedition of, to the Amazon valley, 97-98, 101, 113
Urubamba river, 406
Uruguay, 404
Uruguay river, 228
Uruguay, the, 482
Urungu river, 287
Ussuri river, 236, 237
Utah, 394
Utah Lake, 220, 379, 386, 387, 390
Utah Pass, 387
Uthen, 271
Utrecht, Treaty of, 221
Uzboi river, 240

Vaal river, 203, 311
Vaca, C. de, journey of, from Florida to Mexico, 88, 90, 227 ; in South America, 102, 103
Vadillo, O., in South America, 100
Vaigats Island, 120, 121, 122, 123, 124, 125
Valdivia, P. de, in Chile, 96–97
Valdivia, 96, 97
Valdivia, the, 481
Valikhanov, Captain, in the Tian Shan Mountains, 280
Valle, P. della, in Asia, 182
Vambéry, A., in South-west Asia, 240
Van, Lake, 46, 243, 258
Van de Putte, S., journey of, from Persia to China, 191

549

INDEX

Walsingham, Sir F., 132
Walsingham, Cape, 132
Warburton, P. E., in Australia, 429, 431–432
Ward, F. K., in South-east Asia, 269 n., 278
Waria river, 440, 441
Warner Lake, 386
Warrego river, 426, 427, 430
Warren, G. K., on Bonneville, 383 ; on Nicollet, 383–384 ; in the United States, 392
Warrina, 433
Wasatch Mountains, 386, 390, 391
Washington, the, 174, 226
Washington (D.C.), 384
Watkins, H. G., in Labrador, 375 n. ; in Greenland, 471–472
Watling Island, landfall of Columbus, 79
Waugh, Sir A. S., organizes Indian surveys, 262
Wauters, A. J., map of the Congo by, 348
Wavell, A. J. B., in Arabia, 254
Waxel, S., in the North Pacific Ocean, 158
Waymouth, G., enters Hudson Strait, 137 ; on the east coast of North America, 211
Waziristan, 259
Weatherley, P., in Central Africa, 347
Webb, W. S., in India, 263
Webbe river, 352
Weddell, J., in the Antarctic, 478, 477
Weddell Sea, 478 n., 480, 482, 484, 486
Wegener, A., in Greenland, 471, 472
Weiser, C., in North America, 214, 215
Wejh, 254
Wellby, M. S., in Tibet, 298 ; in North-east Africa, 353
Welle river, 319, 320, 321, 322, 323, 342, 348, 356, 357
Wellington, 436, 437
Wellington Channel, 457, 459, 460
Wellman, W., in the Arctic, 467, 473
Wells, J. W., in South America, 414
Wells, L. A., in Australia, 433
Wellsted, J., in Arabia, 249, 251
Welsh, and discovery of America, 496
Welwitsch, F., in Angola, 332
Wentworth, W. C., in Australia, 419
Wenzel, —, in Lower California, 219
Werne, F., in North Africa, 309–310
Werner, A. G., 401
Werthemann, A., in South America, 408, 412
Wessels, C., on Goes and Andrade, 190
West, R. H., in Syria, 245
West Indies, 206, 305

Western Port, 418
Western river, 419
Western Union Telegraph Company, 399, 400
Weston, S., in Australia, 434
Wetzstein, J. G., in Syria, 244
Weyprecht, C., in the Arctic, 465
Whale Island, 225
Whales, Bay of, 483, 485, 487
Wheeler, G. M., in the United States, 394
Wheeling, 216, 380
Whidbey, J., surveys of, 174
Whipple, A. W., in the United States, 391
White, Captain, in Burma, 265
White, J. C., in Bhutan, 262
White, R. B., in Colombia, 412
White Island, 453 n., 475
White river, 387
White Sea, 36, 120, 122
White Snow Mountains, 378
Whitelock, Lieutenant, in Arabia, 249, 251
Whitely, H., in South America, 413
Wickenburg, Count E. von, in North-east Africa, 353
Wickham, J. C., in Australia, 425
Wickham river, 440
Wied-Neuwied, Prince Maximilian of, in Brazil, 403
Wiener, C., in South America, 412
Wiese, W., 466
Wiese Land, 465
Wilcox, R., in India, 263 ; in Burma, 266
Wilczek Island, 467
Wild, F., in the Antarctic, 484
Wilhelmina Peak, 442, 443
Wilkes, C., in the United States, 385 ; in the Pacific Ocean, 450 ; in the Antarctic, 450, 479, 480, 484, 486, 487
Wilkes Land, 450, 479, 482
Wilkins, Sir H., in the Arctic, 463 ; in the Antarctic, 485, 487, 491
Willamette river, 380, 383, 385
Willcocks, Sir W., map of Mesopotamia by, 247
Willes, R., on the North-west Passage, 128
William, the, 122
Williams, Bill, with J. C. Frémont, 389
Williams, E., on the ' passage ' to the South Sea, 212
Williams, —, in Uganda, 351
Williamson, A., in China, 275
Williamson, Dr J. A., on the second voyage of John Cabot, 83
Williamson, N., in India, 263

551

INDEX